INSTRUCTOR'S SOLUTIONS MANUAL

VOLUME I

Mark McCombs

ALGEBRA &
TRIGONOMETRY

SIXTH EDITION

Michael Sullivan

Prentice
Hall

Upper Saddle River, NJ 07458

Editor in Chief: Sally Yagan
Associate Editor: Dawn Murrin
Assistant Managing Editor: John Matthews
Production Editor: Donna Crilly
Supplement Cover Manager: Paul Gourhan
Supplement Cover Designer: PM Workshop Inc.
Manufacturing Buyer: Lisa McDowell

© 2002 by Prentice-Hall, Inc.
Upper Saddle River, NJ 07458

Printed in the United States of America

10 9 8 7 6 5 4 3 2 1

ISBN   0-13-097061-1

Prentice-Hall International (UK) Limited, London
Prentice-Hall of Australia Pty. Limited, Sydney
Prentice-Hall Canada, Inc., Toronto
Prentice-Hall Hispanoamericana, S.A., Mexico City
Prentice-Hall of India Private Limited, New Delhi
Pearson Education Asia Pte. Ltd., Singapore
Prentice-Hall of Japan, Inc., Tokyo
Editora Prentice-Hall do Brazil, Ltda., Rio de Janeiro

Contents

Preface   vii

Chapter R   Review

R.1   Real Numbers   1
R.2   Algebra Review   5
R.3   Geometry Review   9
R.4   Integer Exponents   13
R.5   Polynomials   18
R.6   Factoring Polynomials   29
R.7   Rational Expressions   34
R.8   Square Roots; Radicals   43
R.9   Rational Exponents   49
R.R   Chapter Review   56

Chapter 1   Equations and Inequalities

1.1   Equations   68
1.2   Setting Up Equations: Applications   87
1.3   Quadratic Equations   102
1.4   Radical Equations; Equations Quadratic in Form   121
1.5   Solving Inequalities   144
1.6   Equations and Inequalities Involving Absolute Value   156
1.R   Chapter Review   166

Chapter 2   Graphs

2.1   Rectangular Coordinates   185
2.2   Graphs of Equations   196
2.3   Lines   207
2.4   Parallel and Perpendicular Lines; Circles   219
2.5   Scatter Diagrams; Linear Curve Fitting   233
2.6   Variation   241
2.R   Chapter Review   246

Chapter 3   Functions

3.1   Functions   257
3.2   Properties of Functions   275
3.3   Library of Functions; Piecewise Defined Functions   284
3.4   Graphing Techniques: Transformations   292
3.5   Operations on Functions; Composite Functions   310
3.6   Mathematical Models: Constructing Functions   326
3.R   Chapter Review   337

Chapter 4   Polynomial and Rational Functions

4.1	Quadratic Functions and Models	356
4.2	Polynomial Functions	380
4.3	Rational Functions I	402
4.4	Rational Functions II: Analyzing Graphs	411
4.5	Polynomial and Rational Inequalities	442
4.R	Chapter Review	457

Chapter 5   The Zeros of a Polynomial Function

5.1	Synthetic Division	483
5.2	The Real Zeros of a Polynomial Function	487
5.3	Complex Numbers; Quadratic Equations with a Negative Discriminant	522
5.4	Complex Zeros; Fundamental Theorem of Algebra	530
5.R	Chapter Review	540

Chapter 6   Exponential and Logarithmic Functions

6.1	One-to-One Functions; Inverse Functions	563
6.2	Exponential Functions	582
6.3	Logarithmic Functions	596
6.4	Properties of Logarithms; Exponential and Logarithmic Models	608
6.5	Logarithmic and Exponential Equations	619
6.6	Compound Interest	629
6.7	Growth and Decay; Newton's Law; Logistic Models	636
6.8	Logarithmic Scales	643
6.R	Chapter Review	646

Chapter 7   Trigonometric Functions

7.1	Angles and Their Measure	659
7.2	Right Triangle Trigonometry	669
7.3	Computing Values of Trigonometric Functions of Given Angles	685
7.4	Trigonometric Functions of General Angles	692
7.5	Properties of Trigonometric Functions: Unit Circle Approach	715
7.6	Graphs of the Sine and Cosine Functions	724
7.7	Graphs of the Tangent, Cotangent, Secant and Cosecant Functions	735
7.8	Phase Shift; Sinusoidal Curve Fitting	740
7.R	Chapter Review	752

Chapter 8   Analytic Trigonometry

8.1	The Inverse Sine, Cosine and Tangent Functions	770
8.2	The Inverse Trigonometric Functions (Continued)	777
8.3	Trigonometric Identities	789
8.4	Sum and Difference Formulas	799

8.5	Double-Angle and Half-Angle Formulas	819
8.6	Product-to-Sum and Sum-to-Product Formulas	838
8.7	Trigonometric Equations (I)	844
8.8	Trigonometric Equations (II)	852
8.R	Chapter Review	866

Chapter 9   Applications of Trigonometric Functions

9.1	Applications Involving Right Triangles	888
9.2	The Law of Sines	897
9.3	The Law of Cosines	910
9.4	The Area of a Triangle	919
9.5	Simple Harmonic Motion: Damped Motion	927
9.R	Chapter Review	932

Chapter 10   Polar Coordinates; Vectors

10.1	Polar Coordinates	944
10.2	Polar Equations and Graphs	952
10.3	The Complex Plane; DeMoivre's Theorem	978
10.4	Vectors	991
10.5	The Dot Product	999
10.R	Chapter Review	1008

Chapter 11   Analytic Geometry

11.2	The Parabola	1024
11.3	The Ellipse	1040
11.4	The Hyperbola	1060
11.5	Rotation of Axes; General Form of a Conic	1080
11.6	Polar Equations of Conics	1092
11.7	Plane Curves and Parametric Equations	1100
11.R	Chapter Review	1115

Chapter 12   Systems of Equations and Inequalities

12.1	Systems of Linear Equations: Two Equations Containing Two Variables	1136
12.2	Systems of Linear Equations: Three Equations Containing Three Variables	1151
12.3	Systems of Linear Equations: Matrices	1166
12.4	Systems of Linear Equations: Determinants	1196
12.5	Matrix Algebra	1215
12.6	Partial Fraction Decomposition	1229
12.7	Systems of Nonlinear Equations	1247
12.8	Systems of Inequalities	1279
12.9	Linear Programming	1302
12.R	Chapter Review	1322

Chapter 13 Sequences; Induction; The Binomial Theorem

13.1	Sequences	1362
13.2	Arithmetic Sequences	1368
13.3	Geometric Sequences; Geometric Series	1375
13.4	Mathematical Induction	1386
13.5	The Binomial Theorem	1395
13.R	Chapter Review	1401

Chapter 14 Counting and Probability

14.1	Sets and Counting	1409
14.2	Permutations and Combinations	1413
14.3	Probability	1418
14.R	Chapter Review	1427

Appendix Graphing Utilities

A.1	The Viewing Rectangle	1431
A.2	Using a Graphing Utility to Graph Equations	1433
A.3	Using a Graphing Utility to Locate Intercepts and Check for Symmetry	1451
A.5	Square Screens	1456

Preface

The *Instructor's Solutions Manual to Accompany Algebra & Trigonometry, 6th Edition* by Michael Sullivan contains detailed solutions to all of the problems in the textbook. TI-83 graphing calculator screens have been included to demonstrate the use of the graphics calculator in solving and in checking solutions to the problems where requested. Every attempt has been made to make this manual as error-free as possible. If you have suggestions, corrections, or comments please feel free to write to me about them.

A number of people need to be recognized for their contributions in the preparation of this manual. Thanks go to Sally Yagan, Dawn Murrin and Audra Walsh at Prentice Hall. Thanks also to Rachelle DeCoste, Kyle Kneisl, Laura Stevens and Scott Young for thoroughly checking the solutions for errors.

I especially wish to thank my mother, Sarah, and my brothers, Kirk and Doug, for their unwavering support and encouragement.

Finally, I want to thank Lily for her invaluable help in formatting the manual.

Mark A. McCombs
Department of Mathematics
Campus Box 3250
University of North Carolina at Chapel Hill
Chapel Hill, NC 27599
mccombs@math.unc.edu

Review

R.1 Real Numbers

1. (a) $\{2, 5\}$
   (b) $\{-6, 2, 5\}$
   (c) $\left\{-6, \dfrac{1}{2}, -1.333\ldots, 2, 5\right\}$
   (d) $\{\pi\}$
   (e) $\left\{-6, \dfrac{1}{2}, -1.333\ldots, \pi, 2, 5\right\}$

2. (a) $\{1\}$
   (b) $\{0, 1\}$
   (c) $\left\{-\dfrac{5}{3}, 2.060606\ldots, 1.25, 0, 1\right\}$
   (d) $\{\sqrt{5}\}$
   (e) $\left\{-\dfrac{5}{3}, 2.060606\ldots, 1.25, 0, 1, \sqrt{5}\right\}$

3. (a) $\{1\}$
   (b) $\{0, 1\}$
   (c) $\left\{0, 1, \dfrac{1}{2}, \dfrac{1}{3}, \dfrac{1}{4}\right\}$
   (d) None
   (e) $\left\{0, 1, \dfrac{1}{2}, \dfrac{1}{3}, \dfrac{1}{4}\right\}$

4. (a) None
   (b) $\{-1\}$
   (c) $\{-1, -1.1, -1.2, -1.3\}$
   (d) None
   (e) $\{-1, -1.1, -1.2, -1.3\}$

5. (a) None
   (b) None
   (c) None
   (d) $\left\{\sqrt{2}, \pi, \sqrt{2}+1, \pi+\dfrac{1}{2}\right\}$
   (e) $\left\{\sqrt{2}, \pi, \sqrt{2}+1, \pi+\dfrac{1}{2}\right\}$

6. (a) None
   (b) None
   (c) $\left\{\dfrac{1}{2}+10.3\right\}$
   (d) $\left\{-\sqrt{2}, \pi+\sqrt{2}\right\}$
   (e) $\left\{-\sqrt{2}, \pi+\sqrt{2}, \dfrac{1}{2}+10.3\right\}$

7. (a) 18.953
   (b) 18.952

8. (a) 25.861
   (b) 25.861

9. (a) 28.653
   (b) 28.653

10. (a) 99.052
    (b) 99.052

11. (a) 0.063
    (b) 0.062

12. (a) 0.054
    (b) 0.053

13. (a) 9.998
    (b) 9.998

14. (a) 1.001
    (b) 1.000

15. (a) 0.429
    (b) 0.428

16. (a) 0.556
(b) 0.555

17. (a) 34.733
(b) 34.733

18. (a) 16.200
(b) 16.200

19. $3 + 2 = 5$

20. $(5)(2) = 10$

21. $x + 2 = (3)(4)$

22. $3 + y = 2 + 2$

23. $3y = 1 + 2$

24. $2x = (4)(6)$

25. $x - 2 = 6$

26. $2 - y = 6$

27. $\dfrac{x}{2} = 6$

28. $\dfrac{2}{x} = 6$

29. $9 - 4 + 2 = 5 + 2 = 7$

30. $6 - 4 + 3 = 2 + 3 = 5$

31. $-6 + 4 \cdot 3 = -6 + 12 = 6$

32. $8 - 4 \cdot 2 = 8 - 8 = 0$

33. $4 + 5 - 8 = 9 - 8 = 1$

34. $8 - 3 - 4 = 5 - 4 = 1$

35. $4 + \dfrac{1}{3} = \dfrac{12 + 1}{3} = \dfrac{13}{3}$

36. $2 - \dfrac{1}{2} = \dfrac{4 - 1}{2} = \dfrac{3}{2}$

37.
$$6 - \left[3 \cdot 5 + 2 \cdot (3 - 2) \right]$$
$$= 6 - \left[15 + 2 \cdot (1) \right]$$
$$= 6 - 17 = -11$$

38.
$$2 \cdot \left[8 - 3 \cdot (4 + 2) \right] - 3$$
$$= 2 \cdot \left[8 - 3 \cdot (6) \right] - 3$$
$$= 2 \cdot \left[8 - 18 \right] - 3$$
$$= 2 \cdot \left[-10 \right] - 3 = -20 - 3$$
$$= -23$$

39.
$$2 \cdot (3 - 5) + 8 \cdot 2 - 1$$
$$= 2 \cdot (-2) + 16 - 1$$
$$= -4 + 16 - 1$$
$$= 12 - 1 = 11$$

40.
$$1 - (4 \cdot 3 - 2 + 2)$$
$$= 1 - (12 - 2 + 2)$$
$$= 1 - (10 + 2)$$
$$= 1 - 12 = -11$$

41.
$$10 - \left[6 - 2 \cdot 2 + (8 - 3) \right] \cdot 2$$
$$= 10 - \left[6 - 4 + (5) \right] \cdot 2$$
$$= 10 - \left[2 + 5 \right] \cdot 2$$
$$= 10 - 7 \cdot 2$$
$$= 10 - 14 = -4$$

42.
$$2 - 5 \cdot 4 - \left[6 \cdot (3 - 4) \right]$$
$$= 2 - 20 - \left[6 \cdot (-1) \right]$$
$$= 2 - 20 - (-6)$$
$$= -18 + 6 = -12$$

43. $(5 - 3)\dfrac{1}{2} = (2)\dfrac{1}{2} = 1$

44. $(5 + 4)\dfrac{1}{3} = (9)\dfrac{1}{3} = 3$

45. $\dfrac{4 + 8}{5 - 3} = \dfrac{12}{2} = 6$

46. $\dfrac{2 - 4}{5 - 3} = \dfrac{-2}{2} = -1$

47. $\dfrac{3}{5} \cdot \dfrac{10}{21} = \dfrac{2}{7}$

48. $\dfrac{5}{9} \cdot \dfrac{3}{10} = \dfrac{1}{6}$

49. $\dfrac{6}{25} \cdot \dfrac{10}{27} = \dfrac{4}{15}$

50. $\dfrac{21}{25} \cdot \dfrac{100}{3} = 28$

51. $\dfrac{3}{4} + \dfrac{2}{5} = \dfrac{15 + 8}{20} = \dfrac{23}{20}$

52. $\dfrac{4}{3} + \dfrac{1}{2} = \dfrac{8+3}{6} = \dfrac{11}{6}$

53. $\dfrac{5}{6} + \dfrac{9}{5} = \dfrac{25+54}{30} = \dfrac{79}{30}$

54. $\dfrac{8}{9} + \dfrac{15}{2} = \dfrac{16+135}{18} = \dfrac{151}{18}$

55. $\dfrac{5}{18} + \dfrac{1}{12} = \dfrac{10+3}{36} = \dfrac{13}{36}$

56. $\dfrac{2}{15} + \dfrac{8}{9} = \dfrac{6+40}{45} = \dfrac{46}{45}$

57.
$$\dfrac{1}{30} - \dfrac{7}{18} = \dfrac{3-35}{90}$$
$$= -\dfrac{32}{90} = -\dfrac{16}{45}$$

58. $\dfrac{3}{14} - \dfrac{2}{21} = \dfrac{9+4}{42} = \dfrac{13}{42}$

59.
$$\dfrac{3}{20} - \dfrac{2}{15} = \dfrac{9-8}{60}$$
$$= \dfrac{1}{60}$$

60.
$$\dfrac{6}{35} - \dfrac{3}{14} = \dfrac{12-15}{70}$$
$$= -\dfrac{3}{70}$$

61.
$$\dfrac{\left(\dfrac{5}{18}\right)}{\left(\dfrac{11}{27}\right)} = \dfrac{5}{18} \cdot \dfrac{27}{11} = \dfrac{15}{22}$$

62.
$$\dfrac{\left(\dfrac{5}{21}\right)}{\left(\dfrac{2}{35}\right)} = \dfrac{5}{21} \cdot \dfrac{35}{2} = \dfrac{175}{42}$$
$$= \dfrac{25}{6}$$

63.
$$6(x+4) = 6x + 24$$

64.
$$4(2x-1) = 8x - 4$$

65.
$$x(x-4) = x^2 - 4x$$

66.
$$4x(x+3) = 4x^2 + 12x$$

67. $(x+2)(x+4)$
$= x^2 + 4x + 2x + 8$
$= x^2 + 6x + 8$

68. $(x+5)(x+1)$
$= x^2 + x + 5x + 5$
$= x^2 + 6x + 5$

69. $(x-2)(x+1)$
$= x^2 + x - 2x - 2$
$= x^2 - x - 2$

70. $(x-4)(x+1)$
$= x^2 + x - 4x - 4$
$= x^2 - 3x - 4$

71. $(x-8)(x-2)$
$= x^2 - 2x - 8x + 16$
$= x^2 - 10x + 16$

72. $(x-4)(x-2)$
$= x^2 - 2x - 4x + 8$
$= x^2 - 6x + 8$

73. $(x+2)(x-2)$
$= x^2 - 2x + 2x - 4$
$= x^2 - 4$

74. $(x-3)(x+3)$
$= x^2 + 3x - 3x - 9$
$= x^2 - 9$

75. $2x + 3x$
$= x(2+3)$
$= x(5) = 5x$

76. $2 + 3 \cdot 4 = 2 + 12 = 14$ since multiplication comes before addition in the Order of Operations for real numbers

$(2+3) \cdot 4 = 5 \cdot 4 = 20$ since operations inside parentheses come before multiplication in the Order of Operations for real numbers.

77. $2(3 \cdot 4)$ means the same thing as $3 \cdot 4 + 3 \cdot 4 = 12 + 12 = 24$

  $(2 \cdot 3) \cdot (2 \cdot 4)$ means the same thing as $(3 + 3) \cdot (4 + 4) = (6)(8) = 8 + 8 + 8 + 8 + 8 + 8 = 48$

78. $\dfrac{4+3}{2+5} = \dfrac{7}{7} = 1$, but $\dfrac{4}{2} + \dfrac{3}{5} = \dfrac{4 \cdot 5 + 3 \cdot 2}{10} = \dfrac{20+6}{10} = \dfrac{26}{10} = 2.6$

79. Subtraction is not commutative; for example: $1 - 4 = -3$, but $4 - 1 = 3$.

80. Subtraction is not associative; for example: $(1 - 4) - 2 = -3 - 2 = -5$,

  but $1 - (4 - 2) = 1 - 2 = -1$

81. Division is not commutative; for example: $\dfrac{6}{2} = 3$, but $\dfrac{2}{6} = \dfrac{1}{3}$.

82. Division is not associative; for example: $\dfrac{\left(\frac{6}{2}\right)}{4} = \dfrac{3}{4}$, but $\dfrac{6}{\left(\frac{2}{4}\right)} = 6 \cdot \left(\dfrac{4}{2}\right) = 12$.

83. The Symmetric Property of Equality implies that if $2 = x$, then $x = 2$.

84. If $x = 5$, then $(x)(x) = (5)(5) \rightarrow x^2 = 25 \rightarrow x^2 + x = 25 + 5 \rightarrow x^2 + x = 30$

85. There are no real numbers that are both rational and irrational, since an irrational number, by definition, is a number that cannot be expressed as the ratio of two integers.

  Every real number is either a rational number or an irrational number, since the decimal form of a real number either involves an infinitely repeating pattern of digits or an infinite, non-repeating string of digits.

86. The sum of an irrational number and a rational number must be irrational. Otherwise, the irrational number would then be the difference of two rational numbers, and therefore would have to be rational.

87. $x = 0.\overline{9} \rightarrow 10x = 9.\overline{9}$

  Now compute $10x = 9.\overline{9}$

  $\underline{\quad - x = 0.\overline{9}\quad}$

  $9x = 9 \rightarrow x = \dfrac{9}{9} = 1$

  So $0.99999\ldots\ldots$ equals 1.

Review

R.2 Algebra Review

1.

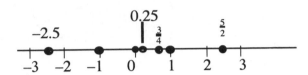

2.

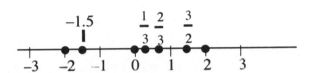

3. $\dfrac{1}{2} > 0$

4. $5 < 6$

5. $-1 > -2$

6. $-3 < -\dfrac{5}{2}$

7. $\pi > 3.14$

8. $\sqrt{2} > 1.41$

9. $\dfrac{1}{2} = 0.5$

10. $\dfrac{1}{3} > 0.33$

11. $\dfrac{2}{3} < 0.67$

12. $\dfrac{1}{4} = 0.25$

13. $x > 0$

14. $z < 0$

15. $x < 2$

16. $y > -5$

17. $x \le 1$

18. $x \ge 2$

19. Graph on the number line: $x \ge -2$

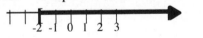

20. Graph on the number line: $x < 4$

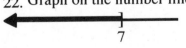

21. Graph on the number line: $x > -1$

22. Graph on the number line: $x \le 7$

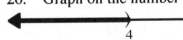

23. $d(C,D) = d(0,1) = |1 - 0| = |1| = 1$

24. $d(C,A) = d(0,-3) = |-3 - 0| = |-3| = 3$

25. $d(D,E) = d(1,3) = |3 - 1| = |2| = 2$

26. $d(C,E) = d(0,3) = |3 - 0| = |3| = 3$

27. $d(A,E) = d(-3,3) = |3-(-3)| = |6| = 6$ 28. $d(D,B) = d(1,-1) = |-1-1| = |-2| = 2$

29. $x + 2y = -2 + 2 \cdot 3 = -2 + 6 = 4$ 30. $3x + y = 3(-2) + 3 = -6 + 3 = -3$

31. $5xy + 2 = 5(-2)(3) + 2 = -30 + 2 = -28$

32. $-2x + xy = -2(-2) + (-2)(3) = 4 - 6 = -2$

33. $\dfrac{2x}{x-y} = \dfrac{2(-2)}{-2-3} = \dfrac{-4}{-5} = \dfrac{4}{5}$ 34. $\dfrac{x+y}{x-y} = \dfrac{-2+3}{-2-3} = \dfrac{1}{-5} = -\dfrac{1}{5}$

35. $\dfrac{3x+2y}{2+y} = \dfrac{3(-2)+2(3)}{2+3} = \dfrac{-6+6}{5} = \dfrac{0}{5} = 0$

36. $\dfrac{2x-3}{y} = \dfrac{2(-2)-3}{3} = \dfrac{-4-3}{3} = -\dfrac{7}{3}$ 37. $|x+y| = |3+(-2)| = |1| = 1$

38. $|x-y| = |3-(-2)| = |5| = 5$ 39. $|x|+|y| = |3|+|-2| = 3+2 = 5$

40. $|x|-|y| = |3|-|-2| = 3-2 = 1$ 41. $\dfrac{|x|}{x} = \dfrac{|3|}{3} = \dfrac{3}{3} = 1$

42. $\dfrac{|y|}{y} = \dfrac{|-2|}{-2} = \dfrac{2}{-2} = -1$

43. $|4x-5y| = |4(3)-5(-2)| = |12+10| = |22| = 22$

44. $|3x+2y| = |3(3)+2(-2)| = |9-4| = |5| = 5$

45. $||4x|-|5y|| = ||4(3)|-|5(-2)|| = ||12|-|-10|| = |12-10| = |2| = 2$

46. $3|x|+2|y| = 3|3|+2|-2| = 3\cdot3+2\cdot2 = 9+4 = 13$

47. $\dfrac{x^2-1}{x}$ Part (c) must be excluded.

The value $x = 0$ must be excluded from the domain because it causes division by 0.

48. $\dfrac{x^2+1}{x}$ Part (c) must be excluded.

The value $x = 0$ must be excluded from the domain because it causes division by 0.

49. $\dfrac{x}{x^2-9} = \dfrac{x}{(x-3)(x+3)}$ Part (a) must be excluded.

The values $x = -3$ and $x = 3$ must be excluded from the domain because they cause division by 0.

50. $\dfrac{x}{x^2+9}$ None of the given values are excluded. The domain is all real numbers.

51. $\dfrac{x^2}{x^2+1}$ None of the given values are excluded. The domain is all real numbers.

52. $\dfrac{x^3}{x^2-1}=\dfrac{x^3}{(x-1)(x+1)}$ Parts (b) and (d) must be excluded.
The values $x = 1$, and $x = -1$ must be excluded from the domain because they cause division by 0.

53. $\dfrac{x^2+5x-10}{x^3-x}=\dfrac{x^2+5x-10}{x(x-1)(x+1)}$ Parts (b), (c), and (d) must be excluded.
The values $x = 0$, $x = 1$, and $x = -1$ must be excluded from the domain because they cause division by 0.

54. $\dfrac{-9x^2-x+1}{x^3+x}=\dfrac{-9x^2-x+1}{x(x^2+1)}$ Part (c) must be excluded.
The value $x = 0$ must be excluded from the domain because it causes division by 0.

55. $\dfrac{4}{x-5}$ Domain $=\left\{x\middle|x\neq5\right\}$ 56. $\dfrac{-6}{x+4}$ Domain $=\left\{x\middle|x\neq-4\right\}$

57. $\dfrac{x}{x+4}$ Domain $=\left\{x\middle|x\neq-4\right\}$ 58. $\dfrac{x-2}{x-6}$ Domain $=\left\{x\middle|x\neq6\right\}$

59. $C=\dfrac{5}{9}(F-32)=\dfrac{5}{9}(32-32)=\dfrac{5}{9}(0)=0$

60. $C=\dfrac{5}{9}(F-32)=\dfrac{5}{9}(212-32)=\dfrac{5}{9}(180)=100$

61. $C=\dfrac{5}{9}(F-32)=\dfrac{5}{9}(77-32)=\dfrac{5}{9}(45)=25$

62. $C=\dfrac{5}{9}(F-32)=\dfrac{5}{9}(-4-32)=\dfrac{5}{9}(-36)=-20$

63. $A=l\cdot w$ 64. $P=2(l+w)$ 65. $C=\pi\cdot d$

66. $A=\dfrac{1}{2}b\cdot h$ 67. $A=\dfrac{\sqrt{3}}{4}\cdot x^2$ 68. $P=3\cdot x$

69. $V=\dfrac{4}{3}\pi\cdot r^3$ 70. $S=4\pi\cdot r^2$ 71. $V=x^3$

72. $S=6\cdot x^2$

73. (a) If $x = 1000$, $C = 4000 + 2x = 4000 + 2(1000) = 4000 + 2000 = \$6000$
    (b) If $x = 2000$, $C = 4000 + 2x = 4000 + 2(2000) = 4000 + 4000 = \$8000$

74. $210 + 80 - 120 + 25 - 60 - 32 - 5 = \$98$

75. $|x - 115| \le 5$
    (a) $|x - 115| = |113 - 115| = |-2| = 2 \le 5$ 113 volts is acceptable.
    (b) $|x - 115| = |109 - 115| = |-6| = 6 \nleq 5$ 109 volts is _not_ acceptable.

76. $|x - 220| \le 8$
    (a) $|x - 220| = |214 - 220| = |-6| = 6 \le 8$ 214 volts is acceptable.
    (b) $|x - 220| = |209 - 220| = |-11| = 11 \nleq 8$ 209 volts is _not_ acceptable.

77. $|x - 3| \le 0.01$
    (a) $|x - 3| = |2.999 - 3| = |-0.001| = 0.001 \le 0.01$ A radius of 2.999 centimeters is acceptable.
    (b) $|x - 3| = |2.89 - 3| = |-0.11| = 0.11 \nleq 0.01$ A radius of 2.89 centimeters is _not_ acceptable.

78. $|x - 98.6| \ge 1.5$
    (a) $|x - 98.6| = |97 - 98.6| = |-1.6| = 1.6 \ge 1.5$ 97°F is unhealthy.
    (b) $|x - 98.6| = |100 - 98.6| = |1.4| = 1.4 \ngeq 1.5$ 100°F is _not_ unhealthy.

79. $\dfrac{1}{3} = 0.333333\ldots > 0.333$ $\dfrac{1}{3}$ is larger by approximately $0.0003333\ldots$

80. $\dfrac{2}{3} = 0.666666\ldots > 0.666$ $\dfrac{2}{3}$ is larger by approximately $0.0006666\ldots$

81. No.

82. $1 < x^2 < 10 \rightarrow 1 < x < \sqrt{10}$
    $x > \pi \rightarrow x > 3.14159$

    $3.15^2 = 9.9225$

    $3.16^2 = 9.9856$

    $3.17^2 = 10.0489$

    so x could be either 3.15 or 3.16

83. Answers will vary.

Review

R.3   Geometry Review

1. $a = 5, \ b = 12, \quad c^2 = a^2 + b^2 = 5^2 + 12^2 = 25 + 144 = 169 \ \rightarrow \ c = 13$

2. $a = 6, \ b = 8, \quad c^2 = a^2 + b^2 = 6^2 + 8^2 = 36 + 64 = 100 \ \rightarrow \ c = 10$

3. $a = 10, \ b = 24, \quad c^2 = a^2 + b^2 = 10^2 + 24^2 = 100 + 576 = 676 \ \rightarrow \ c = 26$

4. $a = 4, \ b = 3, \quad c^2 = a^2 + b^2 = 4^2 + 3^2 = 16 + 9 = 25 \ \rightarrow \ c = 5$

5. $a = 7, \ b = 24, \quad c^2 = a^2 + b^2 = 7^2 + 24^2 = 49 + 576 = 625 \ \rightarrow \ c = 25$

6. $a = 14, \ b = 48, \quad c^2 = a^2 + b^2 = 14^2 + 48^2 = 196 + 2304 = 2500 \ \rightarrow \ c = 50$

7. $5^2 = 3^2 + 4^2 \ \rightarrow \ 25 = 9 + 16 \ \rightarrow \ 25 = 25$
The given triangle is a right triangle. The hypotenuse is 5.

8. $10^2 = 6^2 + 8^2 \ \rightarrow \ 100 = 36 + 64 \ \rightarrow \ 100 = 100$
The given triangle is a right triangle. The hypotenuse is 10.

9. $6^2 = 4^2 + 5^2 \ \rightarrow \ 36 = 16 + 25 \ \rightarrow \ 36 \neq 41$
The given triangle is not a right triangle.

10. $3^2 = 2^2 + 2^2 \ \rightarrow \ 9 = 4 + 4 \ \rightarrow \ 9 \neq 8$
The given triangle is not a right triangle.

11. $25^2 = 7^2 + 24^2 \ \rightarrow \ 625 = 49 + 576 \ \rightarrow \ 625 = 625$
The given triangle is a right triangle. The hypotenuse is 25.

12. $26^2 = 10^2 + 24^2 \ \rightarrow \ 676 = 100 + 576 \ \rightarrow \ 676 = 676$
The given triangle is a right triangle. The hypotenuse is 26.

13. $6^2 = 3^2 + 4^2 \ \rightarrow \ 36 = 9 + 16 \ \rightarrow \ 36 \neq 25$
The given triangle is not a right triangle.

14. $7^2 = 5^2 + 4^2 \ \rightarrow \ 49 = 25 + 16 \ \rightarrow \ 49 \neq 41$
The given triangle is not a right triangle.

15. $A = l \cdot w = 4 \cdot 2 = 8 \ \text{in}^2$

16. $A = l \cdot w = 9 \cdot 4 = 36 \ \text{cm}^2$

17. $A = \dfrac{1}{2}b \cdot h = \dfrac{1}{2}(2)(4) = 4 \text{ in}^2$ 18. $A = \dfrac{1}{2}b \cdot h = \dfrac{1}{2}(4)(9) = 18 \text{ cm}^2$

19. $A = \pi r^2 = \pi(5)^2 = 25\pi \text{ m}^2$ $C = 2\pi r = 2\pi(5) = 10\pi \text{ m}$

20. $A = \pi r^2 = \pi(2)^2 = 4\pi \text{ ft}^2$ $C = 2\pi r = 2\pi(2) = 4\pi \text{ ft}$

21. $V = lwh = 8 \cdot 4 \cdot 7 = 224 \text{ ft}^2$ 22. $V = lwh = 9 \cdot 4 \cdot 8 = 288 \text{ in}^3$

23. $V = \dfrac{4}{3}\pi r^3 = \dfrac{4}{3}\pi \cdot 4^3 = \dfrac{256}{3}\pi \text{ cm}^3$ $S = 4\pi r^2 = 4\pi \cdot 4^2 = 64\pi \text{ cm}^2$

24. $V = \dfrac{4}{3}\pi r^3 = \dfrac{4}{3}\pi \cdot 3^3 = 36\pi \text{ ft}^3$ $S = 4\pi r^2 = 4\pi \cdot 3^2 = 36\pi \text{ ft}^2$

25. $V = \pi r^2 h = \pi(9)^2(8) = 648\pi \text{ in}^3$ 26. $V = \pi r^2 h = \pi(8)^2(9) = 576\pi \text{ in}^3$

27. The diameter of the circle is 2, so its radius is 1. $A = \pi r^2 = \pi(1)^2 = \pi$ square units

28. The diameter of the circle is 2, so its radius is 1. $A = 2^2 - \pi(1)^2 = 4 - \pi$ square units

29. The diameter of the circle is the length of the diagonal of the square.
$$d^2 = 2^2 + 2^2 = 4 + 4 = 8 \;\rightarrow\; d = \sqrt{8} = 2\sqrt{2} \qquad r = \sqrt{2}$$
The area of the circle is: $A = \pi r^2 = \pi\left(\sqrt{2}\right)^2 = 2\pi$ square units

30. The diameter of the circle is the length of the diagonal of the square.
$$d^2 = 2^2 + 2^2 = 4 + 4 = 8 \;\rightarrow\; d = \sqrt{8} = 2\sqrt{2} \qquad r = \sqrt{2}$$
The area is: $A = \pi\left(\sqrt{2}\right)^2 - 2^2 = 2\pi - 4$ square units

31. The total distance traveled is 4 times the circumference of the wheel.
Total distance $= 4C = 4(\pi d) = 4\pi \cdot 16 = 64\pi = 201.1$ inches

32. The distance traveled in one revolution is the circumference of the disk 4π.
The number of revolutions $= \dfrac{\text{distance traveled}}{\text{circumference}} = \dfrac{20}{4\pi} = \dfrac{5}{\pi} \approx 1.59$ revolutions

33. Area of the border $=$ area of EFGH $-$ area of ABCD $= 10^2 - 6^2 = 100 - 36 = 64 \text{ ft}^2$

34. FG $= 4$ feet, BC $= 10$ feet, so CG$= 6$ feet. The area of the triangle CGF is:
$$A = \dfrac{1}{2} \cdot (4)(6) = 12 \text{ ft}^2$$

35.   Area of the window = area of the rectangle + area of the semicircle.

$$A = (6)(4) + \frac{1}{2} \cdot \pi \cdot 2^2 = 24 + 2\pi = 30.28 \text{ ft}^2$$

Perimeter of the window = 2 heights + width + one-half the circumference.

$$P = 2(6) + 4 + \frac{1}{2} \cdot \pi(4) = 12 + 4 + 2\pi = 16 + 2\pi = 22.28 \text{ feet}$$

36.   Area of the deck = area of the pool and deck – area of the pool.

$$A = \pi(13)^2 - \pi(10)^2 = 169\pi - 100\pi = 69\pi \text{ ft}^2$$

The amount of fence is the circumference of the circle with radius 13 feet.

$$C = 2\pi(13) = 26\pi \text{ ft}$$

37.   Convert 20 feet to miles, and solve the Pythagorean theorem to find the distance:

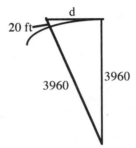

$$20 \text{ feet } = 20 \text{ feet } \cdot \frac{1 \text{ mile}}{5280 \text{ feet}} = 0.003788 \text{ miles}$$

$$d^2 = (3960 + 0.003788)^2 - 3960^2 = 30$$

$$d \approx 5.477 \text{ miles}$$

38.   Convert 6 feet to miles, and solve the Pythagorean theorem to find the distance:

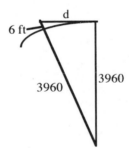

$$6 \text{ feet } = 6 \text{ feet } \cdot \frac{1 \text{ mile}}{5280 \text{ feet}} = 0.001136 \text{ miles}$$

$$d^2 = (3960 + 0.001136)^2 - 3960^2 = 9$$

$$d \approx 3 \text{ miles}$$

39.   Convert 100 feet to miles, and solve the Pythagorean theorem to find the distance:

$$100 \text{ feet } = 100 \text{ feet } \cdot \frac{1 \text{ mile}}{5280 \text{ feet}} = 0.018939 \text{ miles}$$

$$d^2 = (3960 + 0.018939)^2 - 3960^2 = 150$$

$$d \approx 12.247 \text{ miles}$$

Convert 150 feet to miles, and solve the Pythagorean theorem to find the distance:

$$150 \text{ feet } = 150 \text{ feet } \cdot \frac{1 \text{ mile}}{5280 \text{ feet}} = 0.028409 \text{ miles}$$

$$d^2 = (3960 + 0.028409)^2 - 3960^2 = 225$$

$$d \approx 15 \text{ miles}$$

40.   given $m > 0, n > 0$ and $m > n$

if $a = m^2 - n^2, b = 2mn$ and $c = m^2 + n^2$, then

$$a^2 + b^2 = \left(m^2 - n^2\right)^2 + (2mn)^2$$

$$= m^4 - 2m^2n^2 + n^2 + 4m^2n^2 = m^4 + 2m^2n^2 + n^2$$

and $c^2 = \left(m^2 + n^2\right)^2 = m^4 + 2m^2n^2 + n^2$

$\therefore a^2 + b^2 = c^2 \rightarrow a, b$ and c represent the sides of a right triangle.

41. Given a rectangle with perimeter = 1000 feet, the largest area will be enclosed by a square with dimensions 250 by 250 feet.   That is, the area = $250^2 = 62500$ square feet.

A circular pool with circumference = 1000 feet yields the equation : $2\pi r = 1000 \rightarrow r = \dfrac{500}{\pi}$

The area enclosed by the circular pool is: $A = \pi r^2 = \pi \left(\dfrac{500}{\pi}\right)^2 = \dfrac{500^2}{\pi} \approx 79577.47$ square feet

Therefore, a circular pool will enclose the most area.

Review

R.4 Integer Exponents

1. $4^2 = 16$

2. $-4^2 = -(4)^2 = -16$

3. $4^{-2} = \dfrac{1}{4^2} = \dfrac{1}{16}$

4. $(-4)^2 = (-4)(-4) = 16$

5. $-4^{-2} = -\dfrac{1}{4^2} = -\dfrac{1}{16}$

6. $(-4)^{-2} = \dfrac{1}{(-4)^2} = \dfrac{1}{-4} \cdot \dfrac{1}{-4} = \dfrac{1}{16}$

7. $4^0 \cdot 2^{-3} = 1 \cdot \dfrac{1}{2^3} = 1 \cdot \dfrac{1}{8} = \dfrac{1}{8}$

8. $(-2)^{-3} \cdot 3^0 = \dfrac{1}{(-2)^3} \cdot 1 = \dfrac{1}{-8} = -\dfrac{1}{8}$

9. $2^{-3} + \left(\dfrac{1}{2}\right)^3 = \dfrac{1}{2^3} + \dfrac{1^3}{2^3} = \dfrac{1}{8} + \dfrac{1}{8} = \dfrac{1}{4}$

10. $3^{-2} + \left(\dfrac{1}{3}\right)^2 = \dfrac{1}{3^2} + \dfrac{1^2}{3^2} = \dfrac{1}{9} + \dfrac{1}{9} = \dfrac{2}{9}$

11. $3^{-6} \cdot 3^4 = 3^{-6+4} = 3^{-2} = \dfrac{1}{3^2} = \dfrac{1}{9}$

12. $4^{-2} \cdot 4^3 = 4^{-2+3} = 4^1 = 4$

13. $\dfrac{\left(3^2\right)^2}{\left(2^3\right)^2} = \dfrac{3^4}{2^6} = \dfrac{81}{64}$

14. $\dfrac{\left(2^3\right)^3}{\left(2^2\right)^3} = \dfrac{2^9}{2^6} = 2^{9-6} = 2^3 = 8$

15. $\left(\dfrac{2}{3}\right)^{-3} = \dfrac{1}{\left(\dfrac{2}{3}\right)^3} = \dfrac{1}{\left(\dfrac{2^3}{3^3}\right)} = \dfrac{3^3}{2^3} = \dfrac{27}{8}$

16. $\left(\dfrac{3}{2}\right)^{-2} = \dfrac{1}{\left(\dfrac{3}{2}\right)^2} = \dfrac{1}{\left(\dfrac{3^2}{2^2}\right)} = \dfrac{2^2}{3^2} = \dfrac{4}{9}$

17. $\dfrac{2^3 \cdot 3^2}{2^4 \cdot 3^{-2}} = \dfrac{2^3}{2^4} \cdot \dfrac{3^2}{3^{-2}} = 2^{3-4} \cdot 3^{2-(-2)} = 2^{-1} \cdot 3^4 = \dfrac{1}{2} \cdot 81 = \dfrac{81}{2}$

18. $\dfrac{3^{-2} \cdot 5^3}{3^2 \cdot 5} = \dfrac{3^{-2}}{3^2} \cdot \dfrac{5^3}{5} = 3^{-2-2} \cdot 5^{3-1} = 3^{-4} \cdot 5^2 = \dfrac{1}{3^4} \cdot 25 = \dfrac{25}{81}$

19. $\left(\dfrac{9}{2}\right)^{-2} = \dfrac{1}{\left(\dfrac{9}{2}\right)^2} = \dfrac{1}{\left(\dfrac{9^2}{2^2}\right)} = \dfrac{2^2}{9^2} = \dfrac{4}{81}$

20. $\left(\dfrac{6}{5}\right)^{-3} = \dfrac{1}{\left(\dfrac{6}{5}\right)^3} = \dfrac{1}{\left(\dfrac{6^3}{5^3}\right)} = \dfrac{5^3}{6^3} = \dfrac{125}{216}$

21. $\dfrac{2^{-2}}{3} = \dfrac{\left(\dfrac{1}{2^2}\right)}{3} = \dfrac{\left(\dfrac{1}{4}\right)}{3} = \dfrac{1}{4} \cdot \dfrac{1}{3} = \dfrac{1}{12}$

22. $\dfrac{3^{-2}}{2} = \dfrac{\left(\dfrac{1}{3^2}\right)}{2} = \dfrac{\left(\dfrac{1}{9}\right)}{2} = \dfrac{1}{9} \cdot \dfrac{1}{2} = \dfrac{1}{18}$

23. $\dfrac{-3^{-1}}{2^{-1}} = \dfrac{\left(-\dfrac{1}{3}\right)}{\left(\dfrac{1}{2}\right)} = -\dfrac{1}{3} \cdot \dfrac{2}{1} = -\dfrac{2}{3}$

24. $\dfrac{-2^{-3}}{-1} = \dfrac{\left(-\dfrac{1}{2^3}\right)}{-1} = -\dfrac{1}{8} \cdot \dfrac{1}{-1} = \dfrac{1}{8}$

25. $x^0 y^2 = 1 \cdot y^2 = y^2$

26. $x^{-1}y = \dfrac{1}{x} \cdot y = \dfrac{y}{x}$

27. $x\,y^{-2} = x \cdot \dfrac{1}{y^2} = \dfrac{x}{y^2}$

28. $x^0\,y^4 = 1 \cdot y^4 = y^4$

29. $\left(8x^3\right)^{-2} = \dfrac{1}{\left(8x^3\right)^2} = \dfrac{1}{8^2 \cdot x^6} = \dfrac{1}{64x^6}$

30. $\left(-8x^3\right)^{-2} = \dfrac{1}{\left(-8x^3\right)^2} = \dfrac{1}{(-8)^2 \cdot x^6} = \dfrac{1}{64x^6}$

31. $-4x^{-1} = -4 \cdot \dfrac{1}{x} = -\dfrac{4}{x}$

32. $(-4x)^{-1} = \dfrac{1}{-4x} = -\dfrac{1}{4x}$

33. $3x^0 = 3 \cdot 1 = 3$

34. $(3x)^0 = 1$

35. $\dfrac{x^{-2}\,y^3}{x\,y^4} = \dfrac{x^{-2}}{x} \cdot \dfrac{y^3}{y^4} = x^{-2-1}\,y^{3-4} = x^{-3}y^{-1} = \dfrac{1}{x^3} \cdot \dfrac{1}{y} = \dfrac{1}{x^3 y}$

36. $\dfrac{x^{-2}\,y}{x\,y^2} = \dfrac{x^{-2}}{x} \cdot \dfrac{y}{y^2} = x^{-2-1}y^{1-2} = x^{-3}y^{-1} = \dfrac{1}{x^3} \cdot \dfrac{1}{y} = \dfrac{1}{x^3 y}$

37. $x^{-1}y^{-1} = \dfrac{1}{x} \cdot \dfrac{1}{y} = \dfrac{1}{xy}$

38. $\dfrac{x^{-2}y^{-3}}{x} = \dfrac{x^{-2}}{x} \cdot \dfrac{1}{y^3} = x^{-2-1} \cdot \dfrac{1}{y^3} = x^{-3} \cdot \dfrac{1}{y^3} = \dfrac{1}{x^3} \cdot \dfrac{1}{y^3} = \dfrac{1}{x^3 y^3}$

39. $\dfrac{x^{-1}}{y^{-1}} = \dfrac{\left(\dfrac{1}{x}\right)}{\left(\dfrac{1}{y}\right)} = \dfrac{1}{x} \cdot \dfrac{y}{1} = \dfrac{y}{x}$

40. $\left(\dfrac{2x}{3}\right)^{-1} = \dfrac{3}{2x}$

41. $\left(\dfrac{4y}{5x}\right)^{-2} = \dfrac{1}{\left(\dfrac{4y}{5x}\right)^2} = \dfrac{1}{\left(\dfrac{(4y)^2}{(5x)^2}\right)} = \dfrac{(5x)^2}{(4y)^2} = \dfrac{5^2 \cdot x^2}{4^2 \cdot y^2} = \dfrac{25x^2}{16y^2}$

42. $\left(x^2 y\right)^{-2} = \dfrac{1}{\left(x^2 y\right)^2} = \dfrac{1}{\left(x^2\right)^2 y^2} = \dfrac{1}{x^4 y^2}$

43. $x^{-2} y^{-2} = \dfrac{1}{x^2} \cdot \dfrac{1}{y^2} = \dfrac{1}{x^2 y^2}$ 44. $x^{-1} y^{-1} = \dfrac{1}{x} \cdot \dfrac{1}{y} = \dfrac{1}{xy}$

45. $\dfrac{x^{-1} y^{-2} z^3}{x^2 y z^3} = \dfrac{x^{-1}}{x^2} \cdot \dfrac{y^{-2}}{y} \cdot \dfrac{z^3}{z^3} = x^{-1-2} y^{-2-1} z^{3-3} = x^{-3} y^{-3} z^0 = \dfrac{1}{x^3} \cdot \dfrac{1}{y^3} \cdot 1 = \dfrac{1}{x^3 y^3}$

46. $\dfrac{3 x^{-2} y z^2}{x^4 y^{-3} z^2} = 3 \dfrac{x^{-2}}{x^4} \cdot \dfrac{y}{y^{-3}} \cdot \dfrac{z^2}{z^2} = 3 x^{-2-4} y^{1-(-3)} z^{2-2} = 3 x^{-6} y^4 z^0 = 3 \dfrac{1}{x^6} \cdot y^4 \cdot 1 = \dfrac{3 y^4}{x^6}$

47. $\dfrac{(-2)^3 x^4 (y z)^2}{3^2 x y^3 z^4} = \dfrac{-8 x^4 y^2 z^2}{9 x y^3 z^4} = \dfrac{-8}{9} x^{4-1} y^{2-3} z^{2-4} = \dfrac{-8}{9} x^3 y^{-1} z^{-2} = \dfrac{-8}{9} x^3 \cdot \dfrac{1}{y} \cdot \dfrac{1}{z^2} = \dfrac{-8 x^3}{9 y z^2}$

48. $\dfrac{4 x^{-2} (y z)^{-1}}{(-5)^2 x^4 y^2 z^{-2}} = \dfrac{4 x^{-2} y^{-1} z^{-1}}{25 x^4 y^2 z^{-2}} = \dfrac{4}{25} x^{-2-4} y^{-1-2} z^{-1-(-2)} = \dfrac{4}{25} x^{-6} y^{-3} z^1$

   $= \dfrac{4}{25} \dfrac{1}{x^6} \cdot \dfrac{1}{y^3} \cdot z = \dfrac{4 z}{25 x^6 y^3}$

49. $\dfrac{\left(\dfrac{x}{y}\right)^{-2} \cdot \left(\dfrac{y}{x}\right)^4}{x^2 y^3} = \dfrac{\left(\dfrac{y^2}{x^2} \cdot \dfrac{y^4}{x^4}\right)}{x^2 y^3} = \dfrac{y^6}{x^6} \cdot \dfrac{1}{x^2 y^3} = \dfrac{y^3}{x^8}$ 50. $\dfrac{\left(\dfrac{y}{x}\right)^2}{x^{-2} y} = \dfrac{\left(\dfrac{y^2}{x^2}\right)}{\left(\dfrac{y}{x^2}\right)} = \dfrac{y^2}{x^2} \cdot \dfrac{x^2}{y} = y$

51. $\left(\dfrac{3 x^{-1}}{4 y^{-1}}\right)^{-2} = \dfrac{1}{\left(\dfrac{3 x^{-1}}{4 y^{-1}}\right)^2} = \dfrac{1}{\dfrac{\left(3 x^{-1}\right)^2}{\left(4 y^{-1}\right)^2}} = \dfrac{\left(4 y^{-1}\right)^2}{\left(3 x^{-1}\right)^2} = \dfrac{4^2 y^{-2}}{3^2 x^{-2}} = \dfrac{\left(16 \cdot \dfrac{1}{y^2}\right)}{\left(9 \cdot \dfrac{1}{x^2}\right)} = \dfrac{16}{9} \cdot \dfrac{x^2}{y^2} = \dfrac{16 x^2}{9 y^2}$

52. $\left(\dfrac{5 x^{-2}}{6 y^{-2}}\right)^{-3} = \dfrac{1}{\left(\dfrac{5 x^{-2}}{6 y^{-2}}\right)^3} = \dfrac{1}{\dfrac{\left(5 x^{-2}\right)^3}{\left(6 y^{-2}\right)^3}} = \dfrac{\left(6 y^{-2}\right)^3}{\left(5 x^{-2}\right)^3} = \dfrac{6^3 y^{-6}}{5^3 x^{-6}} = \dfrac{\left(216 \cdot \dfrac{1}{y^6}\right)}{\left(125 \cdot \dfrac{1}{x^6}\right)} = \dfrac{216}{125} \cdot \dfrac{x^6}{y^6} = \dfrac{216 x^6}{125 y^6}$

53. $\dfrac{\left(x y^{-1}\right)^{-2}}{x y^3} = \dfrac{x^{-2} y^2}{x y^3} = \dfrac{x^{-2}}{x} \cdot \dfrac{y^2}{y^3} = x^{-2-1} y^{2-3} = x^{-3} y^{-1} = \dfrac{1}{x^3 y}$

54. $\dfrac{\left(3 x y^{-1}\right)^2}{\left(2 x^{-1} y\right)^3} = \dfrac{3^2 x^2 y^{-2}}{2^3 x^{-3} y^3} = \dfrac{9}{8} \cdot \dfrac{x^2}{x^{-3}} \cdot \dfrac{y^{-2}}{y^3} = \dfrac{9}{8} x^{2-(-3)} y^{-2-3} = \dfrac{9}{8} x^5 y^{-5} = \dfrac{9 x^5}{8 y^5}$

55. $\left(\dfrac{x}{y^2}\right)^{-2} \cdot \left(y^2\right)^{-1} = \dfrac{x^{-2}}{\left(y^2\right)^{-2}} \cdot \dfrac{1}{y^2} = \dfrac{x^{-2}}{y^{-4}y^2} = \dfrac{x^{-2}}{y^{-2}} = \dfrac{\left(\dfrac{1}{x^2}\right)}{\left(\dfrac{1}{y^2}\right)} = \dfrac{y^2}{x^2}$

56. $\dfrac{\left(x^2\right)^{-3}y^3}{\left(x^3y\right)^{-2}} = \dfrac{x^{-6}y^3}{x^{-6}y^{-2}} = x^{-6-(-6)}y^{3-(-2)} = x^0 y^5 = y^5$

57. If $x = 2$, $\;2x^3 - 3x^2 + 5x - 4 = 2\cdot 2^3 - 3\cdot 2^2 + 5\cdot 2 - 4 = 16 - 12 + 10 - 4 = 10$
    If $x = 1$, $\;2x^3 - 3x^2 + 5x - 4 = 2\cdot 1^3 - 3\cdot 1^2 + 5\cdot 1 - 4 = 2 - 3 + 5 - 4 = 0$

58. If $x = 1$, $\;4x^3 + 3x^2 - x + 2 = 4\cdot 1^3 + 3\cdot 1^2 - 1 + 2 = 4 + 3 - 1 + 2 = 8$
    If $x = 2$, $\;4x^3 + 3x^2 - x + 2 = 4\cdot 2^3 + 3\cdot 2^2 - 2 + 2 = 32 + 12 - 2 + 2 = 44$

59. $\dfrac{(666)^4}{(222)^4} = \left(\dfrac{666}{222}\right)^4 = 3^4 = 81$

60. $(0.1)^3 (20)^3 = \left(\dfrac{1}{10}\right)^3 \cdot (2\cdot 10)^3 = \dfrac{1}{10^3} \cdot 2^3 \cdot 10^3 = 2^3 = 8$

61. $(8.2)^6 \approx 304,006.671$ 62. $(3.7)^5 \approx 693.440$

63. $(6.1)^{-3} \approx 0.004$ 64. $(2.2)^{-5} \approx 0.019$

65. $(-2.8)^6 \approx 481.890$ 66. $-(2.8)^6 \approx -481.890$

67. $(-8.11)^{-4} \approx 0.000$ 68. $-(8.11)^{-4} \approx 0.000$

69. $454.2 = 4.542 \times 10^2$ 70. $32.14 = 3.214 \times 10^1$

71. $0.013 = 1.3 \times 10^{-2}$ 72. $0.00421 = 4.21 \times 10^{-3}$

73. $32,155 = 3.2155 \times 10^4$ 74. $21,210 = 2.121 \times 10^4$

75. $0.000423 = 4.23 \times 10^{-4}$ 76. $0.0514 = 5.14 \times 10^{-2}$

77. $6.15 \times 10^4 = 61,500$ 78. $9.7 \times 10^3 = 9700$

79. $1.214 \times 10^{-3} = 0.001214$ 80. $9.88 \times 10^{-4} = 0.000988$

81. $1.1 \times 10^8 = 110,000,000$ 82. $4.112 \times 10^2 = 411.2$

83. $8.1 \times 10^{-2} = 0.081$ 84. $6.453 \times 10^{-1} = 0.6453$

85. $4 \times 10^8 = 400,000,000$ meters   86. $8872 = 8.872 \times 10^3$ meters

87. $5 \times 10^{-7} = 0.0000005$

88. $1 \times 10^{-10} = 0.0000000001$ meters

89. $0.0005 = 5 \times 10^{-4}$

90. $0.05 = 5 \times 10^{-2}$ centimeters

91. $64,000,000 \cdot 30 = (6.4 \times 10^7)(3 \times 10^1) = 19.2 \times 10^8 = 1.92 \times 10^9$

92. $17,640,000 \cdot 42 = (1.764 \times 10^7)(4.2 \times 10^1) = 7.4088 \times 10^8$ gallons

93. $186,000 \cdot 60 \cdot 60 \cdot 24 \cdot 365 = (1.86 \times 10^5)(6 \times 10^1)(6 \times 10^1)(2.4 \times 10^1)(3.65 \times 10^2)$
$$= 586.5696 \times 10^{10} = 5.865696 \times 10^{12}$$

94. $\dfrac{93,000,000}{186,000} = \dfrac{9.3 \times 10^7}{1.86 \times 10^5} = 5 \times 10^2 = 500$ seconds ≈ 8 minutes 20 seconds

95. Answers will vary.

96. Answers will vary.

Review

R.5 Polynomials

1. $2x^3$ Monomial; Variable: x; Coefficient: 2; Degree: 3

2. $-4x^2$ Monomial; Variable: x; Coefficient: –4; Degree: 2

3. $\dfrac{8}{x}$ Not a monomial. 4. $-2x^{-3} = \dfrac{-2}{x^3}$ Not a monomial.

5. $-2xy^2$ Monomial; Variable: x, y; Coefficient: –2; Degree: 3

6. $5x^2y^3$ Monomial; Variable: x, y; Coefficient: 5; Degree: 5

7. $\dfrac{8x}{y}$ Not a monomial 8. $\dfrac{-2x^2}{y^3}$ Not a monomial

9. $x^2 + y^2$ Not a monomial. 10. $3x^2 + 4$ Not a monomial.

11. $3x^2 - 5$ Polynomial; Degree: 2 12. $1 - 4x$ Polynomial; Degree: 1

13. 5 Polynomial; Degree: 0 14. $-\pi$ Polynomial; Degree: 0

15. $3x^2 - \dfrac{5}{x}$ Not a polynomial. 16. $\dfrac{3}{x} + 2$ Not a polynomial.

17. $2y^3 - \sqrt{2}$ Polynomial; Degree: 3 18. $10z^2 + z$ Polynomial; Degree: 2

19. $\dfrac{x^2 + 5}{x^3 - 1}$ Not a polynomial. 20. $\dfrac{3x^3 + 2x - 1}{x^2 + x + 1}$ Not a polynomial.

21. $(x^2 + 4x + 5) + (3x - 3) = x^2 + (4x + 3x) + (5 - 3) = x^2 + 7x + 2$

22. $(x^3 + 3x^2 + 2) + (x^2 - 4x + 4) = x^3 + (3x^2 + x^2) + (-4x) + (2 + 4) = x^3 + 4x^2 - 4x + 6$

23. $(x^3 - 2x^2 + 5x + 10) - (2x^2 - 4x + 3) = x^3 - 2x^2 + 5x + 10 - 2x^2 + 4x - 3$
$$= x^3 + (-2x^2 - 2x^2) + (5x + 4x) + (10 - 3)$$
$$= x^3 - 4x^2 + 9x + 7$$

24. $(x^2 - 3x - 4) - (x^3 - 3x^2 + x + 5) = x^2 - 3x - 4 - x^3 + 3x^2 - x - 5$
$$= -x^3 + (x^2 + 3x^2) + (-3x - x) + (-4 - 5)$$
$$= -x^3 + 4x^2 - 4x - 9$$

25. $(6x^5 + x^3 + x) + (5x^4 - x^3 + 3x^2) = 6x^5 + 5x^4 + 3x^2 + x$

26. $(10x^5 - 8x^2) + (3x^3 - 2x^2 + 6) = 10x^5 + 3x^3 - 10x^2 + 6$

27. $(x^2 - 3x + 1) + 2(3x^2 + x - 4) = x^2 - 3x + 1 + 6x^2 + 2x - 8 = 7x^2 - x - 7$

28. $-2(x^2 + x + 1) + (-5x^2 - x + 2) = -2x^2 - 2x - 2 - 5x^2 - x + 2 = -7x^2 - 3x$

29. $6(x^3 + x^2 - 3) - 4(2x^3 - 3x^2) = 6x^3 + 6x^2 - 18 - 8x^3 + 12x^2 = -2x^3 + 18x^2 - 18$

30. $8(4x^3 - 3x^2 - 1) - 6(4x^3 + 8x - 2) = 32x^3 - 24x^2 - 8 - 24x^3 - 48x + 12$
$$= 8x^3 - 24x^2 - 48x + 4$$

31. $(x^2 - x + 2) + (2x^2 - 3x + 5) - (x^2 + 1) = x^2 - x + 2 + 2x^2 - 3x + 5 - x^2 - 1$
$$= 2x^2 - 4x + 6$$

32. $(x^2 + 1) - (4x^2 + 5) - (x^2 + x - 2) = x^2 + 1 - 4x^2 - 5 - x^2 - x + 2$
$$= -4x^2 - x - 2$$

33. $9(y^2 - 3y + 4) - 6(1 - y^2) = 9y^2 - 27y + 36 - 6 + 6y^2 = 15y^2 - 27y + 30$

34. $8(1 - y^2) + 4(1 + y + y^2 + y^3) = 8 - 8y^2 + 4 + 4y + 4y^2 + 4y^3$
$$= 4y^3 - 4y^2 + 4y + 12$$

35. $x(x^2 + x - 4) = x^3 + x^2 - 4x$ 　　　　36.　　$4x^2(x^3 - x + 2) = 4x^5 - 4x^3 + 8x^2$

37. $-2x^2(4x^3 + 5) = -8x^5 - 10x^2$ 　　　38.　　$5x^3(3x - 4) = 15x^4 - 20x^3$

39. $(x + 1)(x^2 + 2x - 4) = x(x^2 + 2x - 4) + 1(x^2 + 2x - 4)$
$$= x^3 + 2x^2 - 4x + x^2 + 2x - 4$$
$$= x^3 + 3x^2 - 2x - 4$$

40. $(2x - 3)(x^2 + x + 1) = 2x(x^2 + x + 1) - 3(x^2 + x + 1)$
$$= 2x^3 + 2x^2 + 2x - 3x^2 - 3x - 3$$
$$= 2x^3 - x^2 - x - 3$$

41. $(x + 2)(x + 4) = x^2 + 4x + 2x + 8 = x^2 + 6x + 8$

42. $(x + 3)(x + 5) = x^2 + 5x + 3x + 15 = x^2 + 8x + 15$

43. $(2x+5)(x+2) = 2x^2 + 4x + 5x + 10 = 2x^2 + 9x + 10$

44. $(3x+1)(2x+1) = 6x^2 + 3x + 2x + 1 = 6x^2 + 5x + 1$

45. $(x-4)(x+2) = x^2 + 2x - 4x - 8 = x^2 - 2x - 8$

46. $(x+4)(x-2) = x^2 - 2x + 4x - 8 = x^2 + 2x - 8$

47. $(x-3)(x-2) = x^2 - 2x - 3x + 6 = x^2 - 5x + 6$

48. $(x-5)(x-1) = x^2 - x - 5x + 5 = x^2 - 6x + 5$

49. $(2x+3)(x-2) = 2x^2 - 4x + 3x - 6 = 2x^2 - x - 6$

50. $(2x-4)(3x+1) = 6x^2 + 2x - 12x - 4 = 6x^2 - 10x - 4$

51. $(-2x+3)(x-4) = -2x^2 + 8x + 3x - 12 = -2x^2 + 11x - 12$

52. $(-3x-1)(x+1) = -3x^2 - 3x - x - 1 = -3x^2 - 4x - 1$

53. $(-x-2)(-2x-4) = 2x^2 + 4x + 4x + 8 = 2x^2 + 8x + 8$

54. $(-2x-3)(3-x) = -6x + 2x^2 - 9 + 3x = 2x^2 - 3x - 9$

55. $(x-2y)(x+y) = x^2 + xy - 2xy - 2y^2 = x^2 - 3xy - 2y^2$

56. $(2x+3y)(x-y) = 2x^2 + 2xy + 3xy - 3y^2 = 2x^2 + 5xy - 3y^2$

57. $(-2x-3y)(3x+2y) = -6x^2 - 4xy - 9xy - 6y^2 = -6x^2 - 13xy - 6y^2$

58. $(x-3y)(-2x+y) = -2x^2 + xy + 6xy - 3y^2 = -2x^2 + 7xy - 3y^2$

59. $(x-7)(x+7) = x^2 - 7^2 = x^2 - 49$

60. $(x-1)(x+1) = x^2 - 1^2 = x^2 - 1$

61. $(2x+3)(2x-3) = (2x)^2 - 3^2 = 4x^2 - 9$

62. $(3x+2)(3x-2) = (3x)^2 - 2^2 = 9x^2 - 4$

63. $(x+4)^2 = x^2 + 2 \cdot x \cdot 4 + 4^2 = x^2 + 8x + 16$

64. $(x+5)^2 = x^2 + 2 \cdot x \cdot 5 + 5^2 = x^2 + 10x + 25$

65. $(x-4)^2 = x^2 - 2 \cdot x \cdot 4 + 4^2 = x^2 - 8x + 16$

66. $(x-5)^2 = x^2 - 2 \cdot x \cdot 5 + 5^2 = x^2 - 10x + 25$

67. $(3x+4)(3x-4) = (3x)^2 - 4^2 = 9x^2 - 16$

68. $(5x-3)(5x+3) = (5x)^2 - 3^2 = 25x^2 - 9$

69. $(2x-3)^2 = (2x)^2 - 2(2x)(3) + 3^2 = 4x^2 - 12x + 9$

70. $(3x-4)^2 = (3x)^2 - 2(3x)(4) + 4^2 = 9x^2 - 24x + 16$

71. $(x+y)(x-y) = (x)^2 - (y)^2 = x^2 - y^2$

72. $(x+3y)(x-3y) = (x)^2 - (3y)^2 = x^2 - 9y^2$

73. $(3x+y)(3x-y) = (3x)^2 - (y)^2 = 9x^2 - y^2$

74. $(3x+4y)(3x-4y) = (3x)^2 - (4y)^2 = 9x^2 - 16y^2$

75. $(x+y)^2 = x^2 + 2xy + y^2$

76. $(x-y)^2 = x^2 - 2xy + y^2$

77. $(x-2y)^2 = x^2 + 2(x \cdot (-2y)) + (2y)^2 = x^2 - 4xy + 4y^2$

78. $(2x+3y)^2 = (2x)^2 + 2(2x \cdot 3y) + (3y)^2 = 4x^2 + 12xy + 9y^2$

79. $(x-2)^3 = x^3 - 3 \cdot x^2 \cdot 2 + 3 \cdot x \cdot 2^2 - 2^3 = x^3 - 6x^2 + 12x - 8$

80. $(x+1)^3 = x^3 + 3 \cdot x^2 \cdot 1 + 3 \cdot x \cdot 1^2 + 1^3 = x^3 + 3x^2 + 3x + 1$

81. $(2x+1)^3 = (2x)^3 + 3(2x)^2(1) + 3(2x) \cdot 1^2 + 1^3 = 8x^3 + 12x^2 + 6x + 1$

82. $(3x-2)^3 = (3x)^3 - 3(3x)^2(2) + 3(3x) \cdot 2^2 - 2^3 = 27x^3 - 54x^2 + 36x - 8$

83. Divide:

$$
\begin{array}{r}
4x^2 - 3x + 1 \\
x\overline{\smash{\big)}\, 4x^3 - 3x^2 + x + 1} \\
\underline{4x^3} \\
-3x^2 + x + 1 \\
\underline{-3x^2} \\
x + 1 \\
\underline{x} \\
1
\end{array}
$$

Check:

$(x)(4x^2 - 3x + 1) + (1)$
$= 4x^3 - 3x^2 + x + 1$

The quotient is $4x^2 - 3x + 1$; the remainder is 1.

84. Divide:

$$
\begin{array}{r}
3x^2 - x + 1 \\
x\overline{\smash{\big)}\, 3x^3 - x^2 + x - 2} \\
\underline{3x^3} \\
-x^2 + x - 2 \\
\underline{-x^2} \\
x - 2 \\
\underline{x} \\
-2
\end{array}
$$

Check:

$(x)(3x^2 - x + 1) + (-2)$
$= 3x^3 - x^2 + x - 2$

The quotient is $3x^2 - x + 1$; the remainder is –2.

85. Divide:

$$
\begin{array}{r}
4x^2 - 11x + 23 \\
x + 2\overline{\smash{\big)}\, 4x^3 - 3x^2 + x + 1} \\
\underline{4x^3 + 8x^2} \\
-11x^2 + x \\
\underline{-11x^2 - 22x} \\
23x + 1 \\
\underline{23x + 46} \\
-45
\end{array}
$$

Check:

$(x + 2)(4x^2 - 11x + 23) + (-45)$
$= 4x^3 - 11x^2 + 23x + 8x^2 - 22x + 46 - 45$
$= 4x^3 - 3x^2 + x + 1$

The quotient is $4x^2 - 11x + 23$; the remainder is –45.

86. Divide:

$$x+2\overline{)3x^3-\ x^2+\ \ x-2}$$

quotient: $3x^2-7x+15$

$$\frac{3x^3+6x^2}{\ \ -7x^2+\ \ x}$$
$$\frac{-7x^2-14x}{\ \ 15x-\ 2}$$
$$\frac{15x+30}{-32}$$

Check:

$(x+2)(3x^2-7x+15)+(-32)$

$=3x^3-7x^2+15x+6x^2-14x+30-32$

$=3x^3-x^2+x-2$

The quotient is $3x^2-7x+15$; the remainder is -32.

87. Divide:

$$x^2\overline{)4x^3-3x^2+\ x+1}$$

quotient: $4x-3$

$$\frac{4x^3}{-3x^2+x+1}$$
$$\frac{-3x^2}{x+1}$$

Check:

$(x^2)(4x-3)+(x+1)$

$=4x^3-3x^2+x+1$

The quotient is $4x-3$; the remainder is $x+1$.

88. Divide:

$$x^2\overline{)3x^3-\ x^2+x-2}$$

quotient: $3x+1$

$$\frac{3x^3+}{x^2+x-2}$$
$$\frac{x^2}{x-2}$$

Check:

$(x^2)(3x+1)+(x-2)$

$=3x^3+x^2+x-2$

The quotient is $3x+1$; the remainder is $x-2$.

89. Divide:

$$x^2+2\overline{)4x^3-\ 3x^2+\ x+\ 1}$$

quotient: $4x-3$

$$\frac{4x^3\qquad+8x}{-3x^2-7x}$$
$$\frac{-3x^2\qquad-6}{-7x+\ 7}$$

Check:

$(x^2+2)(4x-3)+(-7x+7)$

$=4x^3-3x^2+8x-6-7x+7$

$=4x^3-3x^2+x+1$

The quotient is $4x-3$; the remainder is $-7x+7$.

90.   Divide:

$$
\begin{array}{r}
3x - 1 \\
x^2+2\overline{\smash{\big)}\,3x^3 - x^2 + x - 2} \\
\underline{3x^3 \qquad + 6x} \\
-x^2 - 5x \\
\underline{-x^2 \qquad -2} \\
-5x
\end{array}
$$

Check:

$(x^2+2)(3x-1)+(-5x)$

$=3x^3-x^2+6x-2-5x$

$=3x^3-x^2+x-2$

The quotient is $3x-1$; the remainder is $-5x$.

91.   Divide:

$$
\begin{array}{r}
2 \\
2x^3-1\overline{\smash{\big)}\,4x^3 - 3x^2 + x + 1} \\
\underline{4x^3 \qquad\quad -2} \\
-3x^2 + x + 3
\end{array}
$$

Check:

$(2x^3-1)(2)+(-3x^2+x+3)$

$=4x^3-2-3x^2+x+3$

$=4x^3-3x^2+x+1$

The quotient is 2; the remainder is $-3x^2+x+3$.

92.   Divide:

$$
\begin{array}{r}
1 \\
3x^3-1\overline{\smash{\big)}\,3x^3 - x^2 + x - 2} \\
\underline{3x^3 \qquad\quad -1} \\
-x^2 + x - 1
\end{array}
$$

Check:

$(3x^3-1)(1)+(-x^2+x-1)$

$=3x^3-1-x^2+x-1$

$=3x^3-x^2+x-2$

The quotient is 1; the remainder is $-x^2+x-1$.

93.   Divide:

$$
\begin{array}{r}
2x-\dfrac{5}{2} \\
2x^2+x+1\overline{\smash{\big)}\,4x^3 - 3x^2 + x + 1} \\
\underline{4x^3 + 2x^2 + 2x} \\
-5x^2 - x \\
\underline{-5x^2 - \dfrac{5}{3}x - \dfrac{5}{2}} \\
\dfrac{3}{2}x + \dfrac{7}{2}
\end{array}
$$

Check :

$(2x^2+x+1)(2x-\dfrac{5}{2})+\left(\dfrac{3}{2}x+\dfrac{7}{2}\right)$

$=4x^3-5x^2+2x^2-\dfrac{5}{2}x+2x-\dfrac{5}{2}+\dfrac{3}{2}x+\dfrac{7}{2}=4x^3-3x^2+x+1$

The quotient is $2x-\dfrac{5}{2}$; the remainder is $\dfrac{3}{2}x+\dfrac{7}{2}$.

94. Divide:

$$\begin{array}{r} x - \dfrac{2}{3} \\ 3x^2 + x + 1\overline{\smash{\big)}\,3x^3 - x^2 + x - 2} \\ \underline{3x^3 + x^2 + x} \\ -2x^2 \end{array}$$

$$\begin{array}{r} -2x^2 - \dfrac{2}{3}x - \dfrac{2}{3} \\ \underline{} \\ \dfrac{2}{3}x - \dfrac{4}{3} \end{array}$$

Check:

$$(3x^2 + x + 1)\left(x - \dfrac{2}{3}\right) + \left(\dfrac{2}{3}x - \dfrac{4}{3}\right)$$

$$= 3x^3 - 2x^2 + x^2 - \dfrac{2}{3}x + x - \dfrac{2}{3} + \dfrac{2}{3}x - \dfrac{4}{2}$$

$$= 3x^3 - x^2 + x - 2$$

The quotient is $x - \dfrac{2}{3}$; the remainder is $\dfrac{2}{3}x - \dfrac{4}{3}$.

95. Divide:

$$\begin{array}{r} -4x^2 - 3x - 3 \\ x - 1\overline{\smash{\big)}\,-4x^3 + x^2 + 0x - 4} \\ \underline{-4x^3 + 4x^2} \\ -3x^2 \\ \underline{-3x^2 + 3x} \\ -3x - 4 \\ \underline{-3x + 3} \\ -7 \end{array}$$

Check:

$$(x - 1)(-4x^2 - 3x - 3) + (-7)$$

$$= -4x^3 - 3x^2 - 3x + 4x^2 + 3x + 3 - 7$$

$$= -4x^3 + x^2 - 4$$

The quotient is $-4x^2 - 3x - 3$; the remainder is -7.

96. Divide:

$$\begin{array}{r} -3x^3 - 3x^2 - 3x - 5 \\ x - 1\overline{\smash{\big)}\,-3x^4 + 0x^3 + 0x^2 - 2x - 1} \\ \underline{-3x^4 + 3x^3} \\ -3x^3 \\ \underline{-3x^3 + 3x^2} \\ -3x^2 - 2x \\ \underline{-3x^2 + 3x} \\ -5x - 1 \\ \underline{-5x + 5} \\ -6 \end{array}$$

Check:

$$(x - 1)(-3x^3 - 3x^2 - 3x - 5) + (-6)$$

$$= -3x^4 - 3x^3 - 3x^2 - 5x + 3x^3 + 3x^2 + 3x + 5 - 6$$

$$= -3x^4 - 2x - 1$$

The quotient is $-3x^3 - 3x^2 - 3x - 5$; the remainder is -6.

97. Divide:

$$
\begin{array}{r}
x^2 - x - 1 \\
x^2 + x + 1 \overline{\smash{)} x^4 + 0x^3 - \ x^2 + 0x + 1} \\
\underline{x^4 + \ x^3 + \ x^2} \\
- x^3 - 2x^2 \\
\underline{- x^3 - \ x^2 - x} \\
- x^2 + x + 1 \\
\underline{-x^2 - x - 1} \\
2x + 2
\end{array}
$$

Check:

$(x^2 + x + 1)(x^2 - x - 1) + 2x + 2$

$= x^4 + x^3 + x^2 - x^3 - x^2 - x - x^2 - x - 1 + 2x + 2$

$= x^4 - x^2 + 1$

The quotient is $x^2 - x - 1$; the remainder is $2x + 2$.

98. Divide:

$$
\begin{array}{r}
x^2 + x - 1 \\
x^2 - x + 1 \overline{\smash{)} x^4 + 0x^3 - \ x^2 + 0x + 1} \\
\underline{x^4 - \ x^3 + \ x^2} \\
x^3 - 2x^2 \\
\underline{x^3 - \ x^2 + x} \\
- x^2 - x + 1 \\
\underline{-x^2 + x - 1} \\
- 2x + 2
\end{array}
$$

Check:

$(x^2 - x + 1)(x^2 + x - 1) + (-2x + 2)$

$= x^4 + x^3 - x^2 - x^3 - x^2 + x + x^2 + x - 1 - 2x + 2$

$= x^4 - x^2 + 1$

The quotient is $x^2 + x - 1$; the remainder is $-2x + 2$.

99. Divide:

$$
\begin{array}{r}
x^2 + ax + a^2 \\
x - a \overline{\smash{)} x^3 + 0x^2 + \ 0x - a^3} \\
\underline{x^3 - ax^2} \\
ax^2 \\
\underline{ax^2 - a^2 x} \\
a^2 x - a^3 \\
\underline{a^2 x - a^3} \\
0
\end{array}
$$

Check:

$(x - a)(x^2 + ax + a^2) + 0$

$= x^3 + ax^2 + a^2 x - ax^2 - a^2 x - a^3$

$= x^3 - a^3$

The quotient is $x^2 + ax + a^2$; the remainder is 0.

100. Divide:

$$x - a \overline{)\begin{array}{r} x^4 + ax^3 + a^2x^2 + a^3x + a^4 \\ x^5 + 0x^4 + 0x^3 + 0x^2 + 0x - a^5 \end{array}}$$

$$\underline{x^5 - ax^4}$$
$$ax^4$$
$$\underline{ax^4 - a^2x^3}$$
$$a^2x^3$$
$$\underline{a^2x^3 - a^3x^2}$$
$$a^3x^2$$
$$\underline{a^3x^2 - a^4x}$$
$$a^4x - a^5$$
$$\underline{a^4x - a^5}$$
$$0$$

Check:

$$(x - a)(x^4 + ax^3 + a^2x^2 + a^3x + a^4) + 0$$
$$= x^5 + ax^4 + a^2x^3 + a^3x^2 + a^4x - ax^4 - a^2x^3 - a^3x^2 - a^4x - a^5$$
$$= x^5 - a^5$$

The quotient is $x^4 + ax^3 + a^2x^2 + a^3x + a^4$; the remainder is 0.

101.

$$\frac{x^3 - 2x^2 + 3x + 5}{x + 2} = ax^2 + bx + c + \frac{d}{x + 2}$$

In order to find $a + b + c + d$, we do the long division and then look at the coefficients of the quotient and remainder.

$$x + 2 \overline{)\begin{array}{r} x^2 - 4x + 11 \\ x^3 - 2x^2 + 3x - 5 \end{array}}$$

$$\underline{x^3 + 2x^2}$$
$$-4x^2 + 3x - 5$$
$$\underline{-4x^2 - 8x}$$
$$11x - 5$$
$$\underline{11x + 22}$$
$$-27$$

therefore,

$$\frac{x^3 - 2x^2 + 3x + 5}{x + 2} = x^2 - 4x + 11 + \frac{-27}{x + 2}$$

$$a + b + c + d = 1 - 4 + 11 - 27 = -19$$

102. When we multiply polynomials $p_1(x)$ and $p_2(x)$, each term of $p_1(x)$ will be multiplied by each term of $p_2(x)$. So when the highest powered term of $p_1(x)$ multiplies by the highest powered term of $p_2(x)$, the exponents on the variables in those terms will add according to the basic rules of exponents. Therefore, the highest powered term of the product polynomial will have degree equal to the sum of the degrees of $p_1(x)$ and $p_2(x)$.

103. When we add two polynomials $p_1(x)$ and $p_2(x)$, where the degree of $p_1(x) \neq$ the degree of $p_2(x)$, each term of $p_1(x)$ will be added to each term of $p_2(x)$. Since only the terms with equal degrees will combine via addition, the degree of the sum polynomial will be the degree of the highest powered term overall, that is, the degree of the polynomial that had the higher degree.

104. When we add two polynomials $p_1(x)$ and $p_2(x)$, where the degree of $p_1(x) =$ the degree of $p_2(x)$, the new polynomial will degree $\leq$ the degree of $p_1(x)$ and $p_2(x)$.

105. Answers will vary.

106. Answers will vary.

Review

R.6   Factoring Polynomials

1. $3x + 6 = 3(x + 2)$

2. $7x - 14 = 7(x - 2)$

3. $ax^2 + a = a(x^2 + 1)$

4. $ax - a = a(x - 1)$

5. $x^3 + x^2 + x = x(x^2 + x + 1)$

6. $x^3 - x^2 + x = x(x^2 - x + 1)$

7. $2x^2 - 2x = 2x(x - 1)$

8. $3x^2 - 3x = 3x(x - 1)$

9. $3x^2y - 6xy^2 + 12xy = 3xy(x - 2y + 4)$

10. $60x^2y - 48xy^2 + 72x^3y = 12xy(5x - 4y + 6x^2)$

11. $x^2 - 1 = x^2 - 1^2 = (x - 1)(x + 1)$

12. $x^2 - 4 = x^2 - 2^2 = (x - 2)(x + 2)$

13. $4x^2 - 1 = (2x)^2 - 1^2 = (2x - 1)(2x + 1)$

14. $9x^2 - 1 = (3x)^2 - 1^2 = (3x - 1)(3x + 1)$

15. $x^2 - 16 = x^2 - 4^2 = (x - 4)(x + 4)$

16. $x^2 - 25 = x^2 - 5^2 = (x - 5)(x + 5)$

17. $25x^2 - 4 = (5x - 2)(5x + 2)$

18. $36x^2 - 9 = 9(4x^2 - 1) = 9(2x - 1)(2x + 1)$

19. $x^2 + 2x + 1 = (x + 1)^2$

20. $x^2 - 4x + 4 = (x - 2)^2$

21. $x^2 + 4x + 4 = (x + 2)^2$

22. $x^2 - 2x + 1 = (x + 1)^2$

23. $x^2 - 10x + 25 = (x - 5)^2$

24. $x^2 + 10x + 25 = (x + 5)^2$

25. $4x^2 + 4x + 1 = (2x + 1)^2$

26. $9x^2 + 6x + 1 = (3x + 1)^2$

27. $16x^2 + 8x + 1 = (4x + 1)^2$

28. $25x^2 + 10x + 1 = (5x + 1)^2$

29. $x^3 - 27 = x^3 - 3^3 = (x - 3)(x^2 + 3x + 9)$

30. $x^3 + 125 = x^3 + 5^3 = (x + 5)(x^2 - 5x + 25)$

31. $x^3 + 27 = x^3 + 3^3 = (x + 3)(x^2 - 3x + 9)$

32. $27 - 8x^3 = 3^3 - (2x)^3 = (3 - 2x)(9 + 6x + 4x^2)$

33. $8x^3 + 27 = (2x)^3 + 3^3 = (2x+3)(4x^2 - 6x + 9)$

34. $64 - 27x^3 = 4^3 - (3x)^3 = (4-3x)(16+12x+9x^2)$

35. $x^2 + 5x + 6 = (x+2)(x+3)$
36. $x^2 + 6x + 8 = (x+2)(x+4)$

37. $x^2 + 7x + 6 = (x+6)(x+1)$
38. $x^2 + 9x + 8 = (x+8)(x+1)$

39. $x^2 + 7x + 10 = (x+2)(x+5)$
40. $x^2 + 11x + 10 = (x+10)(x+1)$

41. $x^2 - 10x + 16 = (x-2)(x-8)$
42. $x^2 - 17x + 16 = (x-16)(x-1)$

43. $x^2 - 7x - 8 = (x+1)(x-8)$
44. $x^2 - 2x - 8 = (x+2)(x-4)$

45. $x^2 + 7x - 8 = (x+8)(x-1)$
46. $x^2 + 2x - 8 = (x+4)(x-2)$

47. $2x^2 + 4x + 3x + 6 = 2x(x+2) + 3(x+2) = (x+2)(2x+3)$

48. $3x^2 - 3x + 2x - 2 = 3x(x-1) + 2(x-1) = (x-1)(3x+2)$

49. $2x^2 - 4x + x - 2 = 2x(x-2) + 1(x-2) = (x-2)(2x+1)$

50. $3x^2 + 6x - x - 2 = 3x(x+2) - 1(x+2) = (x+2)(3x-1)$

51. $6x^2 + 9x + 4x + 6 = 3x(2x+3) + 2(2x+3) = (2x+3)(3x+2)$

52. $9x^2 - 6x + 3x - 2 = 3x(3x-2) + 1(3x-2) = (3x-2)(3x+1)$

53. $3x^2 + 4x + 1 = (3x+1)(x+1)$
54. $2x^2 + 3x + 1 = (2x+1)(x+1)$

55. $2z^2 + 5z + 3 = (2z+3)(z+1)$
56. $6z^2 + 5z + 1 = (3z+1)(2z+1)$

57. $3x^2 - 2x - 8 = (3x+4)(x-2)$
58. $3x^2 - 10x + 8 = (3x-4)(x-2)$

59. $3x^2 - 2x - 8 = (3x-4)(x+2)$
60. $3x^2 - 10x + 8 = (3x-4)(x-2)$

61. $3x^2 + 14x + 8 = (3x+2)(x+4)$
62. $3x^2 - 14x + 8 = (3x-2)(x-4)$

63. $3x^2 + 10x - 8 = (3x-2)(x+4)$
64. $3x^2 - 10x - 8 = (3x+2)(x-4)$

65. $x^2 - 36 = (x-6)(x+6)$
66. $x^2 - 9 = (x-3)(x+3)$

67. $2 - 8x^2 = 2(1-4x^2) = 2(1-2x)(1+2x)$

68. $3 - 27x^2 = 3(1 - 9x^2) = 3(1 - 3x)(1 + 3x)$

69. $x^2 + 7x + 10 = (x + 2)(x + 5)$

70. $x^2 + 5x + 4 = (x + 4)(x + 1)$

71. $x^2 - 10x + 21 = (x - 7)(x - 3)$

72. $x^2 - 6x + 8 = (x - 2)(x - 4)$

73. $4x^2 - 8x + 32 = 4(x^2 - 2x + 8)$

74. $3x^2 - 12x + 15 = 3(x^2 - 4x + 5)$

75. $x^2 + 4x + 16$ is prime because there are no factors of 16 whose sum is 4.

76. $x^2 + 12x + 36 = (x + 6)^2$

77. $15 + 2x - x^2 = -(x^2 - 2x - 15) = -(x - 5)(x + 3)$

78. $14 + 6x - x^2 = -(x^2 - 6x - 14)$ is prime because there are no factors of -14 whose sum is -6.

79. $3x^2 - 12x - 36 = 3(x^2 - 4x - 12) = 3(x - 6)(x + 2)$

80. $x^3 + 8x^2 - 20x = x(x^2 + 8x - 20) = x(x + 10)(x - 2)$

81. $y^4 + 11y^3 + 30y^2 = y^2(y^2 + 11y + 30) = y^2(y + 5)(y + 6)$

82. $3y^3 - 18y^2 - 48y = 3y(y^2 - 6y - 16) = 3y(y + 2)(y - 8)$

83. $4x^2 + 12x + 9 = (2x + 3)^2$

84. $9x^2 - 12x + 4 = (3x - 2)^2$

85. $6x^2 + 8x + 2 = 2(3x^2 + 4x + 1) = 2(3x + 1)(x + 1)$

86. $8x^2 + 6x - 2 = 2(4x^2 + 3x - 1) = 2(4x - 1)(x + 1)$

87. $x^4 - 81 = (x^2 - 9)(x^2 + 9) = (x - 3)(x + 3)(x^2 + 9)$

88. $x^4 - 1 = (x^2 - 1)(x^2 + 1) = (x - 1)(x + 1)(x^2 + 1)$

89. $x^6 - 2x^3 + 1 = (x^3 - 1)^2 = \left[(x - 1)(x^2 + x + 1)\right]^2 = (x - 1)^2(x^2 + x + 1)^2$

90. $x^6 + 2x^3 + 1 = (x^3 + 1)^2 = \left[(x + 1)(x^2 - x + 1)\right]^2 = (x + 1)^2(x^2 - x + 1)^2$

91. $x^7 - x^5 = x^5(x^2 - 1) = x^5(x - 1)(x + 1)$

92. $x^8 - x^5 = x^5(x^3 - 1) = x^5(x - 1)(x^2 + x + 1)$

93. $16x^2 + 24x + 9 = (4x + 3)^2$

94. $9x^2 - 24x + 16 = (3x - 4)^2$

95. $5 + 16x - 16x^2 = -(16x^2 - 16x - 5) = -(4x - 5)(4x + 1)$

96. $5 + 11x - 16x^2 = -(16x^2 - 11x - 5) = -(16x + 5)(x - 1)$

97. $4y^2 - 16y + 15 = (2y - 5)(2y - 3)$ 98. $9y^2 + 9y - 4 = (3y + 4)(3y - 1)$

99. $1 - 8x^2 - 9x^4 = -(9x^4 + 8x^2 - 1) = -(9x^2 - 1)(x^2 + 1) = -(3x - 1)(3x + 1)(x^2 + 1)$

100. $4 - 14x^2 - 8x^4 = -2(4x^4 + 7x^2 - 2) = -2(4x^2 - 1)(x^2 + 2)$
$$= -2(2x - 1)(2x + 1)(x^2 + 2)$$

101. $x(x + 3) - 6(x + 3) = (x + 3)(x - 6)$

102. $5(3x - 7) + x(3x - 7) = (3x - 7)(x + 5)$

103. $(x + 2)^2 - 5(x + 2) = (x + 2)[(x + 2) - 5] = (x + 2)(x - 3)$

104. $(x - 1)^2 - 2(x - 1) = (x - 1)[(x - 1) - 2] = (x - 1)(x - 3)$

105. $(3x - 2)^3 - 27 = [(3x - 2) - 3][(3x - 2)^2 + 3(3x - 2) + 9]$
$$= (3x - 5)(9x^2 - 12x + 4 + 9x - 6 + 9) = (3x - 5)(9x^2 - 3x + 7)$$

106. $(5x + 1)^3 - 1 = [(5x + 1) - 1][(5x + 1)^2 + (1)(5x + 1) + 1]$
$$= (5x)(25x^2 + 10x + 1 + 5x + 1 + 1) = (3x - 5)(25x^2 + 15x + 3)$$

107. $3(x^2 + 10x + 25) - 4(x + 5) = 3(x + 5)^2 - 4(x + 5)$
$$= (x + 5)[3(x + 5) - 4] = (x + 5)(3x + 15 - 4) = (x + 5)(3x + 11)$$

108. $7(x^2 - 6x + 9) + 5(x - 3) = 7(x - 3)^2 + 5(x - 3)$
$$= (x - 3)[7(x - 3) + 5] = (x - 3)(7x - 21 + 5) = (x - 3)(7x - 16)$$

109. $x^3 + 2x^2 - x - 2 = x^2(x + 2) - (x + 2) = (x + 2)(x^2 - 1) = (x + 2)(x - 1)(x + 1)$

110. $x^3 - 3x^2 - x + 3 = x^2(x - 3) - (x - 3) = (x - 3)(x^2 - 1) = (x - 3)(x - 1)(x + 1)$

111. $x^4 - x^3 + x - 1 = x^3(x - 1) + (x - 1) = (x - 1)(x^3 + 1) = (x - 1)(x + 1)(x^2 - x + 1)$

112. $x^4 + x^3 + x + 1 = x^3(x + 1) + (x + 1) = (x + 1)(x^3 + 1) = (x + 1)(x + 1)(x^2 - x + 1)$
$$= (x + 1)^2(x^2 - x + 1)$$

113.

Factors of 4	1, 4	2, 2	−1, −4	−2, −2
Sum	5	4	−5	−4

None of the sums of the factors is 0, so $x^2 + 4$ is prime.

114.

Factors of 1	1, 1	−1, −1
Sum	2	−2

None of the sums of the factors is 1, so $x^2 + x + 1$ is prime.

115. Answers will vary.

116. Answers will vary.

Review

R.7 Rational Expressions

1. $\dfrac{3x+9}{x^2-9} = \dfrac{3(x+3)}{(x-3)(x+3)} = \dfrac{3}{x-3}$

2. $\dfrac{4x^2+8x}{12x+24} = \dfrac{4x(x+2)}{12(x+2)} = \dfrac{x}{3}$

3. $\dfrac{x^2-2x}{3x-6} = \dfrac{x(x-2)}{3(x-2)} = \dfrac{x}{3}$

4. $\dfrac{15x^2+24x}{3x^2} = \dfrac{3x(5x+8)}{3x^2} = \dfrac{5x+8}{x}$

5. $\dfrac{24x^2}{12x^2-6x} = \dfrac{24x^2}{6x(2x-1)} = \dfrac{4x}{2x-1}$

6. $\dfrac{x^2+4x+4}{x^2-16} = \dfrac{(x+2)^2}{(x-4)(x+4)}$

7. $\dfrac{y^2-25}{2y^2-8y-10} = \dfrac{(y+5)(y-5)}{2(y^2-4y-5)} = \dfrac{(y+5)(y-5)}{2(y-5)(y+1)} = \dfrac{y+5}{2(y+1)}$

8. $\dfrac{3y^2-y-2}{3y^2+5y+2} = \dfrac{(3y+1)(y-2)}{(3y+2)(y+1)}$

9. $\dfrac{x^2+4x-5}{x^2-2x+1} = \dfrac{(x+5)(x-1)}{(x-1)(x-1)} = \dfrac{x+5}{x-1}$

10. $\dfrac{x-x^2}{x^2+x-2} = \dfrac{-x(x-1)}{(x+2)(x-1)} = \dfrac{-x}{x+2}$

11. $\dfrac{x^2+5x-14}{2-x} = \dfrac{(x+7)(x-2)}{2-x} = \dfrac{(x+7)(x-2)}{(-1)(-2+x)} = \dfrac{(x+7)(x-2)}{(-1)(x-2)} = -(x+7)$

12. $\dfrac{2x^2+5x-3}{1-2x} = \dfrac{(2x-1)(x+3)}{-1(2x-1)} = -(x+3)$

13. $\dfrac{3x+6}{5x^2} \cdot \dfrac{x}{x^2-4} = \dfrac{3(x+2)}{5x^2} \cdot \dfrac{x}{(x-2)(x+2)} = \dfrac{3}{5x(x-2)}$

14. $\dfrac{3}{2x} \cdot \dfrac{x^2}{6x+10} = \dfrac{3}{2} \cdot \dfrac{x}{2(3x+5)} = \dfrac{3x}{4(3x+5)}$

15. $\dfrac{4x^2}{x^2-16} \cdot \dfrac{x-4}{2x} = \dfrac{4x^2}{(x-4)(x+4)} \cdot \dfrac{x-4}{2x} = \dfrac{2x}{x+4}$

16. $\dfrac{12}{x^2-x} \cdot \dfrac{x^2-1}{4x-2} = \dfrac{12}{x(x-1)} \cdot \dfrac{(x-1)(x+1)}{2(2x-1)} = \dfrac{6(x+1)}{x(2x-1)}$

17. $\dfrac{4x-8}{-3x} \cdot \dfrac{12}{12-6x} = \dfrac{4(x-2)}{-3x} \cdot \dfrac{12}{6(2-x)} = \dfrac{4(x-2)}{-3x} \cdot \dfrac{2}{(-1)(x-2)} = \dfrac{8}{3x}$

18. $\dfrac{6x-27}{5x} \cdot \dfrac{2}{4x-18} = \dfrac{3(2x-9)}{5x} \cdot \dfrac{2}{2(2x-9)} = \dfrac{3}{5x}$

19. $\dfrac{x^2-3x-10}{x^2+2x-35} \cdot \dfrac{x^2+4x-21}{x^2+9x+14} = \dfrac{(x-5)(x+2)}{(x+7)(x-5)} \cdot \dfrac{(x+7)(x-3)}{(x+7)(x+2)} = \dfrac{x-3}{x+7}$

20. $\dfrac{x^2+x-6}{x^2+4x-5} \cdot \dfrac{x^2-25}{x^2+2x-15} = \dfrac{(x-2)(x+3)}{(x+5)(x-1)} \cdot \dfrac{(x+5)(x-5)}{(x+5)(x-3)} = \dfrac{(x-2)(x+3)(x-5)}{(x+5)(x-1)(x-3)}$

21. $\dfrac{\left(\dfrac{6x}{x^2-4}\right)}{\left(\dfrac{3x-9}{2x+4}\right)} = \dfrac{6x}{x^2-4} \cdot \dfrac{2x+4}{3x-9} = \dfrac{6x}{(x-2)(x+2)} \cdot \dfrac{2(x+2)}{3(x-3)} = \dfrac{4x}{(x-2)(x-3)}$

22. $\dfrac{\left(\dfrac{12x}{5x+20}\right)}{\left(\dfrac{4x^2}{x^2-16}\right)} = \dfrac{12x}{5x+20} \cdot \dfrac{x^2-16}{4x^2} = \dfrac{12x}{5(x+4)} \cdot \dfrac{(x+4)(x-4)}{4x^2} = \dfrac{3(x-4)}{5x}$

23. $\dfrac{\left(\dfrac{8x}{x^2-1}\right)}{\left(\dfrac{10}{x+1}\right)} = \dfrac{8x}{x^2-1} \cdot \dfrac{x+1}{10} = \dfrac{8x}{(x-1)(x+1)} \cdot \dfrac{x+1}{10} = \dfrac{4x}{5(x-1)}$

24. $\dfrac{\left(\dfrac{x-2}{4x}\right)}{\left(\dfrac{x^2-4x+4}{12x}\right)} = \dfrac{x-2}{4x} \cdot \dfrac{12x}{x^2-4x+4} = \dfrac{x-2}{4x} \cdot \dfrac{12x}{(x-2)(x-2)} = \dfrac{3}{x-2}$

25. $\dfrac{\left(\dfrac{4-x}{4+x}\right)}{\left(\dfrac{4x}{x^2-16}\right)} = \dfrac{4-x}{4+x} \cdot \dfrac{x^2-16}{4x} = \dfrac{4-x}{4+x} \cdot \dfrac{(x+4)(x-4)}{4x} = \dfrac{(4-x)(x-4)}{4x} = \dfrac{-(x-4)^2}{4x}$

26. $\dfrac{\left(\dfrac{3+x}{3-x}\right)}{\left(\dfrac{x^2-9}{9x^3}\right)} = \dfrac{3+x}{3-x} \cdot \dfrac{9x^3}{x^2-9} = \dfrac{3+x}{3-x} \cdot \dfrac{9x^3}{(x+3)(x-3)} = \dfrac{9x^3}{(3-x)(x-3)} = \dfrac{9x^3}{-(x-3)^2}$

27. $\dfrac{\left(\dfrac{x^2+7x+12}{x^2-7x+12}\right)}{\left(\dfrac{x^2+x-12}{x^2-x-12}\right)} = \dfrac{x^2+7x+12}{x^2-7x+12} \cdot \dfrac{x^2-x-12}{x^2+x-12} = \dfrac{(x+3)(x+4)}{(x-3)(x-4)} \cdot \dfrac{(x-4)(x+3)}{(x+4)(x-3)} = \dfrac{(x+3)^2}{(x-3)^2}$

28. $\dfrac{\left(\dfrac{x^2+7x+6}{x^2+x-6}\right)}{\left(\dfrac{x^2+5x-6}{x^2+5x+6}\right)} = \dfrac{x^2+7x+6}{x^2+x-6} \cdot \dfrac{x^2+5x+6}{x^2+5x-6} = \dfrac{(x+6)(x+1)}{(x+3)(x-2)} \cdot \dfrac{(x+2)(x+3)}{(x+6)(x-1)}$

$\qquad = \dfrac{(x+1)(x+2)}{(x-2)(x-1)}$

29. $\dfrac{\left(\dfrac{2x^2-x-28}{3x^2-x-2}\right)}{\left(\dfrac{4x^2+16x+7}{3x^2+11x+6}\right)} = \dfrac{2x^2-x-28}{3x^2-x-2} \cdot \dfrac{3x^2+11x+6}{4x^2+16x+7} = \dfrac{(2x+7)(x-4)}{(3x+2)(x-1)} \cdot \dfrac{(3x+2)(x+3)}{(2x+7)(2x+1)}$

$\qquad = \dfrac{(x-4)(x+3)}{(x-1)(2x+1)}$

30. $\dfrac{\left(\dfrac{9x^2+3x-2}{12x^2+5x-2}\right)}{\left(\dfrac{9x^2-6x+1}{8x^2-10x-3}\right)} = \dfrac{9x^2+3x-2}{12x^2+5x-2} \cdot \dfrac{8x^2-10x-3}{9x^2-6x+1} = \dfrac{(3x+2)(3x-1)}{(3x+2)(4x-1)} \cdot \dfrac{(4x+1)(2x-3)}{(3x-1)(3x-1)}$

$\qquad = \dfrac{(4x+1)(2x-3)}{(4x-1)(3x-1)}$

31. $\dfrac{x}{2} + \dfrac{5}{2} = \dfrac{5+x}{2}$

32. $\dfrac{3}{x} - \dfrac{6}{x} = \dfrac{3-6}{x} = \dfrac{-2}{x}$

33. $\dfrac{x^2}{2x-3} - \dfrac{4}{2x-3} = \dfrac{x^2-4}{2x-3} = \dfrac{(x+2)(x-2)}{2x-3}$

34. $\dfrac{3x^2}{2x-1} - \dfrac{9}{2x-1} = \dfrac{3x^2-9}{2x-1} = \dfrac{3(x^2-3)}{2x-1}$

35. $\dfrac{x+1}{x-3} + \dfrac{2x-3}{x-3} = \dfrac{x+1+2x-3}{x-3} = \dfrac{3x-2}{x-3}$

36. $\dfrac{2x-5}{3x+2} + \dfrac{x+4}{3x+2} = \dfrac{2x-5+x+4}{3x+2} = \dfrac{3x-1}{3x+2}$

37. $\dfrac{3x+5}{2x-1} - \dfrac{2x-4}{2x-1} = \dfrac{(3x+5)-(2x-4)}{2x-1} = \dfrac{3x+5-2x+4}{2x-1} = \dfrac{x+9}{2x-1}$

38. $\dfrac{5x-4}{3x+4} - \dfrac{x+1}{3x+4} = \dfrac{(5x-4)-(x+1)}{3x+4} = \dfrac{5x-4-x-1}{3x+4} = \dfrac{4x-5}{3x+4}$

39. $\dfrac{4}{x-2} + \dfrac{x}{2-x} = \dfrac{4}{x-2} - \dfrac{x}{x-2} = \dfrac{4-x}{x-2}$

40. $\dfrac{6}{x-1} - \dfrac{x}{1-x} = \dfrac{6}{x-1} + \dfrac{x}{x-1} = \dfrac{x+6}{x-1}$

41. $\dfrac{4}{x-1} - \dfrac{2}{x+2} = \dfrac{4(x+2)}{(x-1)(x+2)} - \dfrac{2(x-1)}{(x+2)(x-1)} = \dfrac{4x+8-2x+2}{(x+2)(x-1)} = \dfrac{2x+10}{(x+2)(x-1)}$

$= \dfrac{2(x+5)}{(x+2)(x-1)}$

42. $\dfrac{2}{x+5} - \dfrac{5}{x-5} = \dfrac{2(x-5)}{(x+5)(x-5)} - \dfrac{5(x+5)}{(x+5)(x-5)} = \dfrac{2x-10-5x-25}{(x+5)(x-5)} = \dfrac{-3x-35}{(x+5)(x-5)}$

43. $\dfrac{x}{x+1} + \dfrac{2x-3}{x-1} = \dfrac{x(x-1)}{(x+1)(x-1)} + \dfrac{(2x-3)(x+1)}{(x-1)(x+1)} = \dfrac{x^2-x+2x^2-x-3}{(x-1)(x+1)}$

$= \dfrac{3x^2-2x-3}{(x-1)(x+1)}$

44. $\dfrac{3x}{x-4} + \dfrac{2x}{x+3} = \dfrac{3x(x+3)}{(x-4)(x+3)} + \dfrac{2x(x-4)}{(x-4)(x+3)} = \dfrac{3x^2+9x+2x^2-8x}{(x-4)(x+3)}$

$= \dfrac{5x^2+x}{(x-4)(x+3)} = \dfrac{x(5x+1)}{(x-4)(x+3)}$

45. $\dfrac{x-3}{x+2} - \dfrac{x+4}{x-2} = \dfrac{(x-3)(x-2)}{(x+2)(x-2)} - \dfrac{(x+4)(x+2)}{(x-2)(x+2)} = \dfrac{x^2-5x+6-(x^2+6x+8)}{(x+2)(x-2)}$

$= \dfrac{x^2-5x+6-x^2-6x-8}{(x+2)(x-2)} = \dfrac{-11x-2}{(x+2)(x-2)}$

46. $\dfrac{2x-3}{x-1} - \dfrac{2x+1}{x+1} = \dfrac{(2x-3)(x+1)}{(x-1)(x+1)} - \dfrac{(2x+1)(x-1)}{(x+1)(x-1)} = \dfrac{2x^2-x-3-(2x^2-x-1)}{(x+1)(x-1)}$

$= \dfrac{2x^2-x-3-2x^2+x+1}{(x+1)(x-1)} = \dfrac{-2}{(x+1)(x-1)}$

47. $\dfrac{x}{x^2-4} + \dfrac{1}{x} = \dfrac{x^2+x^2-4}{(x)(x^2-4)} = \dfrac{2x^2-4}{(x)(x^2-4)} = \dfrac{2(x^2-2)}{(x)(x-2)(x+2)}$

48. $\dfrac{x-1}{x^3} + \dfrac{x}{x^2+1} = \dfrac{(x-1)(x^2+1)+x^4}{(x^3)(x^2+1)} = \dfrac{x^3-x^2+x-1+x^4}{(x^3)(x^2+1)} = \dfrac{x^4+x^3-x^2+x-1}{(x^3)(x^2+1)}$

49. $x^2-4 = (x+2)(x-2)$

$x^2-x-2 = (x+1)(x-2)$

$\therefore$ LCM is $(x+2)(x-2)(x+1)$

50. $x^2 - x - 12 = (x + 3)(x - 4)$
$x^2 - 8x + 16 = (x - 4)(x - 4)$
$$\therefore \text{LCM is } (x + 3)(x - 4)^2$$

51. $x^3 - x = x(x^2 - 1) = x(x + 1)(x - 1)$
$x^2 - x = x(x - 1)$
$$\therefore \text{LCM is } x(x + 1)(x - 1)$$

52. $3x^2 - 27 = 3(x^2 - 9) = 3(x + 3)(x - 3)$
$2x^2 - x - 15 = (2x + 5)(x - 3)$
$$\therefore \text{LCM is } 3(2x + 5)(x - 3)(x + 3)$$

53. $4x^3 - 4x^2 + x = x(4x^2 - 4x + 1) = x(2x - 1)(2x - 1)$
$2x^3 - x^2 = x^2(2x - 1)$
$$x^3$$
$$\therefore \text{LCM is } x^3(2x - 1)^2$$

54. $x - 3$
$x^2 + 3x = x(x + 3)$
$x^3 - 9x = x(x^2 - 9) = x(x + 3)(x - 3)$
$$\therefore \text{LCM is } x(x + 3)(x - 3)$$

55. $x^3 - x = x(x^2 - 1) = x(x + 1)(x - 1)$
$x^3 - 2x^2 + x = x(x^2 - 2x + 1) = x(x - 1)^2$
$x^3 - 1 = (x - 1)(x^2 + x + 1)$
$$\therefore \text{LCM is } x(x + 1)(x - 1)^2(x^2 + x + 1)$$

56. $x^2 + 4x + 4 = (x + 2)^2$
$x^3 + 2x^2 = x^2(x + 2)$
$$(x + 2)^3$$
$$\therefore \text{LCM is } x^2(x + 2)^3$$

57. $\dfrac{x}{x^2 - 7x + 6} - \dfrac{x}{x^2 - 2x - 24} = \dfrac{x}{(x - 6)(x - 1)} - \dfrac{x}{(x - 6)(x + 4)}$
$$= \dfrac{x(x + 4)}{(x - 6)(x - 1)(x + 4)} - \dfrac{x(x - 1)}{(x - 6)(x + 4)(x - 1)}$$
$$= \dfrac{x^2 + 4x - x^2 + x}{(x - 6)(x + 4)(x - 1)} = \dfrac{5x}{(x - 6)(x + 4)(x - 1)}$$

58. $\dfrac{x}{x - 3} - \dfrac{x + 1}{x^2 + 5x - 24} = \dfrac{x}{(x - 3)} - \dfrac{x + 1}{(x - 3)(x + 8)} = \dfrac{x(x + 8)}{(x - 3)(x + 8)} - \dfrac{x + 1}{(x - 3)(x + 8)}$
$$= \dfrac{x^2 + 8x - x - 1}{(x - 3)(x + 8)} = \dfrac{x^2 + 7x - 1}{(x - 3)(x + 8)}$$

59. $\dfrac{4x}{x^2-4} - \dfrac{2}{x^2+x-6} = \dfrac{4x}{(x-2)(x+2)} - \dfrac{2}{(x+3)(x-2)}$

$$= \dfrac{4x(x+3)}{(x-2)(x+2)(x+3)} - \dfrac{2(x+2)}{(x+3)(x-2)(x+2)}$$

$$= \dfrac{4x^2+12x-2x-4}{(x-2)(x+2)(x+3)} = \dfrac{4x^2+10x-4}{(x-2)(x+2)(x+3)}$$

$$= \dfrac{2(2x^2+5x-2)}{(x-2)(x+2)(x+3)}$$

60. $\dfrac{3x}{x-1} - \dfrac{x-4}{x^2-2x+1} = \dfrac{3x}{(x-1)} - \dfrac{x-4}{(x-1)^2} = \dfrac{3x(x-1)}{(x-1)(x-1)} - \dfrac{x-4}{(x-1)^2} = \dfrac{3x^2-3x-x+4}{(x-1)^2}$

$$= \dfrac{3x^2-4x+4}{(x-1)^2}$$

61. $\dfrac{3}{(x-1)^2(x+1)} + \dfrac{2}{(x-1)(x+1)^2} = \dfrac{3(x+1)+2(x-1)}{(x-1)^2(x+1)^2} = \dfrac{3x+3+2x-2}{(x-1)^2(x+1)^2}$

$$= \dfrac{5x+1}{(x-1)^2(x+1)^2}$$

62. $\dfrac{2}{(x+2)^2(x-1)} - \dfrac{6}{(x+2)(x-1)^2} = \dfrac{2(x-1)-6(x+2)}{(x-1)^2(x+1)^2} = \dfrac{2x-2-6x-12}{(x-1)^2(x+1)^2}$

$$= \dfrac{-4x-14}{(x-1)^2(x+1)^2} = \dfrac{-2(2x+7)}{(x-1)^2(x+1)^2}$$

63. $\dfrac{x+4}{x^2-x-2} - \dfrac{2x+3}{x^2+2x-8} = \dfrac{x+4}{(x-2)(x+1)} - \dfrac{2x+3}{(x+4)(x-2)}$

$$= \dfrac{(x+4)(x+4)}{(x-2)(x+1)(x+4)} - \dfrac{(2x+3)(x+1)}{(x+4)(x-2)(x+1)}$$

$$= \dfrac{x^2+8x+16-(2x^2+5x+3)}{(x-2)(x+1)(x+4)} = \dfrac{-x^2+3x+13}{(x-2)(x+1)(x+4)}$$

64. $\dfrac{2x-3}{x^2+8x+7} - \dfrac{x-2}{(x+1)^2} = \dfrac{2x-3}{(x+1)(x+7)} - \dfrac{x-2}{(x+1)^2}$

$$= \dfrac{(2x-3)(x+1)}{(x+1)(x+7)(x+1)} - \dfrac{(x-2)(x+7)}{(x+1)^2(x+7)} = \dfrac{2x^2-x-3-(x^2+5x-14)}{(x+1)^2(x+7)}$$

$$= \dfrac{x^2-6x+11}{(x+1)^2(x+7)}$$

65. $\dfrac{1}{x} - \dfrac{2}{x^2+x} + \dfrac{3}{x^3-x^2} = \dfrac{1}{x} - \dfrac{2}{x(x+1)} + \dfrac{3}{x^2(x-1)} = \dfrac{x(x+1)(x-1)-2x(x-1)+3(x+1)}{x^2(x+1)(x-1)}$

$$= \dfrac{x(x^2-1)-2x^2+2x+3x+3}{x^2(x+1)(x-1)} = \dfrac{x^3-x-2x^2+5x+3}{x^2(x+1)(x-1)} = \dfrac{x^3-2x^2+4x+3}{x^2(x+1)(x-1)}$$

66. $\dfrac{x}{(x-1)^2}+\dfrac{2}{x}-\dfrac{x+1}{x^3-x^2}=\dfrac{x}{(x-1)^2}+\dfrac{2}{x}-\dfrac{x+1}{x^2(x-1)}=\dfrac{x^3+2x(x-1)^2-(x+1)(x-1)}{x^2(x-1)^2}$

$=\dfrac{x^3+2x(x^2-2x+1)-(x^2-1)}{x^2(x-1)^2}=\dfrac{x^3+2x^3-4x^2+2x-x^2+1}{x^2(x-1)^2}=\dfrac{3x^3-5x^2+2x+1}{x^2(x-1)^2}$

67. $\dfrac{1}{h}\left(\dfrac{1}{x+h}-\dfrac{1}{x}\right)=\dfrac{1}{h}\left(\dfrac{1\cdot x}{(x+h)x}-\dfrac{1(x+h)}{x(x+h)}\right)=\dfrac{1}{h}\left(\dfrac{x-x-h}{x(x+h)}\right)=\dfrac{-h}{hx(x+h)}=\dfrac{-1}{x(x+h)}$

68. $\dfrac{1}{h}\left(\dfrac{1}{(x+h)^2}-\dfrac{1}{x^2}\right)=\dfrac{1}{h}\left(\dfrac{1\cdot x^2}{(x+h)^2 x^2}-\dfrac{1(x+h)^2}{x^2(x+h)^2}\right)=\dfrac{1}{h}\left(\dfrac{x^2-(x^2+2xh+h^2)}{x^2(x+h)^2}\right)$

$=\dfrac{-2xh-h^2}{hx^2(x+h)^2}=\dfrac{h(-2x-h)}{hx^2(x+h)^2}=\dfrac{-2x-h}{x^2(x+h)^2}$

69. $\dfrac{1+\dfrac{1}{x}}{1-\dfrac{1}{x}}=\dfrac{\left(\dfrac{x}{x}+\dfrac{1}{x}\right)}{\left(\dfrac{x}{x}-\dfrac{1}{x}\right)}=\dfrac{\left(\dfrac{x+1}{x}\right)}{\left(\dfrac{x-1}{x}\right)}=\dfrac{x+1}{x}\cdot\dfrac{x}{x-1}=\dfrac{x+1}{x-1}$

70. $\dfrac{4+\dfrac{1}{x^2}}{3-\dfrac{1}{x^2}}=\dfrac{\left(\dfrac{4x^2}{x^2}+\dfrac{1}{x^2}\right)}{\left(\dfrac{3x^2}{x^2}-\dfrac{1}{x^2}\right)}=\dfrac{\left(\dfrac{4x^2+1}{x^2}\right)}{\left(\dfrac{3x^2-1}{x^2}\right)}=\dfrac{4x^2+1}{x^2}\cdot\dfrac{x^2}{3x^2-1}=\dfrac{4x^2+1}{3x^2-1}$

71. $\dfrac{x-\dfrac{1}{x}}{x+\dfrac{1}{x}}=\dfrac{\left(\dfrac{x^2}{x}-\dfrac{1}{x}\right)}{\left(\dfrac{x^2}{x}+\dfrac{1}{x}\right)}=\dfrac{\left(\dfrac{x^2-1}{x}\right)}{\left(\dfrac{x^2+1}{x}\right)}=\dfrac{x^2-1}{x}\cdot\dfrac{x}{x^2+1}=\dfrac{(x-1)(x+1)}{x^2+1}$

72. $\dfrac{1-\dfrac{x}{x+1}}{2-\dfrac{x-1}{x}}=\dfrac{\left(\dfrac{x+1}{x+1}-\dfrac{x}{x+1}\right)}{\left(\dfrac{2x}{x}-\dfrac{x-1}{x}\right)}=\dfrac{\left(\dfrac{1}{x+1}\right)}{\left(\dfrac{x+1}{x}\right)}=\dfrac{1}{x+1}\cdot\dfrac{x}{x+1}=\dfrac{x}{(x+1)^2}$

73. $\dfrac{\left(\dfrac{x+4}{x-2}-\dfrac{x-3}{x+1}\right)}{x+1}=\dfrac{\left(\dfrac{(x+4)(x+1)}{(x-2)(x+1)}-\dfrac{(x-3)(x-2)}{(x+1)(x-2)}\right)}{x+1}=\dfrac{\left(\dfrac{x^2+5x+4-(x^2-5x+6)}{(x-2)(x+1)}\right)}{x+1}$

$=\dfrac{10x-2}{(x-2)(x+1)}\cdot\dfrac{1}{x+1}=\dfrac{2(5x-1)}{(x-2)(x+1)^2}$

74. $\dfrac{\left(\dfrac{x-2}{x+1}-\dfrac{x}{x-2}\right)}{x+3}=\dfrac{\left(\dfrac{(x-2)(x-2)}{(x+1)(x-2)}-\dfrac{x(x+1)}{(x-2)(x+1)}\right)}{x+3}=\dfrac{\left(\dfrac{x^2-4x+4-(x^2+x)}{(x-2)(x+1)}\right)}{x+3}$

$$=\dfrac{-5x+4}{(x-2)(x+1)}\cdot\dfrac{1}{x+3}=\dfrac{-5x+4}{(x-2)(x+1)(x+3)}$$

75. $\dfrac{\left(\dfrac{x-2}{x+2}+\dfrac{x-1}{x+1}\right)}{\left(\dfrac{x}{x+1}-\dfrac{2x-3}{x}\right)}=\dfrac{\left(\dfrac{(x-2)(x+1)}{(x+2)(x+1)}+\dfrac{(x-1)(x+2)}{(x+1)(x+2)}\right)}{\left(\dfrac{x^2}{(x+1)(x)}-\dfrac{(2x-3)(x+1)}{x(x+1)}\right)}=\dfrac{\left(\dfrac{x^2-x-2+x^2+x-2}{(x+2)(x+1)}\right)}{\left(\dfrac{x^2-(2x^2-x-3)}{x(x+1)}\right)}$

$$=\dfrac{\left(\dfrac{2x^2-4}{(x+2)(x+1)}\right)}{\left(\dfrac{-x^2+x+3}{x(x+1)}\right)}=\dfrac{2(x^2-2)}{(x+2)(x+1)}\cdot\dfrac{x(x+1)}{-(x^2-x-3)}=\dfrac{2x(x^2-2)}{-(x+2)(x^2-x-3)}$$

76. $\dfrac{\left(\dfrac{2x+5}{x}-\dfrac{x}{x-3}\right)}{\left(\dfrac{x^2}{x-3}-\dfrac{(x+1)^2}{x+3}\right)}=\dfrac{\left(\dfrac{(2x+5)(x-3)}{x(x-3)}-\dfrac{x(x)}{x(x-3)}\right)}{\left(\dfrac{x^2(x+3)}{(x-3)(x+3)}-\dfrac{(x-3)(x+1)^2}{(x-3)(x+3)}\right)}=\dfrac{\left(\dfrac{2x^2-x-15-x^2}{x(x-3)}\right)}{\left(\dfrac{x^3+3x^2-(x^3-x^2-5x-3)}{(x-3)(x+3)}\right)}$

$$=\dfrac{\left(\dfrac{x^2-x-15}{x(x-3)}\right)}{\left(\dfrac{4x^2+5x+3}{(x-3)(x+3)}\right)}=\dfrac{x^2-x-15}{x(x-3)}\cdot\dfrac{(x-3)(x+3)}{4x^2+5x+3}=\dfrac{(x^2-x-15)(x+3)}{x(4x^2+5x+3)}$$

77. $1-\dfrac{1}{\left(1-\dfrac{1}{x}\right)}=1-\dfrac{1}{\left(\dfrac{x-1}{x}\right)}=1-1\cdot\dfrac{x}{x-1}=\dfrac{x-1-x}{x-1}=\dfrac{-1}{x-1}$

78. $1-\dfrac{1}{\left(1-\dfrac{1}{1-x}\right)}=1-\dfrac{1}{\left(\dfrac{1-x-1}{1-x}\right)}=1-\dfrac{1}{\left(\dfrac{-x}{1-x}\right)}=1-1\cdot\dfrac{1-x}{-x}=1+1\cdot\dfrac{1-x}{x}=\dfrac{x+1-x}{x}=\dfrac{1}{x}$

79. $\dfrac{1}{f}=(n-1)\left(\dfrac{1}{R_1}+\dfrac{1}{R_2}\right)$

$$\dfrac{R_1\cdot R_2}{f}=(n-1)\left(\dfrac{1}{R_1}+\dfrac{1}{R_2}\right)R_1\cdot R_2 \rightarrow \dfrac{R_1\cdot R_2}{f}=(n-1)(R_2+R_1)$$

$$\dfrac{f}{R_1\cdot R_2}=\dfrac{1}{(n-1)(R_2+R_1)}\rightarrow f=\dfrac{R_1\cdot R_2}{(n-1)(R_2+R_1)}$$

$$f=\dfrac{0.1(0.2)}{(1.5-1)(0.2+0.1)}=\dfrac{0.02}{0.5(0.3)}=\dfrac{0.02}{0.15}=\dfrac{2}{15}$$

80. $\dfrac{1}{R} = \dfrac{1}{R_1} + \dfrac{1}{R_2} + \dfrac{1}{R_3} = \dfrac{R_2 R_3 + R_1 R_3 + R_1 R_2}{R_1 R_2 R_3}$

$R = \dfrac{R_1 R_2 R_3}{R_2 R_3 + R_1 R_3 + R_1 R_2} = \dfrac{5 \cdot 4 \cdot 10}{4 \cdot 10 + 5 \cdot 10 + 5 \cdot 4} = \dfrac{200}{110} = \dfrac{20}{11}$

81. $1 + \dfrac{1}{x} = \dfrac{x+1}{x} \rightarrow a = 1, b = 1, c = 0$

$1 + \dfrac{1}{1 + \dfrac{1}{x}} = 1 + \dfrac{1}{\left(\dfrac{x+1}{x}\right)} = 1 + \dfrac{x}{x+1} = \dfrac{x+1+x}{x+1} = \dfrac{2x+1}{x+1} \rightarrow a = 2, b = 1, c = 1$

$1 + \dfrac{1}{1 + \dfrac{1}{1 + \dfrac{1}{x}}} = 1 + \dfrac{1}{\left(\dfrac{2x+1}{x+1}\right)} = 1 + \dfrac{x+1}{2x+1} = \dfrac{2x+1+x+1}{2x+1} = \dfrac{3x+2}{2x+1} \rightarrow a = 3, b = 2, c = 1$

$1 + \dfrac{1}{1 + \dfrac{1}{1 + \dfrac{1}{1 + \dfrac{1}{x}}}} = 1 + \dfrac{1}{\left(\dfrac{3x+2}{2x+1}\right)} = 1 + \dfrac{2x+1}{3x+2} = \dfrac{3x+2+2x+1}{3x+2} = \dfrac{5x+3}{3x+2} \rightarrow a = 5, b = 3, c = 2$

If we continue this process, the values of a, b and c produce the following sequences:

$a : 1, 2, 3, 5, 8, 13, 21, ...$

$b : 1, 1, 2, 3, 5, 8, 13, 21, ...$

$c : 0, 1, 1, 2, 3, 5, 8, 13, 21, ...$

in each case we have the *Fibonacci Sequence*, where the next value in the list is obtained from the sum of the previous 2 values in the list.

82.   Answers will vary.

83.   Answers will vary.

Review

R.8   Square Roots; Radicals

1. $\sqrt{25} = 5$

2. $\sqrt{81} = 9$

3. $\sqrt[3]{27} = 3$

4. $\sqrt[3]{125} = 5$

5. $\sqrt[3]{-64} = -4$

6. $\sqrt[3]{-8} = -2$

7. $\sqrt{\dfrac{1}{9}} = \dfrac{1}{3}$

8. $\sqrt[3]{\dfrac{27}{8}} = \dfrac{3}{2}$

9. $\sqrt{25x^4} = 5x^2$

10. $\sqrt[3]{64x^6} = 4x^2$

11. $\sqrt[3]{8(1+x)^3} = 2(1+x)$

12. $\sqrt{4(x+4)^2} = 2|x+4|$

13. $\sqrt{8} = \sqrt{4 \cdot 2} = 2\sqrt{2}$

14. $\sqrt{27} = \sqrt{9 \cdot 3} = 3\sqrt{3}$

15. $\sqrt{50} = \sqrt{25 \cdot 2} = 5\sqrt{2}$

16. $\sqrt{72} = \sqrt{36 \cdot 2} = 6\sqrt{2}$

17. $\sqrt[3]{16} = \sqrt[3]{8 \cdot 2} = 2\sqrt[3]{2}$

18. $\sqrt[3]{24} = \sqrt[3]{8 \cdot 3} = 2\sqrt[3]{3}$

19. $\sqrt[3]{-16} = \sqrt[3]{-8 \cdot 2} = -2\sqrt[3]{2}$

20. $-\sqrt[3]{16} = -\sqrt[3]{8 \cdot 2} = -2\sqrt[3]{2}$

21. $\sqrt{\dfrac{25x^3}{9x}}, x \neq 0 \ = \sqrt{\dfrac{25x^2}{9}} = \dfrac{5}{3}|x|$

22. $\sqrt[3]{\dfrac{x}{8x^4}} = \sqrt[3]{\dfrac{1}{8x^3}} = \dfrac{\sqrt[3]{1}}{\sqrt[3]{8x^3}} = \dfrac{1}{2x}$

23. $\sqrt[4]{x^{12}y^8} = \sqrt[4]{\left(x^3\right)^4\left(y^2\right)^4} = x^3 y^2$

24. $\sqrt[5]{x^{10}y^5} = \sqrt[5]{\left(x^2\right)^5\left(y^5\right)} = x^2 y$

25. $\sqrt{36x} = 6\sqrt{x}$

26. $\sqrt{9x^5} = 3\sqrt{x^4 \cdot x} = 3x^2\sqrt{x}$

27. $\sqrt{3x^2}\sqrt{12x} = \sqrt{36x^2 \cdot x} = 6x\sqrt{x}$

28. $\sqrt{5x}\sqrt{20x^3} = \sqrt{100x^4} = 10x^2$

29. $\dfrac{\sqrt{3xy^3}\sqrt{2x^2y}}{\sqrt{6x^3y^4}}, x > 0, y > 0$

$= \sqrt{\dfrac{\left(3xy^3\right)\left(2x^2y\right)}{6x^3y^4}} = \sqrt{\dfrac{6x^3y^4}{6x^3y^4}} = \sqrt{1} = 1$

30. $\dfrac{\sqrt[3]{x^2y}\ \sqrt[3]{125x^3}}{\sqrt[3]{8x^3y^4}}, x \neq 0, y \neq 0$ $= \sqrt[3]{\dfrac{(x^2y)(125x^3)}{8x^3y^4}} = \sqrt[3]{\dfrac{(x^2)(125)}{8y^3}} = \dfrac{5}{2y}\sqrt[3]{x^2}$

31. $\sqrt{\dfrac{16y^4}{9x^2}}, x > 0, y \geq 0$ $= \dfrac{4y^2}{3x}$

32. $\sqrt{\dfrac{9x^4}{16y^6}}, x \geq 0, y > 0$ $= \dfrac{3x^2}{4y^3}$

33. $\left(\sqrt{5}\ \sqrt[3]{9}\right)^2 = 5\sqrt[3]{81} = 5\sqrt[3]{27\cdot3} = 5\cdot3\sqrt[3]{3} = 15\sqrt[3]{3}$

34. $\left(\sqrt[3]{3}\sqrt{10}\right)^4 = \sqrt[3]{81}\sqrt{10000} = 100\sqrt[3]{27\cdot3} = 100\cdot3\sqrt[3]{3} = 300\sqrt[3]{3}$

35. $\sqrt{\dfrac{2x-3}{2x^4+3x^3}}\sqrt{\dfrac{x}{4x^2-9}}, x > \dfrac{3}{2}$

$= \sqrt{\dfrac{2x-3}{2x^4+3x^3}\cdot\dfrac{x}{4x^2-9}} = \sqrt{\dfrac{2x-3}{x^3(2x+3)}\cdot\dfrac{x}{(2x+3)(2x-3)}} = \sqrt{\dfrac{1}{x^2(2x+3)^2}} = \dfrac{1}{x(2x+3)}$

36. $\sqrt[3]{\dfrac{x-1}{x^2+2x+1}}\sqrt[3]{\dfrac{(x-1)^2}{x+1}}, x \neq -1$

$= \sqrt[3]{\dfrac{x-1}{x^2+2x+1}\cdot\dfrac{(x-1)^2}{x+1}} = \sqrt[3]{\dfrac{x-1}{(x+1)^2}\cdot\dfrac{(x-1)^2}{x+1}} = \sqrt[3]{\dfrac{(x-1)^3}{(x+1)^3}} = \dfrac{x-1}{x+1}$

37. $\sqrt{\dfrac{x-1}{x+1}}\sqrt{\dfrac{x^2+2x+1}{x^2-1}}, x > 1$

$= \sqrt{\dfrac{x-1}{x+1}\cdot\dfrac{x^2+2x+1}{x^2-1}} = \sqrt{\dfrac{x-1}{x+1}\cdot\dfrac{(x+1)^2}{(x-1)(x+1)}} = \sqrt{\dfrac{(x+1)^2}{(x+1)^2}} = \sqrt{1} = 1$

38. $\sqrt{\dfrac{x^2+4}{x(x^2-4)}}\sqrt{\dfrac{4x^2}{x^4-16}}, x > 2$

$= \sqrt{\dfrac{x^2+4}{x(x^2-4)}\cdot\dfrac{4x^2}{x^4-16}} = \sqrt{\dfrac{x^2+4}{x(x^2-4)}\cdot\dfrac{4x^2}{(x^2-4)(x^2+4)}} = \sqrt{\dfrac{4x}{(x^2-4)^2}} = \dfrac{2}{x^2-4}\sqrt{x}$

39. $3\sqrt{2} + 4\sqrt{2} = 7\sqrt{2}$ 40. $6\sqrt{5} - 4\sqrt{5} = 2\sqrt{5}$

41. $-\sqrt{18} + 2\sqrt{8} = -\sqrt{9\cdot 2} + 2\sqrt{4\cdot 2} = -3\sqrt{2} + 4\sqrt{2} = \sqrt{2}$

42. $2\sqrt{12} - 3\sqrt{27} = 2\sqrt{4\cdot 3} - 3\sqrt{9\cdot 3} = 4\sqrt{3} - 9\sqrt{3} = -5\sqrt{3}$

43. $5\sqrt[3]{2} - 2\sqrt[3]{54} = 5\sqrt[3]{2} - 2\sqrt[3]{27\cdot 2} = 5\sqrt[3]{2} - 6\sqrt[3]{2} = -\sqrt[3]{2}$

44. $9\sqrt[3]{24} - \sqrt[3]{81} = 9\sqrt[3]{8\cdot 3} - \sqrt[3]{27\cdot 3} = 18\sqrt[3]{3} - 3\sqrt[3]{3} = 15\sqrt[3]{3}$

45. $\sqrt{8x^3} - 3\sqrt{50x}, x \ge 0$

$\sqrt{4\cdot 2x^3} - 3\sqrt{25\cdot 2x} = 2x\sqrt{2x} - 15\sqrt{2x} = \sqrt{2x}\,(2x - 15)$

46. $3x\sqrt{9y} + 4\sqrt{25y}, y \ge 0$

$9x\sqrt{y} + 20\sqrt{y} = \sqrt{y}\,(9x + 20)$

47. $\sqrt[3]{16x^4 y} - 3x\sqrt[3]{2xy} + 5\sqrt[3]{-2xy^4} = \sqrt[3]{8\cdot 2x^4 y} - 3x\sqrt[3]{2xy} - 5y\sqrt[3]{2xy}$

$= 2x\sqrt[3]{2xy} - 3x\sqrt[3]{2xy} - 5y\sqrt[3]{2xy} = \sqrt[3]{2xy}\,(2x - 3x - 5y) = \sqrt[3]{2xy}\,(-x - 5y)$

48. $8xy - \sqrt{25x^2 y^2} + \sqrt[3]{8x^3 y^3}, x \ge 0, y \ge 0$

$8xy - 5xy + 2xy = 5xy$

49. $\left(3\sqrt{6}\right)\left(4\sqrt{3}\right) = 12\sqrt{18} = 12\sqrt{9\cdot 2} = 36\sqrt{2}$

50. $\left(5\sqrt{8}\right)\left(-3\sqrt{6}\right) = -15\sqrt{48} = -15\sqrt{16\cdot 3} = -60\sqrt{3}$

51. $\sqrt{3}\left(\sqrt{3} - 4\right) = 3 - 4\sqrt{3}$ 52. $\sqrt{5}\left(\sqrt{5} + 6\right) = 5 + 6\sqrt{5}$

53. $3\sqrt{7}\left(2\sqrt{7} + 3\right) = 6\cdot 7 + 9\sqrt{7} = 42 + 9\sqrt{7}$

54. $\left(2\sqrt{6} + 3\right)\left(3\sqrt{6}\right) = 6\cdot 6 + 9\sqrt{6} = 36 + 9\sqrt{6}$

55. $\left(\sqrt{2} - 1\right)^2 = \left(\sqrt{2}\right)^2 - 2\sqrt{2} + 1 = 2 - 2\sqrt{2} + 1 = 3 - 2\sqrt{2}$

56. $\left(\sqrt{3} + \sqrt{5}\right)^2 = \left(\sqrt{3}\right)^2 + 2\sqrt{3}\sqrt{5} + \left(\sqrt{5}\right)^2 = 3 + 2\sqrt{15} + 5 = 8 + 2\sqrt{15}$

57. $\left(\sqrt[3]{2}-1\right)^3 = \left(\sqrt[3]{2}\right)^3 - 3\left(\sqrt[3]{2}\right)^2 + 3\left(\sqrt[3]{2}\right) - 1 = 2 - 3\left(\sqrt[3]{2}\right)^2 + 3\left(\sqrt[3]{2}\right) - 1$

$$= 1 - 3\left(\sqrt[3]{2}\right)\left(\sqrt[3]{2}-1\right)$$

58. $\left(\sqrt[3]{4}+2\right)^3 = \left(\sqrt[3]{4}\right)^3 + 6\left(\sqrt[3]{4}\right)^2 + 12\left(\sqrt[3]{4}\right) + 8 = 4 + 6\left(\sqrt[3]{4}\right)^2 + 12\left(\sqrt[3]{4}\right) + 8$

$$= 12 + 6\left(\sqrt[3]{4}\right)\left(\sqrt[3]{4}+2\right)$$

59. $\left(2\sqrt{x}-3\right)\left(2\sqrt{x}+5\right), x \geq 0 \qquad = 4x - 6\sqrt{x} + 10\sqrt{x} - 15 = 4x + 4\sqrt{x} - 15$

60. $\left(4\sqrt{x}-3\right)\left(\sqrt{x}+3\right), x \geq 0 \qquad = 4x + 12\sqrt{x} - 3\sqrt{x} - 9 = 4x + 9\sqrt{x} - 9$

61. $\sqrt{1-x^2} - \dfrac{1}{\sqrt{1-x^2}}, -1 < x < 1 \quad = \dfrac{\sqrt{1-x^2}\cdot\sqrt{1-x^2}-1}{\sqrt{1-x^2}} = \dfrac{1-x^2-1}{\sqrt{1-x^2}} = \dfrac{-x^2}{\sqrt{1-x^2}}\cdot\dfrac{\sqrt{1-x^2}}{\sqrt{1-x^2}}$

$$= \dfrac{-x^2\sqrt{1-x^2}}{(1+x)(1-x)}$$

62. $\sqrt{1-x^2} + \dfrac{1}{\sqrt{1-x^2}}, -1 < x < 1 \quad = \dfrac{\sqrt{1-x^2}\cdot\sqrt{1-x^2}+1}{\sqrt{1-x^2}} = \dfrac{1-x^2+1}{\sqrt{1-x^2}} = \dfrac{2-x^2}{\sqrt{1-x^2}}\cdot\dfrac{\sqrt{1-x^2}}{\sqrt{1-x^2}}$

$$= \dfrac{(2-x^2)\sqrt{1-x^2}}{(1+x)(1-x)}$$

63. $\dfrac{2}{\sqrt{5}}\cdot\dfrac{\sqrt{5}}{\sqrt{5}} = \dfrac{2\sqrt{5}}{5}$

64. $\dfrac{\sqrt{3}}{\sqrt{5}}\cdot\dfrac{\sqrt{5}}{\sqrt{5}} = \dfrac{\sqrt{15}}{5}$

65. $\dfrac{8}{\sqrt{6}}\cdot\dfrac{\sqrt{6}}{\sqrt{6}} = \dfrac{8\sqrt{6}}{6} = \dfrac{4\sqrt{6}}{3}$

66. $\dfrac{5}{\sqrt{10}}\cdot\dfrac{\sqrt{10}}{\sqrt{10}} = \dfrac{5\sqrt{10}}{10} = \dfrac{\sqrt{10}}{2}$

67. $\dfrac{1}{\sqrt{x}}, x > 0 \qquad \dfrac{1}{\sqrt{x}}\cdot\dfrac{\sqrt{x}}{\sqrt{x}} = \dfrac{\sqrt{x}}{x}$

68. $\dfrac{x}{\sqrt{x^2+4}}\cdot\dfrac{\sqrt{x^2+4}}{\sqrt{x^2+4}} = \dfrac{x\sqrt{x^2+4}}{x^2+4}$

69. $\dfrac{3}{5+\sqrt{2}}\cdot\dfrac{5-\sqrt{2}}{5-\sqrt{2}} = \dfrac{3\left(5-\sqrt{2}\right)}{25-2} = \dfrac{3\left(5-\sqrt{2}\right)}{23}$

70. $\dfrac{2}{\sqrt{7}-2} \cdot \dfrac{\sqrt{7}+2}{\sqrt{7}+2} = \dfrac{2(\sqrt{7}+2)}{7-4} = \dfrac{2(\sqrt{7}+2)}{3}$

71. $\dfrac{3}{4+\sqrt{7}} \cdot \dfrac{4-\sqrt{7}}{4-\sqrt{7}} = \dfrac{3(4-\sqrt{7})}{16-7} = \dfrac{3(4-\sqrt{7})}{9} = \dfrac{4-\sqrt{7}}{3}$

72. $\dfrac{10}{4-\sqrt{2}} \cdot \dfrac{4+\sqrt{2}}{4+\sqrt{2}} = \dfrac{10(4+\sqrt{2})}{16-2} = \dfrac{10(4+\sqrt{2})}{14} = \dfrac{5(4+\sqrt{2})}{7}$

73. $\dfrac{\sqrt{5}}{2+3\sqrt{5}} \cdot \dfrac{2-3\sqrt{5}}{2-3\sqrt{5}} = \dfrac{\sqrt{5}(2-3\sqrt{5})}{4-9\cdot 5} = \dfrac{\sqrt{5}(2-3\sqrt{5})}{4-45} = \dfrac{\sqrt{5}(2-3\sqrt{5})}{-41} = \dfrac{2\sqrt{5}-15}{-41}$

74. $\dfrac{\sqrt{3}}{2\sqrt{3}+3} \cdot \dfrac{2\sqrt{3}-3}{2\sqrt{3}-3} = \dfrac{\sqrt{3}(2\sqrt{3}-3)}{4\cdot 3-9} = \dfrac{\sqrt{3}(2\sqrt{3}-3)}{12-9} = \dfrac{\sqrt{3}(2\sqrt{3}-3)}{3} = \dfrac{2\cdot 3-3\sqrt{3}}{3} = 2-\sqrt{3}$

75. $\dfrac{\sqrt{3}-\sqrt{2}}{\sqrt{3}+\sqrt{2}} \cdot \dfrac{\sqrt{3}-\sqrt{2}}{\sqrt{3}-\sqrt{2}} = \dfrac{3-2\sqrt{3}\sqrt{2}+2}{3-2} = 5-2\sqrt{6}$

76. $\dfrac{\sqrt{5}+\sqrt{3}}{\sqrt{5}-\sqrt{3}} \cdot \dfrac{\sqrt{5}+\sqrt{3}}{\sqrt{5}+\sqrt{3}} = \dfrac{5+2\sqrt{5}\sqrt{3}+3}{5-3} = \dfrac{8+2\sqrt{15}}{2} = 4+\sqrt{15}$

77. $\dfrac{1}{\sqrt{x}+2}, x \geq 0$ $\dfrac{1}{\sqrt{x}+2} \cdot \dfrac{\sqrt{x}-2}{\sqrt{x}-2} = \dfrac{\sqrt{x}-2}{x-4}$

78. $\dfrac{1}{\sqrt{x}-3}, x \geq 0, x \neq 9$ $\dfrac{1}{\sqrt{x}-3} \cdot \dfrac{\sqrt{x}+3}{\sqrt{x}+3} = \dfrac{\sqrt{x}+3}{x-9}$s

79. $\sqrt{2} \approx 1.41$ 80. $\sqrt{7} \approx 2.65$ 81. $\sqrt[3]{4} \approx 1.59$

82. $\sqrt[3]{-5} \approx -1.71$ 83. $\dfrac{2+\sqrt{3}}{3-\sqrt{5}} \approx 4.88$ 84. $\dfrac{\sqrt{5}-2}{\sqrt{2}+4} \approx 0.04$

85. $\dfrac{3\sqrt[3]{5}-\sqrt{2}}{\sqrt{3}} \approx 2.14$ 86. $\dfrac{2\sqrt{3}-\sqrt[3]{4}}{\sqrt{2}} \approx 1.33$

87.   (a) $V = 40(12)^2 \sqrt{\dfrac{96}{12}-0.608} \approx 15660.422$ gallons

       (b) $V = 40(1)^2 \sqrt{\dfrac{96}{1}-0.608} \approx 390.68$ gallons

88.   (a) $v = \sqrt{64 \cdot 4 + 0^2} = \sqrt{256} = 16$ feet per second

       (b) $v = \sqrt{64 \cdot 16 + 0^2} = \sqrt{1024} = 32$ feet per second

       (c) $v = \sqrt{64 \cdot 2 + 4^2} = \sqrt{144} = 12$ feet per second

89. $T = 2\pi \sqrt{\dfrac{64}{32}} = 2\pi \sqrt{2} \approx 8.89$ seconds

90. $T = 2\pi \sqrt{\dfrac{64}{16}} = 2\pi \sqrt{4} = 4\pi \approx 12.57$ seconds

91. $T = 2\pi \sqrt{\dfrac{64}{\left(\dfrac{8}{12}\right)}} = 2\pi \sqrt{96} \approx 61.56$ seconds

92. $T = 2\pi \sqrt{\dfrac{64}{\left(\dfrac{4}{12}\right)}} = 2\pi \sqrt{192} \approx 87.06$ seconds

93.   if $a = -5$, then $\sqrt{a^2} = \sqrt{(-5)^2} = \sqrt{25} = 5 \neq a$.

       Since we use the principal square root, which is always non-negative,

$$\sqrt{a^2} = \begin{cases} a & \text{if } a \geq 0 \\ -a & \text{if } a < 0 \end{cases}$$

       which is the definition of $|a|$, so $\sqrt{a^2} = |a|$.

Review

R.9 Rational Exponents

1. $8^{2/3} = \left(2^3\right)^{2/3} = 2^2 = 4$

2. $4^{3/2} = \left(2^2\right)^{3/2} = 2^3 = 8$

3. $(-27)^{1/3} = \left((-3)^3\right)^{1/3} = -3$

4. $(-64)^{2/3} = \left(-4^3\right)^{2/3} = (-4)^{6/3} = (-4)^2 = 16$

5. $(4)^{-3/2} = \left(2^2\right)^{-3/2} = (2)^{-6/2} = (2)^{-3} = \dfrac{1}{2^3} = \dfrac{1}{8}$

6. $(-8)^{-5/3} = \left(-2^3\right)^{-5/3} = (-2)^{-15/3} = (-2)^{-5} = \dfrac{1}{-2^5} = -\dfrac{1}{32}$

7. $9^{-3/2} = \left(3^2\right)^{-3/2} = 3^{-3} = \dfrac{1}{3^3} = \dfrac{1}{27}$

8. $25^{-5/2} = \left(5^2\right)^{-5/2} = 5^{-5} = \dfrac{1}{5^5} = \dfrac{1}{3125}$

9. $\left(\dfrac{9}{4}\right)^{3/2} = \left(\dfrac{3^2}{2^2}\right)^{3/2} = \dfrac{3^{6/2}}{2^{6/2}} = \dfrac{3^3}{2^3} = \dfrac{27}{8}$

10. $\left(\dfrac{27}{8}\right)^{2/3} = \dfrac{27^{2/3}}{8^{2/3}} = \dfrac{\left(3^3\right)^{2/3}}{\left(2^3\right)^{2/3}} = \dfrac{3^2}{2^2} = \dfrac{9}{4}$

11. $\left(\dfrac{4}{9}\right)^{-3/2} = \left(\dfrac{2^2}{3^2}\right)^{-3/2} = \dfrac{2^{-6/2}}{3^{-6/2}} = \dfrac{2^{-3}}{3^{-3}} = \dfrac{3^3}{2^3} = \dfrac{27}{8}$

12. $\left(\dfrac{8}{27}\right)^{-2/3} = \left(\dfrac{27}{8}\right)^{2/3} = \dfrac{27^{2/3}}{8^{2/3}} = \dfrac{\left(3^3\right)^{2/3}}{\left(2^3\right)^{2/3}} = \dfrac{3^2}{2^2} = \dfrac{9}{4}$

13. $4^{1.5} = 4^{3/2} = \left(2^2\right)^{3/2} = 2^{6/2} = 2^3 = 8$

14. $16^{-1.5} = 16^{-3/2} = \left(4^2\right)^{-3/2} = 4^{-6/2} = 4^{-3} = \dfrac{1}{4^3} = \dfrac{1}{64}$

15. $\left(\dfrac{1}{4}\right)^{-1.5} = \left(\dfrac{1}{4}\right)^{-3/2} = 4^{3/2} = \left(2^2\right)^{3/2} = 2^{6/2} = 2^3 = 8$

16. $\left(\dfrac{1}{9}\right)^{1.5} = \left(\dfrac{1}{9}\right)^{3/2} = 9^{-3/2} = \left(3^2\right)^{-3/2} = 3^{-6/2} = 3^{-3} = \dfrac{1}{3^3} = \dfrac{1}{27}$

17. $\left(\sqrt{3}\right)^6 = \left(3^{1/2}\right)^6 = 3^{6/2} = 3^3 = 27$

18. $\left(\sqrt[3]{4}\right)^6 = \left(4^{1/3}\right)^6 = 4^{6/3} = 4^2 = 16$ 19. $\left(\sqrt{5}\right)^{-2} = \left(5^{1/2}\right)^{-2} = 5^{-2/2} = 5^{-1} = \dfrac{1}{5}$

20. $\left(\sqrt[4]{3}\right)^{-8} = \left(3^{1/4}\right)^{-8} = 3^{-8/4} = 3^{-2} = \dfrac{1}{3^2} = \dfrac{1}{9}$

21. $3^{1/2} \cdot 3^{3/2} = 3^{1/2+3/2} = 3^2 = 9$

22. $5^{1/3} \cdot 5^{4/3} = 5^{1/3+4/3} = 5^{5/3} = 5^1 \cdot 5^{2/3} = 5\sqrt[3]{5^2} = 5\sqrt[3]{25}$

23. $\dfrac{7^{1/3}}{7^{4/3}} = 7^{1/3-4/3} = 7^{-3/3} = 7^{-1} = \dfrac{1}{7}$ 24. $\dfrac{6^{5/4}}{6^{1/4}} = 6^{5/4-1/4} = 6^{4/4} = 6^1 = 6$

25. $2^{1/3} \cdot 4^{1/3} = (2 \cdot 4)^{1/3} = 8^{1/3} = \left(2^3\right)^{1/3} = 2^{3/3} = 2^1 = 2$

26. $9^{1/3} \cdot 3^{1/3} = (9 \cdot 3)^{1/3} = 27^{1/3} = \left(3^3\right)^{1/3} = 3^{3/3} = 3^1 = 3$

27. $\sqrt[4]{3} \cdot \sqrt[4]{27} = \sqrt[4]{3 \cdot 27} = \sqrt[4]{81} = 81^{1/4} = \left(3^4\right)^{1/4} = 3^{4/4} = 3^1 = 3$

28. $\sqrt[3]{2} \cdot \sqrt[3]{4} = \sqrt[3]{2 \cdot 4} = \sqrt[3]{8} = 8^{1/3} = \left(2^3\right)^{1/3} = 2^{3/3} = 2^1 = 2$

29. $\left(\sqrt[4]{2}\right)^{-4} = \left(2^{1/4}\right)^{-4} = 2^{-4/4} = 2^{-1} = \dfrac{1}{2}$ 30. $\left(\sqrt[5]{3}\right)^{-5} = \left(3^{1/5}\right)^{-5} = 3^{-5/5} = 3^{-1} = \dfrac{1}{3}$

31. $\left(\sqrt[3]{6}\right)^2 = \left(6^{1/3}\right)^2 = 6^{2/3} = \sqrt[3]{6^2} = \sqrt[3]{36}$

32. $\left(\sqrt[4]{5}\right)^3 = \left(5^{1/4}\right)^3 = 5^{3/4} = \sqrt[4]{5^3} = \sqrt[4]{125}$

33. $\sqrt{2}\,\sqrt[3]{2} = 2^{1/2} \cdot 2^{1/3} = 2^{1/2+1/3} = 2^{5/6} = \sqrt[6]{32}$

34. $\sqrt{5}\,\sqrt[3]{5} = 5^{1/2} \cdot 5^{1/3} = 5^{1/2+1/3} = 5^{5/6} = \sqrt[6]{3125}$

35. $\sqrt[8]{x^4} = \left(x^4\right)^{1/8} = x^{4/8} = x^{1/2}$ 36. $\sqrt[6]{x^3} = \left(x^3\right)^{1/6} = x^{3/6} = x^{1/2}$

37. $\sqrt{x^3}\,\sqrt[4]{x} = x^{3/2} \cdot x^{1/4} = x^{3/2+1/4} = x^{7/4}$

38. $\sqrt[3]{x^2}\,\sqrt{x} = x^{2/3} \cdot x^{1/2} = x^{2/3+1/2} = x^{7/6}$

39. $x^{3/2} \cdot x^{-1/2} = x^{3/2-1/2} = x^1 = x$

40. $x^{5/4} \cdot x^{-1/4} = x^{5/4-1/4} = x^1 = x$

41. $\left(x^3 y^6\right)^{1/3} = \left(x^3\right)^{1/3}\left(y^6\right)^{1/3} = x y^2$

42. $\left(x^4 y^8\right)^{3/4} = \left(x^4\right)^{3/4}\left(y^8\right)^{3/4} = x^3 y^6$

43. $\left(x^2 y\right)^{1/3}\left(x y^2\right)^{2/3} = x^{2/3} y^{1/3} x^{2/3} y^{4/3} = x^{4/3} y^{5/3}$

44. $\left(xy\right)^{1/4}\left(x^2 y^2\right)^{1/2} = x^{1/4} y^{1/4} x^1 y^1 = x^{5/4} y^{5/4}$

45. $\left(16 x^2 y^{-1/3}\right)^{3/4} = \left(2^4 x^2 y^{-1/3}\right)^{3/4} = 2^3 x^{3/2} y^{-1/4} = \dfrac{8 x^{3/2}}{y^{1/4}}$

46. $\left(4 x^{-1} y^{1/3}\right)^{3/2} = \left(2^2 x^{-1} y^{1/3}\right)^{3/2} = 2^3 x^{-3/2} y^{1/2} = \dfrac{8 y^{1/2}}{x^{3/2}}$

47. $\left(\dfrac{x^{2/5} y^{-1/5}}{x^{-1/3}}\right)^{15} = \left(\dfrac{x^{2/5} x^{1/3}}{y^{1/5}}\right)^{15} = \dfrac{x^{30/5} x^{15/3}}{y^{15/5}} = \dfrac{x^6 x^5}{y^3} = \dfrac{x^{6+5}}{y^3} = \dfrac{x^{11}}{y^3}$

48. $\left(\dfrac{x^{1/2}}{y^2}\right)^4 \left(\dfrac{y^{1/3}}{x^{-2/3}}\right)^3 = \left(\dfrac{x^{4/2}}{y^{4 \cdot 2}}\right)\left(y^{1/3} x^{2/3}\right)^3 = \left(\dfrac{x^2}{y^8}\right)\left(y^{3/3} x^{6/3}\right) = \left(\dfrac{x^2}{y^8}\right)\left(y^1 x^2\right) = \dfrac{x^{2+2}}{y^{8-1}} = \dfrac{x^4}{y^7}$

49. $\dfrac{x}{(1+x)^{1/2}} + 2(1+x)^{1/2} = \dfrac{x + 2(1+x)^{1/2}(1+x)^{1/2}}{(1+x)^{1/2}} = \dfrac{x + 2(1+x)}{(1+x)^{1/2}} = \dfrac{x + 2 + 2x}{(1+x)^{1/2}} = \dfrac{3x + 2}{(1+x)^{1/2}}$

50. $\dfrac{1+x}{2x^{1/2}} + x^{1/2} = \dfrac{1 + x + x^{1/2} \cdot 2x^{1/2}}{2x^{1/2}} = \dfrac{1 + x + 2x}{2x^{1/2}} = \dfrac{3x + 1}{2x^{1/2}}$

51. $2x\left(x^2 + 1\right)^{1/2} + x^2 \cdot \dfrac{1}{2}\left(x^2 + 1\right)^{-1/2} \cdot 2x = 2x\left(x^2 + 1\right)^{1/2} + \dfrac{x^3}{\left(x^2 + 1\right)^{1/2}}$

$$= \dfrac{2x\left(x^2 + 1\right)^{1/2} \cdot \left(x^2 + 1\right)^{1/2} + x^3}{\left(x^2 + 1\right)^{1/2}} = \dfrac{2x\left(x^2 + 1\right)^{1/2+1/2} + x^3}{\left(x^2 + 1\right)^{1/2}} = \dfrac{2x\left(x^2 + 1\right)^1 + x^3}{\left(x^2 + 1\right)^{1/2}}$$

$$= \dfrac{2x^3 + 2x + x^3}{\left(x^2 + 1\right)^{1/2}} = \dfrac{3x^3 + 2x}{\left(x^2 + 1\right)^{1/2}} = \dfrac{x\left(3x^2 + 2\right)}{\left(x^2 + 1\right)^{1/2}}$$

52. $(x+1)^{1/3} + x \cdot \dfrac{1}{3}(x+1)^{-2/3}, x \neq -1$

$$= (x+1)^{1/3} + \dfrac{x}{3(x+1)^{2/3}} = \dfrac{3(x+1)^{2/3}(x+1)^{1/3} + x}{3(x+1)^{2/3}} = \dfrac{3(x+1)^{2/3+1/3} + x}{3(x+1)^{2/3}}$$

$$= \dfrac{3(x+1)^{1} + x}{3(x+1)^{2/3}} = \dfrac{3x+3+x}{3(x+1)^{2/3}} = \dfrac{4x+3}{3(x+1)^{2/3}}$$

53. $\sqrt{4x+3} \cdot \dfrac{1}{2\sqrt{x-5}} + \sqrt{x-5} \cdot \dfrac{1}{5\sqrt{4x+3}}, x > 5$

$$= \dfrac{\sqrt{4x+3}}{2\sqrt{x-5}} + \dfrac{\sqrt{x-5}}{5\sqrt{4x+3}} = \dfrac{\sqrt{4x+3} \cdot \sqrt{4x+3} + \sqrt{x-5} \cdot \sqrt{x-5}}{10\sqrt{x-5}\sqrt{4x+3}}$$

$$= \dfrac{4x+3+x-5}{10\sqrt{(x-5)(4x+3)}} = \dfrac{5x-2}{10\sqrt{(x-5)(4x+3)}}$$

54. $\dfrac{\sqrt[3]{8x+1}}{3\sqrt[3]{(x-2)^2}} + \dfrac{\sqrt[3]{x-2}}{24\sqrt[3]{(8x+1)^2}}, x \neq 2, x \neq -\dfrac{1}{8}$

$$= \dfrac{8\sqrt[3]{8x+1} \cdot \sqrt[3]{(8x+1)^2} + \sqrt[3]{x-2} \cdot \sqrt[3]{(x-2)^2}}{24\sqrt[3]{(x-2)^2} \cdot \sqrt[3]{(8x+1)^2}} = \dfrac{8\sqrt[3]{(8x+1)^3} + \sqrt[3]{(x-2)^3}}{24\sqrt[3]{(x-2)^2} \cdot \sqrt[3]{(8x+1)^2}}$$

$$= \dfrac{8(8x+1) + x-2}{24\sqrt[3]{(x-2)^2(8x+1)^2}} = \dfrac{64x+8+x-2}{24\sqrt[3]{(x-2)^2(8x+1)^2}} = \dfrac{65x+6}{24\sqrt[3]{(x-2)^2(8x+1)^2}}$$

55. $\dfrac{\left(\sqrt{1+x} - x \cdot \dfrac{1}{2\sqrt{1+x}}\right)}{1+x} = \dfrac{\left(\sqrt{1+x} - \dfrac{x}{2\sqrt{1+x}}\right)}{1+x} = \dfrac{\left(\dfrac{2\sqrt{1+x}\sqrt{1+x} - x}{2\sqrt{1+x}}\right)}{1+x}$

$$= \dfrac{2(1+x)-x}{2(1+x)^{1/2}} \cdot \dfrac{1}{1+x} = \dfrac{2+x}{2(1+x)^{3/2}}$$

56.
$$\frac{\left(\sqrt{x^2+1}-x\cdot\dfrac{2x}{2\sqrt{x^2+1}}\right)}{x^2+1}=\frac{\left(\sqrt{x^2+1}-\dfrac{x^2}{\sqrt{x^2+1}}\right)}{x^2+1}=\frac{\left(\sqrt{x^2+1}\cdot\dfrac{\sqrt{x^2+1}}{\sqrt{x^2+1}}-\dfrac{x^2}{\sqrt{x^2+1}}\right)}{x^2+1}$$

$$=\frac{\left(\dfrac{x^2+1-x^2}{\sqrt{x^2+1}}\right)}{x^2+1}=\frac{1}{\sqrt{x^2+1}}\cdot\frac{1}{x^2+1}=\frac{1}{\left(x^2+1\right)^{3/2}}$$

57.
$$\frac{\left(x+4\right)^{1/2}-2x\left(x+4\right)^{-1/2}}{x+4}=\frac{\left(\left(x+4\right)^{1/2}-\dfrac{2x}{\left(x+4\right)^{1/2}}\right)}{x+4}=\frac{\left(\left(x+4\right)^{1/2}\cdot\dfrac{\left(x+4\right)^{1/2}}{\left(x+4\right)^{1/2}}-\dfrac{2x}{\left(x+4\right)^{1/2}}\right)}{x+4}$$

$$=\frac{\left(\dfrac{x+4-2x}{\left(x+4\right)^{1/2}}\right)}{x+4}=\frac{-x+4}{\left(x+4\right)^{1/2}}\cdot\frac{1}{x+4}=\frac{-x+4}{\left(x+4\right)^{3/2}}$$

58.
$$\frac{\left(9-x^2\right)^{1/2}+x^2\left(9-x^2\right)^{-1/2}}{9-x^2},-3<x<3$$

$$\frac{\left(\left(9-x^2\right)^{1/2}+\dfrac{x^2}{\left(9-x^2\right)^{1/2}}\right)}{9-x^2}=\frac{\left(\dfrac{\left(9-x^2\right)^{1/2}\cdot\left(9-x^2\right)^{1/2}+x^2}{\left(9-x^2\right)^{1/2}}\right)}{9-x^2}$$

$$=\frac{\left(9-x^2\right)^{1/2}\cdot\left(9-x^2\right)^{1/2}+x^2}{\left(9-x^2\right)^{1/2}}\cdot\frac{1}{9-x^2}=\frac{9-x^2+x^2}{\left(9-x^2\right)^{1/2}}\cdot\frac{1}{9-x^2}=\frac{9}{\left(9-x^2\right)^{3/2}}$$

59.
$$\frac{\left(\dfrac{x^2}{\left(x^2-1\right)^{1/2}}-\left(x^2-1\right)^{1/2}\right)}{x^2},x<-1\ \text{or}\ x>1$$

$$=\frac{\left(\dfrac{x^2-\left(x^2-1\right)^{1/2}\cdot\left(x^2-1\right)^{1/2}}{\left(x^2-1\right)^{1/2}}\right)}{x^2}=\frac{x^2-\left(x^2-1\right)^{1/2}\cdot\left(x^2-1\right)^{1/2}}{\left(x^2-1\right)^{1/2}}\cdot\frac{1}{x^2}$$

$$=\frac{x^2-\left(x^2-1\right)}{\left(x^2-1\right)^{1/2}}\cdot\frac{1}{x^2}=\frac{x^2-x^2+1}{\left(x^2-1\right)^{1/2}}\cdot\frac{1}{x^2}=\frac{1}{x^2\left(x^2-1\right)^{1/2}}$$

60. $\dfrac{\left(x^2+4\right)^{1/2}-x^2\left(x^2+4\right)^{-1/2}}{x^2+4}$

$= \dfrac{\left(\left(x^2+4\right)^{1/2}-\dfrac{x^2}{\left(x^2+4\right)^{1/2}}\right)}{x^2+4} = \dfrac{\left(\dfrac{\left(x^2+4\right)^{1/2}\cdot\left(x^2+4\right)^{1/2}-x^2}{\left(x^2+4\right)^{1/2}}\right)}{x^2+4}$

$= \dfrac{\left(x^2+4\right)^{1/2}\cdot\left(x^2+4\right)^{1/2}-x^2}{\left(x^2+4\right)^{1/2}}\cdot\dfrac{1}{x^2+4} = \dfrac{x^2+4-x^2}{\left(x^2+4\right)^{1/2}}\cdot\dfrac{1}{x^2+4} = \dfrac{4}{\left(x^2+4\right)^{3/2}}$

61. $\dfrac{\dfrac{1+x^2}{2\sqrt{x}}-2x\sqrt{x}}{\left(1+x^2\right)^2}, x>0$

$= \dfrac{\left(\dfrac{1+x^2-\left(2\sqrt{x}\right)\left(2x\sqrt{x}\right)}{2\sqrt{x}}\right)}{\left(1+x^2\right)^2} = \dfrac{1+x^2-\left(2\sqrt{x}\right)\left(2x\sqrt{x}\right)}{2\sqrt{x}}\cdot\dfrac{1}{\left(1+x^2\right)^2}$

$= \dfrac{1+x^2-4x^2}{2\sqrt{x}}\cdot\dfrac{1}{\left(1+x^2\right)^2} = \dfrac{1-3x^2}{2\sqrt{x}\left(1+x^2\right)^2}$

62. $\dfrac{2x\left(1-x^2\right)^{1/3}+\dfrac{2}{3}x^3\left(1-x^2\right)^{-2/3}}{\left(1-x^2\right)^{2/3}}, x\neq-1, x\neq1$

$= \dfrac{\left(2x\left(1-x^2\right)^{1/3}+\dfrac{2x^3}{3\left(1-x^2\right)^{2/3}}\right)}{\left(1-x^2\right)^{2/3}} = \dfrac{\left(\dfrac{2x\left(1-x^2\right)^{1/3}3\left(1-x^2\right)^{2/3}+2x^3}{3\left(1-x^2\right)^{2/3}}\right)}{\left(1-x^2\right)^{2/3}}$

$= \dfrac{6x\left(1-x^2\right)^{1/3+2/3}+2x^3}{3\left(1-x^2\right)^{2/3}}\cdot\dfrac{1}{\left(1-x^2\right)^{2/3}} = \dfrac{6x\left(1-x^2\right)+2x^3}{3\left(1-x^2\right)^{2/3+2/3}} = \dfrac{6x-6x^3+2x^3}{3\left(1-x^2\right)^{4/3}}$

$= \dfrac{6x-4x^3}{3\left(1-x^2\right)^{4/3}} = \dfrac{2x\left(3-2x^2\right)}{3\left(1-x^2\right)^{4/3}}$

63. $(x+1)^{3/2} + x \cdot \dfrac{3}{2}(x+1)^{1/2} = (x+1)^{1/2}\left(x+1+\dfrac{3}{2}x\right) = (x+1)^{1/2}\left(\dfrac{5}{2}x+1\right) = \dfrac{1}{2}(x+1)^{1/2}(5x+2)$

64. $(x^2+4)^{4/3} + x \cdot \dfrac{4}{3}(x^2+4)^{1/3} \cdot 2x = (x^2+4)^{1/3}\left(x^2+4+\dfrac{8}{3}x^2\right) = (x^2+4)^{1/3}\left(\dfrac{11}{3}x^2+4\right)$

65. $6x^{1/2}\left(x^2+x\right) - 8x^{3/2} - 8x^{1/2} = 2x^{1/2}\left(3(x^2+x) - 4x - 4\right) = 2x^{1/2}\left(3x^2 - x - 4\right)$
$$= 2x^{1/2}(3x-4)(x+1)$$

66. $6x^{1/2}\left(2x+3\right) + x^{3/2} \cdot 8 = 2x^{1/2}\left(3(2x+3) + 4x\right) = 2x^{1/2}(10x+9)$

67. $3\left(x^2+4\right)^{4/3} + x \cdot 4\left(x^2+4\right)^{1/3} \cdot 2x = \left(x^2+4\right)^{1/3}\left[3\left(x^2+4\right) + 8x^2\right]$
$$= \left(x^2+4\right)^{1/3}\left[3x^2+12+8x^2\right] = \left(x^2+4\right)^{1/3}\left(11x^2+12\right)$$

68. $2x\left(3x+4\right)^{4/3} + x^2 \cdot 4\left(3x+4\right)^{1/3} = 2x\left(3x+4\right)^{1/3}\left[(3x+4)+2x\right] = 2x\left(3x+4\right)^{1/3}(5x+4)$

69. $4\left(3x+5\right)^{1/3}\left(2x+3\right)^{3/2} + 3\left(3x+5\right)^{4/3}\left(2x+3\right)^{1/2}, x \geq -\dfrac{3}{2}$
$$= \left(3x+5\right)^{1/3}\left(2x+3\right)^{1/2}\left[4(2x+3)+3(3x+5)\right] = \left(3x+5\right)^{1/3}\left(2x+3\right)^{1/2}(8x+12+9x+15)$$
$$= \left(3x+5\right)^{1/3}\left(2x+3\right)^{1/2}(17x+27)$$

70. $6\left(6x+1\right)^{1/3}\left(4x-3\right)^{3/2} + 6\left(6x+1\right)^{4/3}\left(4x-3\right)^{1/2}, x \geq \dfrac{3}{4}$
$$= 6\left(6x+1\right)^{1/3}\left(4x-3\right)^{1/2}\left[(4x-3)+(6x+1)\right] = 6\left(6x+1\right)^{1/3}\left(4x-3\right)^{1/2}(10x-2)$$
$$= 6\left(6x+1\right)^{1/3}\left(4x-3\right)^{1/2}(2)(5x-1) = 12\left(6x+1\right)^{1/3}\left(4x-3\right)^{1/2}(5x-1)$$

71. $3x^{-1/2} + \dfrac{3}{2}x^{1/2}, x > 0$

$$= \dfrac{3}{x^{1/2}} + \dfrac{3}{2}x^{1/2} = \dfrac{3 \cdot 2 + 3x^{1/2} \cdot x^{1/2}}{2x^{1/2}} = \dfrac{6+3x}{2x^{1/2}} = \dfrac{3(2+x)}{2x^{1/2}}$$

72. $8x^{1/3} - 4x^{-2/3}, x \neq 0$

$$= 8x^{1/3} - \dfrac{4}{x^{2/3}} = \dfrac{8x^{1/3} \cdot x^{2/3} - 4}{x^{2/3}} = \dfrac{8x-4}{x^{2/3}} = \dfrac{4(2x-1)}{x^{2/3}}$$

Review

R.R   Review Exercises

1. $3-4\cdot 5+6 = 3-20+6 = -17+6 = -11$

2. $8+4\cdot 2-6 = 8+8-6 = 16-6 = 10$

3. $\dfrac{3}{4}-\dfrac{7}{12} = \dfrac{3\cdot 3-7}{12} = \dfrac{9-7}{12} = \dfrac{2}{12} = \dfrac{1}{6}$

4. $\dfrac{9}{8}-\dfrac{3}{4} = \dfrac{9-3\cdot 2}{8} = \dfrac{9-6}{8} = \dfrac{3}{8}$

5. $\dfrac{\left(\dfrac{15}{2}+\dfrac{1}{4}\right)}{\left(\dfrac{2}{3}\right)} = \dfrac{\left(\dfrac{15\cdot 2+1}{4}\right)}{\left(\dfrac{2}{3}\right)} = \dfrac{\left(\dfrac{31}{4}\right)}{\left(\dfrac{2}{3}\right)} = \dfrac{31}{4}\cdot\dfrac{3}{2} = \dfrac{93}{8}$

6. $\dfrac{\left(\dfrac{9}{2}+\dfrac{3}{4}\right)}{\left(\dfrac{4}{3}\right)} = \dfrac{\left(\dfrac{9\cdot 2+3}{4}\right)}{\left(\dfrac{4}{3}\right)} = \dfrac{\left(\dfrac{21}{4}\right)}{\left(\dfrac{4}{3}\right)} = \dfrac{21}{4}\cdot\dfrac{3}{4} = \dfrac{63}{16}$

7. $5^2-3^3\cdot 2 = 25-27\cdot 2 = 25-54 = -29$

8. $2^3+3^2\cdot 4 = 8+9\cdot 4 = 8+36 = 44$

9. $\dfrac{2^{-3}\cdot 5^0}{4^2} = \dfrac{5^0}{2^3\cdot 4^2} = \dfrac{1}{8\cdot 16} = \dfrac{1}{128}$

10. $\dfrac{3^{-2}-4}{2^{-2}} = \dfrac{\left(\dfrac{1}{3^2}-4\right)}{\left(\dfrac{1}{2^2}\right)} = \dfrac{\left(\dfrac{1}{9}-4\right)}{\left(\dfrac{1}{4}\right)} = \dfrac{\left(\dfrac{1-4\cdot 9}{9}\right)}{\left(\dfrac{1}{4}\right)} = \left(\dfrac{1-36}{9}\right)\cdot\left(\dfrac{4}{1}\right) = \dfrac{-35}{9}\cdot\dfrac{4}{1} = -\dfrac{140}{9}$

11. $(2\sqrt{5}-2)(2\sqrt{5}+2) = (2\sqrt{5})^2-2^2 = 4\cdot 5-4 = 20-4 = 16$

12. $(2\sqrt{3}+\sqrt{2})(2\sqrt{3}-\sqrt{2}) = (2\sqrt{3})^2-(\sqrt{2})^2 = 4\cdot 3-2 = 12-2 = 10$

13. $\left(\dfrac{8}{27}\right)^{-2/3} = \left(\dfrac{27}{8}\right)^{2/3} = \dfrac{27^{2/3}}{8^{2/3}} = \dfrac{\left(3^3\right)^{2/3}}{\left(2^3\right)^{2/3}} = \dfrac{3^2}{2^2} = \dfrac{9}{4}$

14. $\left(\dfrac{4}{9}\right)^{-3/2} = \left(\dfrac{9}{4}\right)^{3/2} = \dfrac{3^{6/2}}{2^{6/2}} = \dfrac{3^3}{2^3} = \dfrac{27}{8}$

15. $\left(\sqrt[3]{3}\right)^{-3} = \left(3^{1/3}\right)^{-3} = 3^{-3/3} = 3^{-1} = \dfrac{1}{3}$

16. $\left(4\sqrt{32}\right)^{-1/2} = \left(2^2 \cdot 2^{5/2}\right)^{-1/2} = \left(2^{2+5/2}\right)^{-1/2} = \left(2^{9/2}\right)^{-1/2} = 2^{-9/4} = \dfrac{1}{2^{9/4}} = \dfrac{1}{2^{8/4}2^{1/4}} = \dfrac{1}{2^2 2^{1/4}} = \dfrac{1}{4\sqrt[4]{2}}$

17. $\left|6 - 8^{1/3}\right| = \left|6 - \left(2^3\right)^{1/3}\right| = \left|6 - 2^{3/3}\right| = \left|6 - 2^1\right| = \left|6 - 2\right| = \left|4\right| = 4$

18. $\left|25^{1/2} - 27^{2/3}\right| = \left|\left(5^2\right)^{1/2} - \left(3^3\right)^{2/3}\right| = \left|5^{2/2} - 3^{6/3}\right| = \left|5^1 - 3^2\right| = \left|5 - 9\right| = \left|-4\right| = 4$

19. $\sqrt{\left|3^2 - 5^2\right|} = \sqrt{\left|9 - 25\right|} = \sqrt{\left|-16\right|} = \sqrt{16} = 4$

20. $\sqrt[3]{-\left|4^2 - 2^3\right|} = \sqrt[3]{-\left|16 - 8\right|} = \sqrt[3]{-\left|8\right|} = \sqrt[3]{-8} = -2$

21. $\dfrac{x^{-2}}{y^{-2}} = \dfrac{y^2}{x^2}$

22. $\left(\dfrac{x^{-1}}{y^{-3}}\right)^2 = \left(\dfrac{y^3}{x^1}\right)^2 = \dfrac{y^{3\cdot 2}}{x^{1\cdot 2}} = \dfrac{y^6}{x^2}$

23. $\dfrac{\left(x^2 y\right)^{-4}}{\left(xy\right)^{-3}} = \dfrac{\left(xy\right)^3}{\left(x^2 y\right)^4} = \dfrac{x^3 y^3}{x^{2\cdot 4} \cdot y^4} = \dfrac{x^3 y^3}{x^8 \cdot y^4} = \dfrac{1}{x^{8-3} \cdot y^{4-3}} = \dfrac{1}{x^5 y}$

24. $\dfrac{\left(\dfrac{x}{y}\right)^2}{\left(\dfrac{x}{y}\right)^{-1}} = \left(\dfrac{x}{y}\right)^2 \cdot \left(\dfrac{x}{y}\right)^1 = \left(\dfrac{x}{y}\right)^{2+1} = \left(\dfrac{x}{y}\right)^3 = \dfrac{x^3}{y^3}$

25. $\dfrac{\left(\dfrac{x^2}{y}\right)^2}{\left(\dfrac{x}{y^2}\right)^3} = \dfrac{\left(\dfrac{x^{2\cdot 2}}{y^2}\right)}{\left(\dfrac{x^3}{y^{2\cdot 3}}\right)} = \dfrac{\left(\dfrac{x^4}{y^2}\right)}{\left(\dfrac{x^3}{y^6}\right)} = \dfrac{x^4}{y^2} \cdot \dfrac{y^6}{x^3} = x^{4-3} \cdot y^{6-2} = x^1 y^4 = xy^4$

26. $\dfrac{\left(\dfrac{2x}{3y^2}\right)^{-1}}{\dfrac{4}{y^3}} = \dfrac{\left(\dfrac{3y^2}{2x}\right)^1}{\dfrac{4}{y^3}} = \dfrac{3y^2}{2x}\cdot\dfrac{y^3}{4} = \dfrac{3y^{2+3}}{8x} = \dfrac{3y^5}{8x}$

27. $\dfrac{x^{-2}}{x^{-2}+y^{-2}} = \dfrac{\left(\dfrac{1}{x^2}\right)}{\left(\dfrac{1}{x^2}+\dfrac{1}{y^2}\right)} = \dfrac{\left(\dfrac{1}{x^2}\right)}{\left(\dfrac{y^2+x^2}{x^2y^2}\right)} = \dfrac{1}{x^2}\cdot\dfrac{x^2y^2}{y^2+x^2} = \dfrac{y^2}{y^2+x^2}$

28. $\dfrac{x^{-1}+y^{-1}}{x^{-1}-y^{-1}} = \dfrac{\left(\dfrac{1}{x}+\dfrac{1}{y}\right)}{\left(\dfrac{1}{x}-\dfrac{1}{y}\right)} = \dfrac{\left(\dfrac{x+y}{xy}\right)}{\left(\dfrac{x-y}{xy}\right)} = \dfrac{x+y}{xy}\cdot\dfrac{xy}{x-y} = \dfrac{x+y}{x-y}$

29. . $\left(25x^{-4/3}y^{-2/3}\right)^{3/2} = (25)^{3/2}\left(x^{(-4/3)(3/2)}\right)\left(y^{(-2/3)(3/2)}\right) = \left(5^2\right)^{3/2}\left(x^{-12/6}\right)\left(y^{-6/6}\right)$

$= \left(5^{6/2}\right)\left(x^{-2}\right)\left(y^{-1}\right) = \dfrac{5^3}{x^2y} = \dfrac{125}{x^2y}$

30. $\left(16x^{-2/3}y^{4/3}\right)^{-3/2} = (16)^{-3/2}\left(x^{(-2/3)(-3/2)}\right)\left(y^{(4/3)(-3/2)}\right) = \left(4^2\right)^{-3/2}\left(x^{6/6}\right)\left(y^{-12/6}\right)$

$= \left(4^{-6/2}\right)\left(x^1\right)\left(y^{-2}\right) = \dfrac{x}{4^3y^2} = \dfrac{x}{64y^2}$

31. $\left(\dfrac{2x^{-1/2}}{y^{-3/4}}\right)^{-4} = \dfrac{(2)^{-4}\left(x^{-1/2}\right)^{-4}}{\left(y^{-3/4}\right)^{-4}} = \dfrac{(2)^{-4}\left(x^{4/2}\right)}{\left(y^{12/4}\right)} = \dfrac{x^2}{2^4y^3} = \dfrac{x^2}{16y^3}$

32. $\left(\dfrac{8x^{-3/2}}{y^{-3}}\right)^{-2/3} = \dfrac{(8)^{-2/3}\left(x^{6/6}\right)}{\left(y^{6/6}\right)} = \dfrac{x}{(8)^{2/3}\cdot y} = \dfrac{x}{\left(2^3\right)^{2/3}\cdot y} = \dfrac{x}{2^{6/3}\cdot y} = \dfrac{x}{2^2\cdot y} = \dfrac{x}{4y}$

33. $(2x-3)(-4x+2) = -8x^2+4x+12x-6 = -8x^2+16x-6$

34. $(3x+4)(-8x-2) = -24x^2-6x-32x-8 = -24x^2-38x-8$

35. $4\left(3x^3-2x^2+1\right)-3\left(x^3+4x^2-2x-3\right) = 12x^3-8x^2+4-3x^3-12x^2+6x+9$

$= 9x^3-20x^2+6x+13$

36. $8\left(1-x^2+x^3\right)-4\left(1+2x^2-4x^4\right) = 8-8x^2+8x^3-4-8x^2+16x^4$

$= 16x^4+8x^3-16x^2+4$

37. $(2x-5)\left(3x^2+2\right) = 6x^3+4x-15x^2-10 = 6x^3-15x^2+4x-10$

38. $(1-2x^3)(1-4x) = 1-4x-2x^3+8x^4 = 8x^4-2x^3-4x+1$

39. $(x+1)(x+2)(x-3) = (x^2+2x+x+2)(x-3) = (x^2+3x+2)(x-3)$
$$= x^3-3x^2+3x^2-9x+2x-6 = x^3-7x-6$$

40. $(x+1)(x+3)(x-5) = (x^2+3x+x+3)(x-5) = (x^2+4x+3)(x-5)$
$$= x^3-5x^2+4x^2-20x+3x-15 = x^3-x^2-17x-15$$

41. Divide:

$$\begin{array}{r} 3x^2+8x+25 \\ x-3 \overline{)3x^3-x^2+x+4} \\ \underline{3x^3-9x^2} \\ 8x^2+x+4 \\ \underline{8x^2-24x} \\ 25x+4 \\ \underline{25x-75} \\ 79 \end{array}$$

Check:

$(x-3)(3x^2+8x+25)+(79)$
$= 3x^3+8x^2+25x-9x^2-24x-75+79$
$= 3x^3-x^2+x+4$

The quotient is $3x^2+8x+25$; the remainder is 79.

42. Divide:

$$\begin{array}{r} 2x^2+x+3 \\ x-2 \overline{)2x^3-3x^2+x+1} \\ \underline{2x^3-4x^2} \\ x^2+x+1 \\ \underline{x^2-2x} \\ 3x+1 \\ \underline{3x-6} \\ 7 \end{array}$$

Check:

$(x-2)(2x^2+x+3)+(7)$
$= 2x^3+x^2+3x-4x^2-2x-6+7$
$= 2x^3-3x^2+x+1$

The quotient is $2x^2+x+3$; the remainder is 7.

43. Divide:

$$\begin{array}{r} -3x^2+4 \\ x^2+1 \overline{)-3x^4+0\cdot x^3+x^2+0\cdot x+2} \\ \underline{-3x^4-3x^2} \\ 4x^2+2 \\ \underline{4x^2+4} \\ -2 \end{array}$$

Check:

$(x^2+1)(-3x^2+4)+(-2)$
$= -3x^4+4x^2-3x^2+4-2$
$= -3x^4+x^2+2$

The quotient is $-3x^2+4$; the remainder is -2.

44.   Divide:

$$-4x+1$$
$$x^2-1\overline{)-4x^3+0\cdot x^3+x^2+0\cdot x-2}$$
$$\underline{-4x^3\qquad\qquad +4x}$$
$$x^2-4x\ -2$$
$$\underline{x^2\qquad -1}$$
$$-4x-1$$

Check :

$$(x^2-1)(-4x+1)+(-4x-1)$$
$$=-4x^3+x^2+4x-1-4x-1$$
$$=-4x^3+x^2-2$$

The quotient is $-4x+1$; the remainder is $-4x-1$.

45.   Divide:

$$8x^2+24x+62$$
$$x^2-3x+1\overline{)8x^4+0\cdot x^3-2x^2+5x+1}$$
$$\underline{8x^4\ -24x^3\ +8x^2}$$
$$24x^3-10x^2+5x+1$$
$$\underline{24x^3-72x^2+24x}$$
$$62x^2-19x\quad +1$$
$$\underline{62x^2-186x+62}$$
$$167x-61$$

Check : $(x^2-3x+1)(8x^2+24x+62)+(167x-61)$

$$=8x^4+24x^3+62x^2-24x^3-72x^2-186x+8x^2+24x+62+167x-61$$

$$=8x^4-2x^2+5x+1 \quad \text{The quotient is } 8x^2+24x+62; \text{ the remainder is } 167x-61.$$

46.   Divide:

$$3x^2-10x+36$$
$$x^2+3x-2\overline{)3x^4-x^3+0\cdot x^2-8x+4}$$
$$\underline{3x^4+9x^3-6x^2}$$
$$-10x^3+6x^2-8x+4$$
$$\underline{-10x^3-30x^2+20x}$$
$$36x^2-28x+4$$
$$\underline{36x^2+106x-72}$$
$$-134x+76$$

Check : $(x^2+3x-2)(3x^2-10x+36)+(-134x+76)$

$$=3x^4-10x^3+36x^2+9x^3-30x^2+106x-6x^2+20x-72-134x+76$$

$$=3x^4-x^3-8x+4$$

The quotient is $3x^2-10x+36$; the remainder is $-134x+76$.

47. Divide:

$$x^4 - x^3 + x^2 - x + 1$$

$$x + 1{\overline{\smash{\big)}\,x^5 + 0 \cdot x^4 + 0 \cdot x^3 + 0 \cdot x^2 + 0 \cdot x + 1}}$$

$$\underline{x^5 \quad + x^4}$$

$$- x^4 \qquad\qquad\qquad + 1$$

$$\underline{- x^4 - x^3}$$

$$x^3 \qquad\qquad + 1$$

$$\underline{x^3 + x^2}$$

$$- x^2 \qquad\qquad + 1$$ **Check :**

$$\underline{- x^2 - x \qquad\qquad + 1}$$ $(x + 1)(x^4 - x^3 + x^2 - x + 1) + (0)$

$$x \qquad\qquad + 1$$ $= x^5 - x^4 + x^3 - x^2 + x + x^4 - x^3 + x^2 - x + 1$

$$\underline{x \qquad\qquad + 1}$$ $= x^5 + 1$

$$0$$

The quotient is $x^4 - x^3 + x^2 - x + 1$; the remainder is 0.

48. Divide:

$$x^4 + x^3 + x^2 + x + 1$$

$$x - 1{\overline{\smash{\big)}\,x^5 + 0 \cdot x^4 + 0 \cdot x^3 + 0 \cdot x^2 + 0 \cdot x - 1}}$$

$$\underline{x^5 \quad - x^4}$$

$$x^4 \qquad\qquad\qquad + 1$$

$$\underline{x^4 - x^3}$$

$$x^3 \qquad\qquad\qquad + 1$$

$$\underline{x^3 - x^2}$$

$$x^2 \qquad\qquad + 1$$ **Check :**

$$\underline{x^2 - x \qquad\qquad + 1}$$ $(x - 1)(x^4 + x^3 + x^2 + x + 1) + (0)$

$$x \qquad\qquad - 1$$ $= x^5 + x^4 + x^3 + x^2 + x - x^4 - x^3 - x^2 - x - 1$

$$\underline{x \qquad\qquad - 1}$$ $= x^5 - 1$

$$0$$

The quotient is $x^4 + x^3 + x^2 + x + 1$; the remainder is 0.

49. Divide:

$$3x^4 - 2x^2 + 1$$
$$2x+1\overline{)6x^5 + 3x^4 - 4x^3 - 2x^2 + 2x + 1}$$
$$\underline{6x^5 + 3x^4}$$
$$-4x^3 - 2x^2 + 2x + 1$$
$$\underline{-4x^3 - 2x^2}$$
$$2x + 1$$
$$\underline{2x + 1}$$
$$0$$

Check:

$(2x+1)(3x^4 - 2x^2 + 1) + (0)$

$= 6x^5 - 4x^3 + 2x + 3x^4 - 2x^2 + 1$

$= 6x^5 + 3x^4 - 4x^3 - 2x^2 + 2x + 1$

The quotient is $3x^4 - 2x^2 + 1$; the remainder is 0.

50. Divide:

$$3x^4 - 2x^2 + 1$$
$$2x-1\overline{)6x^5 - 3x^4 - 4x^3 + 2x^2 + 2x - 1}$$
$$\underline{6x^5 - 3x^4}$$
$$-4x^3 + 2x^2 + 2x - 1$$
$$\underline{-4x^3 + 2x^2}$$
$$2x - 1$$
$$\underline{2x + 1}$$
$$0$$

Check:

$(2x-1)(3x^4 - 2x^2 + 1) + (0)$

$= 6x^5 - 4x^3 + 2x - 3x^4 + 2x^2 - 1$

$= 6x^5 - 3x^4 - 4x^3 + 2x^2 + 2x - 1$

The quotient is $3x^4 - 2x^2 + 1$; the remainder is 0.

51. $x^2 + 5x - 14 = (x+7)(x-2)$

52. $x^2 - 9x + 14 = (x-7)(x-2)$

53. $6x^2 - 5x - 6 = (3x+2)(2x-3)$

54. $6x^2 + x - 2 = (3x+2)(2x-1)$

55. $3x^2 - 15x - 42 = (3x+6)(x-7)$

56. $2x^3 + 18x^2 + 28x = 2x(x^2 + 9x + 14) = 2x(x+7)(x+2)$

57. $8x^3 + 1 = (2x+1)((2x)^2 - (2x)(1) + 1^2) = (2x+1)(4x^2 - 2x + 1)$

58. $27x^3 - 8 = (3x-2)((3x)^2 + (3x)(4) + (2)^2) = (3x-2)(9x^2 + 12x + 4)$

59. $2x^3 + 3x^2 - 2x - 3 = x^2(2x+3) - (2x+3) = (2x+3)(x^2-1)$
$= (2x+3)(x-1)(x+1)$

60. $2x^3 + 3x^2 + 2x + 3 = x^2(2x+3) + (2x+3) = (2x+3)(x^2+1)$

61. $25x^2 - 4 = (5x + 2)(5x - 2)$ 62. $16x^2 - 1 = (4x + 1)(4x - 1)$

63. $9x^2 + 1$; a sum of perfect squares is always prime over the set of real numbers

64. $x^2 - x + 1$; prime since the factors of $+ 1$ will not add to produce $- 1$.

65. $\dfrac{2x^2 + 11x + 14}{x^2 - 4} = \dfrac{(2x + 7)(x + 2)}{(x + 2)(x - 2)} = \dfrac{2x + 7}{x - 2}$

66. $\dfrac{x^2 - 5x - 14}{4 - x^2} = \dfrac{(x - 7)(x + 2)}{(2 + x)(2 - x)} = \dfrac{x - 7}{2 - x}$

67. $\dfrac{9x^2 - 1}{x^2 - 9} \cdot \dfrac{3x - 9}{9x^2 + 6x + 1} = \dfrac{(3x + 1)(3x - 1)}{(x + 3)(x - 3)} \cdot \dfrac{3(x - 3)}{(3x + 1)^2} = \dfrac{3(3x - 1)(x - 3)}{(x + 3)(3x + 1)}$

68. $\dfrac{x^2 - 25}{x^3 - 4x^2 - 5x} \cdot \dfrac{x^2 + x}{1 - x^2} = \dfrac{(x + 5)(x - 5)}{x(x^2 - 4x - 5)} \cdot \dfrac{x(x + 1)}{(1 + x)(1 - x)}$

   $= \dfrac{(x + 5)(x - 5)}{x(x - 5)(x + 1)} \cdot \dfrac{x(x + 1)}{(1 + x)(1 - x)} = \dfrac{(x + 5)}{(x + 1)(1 - x)}$

69. $\dfrac{x + 1}{x - 1} - \dfrac{x - 1}{x + 1} = \dfrac{(x + 1)(x + 1) - (x - 1)(x - 1)}{(x - 1)(x + 1)} = \dfrac{(x^2 + 2x + 1) - (x^2 - 2x + 1)}{(x - 1)(x + 1)}$

   $= \dfrac{x^2 + 2x + 1 - x^2 + 2x - 1}{(x - 1)(x + 1)} = \dfrac{4x}{(x - 1)(x + 1)}$

70. $\dfrac{x}{x + 1} - \dfrac{2x}{x + 2} = \dfrac{x(x + 2) - 2x(x + 1)}{(x + 1)(x + 2)} = \dfrac{x^2 + 2x - 2x^2 - 2x}{(x - 1)(x + 1)} = \dfrac{-x^2}{(x - 1)(x + 1)}$

71. $\dfrac{3x + 4}{x^2 - 4} - \dfrac{2x - 3}{x^2 + 4x + 4} = \dfrac{3x + 4}{(x + 2)(x - 2)} - \dfrac{2x - 3}{(x + 2)^2} = \dfrac{(3x + 4)(x - 2) - (2x - 3)(x - 3)}{(x + 2)^2(x - 2)}$

   $= \dfrac{3x^2 - 6x + 4x - 8 - (2x^2 - 6x - 3x + 9)}{(x + 2)^2(x - 2)} = \dfrac{3x^2 - 2x - 8 - (2x^2 - 9x + 9)}{(x + 2)^2(x - 2)}$

   $= \dfrac{3x^2 - 2x - 8 - 2x^2 + 9x - 9}{(x + 2)^2(x - 2)} = \dfrac{x^2 + 7x - 17}{(x + 2)^2(x - 2)}$

72. $\dfrac{x^2}{2x^2+5x-3}+\dfrac{x^2}{2x^2-5x+2}=\dfrac{x^2}{(2x-1)(x+3)}+\dfrac{x^2}{(2x-1)(x-2)}$

$=\dfrac{x^2(x-2)+x^2(x+3)}{(2x-1)(x+3)(x-2)}=\dfrac{x^3-2x^2+x^3+3x^2}{(2x-1)(x+3)(x-2)}=\dfrac{2x^3+x^2}{(2x-1)(x+3)(x-2)}$

$=\dfrac{x^2(2x+1)}{(2x-1)(x+3)(x-2)}$

73. $\dfrac{4}{\sqrt{5}}\cdot\dfrac{\sqrt{5}}{\sqrt{5}}=\dfrac{4\sqrt{5}}{5}$

74. $\dfrac{-2}{\sqrt{3}}\cdot\dfrac{\sqrt{3}}{\sqrt{3}}=\dfrac{-2\sqrt{3}}{3}$

75. $\dfrac{2}{1-\sqrt{2}}\cdot\dfrac{1-\sqrt{2}}{1-\sqrt{2}}=\dfrac{2(1-\sqrt{2})}{1-(\sqrt{2})^2}=\dfrac{2(1-\sqrt{2})}{1-2}=\dfrac{2(1-\sqrt{2})}{-1}=-2(1-\sqrt{2})$

76. $\dfrac{-4}{1+\sqrt{3}}\cdot\dfrac{1-\sqrt{3}}{1-\sqrt{3}}=\dfrac{-4(1-\sqrt{3})}{1-(\sqrt{3})^2}=\dfrac{-4(1-\sqrt{3})}{1-3}=\dfrac{-4(1-\sqrt{3})}{-2}=2(1-\sqrt{3})$

77. $\dfrac{1+\sqrt{5}}{1-\sqrt{5}}\cdot\dfrac{1+\sqrt{5}}{1+\sqrt{5}}=\dfrac{1+2\sqrt{5}+(\sqrt{5})^2}{1-(\sqrt{5})^2}=\dfrac{1+2\sqrt{5}+5}{1-5}=\dfrac{6+2\sqrt{5}}{-4}=\dfrac{-3-\sqrt{5}}{2}$

78. $\dfrac{4\sqrt{3}+2}{2\sqrt{3}+1}\cdot\dfrac{2\sqrt{3}-1}{2\sqrt{3}-1}=\dfrac{8(\sqrt{3})^2-4\sqrt{3}+4\sqrt{3}-2}{(2\sqrt{3})^2-(1)^2}=\dfrac{8\cdot3-2}{4\cdot3-1}=\dfrac{24-2}{12-1}=\dfrac{22}{11}=2$

79. $(2+x^2)^{1/2}+x\cdot\dfrac{1}{2}(2+x^2)^{-1/2}\cdot2x$

$=(2+x^2)^{1/2}+\dfrac{2x^2}{2(2+x^2)^{1/2}}=(2+x^2)^{1/2}+\dfrac{x^2}{(2+x^2)^{1/2}}$

$=\dfrac{(2+x^2)^{1/2}(2+x^2)^{1/2}+x^2}{(2+x^2)^{1/2}}=\dfrac{2+x^2+x^2}{(2+x^2)^{1/2}}=\dfrac{2+2x^2}{(2+x^2)^{1/2}}=\dfrac{2(1+x^2)}{(2+x^2)^{1/2}}$

80. $(x^2+4)^{2/3}+x\cdot\dfrac{2}{3}(x^2+4)^{-1/3}\cdot2x=(x^2+4)^{2/3}+\dfrac{2x^2}{3(x^2+4)^{1/3}}=\dfrac{3(x^2+4)^{1/3}(x^2+4)^{2/3}+2x^2}{3(x^2+4)^{1/3}}$

$=\dfrac{3(x^2+4)+2x^2}{3(x^2+4)^{1/3}}=\dfrac{3x^2+12+2x^2}{3(x^2+4)^{1/3}}=\dfrac{5x^2+12}{3(x^2+4)^{1/3}}$

81. $$\frac{(x+4)^{1/2}\cdot 2x - x^2 \cdot \frac{1}{2}(x+4)^{-1/2}}{x+4}, x>-4$$

$$=\frac{(x+4)^{1/2}\cdot 2x - \dfrac{x^2}{2(x+4)^{1/2}}}{x+4}=\frac{\left(\dfrac{2(x+4)^{1/2}(x+4)^{1/2}\cdot 2x - x^2}{2(x+4)^{1/2}}\right)}{x+4}$$

$$=\frac{\left(\dfrac{2(x+4)\cdot 2x - x^2}{2(x+4)^{1/2}}\right)}{x+4}=\frac{\left(\dfrac{4x^2 - x^2 + 16x}{2(x+4)^{1/2}}\right)}{x+4}=\left(\dfrac{3x^2+16x}{2(x+4)^{1/2}}\right)\left(\dfrac{1}{x+4}\right)=\frac{3x^2+16x}{2(x+4)^{3/2}}=\frac{x(3x+16)}{2(x+4)^{3/2}}$$

82. $$\frac{(x^2+4)^{1/2}\cdot 2x - x^2 \cdot \frac{1}{2}(x^2+4)^{-1/2}\cdot 2x}{x^2+4}$$

$$=\frac{(x^2+4)^{1/2}\cdot 2x - \dfrac{2x}{2(x^2+4)^{1/2}}}{x^2+4}=\frac{\left(\dfrac{2(x^2+4)^{1/2}(x^2+4)^{1/2}\cdot 2x - 2x}{2(x^2+4)^{1/2}}\right)}{x^2+4}$$

$$=\frac{\left(\dfrac{2(x^2+4)\cdot 2x - 2x}{2(x^2+4)^{1/2}}\right)}{x^2+4}=\frac{\left(\dfrac{4x^3 - 2x + 16x}{2(x^2+4)^{1/2}}\right)}{x^2+4}=\left(\dfrac{4x^3-2x+16x}{2(x^2+4)^{1/2}}\right)\left(\dfrac{1}{x^2+4}\right)=\frac{4x^3-2x+16x}{2(x^2+4)^{3/2}}$$

$$=\frac{2x^3+7x}{(x^2+4)^{3/2}}=\frac{x(2x^2+7)}{(x^2+4)^{3/2}}$$

83. $C(x)=3000+6x-\dfrac{x^2}{1000}$

(a) $C(1000)=3000+6(1000)-\dfrac{(1000)^2}{1000}=3000+6000-1000=\$8000$

(b) $C(3000)=3000+6(3000)-\dfrac{(3000)^2}{1000}=3000+18000-9000=\$12000$

84. Total annual earnings per share
    = (1st quarter earnings) + (2nd quarter earnings)
    + (3rd quarter earnings) + (4th quarter earnings)

    = 1.2 − 0.75 − 0.30 + 0.20 = $0.35 per share.

85. The total area enclosed by the window is given by

Total Area = area of the triangle + area of the rectangle

$$\text{Total Area} = \frac{1}{2}(base)(height) + (length)(width)$$

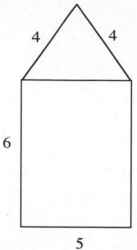

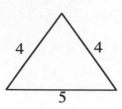

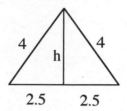

By the Pythagorean Theorem we have

$$(2.5)^2 + h^2 = (4)^2$$

$$h^2 = (4)^2 - (2.5)^2 = 16 - 6.25$$

$$h = \sqrt{9.75}$$

$$\text{Total Area} = \frac{1}{2}(5)\left(\sqrt{9.75}\right) + (6)(5) \approx 37.81 \text{ square feet.}$$

The perimeter of the window $= 4 + 4 + 6 + 5 + 6 = 25$. So the wood frame requires 25 feet of wood.

86.

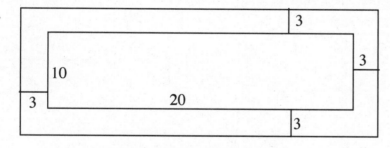

Deck Area = Total Area - Pool Area

$$= (20 + 6)(10 + 6) - (20)(10) = 26 \cdot 16 - 200 = 216 \text{ square feet}$$

Deck Perimeter $= 2(26 + 16) = 84$ feet

87.

Pond Area = area of outer circle - area of inner circle

$$= \pi(5)^2 - \pi(3)^2 = 25\pi - 9\pi = 16\pi \approx 50.27 \text{ square feet}$$

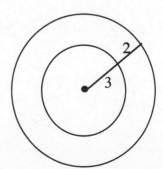

Outer Perimeter $= 2\pi(\text{outer radius}) = 2\pi(5)$

$= 10\pi \approx 314.16$ feet

88.   Recall that 1 mile = 5280 feet.

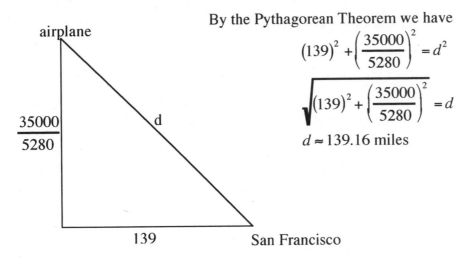

By the Pythagorean Theorem we have

$$(139)^2 + \left(\frac{35000}{5280}\right)^2 = d^2$$

$$\sqrt{(139)^2 + \left(\frac{35000}{5280}\right)^2} = d$$

$$d \approx 139.16 \text{ miles}$$

89.   Answers will vary.

90.   Answers will vary.

91.   Since 1 day = 24 hours, we compute $\frac{12997}{24} = 541.54\overline{16}$.

Now we only need to consider the decimal part of the answer in terms of a 24 hour day. That is, $\left(0.54\overline{16}\right)(24) \approx 13$ hours. So it must be 13 hours later than 12 noon, which makes the time 1 AM CST.

92.   Answers will vary.

Equations and Inequalities

1.1 Equations

1.
$$7x = 21$$
$$\frac{7x}{7} = \frac{21}{7}$$
$$x = 3$$

2.
$$6x = -24$$
$$\frac{6x}{6} = \frac{-24}{6}$$
$$x = -4$$

3.
$$3x + 15 = 0$$
$$3x + 15 - 15 = 0 - 15$$
$$3x = -15$$
$$\frac{3x}{3} = \frac{-15}{3}$$
$$x = -5$$

4.
$$6x + 18 = 0$$
$$6x + 18 - 18 = 0 - 18$$
$$6x = -18$$
$$\frac{6x}{6} = \frac{-18}{6}$$
$$x = -3$$

5.
$$2x - 3 = 0$$
$$2x - 3 + 3 = 0 + 3$$
$$2x = 3$$
$$\frac{2x}{2} = \frac{3}{2}$$
$$x = \frac{3}{2}$$

6.
$$3x + 4 = 0$$
$$3x + 4 - 4 = 0 - 4$$
$$3x = -4$$
$$\frac{3x}{3} = \frac{-4}{3}$$
$$x = -\frac{4}{3}$$

7.
$$\frac{1}{3}x = \frac{5}{12}$$
$$(3)\left(\frac{1}{3}x\right) = \left(\frac{5}{12}\right)(3)$$
$$x = \frac{5}{4}$$

8.
$$\frac{2}{3}x = \frac{9}{2}$$
$$(6)\left(\frac{2}{3}x\right) = \left(\frac{9}{2}\right)(6)$$
$$4x = 27$$
$$\frac{4x}{4} = \frac{27}{4}$$
$$x = \frac{27}{4}$$

9.
$$3x + 4 = x$$
$$3x + 4 - 4 = x - 4$$
$$3x = x - 4$$
$$3x - x = x - 4 - x$$
$$2x = -4$$
$$\frac{2x}{2} = \frac{-4}{2}$$
$$x = -2$$

10.
$$2x + 9 = 5x$$
$$2x + 9 - 9 = 5x - 9$$
$$2x = 5x - 9$$
$$2x - 5x = 5x - 9 - 5x$$
$$-3x = -9$$
$$\frac{-3x}{-3} = \frac{-9}{-3}$$
$$x = 3$$

11.
$$2t - 6 = 3 - t$$
$$2t - 6 + 6 = 3 - t + 6$$
$$2t = 9 - t$$
$$2t + t = 9 - t + t$$
$$3t = 9$$
$$\frac{3t}{3} = \frac{9}{3}$$
$$t = 3$$

12.
$$5y + 6 = -18 - y$$
$$5y + 6 - 6 = -18 - y - 6$$
$$5y = -y - 24$$
$$5y + y = -y - 24 + y$$
$$6y = -24$$
$$\frac{6y}{6} = \frac{-24}{6}$$
$$y = -4$$

13.
$$6 - x = 2x + 9$$
$$6 - x - 6 = 2x + 9 - 6$$
$$-x = 2x + 3$$
$$-x - 2x = 2x + 3 - 2x$$
$$-3x = 3$$
$$\frac{-3x}{-3} = \frac{3}{-3} \rightarrow x = -1$$

14.
$$3 - 2x = 2 - x$$
$$3 - 2x - 3 = 2 - x - 3$$
$$-2x = -x - 1$$
$$-2x + x = -x - 1 + x$$
$$-x = -1$$
$$\frac{-x}{-1} = \frac{-1}{-1} \rightarrow x = 1$$

15.
$$3 + 2n = 4n + 7$$
$$3 + 2n - 3 = 4n + 7 - 3$$
$$2n = 4n + 4$$
$$2n - 4n = 4n + 4 - 4n$$
$$-2n = 4$$
$$\frac{-2n}{-2} = \frac{4}{-2} \rightarrow n = -2$$

16.
$$6 - 2m = 3m + 1$$
$$6 - 2m - 6 = 3m + 1 - 6$$
$$-2m = 3m - 5$$
$$-2m - 3m = 3m - 5 - 3m$$
$$-5m = -5$$
$$\frac{-5m}{-5} = \frac{-5}{-5} \rightarrow m = 1$$

17.
$$2(3 + 2x) = 3(x - 4)$$
$$6 + 4x = 3x - 12$$
$$6 + 4x - 6 = 3x - 12 - 6$$
$$4x = 3x - 18$$
$$4x - 3x = 3x - 18 - 3x$$
$$x = -18$$

18.
$$3(2 - x) = 2x - 1$$
$$6 - 3x = 2x - 1$$
$$6 - 3x - 6 = 2x - 1 - 6$$
$$-3x = 2x - 7$$
$$-3x - 2x = 2x - 7 - 2x$$
$$-5x = -7$$
$$\frac{-5x}{-5} = \frac{-7}{-5} \rightarrow x = \frac{7}{5}$$

19.
$$8x - (3x + 2) = 3x - 10$$
$$8x - 3x - 2 = 3x - 10$$
$$5x - 2 = 3x - 10$$
$$5x - 2 + 2 = 3x - 10 + 2$$
$$5x = 3x - 8$$
$$5x - 3x = 3x - 8 - 3x$$
$$2x = -8$$
$$\frac{2x}{2} = \frac{-8}{2} \rightarrow x = -4$$

20.
$$7 - (2x - 1) = 10$$
$$7 - 2x + 1 = 10$$
$$8 - 2x = 10$$
$$8 - 2x - 8 = 10 - 8$$
$$-2x = 2$$
$$\frac{-2x}{-2} = \frac{2}{-2} \rightarrow x = -1$$

21.
$$\frac{3}{2}x + 2 = \frac{1}{2} - \frac{1}{2}x$$
$$\frac{3}{2}x + 2 - 2 = \frac{1}{2} - \frac{1}{2}x - 2$$
$$\frac{3}{2}x = -\frac{3}{2} - \frac{1}{2}x$$
$$\frac{3}{2}x + \frac{1}{2}x = -\frac{3}{2} - \frac{1}{2}x + \frac{1}{2}x$$
$$2x = -\frac{3}{2}$$
$$\left(\frac{1}{2}\right)(2x) = \left(-\frac{3}{2}\right)\left(\frac{1}{2}\right)$$
$$x = -\frac{3}{4}$$

22.
$$\frac{1}{3}x = 2 - \frac{2}{3}x$$
$$\frac{1}{3}x + \frac{2}{3}x = 2 - \frac{2}{3}x + \frac{2}{3}x$$
$$x = 2$$

23.
$$\frac{1}{2}x - 5 = \frac{3}{4}x$$
$$\frac{1}{2}x - 5 + 5 = \frac{3}{4}x + 5$$
$$\frac{1}{2}x = \frac{3}{4}x + 5$$
$$\frac{1}{2}x - \frac{3}{4}x = \frac{3}{4}x + 5 - \frac{3}{4}x$$
$$\frac{2}{4}x - \frac{3}{4}x = 5$$
$$-\frac{1}{4}x = 5$$
$$(-4)\left(-\frac{1}{4}x\right) = (5)(-4)$$
$$x = -20$$

24.
$$1 - \frac{1}{2}x = 6$$
$$1 - \frac{1}{2}x - 1 = 6 - 1$$
$$-\frac{1}{2}x = 5$$
$$(-2)\left(-\frac{1}{2}x\right) = (5)(-2)$$
$$x = -10$$

25.
$$\tfrac{2}{3}p = \tfrac{1}{2}p + \tfrac{1}{3}$$
$$6\left(\tfrac{2}{3}p\right) = 6\left(\tfrac{1}{2}p + \tfrac{1}{3}\right)$$
$$4p = 3p + 2$$
$$4p - 3p = 3p + 2 - 3p$$
$$p = 2$$

26.
$$\tfrac{1}{2} - \tfrac{1}{3}p = \tfrac{4}{3}$$
$$6\left(\tfrac{1}{2} - \tfrac{1}{3}p\right) = 6 \cdot \tfrac{4}{3}$$
$$3 - 2p = 8$$
$$3 - 2p - 3 = 8 - 3$$
$$-2p = 5$$
$$\frac{-2p}{-2} = \frac{5}{-2} \rightarrow p = -\frac{5}{2}$$

27.
$$0.9t = 0.4 + 0.1t$$
$$0.9t - 0.1t = 0.4 + 0.1t - 0.1t$$
$$0.8t = 0.4$$
$$\frac{0.8t}{0.8} = \frac{0.4}{0.8} \rightarrow t = 0.5$$

28.
$$0.9t = 1 + t$$
$$0.9t - t = 1 + t - t$$
$$-0.1t = 1$$
$$\frac{-0.1t}{-0.1} = \frac{1}{-0.1} \rightarrow t = -10$$

29.
$$\frac{x+1}{3} + \frac{x+2}{7} = 2$$
$$(21)\left(\frac{x+1}{3} + \frac{x+2}{7}\right) = (2)(21)$$
$$(21)\left(\frac{x+1}{3}\right) + (21)\left(\frac{x+2}{7}\right) = 42$$
$$7(x+1) + (3)(x+2) = 42$$
$$7x + 7 + 3x + 6 = 42$$
$$10x + 13 = 42$$
$$10x + 13 - 13 = 42 - 13$$
$$10x = 29$$
$$\frac{10x}{10} = \frac{29}{10}$$
$$x = 2.9$$

30.
$$\frac{2x+1}{3} + 16 = 3x$$
$$3\left(\frac{2x+1}{3} + 16\right) = 3 \cdot 3x$$
$$2x + 1 + 48 = 9x$$
$$2x + 49 = 9x$$
$$2x + 49 - 2x = 9x - 2x$$
$$49 = 7x$$
$$\frac{49}{7} = \frac{7x}{7}$$
$$x = 7$$

31.
$$\frac{2}{y} + \frac{4}{y} = 3$$
$$y\left(\frac{2}{y} + \frac{4}{y}\right) = y(3)$$
$$2 + 4 = 3y$$
$$6 = 3y$$
$$\frac{6}{3} = \frac{3y}{3}$$
$$y = 2$$

and since y = 2 does not cause a denominator to equal zero, the solution set is {2}.

32.
$$\frac{4}{y} - 5 = \frac{5}{2y}$$
$$2y\left(\frac{4}{y} - 5\right) = 2y \cdot \frac{5}{2y}$$
$$8 - 10y = 5$$
$$8 - 10y - 8 = 5 - 8$$
$$-10y = -3$$
$$\frac{-10y}{-10} = \frac{-3}{-10}$$
$$y = \frac{3}{10}$$

and since $y = \frac{3}{10}$ does not cause a denominator to equal zero, the solution set is $\left\{\frac{3}{10}\right\}$.

33.
$$\frac{1}{2} + \frac{2}{x} = \frac{3}{4}$$
$$(4x)\left(\frac{1}{2} + \frac{2}{x}\right) = \left(\frac{3}{4}\right)(4x)$$
$$(4x)\left(\frac{1}{2}\right) + (4x)\left(\frac{2}{x}\right) = 3x$$
$$2x + 8 = 3x$$
$$2x + 8 - 8 = 3x - 8$$
$$2x = 3x - 8$$
$$2x - 3x = 3x - 8 - 3x$$
$$-x = -8$$
$$\frac{-x}{-1} = \frac{-8}{-1}$$
$$x = 8$$

and since x = 8 does not cause any denominator to equal zero, x = 8 solves the original equation.

34.
$$\frac{3}{x} - \frac{1}{3} = \frac{1}{6}$$
$$(6x)\left(\frac{3}{x} - \frac{1}{3}\right) = \left(\frac{1}{6}\right)(6x)$$
$$(6x)\left(\frac{3}{x}\right) - (6x)\left(\frac{1}{3}\right) = x$$
$$18 - 2x = x$$
$$18 - 2x + 2x = x + 2x$$
$$18 = 3x$$
$$\frac{18}{3} = \frac{3x}{3}$$
$$6 = x$$

and since x = 6 does not cause any denominator to equal zero, x = 6 solves the original equation.

35.
$$(x+7)(x-1) = (x+1)^2$$
$$x^2 + 6x - 7 = x^2 + 2x + 1$$
$$x^2 + 6x - 7 - x^2 = x^2 + 2x + 1 - x^2$$
$$6x - 7 = 2x + 1$$
$$6x - 7 + 7 = 2x + 1 + 7$$
$$6x = 2x + 8$$
$$6x - 2x = 2x + 8 - 2x$$
$$4x = 8$$
$$\frac{4x}{4} = \frac{8}{4}$$
$$x = 2$$

36.
$$(x+2)(x-3) = (x+3)^2$$
$$x^2 - x - 6 = x^2 + 6x + 9$$
$$x^2 - x - 6 - x^2 = x^2 + 6x + 9 - x^2$$
$$-x - 6 = 6x + 9$$
$$-x - 6 + 6 = 6x + 9 + 6$$
$$-x = 6x + 15$$
$$-x - 6x = 6x + 15 - 6x$$
$$-7x = 15$$
$$\frac{-7x}{-7} = \frac{15}{-7} \rightarrow x = -\frac{15}{7}$$

37.
$$x(2x-3) = (2x+1)(x-4)$$
$$2x^2 - 3x = 2x^2 - 7x - 4$$
$$2x^2 - 3x - 2x^2 = 2x^2 - 7x - 4 - 2x^2$$
$$-3x = -7x - 4$$
$$-3x + 7x = -7x - 4 + 7x$$
$$4x = -4$$
$$\frac{4x}{4} = \frac{-4}{4} \rightarrow x = -1$$

38.
$$x(1+2x) = (2x-1)(x-2)$$
$$x + 2x^2 = 2x^2 - 5x + 2$$
$$2x^2 + x - 2x^2 = 2x^2 - 5x + 2 - 2x^2$$
$$x = -5x + 2$$
$$x + 5x = -5x + 2 + 5x$$
$$6x = 2$$
$$\frac{6x}{6} = \frac{2}{6} \rightarrow x = \frac{1}{3}$$

39.
$$z(z^2 + 1) = 3 + z^3$$
$$z^3 + z = 3 + z^3$$
$$z^3 + z - z^3 = 3 + z^3 - z^3$$
$$z = 3$$

40.
$$w(4 - w^2) = 8 - w^3$$
$$4w - w^3 = 8 - w^3$$
$$4w - w^3 + w^3 = 8 - w^3 + w^3$$
$$4w = 8$$
$$\frac{4w}{4} = \frac{8}{4} \rightarrow w = 2$$

41.
$$\frac{x}{x-2} + 3 = \frac{2}{x-2}$$
$$(x-2)\left(\frac{x}{x-2} + 3\right) = \left(\frac{2}{x-2}\right)(x-2)$$
$$(x-2)\left(\frac{x}{x-2}\right) + (x-2)(3) = 2$$
$$x + 3x - 6 = 2$$
$$4x - 6 = 2$$
$$4x - 6 + 6 = 2 + 6$$
$$4x = 8$$
$$\frac{4x}{4} = \frac{8}{4} \rightarrow x = 2$$

but x = 2 causes a denominator to equal zero, so we must discard this answer. Therefore the original equation has no real solution.

42.
$$\frac{2x}{x+3} = \frac{-6}{x+3} - 2$$
$$(x+3)\left(\frac{2x}{x+3}\right) = \left(\frac{-6}{x+3} - 2\right)(x+3)$$
$$2x = \left(\frac{-6}{x+3}\right)(x+3) - (2)(x+3)$$
$$2x = -6 - 2x - 6$$
$$2x = -12 - 2x$$
$$2x + 2x = -12 - 2x + 2x$$
$$4x = -12$$
$$\frac{4x}{4} = \frac{-12}{4} \rightarrow x = -3$$

but x = - 3 causes a denominator to equal zero, so we must discard this answer. Therefore the original equation has no real solution.

43.
$$x^2 = 9x$$
$$x^2 - 9x = 0$$
$$x(x - 9) = 0$$
$$x = 0 \text{ or } x = 9$$
The solution set is $\{0, 9\}$.

44.
$$4x^3 = x^2$$
$$4x^3 - x^2 = x^2 - x^2$$
$$4x^3 - x^2 = 0$$
$$x^2(4x - 1) = 0$$
$$x^2 = 0 \text{ or }$$
$$4x - 1 = 0 \rightarrow x = 0$$
$$or \ x = \frac{1}{4}$$
The solution set is $\left\{0, \frac{1}{4}\right\}$

45.
$$t^3 - 9t^2 = 0$$
$$t^2(t - 9) = 0$$
$$t^2 = 0$$
$$or \ t - 9 = 0 \rightarrow t = 0$$
$$or \ t = 9$$
The solution set is $\{0, 9\}$

46.
$$4z^3 - 8z^2 = 0$$
$$4z^2(z - 2) = 0$$
$$4z^2 = 0$$
$$or \ z - 2 = 0 \rightarrow z = 0$$
$$or \ z = 2$$
The solution set is $\{0, 2\}$

47.
$$\frac{2x}{x^2 - 4} = \frac{4}{x^2 - 4} - \frac{3}{x + 2}$$
$$\frac{2x}{(x + 2)(x - 2)} = \frac{4}{(x + 2)(x - 2)} - \frac{3}{x + 2}$$
$$(x + 2)(x - 2)\left(\frac{2x}{(x + 2)(x - 2)}\right) = \left(\frac{4}{(x + 2)(x - 2)} - \frac{3}{x + 2}\right)(x + 2)(x - 2)$$
$$2x = \left(\frac{4}{(x + 2)(x - 2)}\right)(x + 2)(x - 2) - \left(\frac{3}{x + 2}\right)(x + 2)(x - 2)$$
$$2x = 4 - (3)(x - 2)$$
$$2x = 4 - 3x + 6$$
$$2x = 10 - 3x$$
$$2x + 3x = 10 - 3x + 3x$$
$$5x = 10$$
$$\frac{5x}{5} = \frac{10}{5}$$
$$x = 2$$

but $x = 2$ causes a denominator to equal zero, so we must discard this answer.
Therefore the original equation has no real solution.

48.
$$\frac{x}{x^2-9}+\frac{4}{x+3}=\frac{3}{x^2-9}$$

$$\frac{x}{(x+3)(x-3)}+\frac{4}{x+3}=\frac{3}{x^2-9}$$

$$(x+3)(x-3)\left(\frac{x}{(x+3)(x-3)}+\frac{4}{x+3}\right)=\left(\frac{3}{x^2-9}\right)(x+3)(x-3)$$

$$(x+3)(x-3)\left(\frac{x}{(x+3)(x-3)}\right)+(x+3)(x-3)\left(\frac{4}{x+3}\right)=\left(\frac{3}{(x+3)(x-3)}\right)(x+3)(x-3)$$

$$x+(x-3)4=3$$

$$x+4x-12=3$$

$$5x-12=3$$

$$5x-12+12=3+12$$

$$5x=15$$

$$\frac{5x}{5}=\frac{15}{5}$$

$$x=3$$

but $x=3$ causes a denominator to equal zero, so we must discard this answer. Therefore the original equation has no real solution.

49.
$$\frac{x}{x+2}=\frac{3}{2}$$

$$(2)(x+2)\left(\frac{x}{x+2}\right)=\left(\frac{3}{2}\right)(2)(x+2)$$

$$(2)x=3(x+2)$$

$$2x=3x+6$$

$$2x-3x=3x+6-3x$$

$$-x=6$$

$$\frac{-x}{-1}=\frac{6}{-1}\rightarrow x=-6$$

and since x = - 6 does not cause any denominator to equal zero, x = - 6 solves the original equation.

50.
$$\frac{3x}{x-1}=2$$

$$(x-1)\left(\frac{3x}{x-1}\right)=(2)(x-1)$$

$$3x=2x-2$$

$$3x-2x=2x-2-2x$$

$$x=-2$$

and since $x=-2$ does not cause a denominator to equal zero, x = - 2 solves the original equation.

51.
$$\frac{5}{2x-3} = \frac{3}{x+5}$$

$$(2x-3)(x+5)\left(\frac{5}{2x-3}\right) = \left(\frac{3}{x+5}\right)(2x-3)(x+5)$$

$$(x+5)(5) = (3)(2x-3)$$

$$5x+25 = 6x-9$$

$$5x+25-6x = 6x-9-6x$$

$$25-x = -9$$

$$25-x-25 = -9-25$$

$$-x = -34$$

$$\frac{-x}{-1} = \frac{-34}{-1}$$

$$x = 34$$

and since $x = 34$ does not cause any denominator to equal zero, $x = 34$ solves the original equation.

52.
$$\frac{-4}{x+4} = \frac{-3}{x+6}$$

$$(x+6)(x+4)\left(\frac{-4}{x+4}\right) = \left(\frac{-3}{x+6}\right)(x+6)(x+4)$$

$$(x+6)(-4) = (-3)(x+4)$$

$$-4x-24 = -3x-12$$

$$-4x-24+4x = -3x-12+4x$$

$$-24 = -12+x$$

$$-24+12 = -12+x+12$$

$$-12 = x$$

and since $x = -12$ does not cause any denominator to equal zero, $x = -12$ solves the original equation.

53.
$$\frac{6t+7}{4t-1} = \frac{3t+8}{2t-4}$$

$$(4t-1)(2t-4)\left(\frac{6t+7}{4t-1}\right) = \left(\frac{3t+8}{2t-4}\right)(4t-1)(2t-4)$$

$$(2t-4)(6t+7) = (3t+8)(4t-1)$$

$$12t^2+14t-24t-28 = 12t^2-3t+32t-8$$

$$12t^2+14t-24t-28-12t^2 = 12t^2-3t+32t-8-12t^2$$

$$14t-24t-28 = -3t+32t-8$$

$$-10t - 28 = 29t - 8$$

$$-10t - 28 - 29t = 29t - 8 - 29t$$

$$28 - 39t - 28 = -8 - 28$$

$$-39t = -36$$

$$\frac{-39t}{-39} = \frac{-36}{-39}$$

$$t = \frac{12}{13}$$

and since $t = \dfrac{12}{13}$ does not cause any denominator to equal zero, $t = \dfrac{12}{13}$ solves the original equation.

54. $$\frac{8w + 5}{10w - 7} = \frac{4w - 3}{5w + 7}$$

$$(10w - 7)(5w + 7)\left(\frac{8w + 5}{10w - 7}\right) = \left(\frac{4w - 3}{5w + 7}\right)(10w - 7)(5w + 7)$$

$$(5w + 7)(8w + 5) = (4w - 3)(10w - 7)$$

$$40w^2 + 25w + 56w + 35 = 40w^2 - 28w - 30w + 21$$

$$40w^2 + 25w + 56w + 35 - 40w^2 = 40w^2 - 28w - 30w + 21 - 40w^2$$

$$25w + 56w + 35 = -28w - 30w + 21$$

$$81w + 35 = -58w + 21$$

$$81w + 35 + 58w = -58w + 21 + 58w$$

$$139w + 35 = 21$$

$$139w + 35 - 35 = 21 - 35$$

$$139w = -14$$

$$\frac{139w}{139} = \frac{-14}{139}$$

$$w = -\frac{14}{139}$$

and since $w = -14/139$ does not cause any denominator to equal zero, $w = -14/139$ solves the original equation.

55.
$$\frac{4}{x-2} = \frac{-3}{x+5} + \frac{7}{(x+5)(x-2)}$$

$$(x+5)(x-2)\left(\frac{4}{x-2}\right) = \left(\frac{-3}{x+5} + \frac{7}{(x+5)(x-2)}\right)(x+5)(x-2)$$

$$(x+5)(4) = \left(\frac{-3}{x+5}\right)(x+5)(x-2) + \left(\frac{7}{(x+5)(x-2)}\right)(x+5)(x-2)$$

$$4x + 20 = (-3)(x-2) + 7$$
$$4x + 20 = -3x + 6 + 7$$
$$4x + 20 = -3x + 13$$
$$4x + 20 + 3x = -3x - 8 + 3x$$
$$7x + 20 = -8$$
$$7x + 20 - 20 = -8 - 20$$
$$7x = -28$$
$$\frac{7x}{7} = \frac{-28}{7}$$
$$x = -4$$

and since $x = -4$ does not cause any denominator to equal zero, $x = -4$ solves the original equation.

56.
$$\frac{-4}{2x+3} + \frac{1}{x-1} = \frac{1}{(2x+3)(x-1)}$$

$$(2x+3)(x-1)\left(\frac{-4}{2x+3} + \frac{1}{x-1}\right) = \left(\frac{1}{(2x+3)(x-1)}\right)(2x+3)(x-1)$$

$$(2x+3)(x-1)\left(\frac{-4}{2x+3}\right) + (2x+3)(x-1)\left(\frac{1}{x-1}\right) = 1$$

$$(x-1)(-4) + (2x+3)(1) = 1$$
$$-4x + 4 + 2x + 3 = 1$$
$$-2x + 7 = 1$$
$$-2x + 7 + 2x = 1 + 2x$$
$$7 = 1 + 2x$$
$$7 - 1 = 1 + 2x - 1$$
$$6 = 2x$$
$$\frac{6}{2} = \frac{2x}{2}$$
$$3 = x$$

and since $x = 3$ does not cause any denominator to equal zero, $x = 3$ solves the original equation.

57.
$$\frac{2}{y+3}+\frac{3}{y-4}=\frac{5}{y+6}$$

$$(y+3)(y-4)(y+6)\left(\frac{2}{y+3}+\frac{3}{y-4}\right)=\left(\frac{5}{y+6}\right)(y+3)(y-4)(y+6)$$

$$(y+3)(y-4)(y+6)\left(\frac{2}{y+3}\right)+(y+3)(y-4)(y+6)\left(\frac{3}{y-4}\right)=(5)(y+3)(y-4)$$

$$(y-4)(y+6)(2)+(y+3)(y+6)(3)=(5)(y+3)(y-4)$$

$$\left(y^2+6y-4y-24\right)(2)+\left(y^2+6y+3y+18\right)(3)=(5)\left(y^2-4y+3y-12\right)$$

$$\left(y^2+2y-24\right)(2)+\left(y^2+9y+18\right)(3)=(5)\left(y^2-y-12\right)$$

$$2y^2+4y-48+3y^2+27y+54=5y^2-5y-60$$

$$5y^2+31y+6=5y^2-5y-60$$

$$5y^2+31y+6-5y^2=5y^2-5y-60-5y^2$$

$$31y+6=-5y-60$$

$$31y+6+5y=-5y-60+5y$$

$$36y+6=-60$$

$$36y+6-6=-60-6$$

$$36y=-66$$

$$\frac{36y}{36}=\frac{-66}{36}$$

$$y=-\frac{11}{6}$$

and since $y = -11/6$ does not cause any denominator to equal zero, $y = -11/6$ solves the original equation.

58.
$$\frac{5}{5z-11}+\frac{4}{2z-3}=\frac{-3}{5-z}$$

$$(5z-11)(2z-3)(5-z)\left(\frac{5}{5z-11}+\frac{4}{2z-3}\right)=\left(\frac{-3}{5-z}\right)(5z-11)(2z-3)(5-z)$$

$$(5z-11)(2z-3)(5-z)\left(\frac{5}{5z-11}\right)+(5z-11)(2z-3)(5-z)\left(\frac{4}{2z-3}\right)=(-3)(5z-11)(2z-3)$$

$$(2z-3)(5-z)(5)+(5z-11)(5-z)(4)=(-3)(5z-11)(2z-3)$$

$$\left(10z - 2z^2 - 15 + 3z\right)(5) + \left(25z - 5z^2 - 55 + 11z\right)(4) = (-3)\left(10z^2 - 15z - 22z + 33\right)$$

$$\left(-2z^2 + 13z - 15\right)(5) + \left(-5z^2 + 36z - 55\right)(4) = (-3)\left(10z^2 - 37z + 33\right)$$

$$-10z^2 + 85z - 75 - 20z^2 + 144z - 220 = -30z^2 + 111z - 99$$

$$-30z^2 + 229z - 295 = -30z^2 + 111z - 99$$

$$-30z^2 + 229z - 295 + 30z^2 = -30z^2 + 111z - 99 + 30z^2$$

$$229z - 295 = 111z - 99$$

$$229z - 295 - 229z = 111z - 99 - 229z$$

$$-295 = -118z - 99$$

$$-295 + 99 = -118z - 99 + 99$$

$$-196 = -118z$$

$$\frac{-196}{-118} = \frac{-118z}{-118}$$

$$\frac{98}{59} = z$$

and since $z = \dfrac{98}{59}$ does not cause any denominator to equal zero, $z = \dfrac{98}{59}$ solves the original equation.

59.

$$\frac{x}{x^2 - 1} - \frac{x + 3}{x^2 - x} = \frac{-3}{x^2 + x}$$

$$\frac{x}{(x + 1)(x - 1)} - \frac{x + 3}{x(x - 1)} = \frac{-3}{x(x + 1)}$$

$$(x + 1)(x - 1)(x)\left(\frac{x}{(x + 1)(x - 1)} - \frac{x + 3}{x(x - 1)}\right) = \left(\frac{-3}{x(x + 1)}\right)(x + 1)(x - 1)(x)$$

$$(x + 1)(x - 1)(x)\left(\frac{x}{(x + 1)(x - 1)}\right) - (x + 1)(x - 1)(x)\left(\frac{x + 3}{x(x - 1)}\right) = (-3)(x - 1)$$

$$(x)(x) - (x + 1)(x + 3) = -3x + 3$$

$$x^2 - \left(x^2 + 3x + x + 3\right) = -3x + 3$$

$$x^2 - \left(x^2 + 4x + 3\right) = -3x + 3$$

$$x^2 - x^2 - 4x - 3 = -3x + 3$$

$$-4x - 3 = -3x + 3$$

$$-4x - 3 + 4x = -3x + 3 + 4x$$

$$-3 = 3 + x$$

$$-3 - 3 = 3 + x - 3$$

$$-6 = x$$

and since $x = -6$ does not cause any denominator to equal zero, $x = -6$ solves the original equation.

60.
$$\frac{x+1}{x^2+2x} - \frac{x+4}{x^2+x} = \frac{-3}{x^2+3x+2}$$

$$\frac{x+1}{x(x+2)} - \frac{x+4}{x(x+1)} = \frac{-3}{(x+2)(x+1)}$$

$$x(x+2)(x+1)\left(\frac{x+1}{x(x+2)} - \frac{x+4}{x(x+1)}\right) = \left(\frac{-3}{(x+2)(x+1)}\right)x(x+2)(x+1)$$

$$x(x+2)(x+1)\left(\frac{x+1}{x(x+2)}\right) - x(x+2)(x+1)\left(\frac{x+4}{x(x+1)}\right) = (-3)x$$

$$(x+1)(x+1) - (x+2)(x+4) = -3x$$

$$x^2+2x+1 - \left(x^2+4x+2x+8\right) = -3x$$

$$x^2+2x+1 - \left(x^2+6x+8\right) = -3x$$

$$x^2+2x+1 - x^2-6x-8 = -3x$$

$$2x+1-6x-8 = -3x$$

$$-4x-7 = -3x$$

$$-4x-7+4x = -3x+4x$$

$$-7 = x$$

and since $x = -7$ does not cause any denominator to equal zero, $x = -7$ solves the original equation.

61.
$$3.2x + \frac{21.3}{65.871} = 19.23$$

$$3.2x + \frac{21.3}{65.871} - \frac{21.3}{65.871} = 19.23 - \frac{21.3}{65.871}$$

$$3.2x = 19.23 - \frac{21.3}{65.871}$$

$$\left(\frac{1}{3.2}\right)(3.2x) = \left(19.23 - \frac{21.3}{65.871}\right)\left(\frac{1}{3.2}\right)$$

$$x = \left(19.23 - \frac{21.3}{65.871}\right)\left(\frac{1}{3.2}\right)$$

$$x \approx 5.91$$

62.
$$6.2x - \frac{19.1}{83.72} = 0.195$$

$$6.2x - \frac{19.1}{83.72} + \frac{19.1}{83.72} = 0.195 + \frac{19.1}{83.72}$$

$$6.2x = 0.195 + \frac{19.1}{83.72}$$

$$\left(\frac{1}{6.2}\right)(6.2x) = \left(0.195 + \frac{19.1}{83.72}\right)\left(\frac{1}{6.2}\right)$$

$$x = \left(0.195 + \frac{19.1}{83.72}\right)\left(\frac{1}{6.2}\right)$$

$$x \approx 0.07$$

63.
$$14.72 - 21.58x = \frac{18}{2.11}x + 2.4$$

$$14.72 - 21.58x - \frac{18}{2.11}x = \frac{18}{2.11}x + 2.4 - \frac{18}{2.11}x$$

$$14.72 - 21.58x - \frac{18}{2.11}x = 2.4$$

$$14.72 - 21.58x - \frac{18}{2.11}x - 14.72 = 2.4 - 14.72$$

$$-21.58x - \frac{18}{2.11}x = 2.4 - 14.72$$

$$(x)\left(-21.58 - \frac{18}{2.11}\right) = 2.4 - 14.72$$

$$\left(\frac{1}{-21.58 - \frac{18}{2.11}}\right)(x)\left(-21.58 - \frac{18}{2.11}\right) = (2.4 - 14.72)\left(\frac{1}{-21.58 - \frac{18}{2.11}}\right)$$

$$x = (2.4 - 14.72)\left(\frac{1}{-21.58 - \frac{18}{2.11}}\right)$$

$$x \approx 0.41$$

64.
$$18.63x - \frac{21.2}{2.6} = \frac{14}{2.32}x - 20$$

$$18.63x - \frac{21.2}{2.6} - \frac{14}{2.32}x = \frac{14}{2.32}x - 20 - \frac{14}{2.32}x$$

$$18.63x - \frac{21.2}{2.6} - \frac{14}{2.32}x = -20$$

$$18.63x - \frac{21.2}{2.6} - \frac{14}{2.32}x + \frac{21.2}{2.6} = -20 + \frac{21.2}{2.6}$$

$$18.63x - \frac{14}{2.32}x = -20 + \frac{21.2}{2.6}$$

$$(x)\left(18.63 - \frac{14}{2.32}\right) = -20 + \frac{21.2}{2.6}$$

$$\left(\frac{1}{18.63 - \frac{14}{2.32}}\right)(x)\left(18.63 - \frac{14}{2.32}\right) = \left(-20 + \frac{21.2}{2.6}\right)\left(\frac{1}{18.63 - \frac{14}{2.32}}\right)$$

$$x = \left(-20 + \frac{21.2}{2.6}\right)\left(\frac{1}{18.63 - \frac{14}{2.32}}\right)$$

$$x \approx -0.94$$

65.
$$x^2 - 7x + 12 = 0$$
$$(x-4)(x-3) = 0$$
$$x - 4 = 0 \;\rightarrow x = 4$$
$$\text{or } x - 3 = 0 \;\rightarrow\; x = 3$$
Therefore the solution set is $\{3,4\}$

66.
$$x^2 - x - 6 = 0$$
$$(x-3)(x+2) = 0$$
$$x - 3 = 0 \rightarrow x = 3$$
$$\text{or } x + 2 = 0 \;\rightarrow x = -2.$$
Therefore the solution set is $\{-2,3\}$

67.
$$2x^2 + 5x - 3 = 0$$
$$(2x-1)(x+3) = 0$$
$$2x - 1 = 0 \rightarrow x = \frac{1}{2}$$
$$\text{or } x + 3 = 0 \rightarrow x = -3$$
Therefore the solution set is $\left\{-3, \frac{1}{2}\right\}$.

68.
$$3x^2 + 5x - 2 = 0$$
$$(3x-1)(x+2) = 0$$
$$3x - 1 = 0 \rightarrow x = \frac{1}{3}$$
$$\text{or } x + 2 = 0 \rightarrow \; x = -2$$
Therefore the solution set is $\left\{-2, \frac{1}{3}\right\}$.

69.
$$x^3 = 9x$$
$$x^3 - 9x = 0$$
$$x(x^2 - 9) = 0$$
$$x(x+3)(x-3) = 0$$
$$x = 0$$
$$\text{or } x + 3 = 0 \rightarrow x = -3$$
$$\text{or } x - 3 = 0 \rightarrow x = 3$$
Therefore the solution set is $\{-3,0,3\}$.

70.
$$x^4 = x^2$$
$$x^4 - x^2 = 0$$
$$x^2(x^2 - 1) = 0$$
$$x^2(x+1)(x-1) = 0$$
$$x^2 = 0 \rightarrow x = 0$$
$$\text{or } x + 1 = 0 \;\rightarrow x = -1$$
$$\text{or } x - 1 = 0 \rightarrow x = 1$$
Therefore the solution set is $\{-1,0,1\}$.

71.
$$x^3 + x^2 - 20x = 0$$
$$x(x^2 + x - 20) = 0$$
$$x(x+5)(x-4) = 0$$
$$x = 0$$
$$\text{or } x + 5 = 0 \;\rightarrow x = -5$$
$$\text{or } x - 4 = 0 \rightarrow x = 4$$
Therefore the solution set is $\{-5,0,4\}$.

72.
$$x^3 + 6x^2 - 7x = 0$$
$$x(x^2 + 6x - 7) = 0$$
$$x(x+7)(x-1) = 0$$
$$x = 0$$
$$\text{or } x - 1 = 0 \rightarrow x = 1$$
$$\text{or } x + 7 = 0 \rightarrow x = -7$$
Therefore the solution set is $\{-7,0,1\}$.

73. $x^3 + x^2 - x - 1 = 0$

We can factor by grouping to get

$$x^2(x+1) - (x+1) = 0$$
$$(x+1)(x^2-1) = 0$$
$$(x+1)(x+1)(x-1) = 0$$
$$x+1 = 0 \rightarrow x = -1$$
$$\text{or } x-1 = 0 \rightarrow x = 1$$

Therefore the solution set is $\{-1,1\}$.

74. $x^3 + 4x^2 - x - 4 = 0$

We can factor by grouping to get

$$x^2(x+4) - (x+4) = 0$$
$$(x+4)(x^2-1) = 0$$
$$(x+4)(x+1)(x-1) = 0$$
$$x+4 = 0 \rightarrow x = -4$$
$$\text{or } x+1 = 0 \rightarrow x = -1$$
$$\text{or } x-1 = 0 \rightarrow x = 1$$

Therefore the solution set is $\{-4,-1,1\}$.

75. $x^3 - 3x^2 - 4x + 12 = 0$

We can factor by grouping to get

$$x^2(x-3) - 4(x-3) = 0$$
$$(x-3)(x^2-4) = 0$$
$$(x-3)(x+2)(x-2) = 0$$
$$x-3 = 0 \rightarrow x = 3$$
$$\text{or } x+2 = 0 \rightarrow x = -2$$
$$\text{or } x-2 = 0 \rightarrow x = 2$$

Therefore the solution set is $\{-2,2,3\}$.

76. $x^3 - 3x^2 - x + 3 = 0$

We can factor by grouping to get

$$x^2(x-3) - (x-3) = 0$$
$$(x-3)(x^2-1) = 0$$
$$(x-3)(x+1)(x-1) = 0$$
$$x-3 = 0 \rightarrow x = 3$$
$$\text{or } x+1 = 0 \rightarrow x = -1$$
$$\text{or } x-1 = 0 \rightarrow x = 1$$

Therefore the solution set is $\{-1,1,3\}$.

77.
$$ax - b = c, \quad a \neq 0$$
$$ax - b + b = c + b$$
$$ax = c + b$$
$$\frac{ax}{a} = \frac{c+b}{a}$$
$$x = \frac{c+b}{a}$$

78.
$$1 - ax = b, \quad a \neq 0$$
$$1 - ax - 1 = b - 1$$
$$-ax = b - 1$$
$$\frac{-ax}{-a} = \frac{b-1}{-a}$$
$$x = \frac{b-1}{-a} = \frac{1-b}{a}$$

79.
$$\frac{x}{a} + \frac{x}{b} = c, \quad a \neq 0, \ b \neq 0, \ a \neq -b$$
$$ab\left(\frac{x}{a} + \frac{x}{b}\right) = ab \cdot c$$
$$bx + ax = abc$$
$$x(a+b) = abc$$
$$\frac{x(a+b)}{a+b} = \frac{abc}{a+b}$$
$$x = \frac{abc}{a+b}$$

80.
$$\frac{a}{x} + \frac{b}{x} = c, \quad c \neq 0$$
$$x\left(\frac{a}{x} + \frac{b}{x}\right) = x \cdot c$$
$$a + b = cx$$
$$\frac{a+b}{c} = \frac{cx}{c}$$
$$x = \frac{a+b}{c}$$

such that $a \neq -b$

81.
$$\frac{1}{x-a} + \frac{1}{x+a} = \frac{2}{x-1}$$

$$(x-a)(x+a)(x-1)\left(\frac{1}{x-a} + \frac{1}{x+a}\right) = \left(\frac{2}{x-1}\right)(x-a)(x+a)(x-1)$$

$$(x+a)(x-1)(1) + (x-a)(x-1)(1) = (2)(x-a)(x+a)$$

$$x^2 - x + ax - a + x^2 - x - ax + a = 2x^2 - 2a^2$$

$$2x^2 - 2x = 2x^2 - 2a^2$$

$$-2x = -2a^2$$

$$\frac{-2x}{-2} = \frac{-2a^2}{-2}$$

$$x = a^2$$

such that $x \neq \pm a, x \neq 1$

82.
$$\frac{b+c}{x+a} = \frac{b-c}{x-a}, c \neq 0, a \neq 0$$

$$(b+c)(x-a) = (b-c)(x+a)$$

$$bx - ba + cx - ca = bx + ba - cx - ca$$

$$-ba + cx - ca = ba - cx - ca$$

$$-ba + cx = ba - cx$$

$$2cx = 2ba$$

$$\frac{2cx}{2c} = \frac{2ba}{2c}$$

$$x = \frac{ba}{c}$$

such that $x \neq \pm a$

83.
$$x + 2a = 16 + ax - 6a$$

$$x = 4 \rightarrow$$

$$4 + 2a = 16 + a(4) - 6a$$

$$4 + 2a = 16 + 4a - 6a$$

$$4 + 2a = 16 - 2a$$

$$4a = 12$$

$$a = 3$$

84.
$$x + 2b = x - 4 + 2bx$$

$$x = 2 \rightarrow$$

$$2 + 2b = 2 - 4 + 2b(2)$$

$$2 + 2b = 2 - 4 + 4b$$

$$2 + 2b = -2 + 4b$$

$$4 = 2b$$

$$\frac{4}{2} = b \rightarrow b = 2$$

85.   Solving for R:
$$\frac{1}{R} = \frac{1}{R_1} + \frac{1}{R_2}$$

$$RR_1R_2\left(\frac{1}{R}\right) = RR_1R_2\left(\frac{1}{R_1} + \frac{1}{R_2}\right)$$

$$R_1R_2 = RR_2 + RR_1$$

$$R_1R_2 = R(R_2 + R_1)$$

$$\frac{R_1R_2}{R_2 + R_1} = \frac{R(R_2 + R_1)}{R_2 + R_1}$$

$$\frac{R_1R_2}{R_2 + R_1} = R$$

86. Solving for r:

$$A = P(1 + rt)$$
$$A = P + Prt$$
$$A - P = Prt$$
$$\frac{A - P}{Pt} = \frac{Prt}{Pt}$$
$$r = \frac{A - P}{Pt}$$

87. Solving for R:

$$F = \frac{mv^2}{R}$$
$$RF = R\left(\frac{mv^2}{R}\right)$$
$$RF = mv^2$$
$$\frac{RF}{F} = \frac{mv^2}{F} \rightarrow R = \frac{mv^2}{F}$$

88. Solving for T:

$$PV = nRT$$
$$\frac{PV}{nR} = \frac{nRT}{nR}$$
$$T = \frac{PV}{nR}$$

89. Solving for r:

$$S = \frac{a}{1 - r}$$
$$S(1 - r) = \left(\frac{a}{1 - r}\right)(1 - r)$$
$$S - Sr = a$$
$$S - Sr - S = a - S$$
$$-Sr = a - S$$
$$\frac{-Sr}{-S} = \frac{a - S}{-S} \rightarrow r = \frac{S - a}{S}$$

90. Solving for t:

$$v = -gt + v_0$$
$$v - v_0 = -gt$$
$$\frac{v - v_0}{-g} = \frac{-gt}{-g} \rightarrow t = \frac{v - v_0}{-g} = \frac{v_0 - v}{g}$$

91. Step 7 is only allowed if $x \neq 2$. But step 1 states that $x = 2$, so we have a contradiction.

92. $x^2 = 9$ is not equivalent to $x = 3$ since $x^2 = 9$ also has $x = -3$ as a solution.

$x = \sqrt{9}$ is equivalent to $x = 3$ since the equations have equivalent solutions

$(x - 1)(x - 2) = (x - 1)^2$ is not equivalent to $x - 2 = x - 1$ since the first equation has solution set $\{1\}$, but the second equation has no solution.

93. In order to solve $\dfrac{5}{x + 3} + 3 = \dfrac{8 + x}{x + 3}$, we multiply each term by the expression

"$x + 3$" to get $(x + 3)\left(\dfrac{5}{x + 3} + 3\right) = \left(\dfrac{8 + x}{x + 3}\right)(x + 3)$.

Now, provided $x \neq -3$, we can cancel the denominators to get
$$5 + (x + 3)(3) = 8 + x$$
$$5 + 3x + 9 = 8 + x \rightarrow 2x = -6 \rightarrow x = -3$$
However, we already stated that $x \neq -3$. So we have a contradiction.

94. Answers will vary. One example is $3x + 1 = 3x + 6$.

Equations and Inequalities

1.2 Setting Up Equations: Applications

1. Let A represent the area of the circle and r the radius.
The area of a circle is the product of π times the square of the radius. $\quad A = \pi r^2$

2. Let C represent the circumference of a circle and r the radius.
The circumference of a circle is the product of π times twice the radius. $\quad C = 2\pi r$

3. Let A represent the area of the square and s the length of a side.
The area of the square is the square of the length of a side. $\quad A = s^2$

4. Let P represent the perimeter of a square and s the length of a side.
The perimeter of a square is four times the length of a side. $\quad P = 4s$

5. Let F represent the force, m the mass, and a the acceleration.
Force equals the product of the mass times the acceleration. $\quad F = ma$

6. Let P represent the pressure, F the force, and A the area.
Pressure is the force per unit area. $\quad P = \dfrac{F}{A}$

7. Let W represent the work, F the force, and d the distance.
Work equals force times distance. $\quad W = Fd$

8. Let K represent the kinetic energy, m the mass, and v the velocity.
Kinetic energy is one-half the product of the mass and the square of the velocity.
$K = \frac{1}{2}mv^2$

9. C = total variable cost, x = number of dishwashers manufactured.
$C = 150x$

10. R = total revenue, x = number of dishwashers manufactured.
$R = 250x$

11.

Amount in Bonds	Amount in CD's	Total
x	$x - 3000$	20,000

$x + x - 3000 = 20000$

$2x - 3000 = 20000$

$2x = 23000 \rightarrow x = 11500$

$11,500 will be invested in bonds. $8,500 will be invested in CD's.

12.

Amount for Sean	Amount for George	Total
x	$x - 3000$	10,000

$x + x - 3000 = 10000$

$2x - 3000 = 10000$ Sean will receive $6500 and George will receive $3500.

$2x = 13000 \rightarrow x = 6500$

13.

Scott	Alice	Tricia	Total
x	$\frac{3}{4}x$	$\frac{1}{2}x$	900,000

$x + \frac{3}{4}x + \frac{1}{2}x = 900,000$

$\frac{9}{4}x = 900,000$

$x = \frac{4}{9}(900,000) \rightarrow x = 400,000$

Scott receives $400,000. Alice receives $300,000. Tricia receives $200,000.

14.

Canter	Carole	Total
x	$\frac{2}{3}x$	$18

$x + \frac{2}{3}x = 18$ Canter pays $10.80 and Carole pays $7.20.

$\frac{5}{3}x = 18 \rightarrow x = \frac{3}{5}(18) \rightarrow x = 10.80$

15.

	Dollars per hour	Number of hours worked	Money earned
Regular wage	x	40	$40x$
Overtime wage	$1.5x$	8	$(1.5x)(8)$

$40x + (1.5x)(8) = 442$ Sandra's regular hourly wage is $8.50.

$40x + 12x = 442 \rightarrow 52x = 442 \rightarrow x = \frac{442}{52} = 8.50$

16.

	Dollars per hour	Number of hours worked	Money earned
Regular wage	x	40	$40x$
Overtime wage	$1.5x$	6	$(1.5x)(6)$
Sunday wage	$2x$	4	$8x$

$40x + (1.5x)(6) + 8x = 342$ Leah's regular hourly wage is $6.00.

$40x + 9x + 8x = 342 \rightarrow 57x = 342 \rightarrow x = \dfrac{342}{57} = 6$

17.   Let x represent the score on the final exam and construct the table

	Test1	Test2	Test3	Test4	Test5	Final Exam	Final Exam
score	80	83	71	61	95	x	x
weight	1/7	1/7	1/7	1/7	1/7	1/7	1/7

Compute the final average and set equal to 80.

$$\left(\frac{1}{7}\right)(80 + 83 + 71 + 61 + 95 + x + x) = 80$$

Now solve for x:

$$\left(\frac{1}{7}\right)(390 + 2x) = 80$$

$390 + 2x = 560 \rightarrow 2x = 170 \rightarrow x = 85$

Brooke needs to score an 85 on the final exam to get an average of 80 in the course.

18.   Let x represent the score on the final exam and construct the table

	Test1	Test2	Test3	Test4	Final Exam
score	86	80	84	90	x
weight	1/12	1/12	1/12	1/12	2/3

Note: The four tests account for 1/3 of the total average, so each test is

worth $\dfrac{\left(\frac{1}{3}\right)}{4} = \dfrac{1}{12}$. To determine the score Mike needs to earn a B, we compute the final average and set equal to 80.

$$\left(\frac{1}{12}\right)(86 + 80 + 84 + 90) + \left(\frac{2}{3}\right)x = 80$$

Now solve for x: $\left(\frac{1}{12}\right)(340) + \left(\frac{2}{3}\right)x = 80$

$$(12)\left(\left(\frac{1}{12}\right)(340) + \left(\frac{2}{3}\right)x\right) = (80)(12)$$

$$340 + 8x = 960$$
$$8x = 620 \rightarrow x = 77.5$$

Mike must score 77.5 to earn a B.

To determine the score Mike needs to earn an A, we compute the final average and set equal to 90.

$$\left(\frac{1}{12}\right)(86 + 80 + 84 + 90) + \left(\frac{2}{3}\right)x = 90$$

Now solve for x: $\left(\frac{1}{12}\right)(340) + \left(\frac{2}{3}\right)x = 90$

$$(12)\left(\left(\frac{1}{12}\right)(340) + \left(\frac{2}{3}\right)x\right) = (90)(12)$$

$$340 + 8x = 1080$$
$$8x = 740 \rightarrow x = 92.5$$

Mike must score 92.5 to earn an A.

19. Let x represent the original price of the house.
Then $0.15x$ represents the reduction in the price of the house.
  original price – reduction = new price
      $x - 0.15x = 125,000$

      $0.85x = 125,000 \rightarrow x = 147,058.82$
The original price of the house was \$147,058.82.
The amount of the savings is $0.15(\$147,058.82) = \$22,058.82$.

20. Let x represent the original price of the car.
Then $0.15x$ represents the reduction in the price of the car.
  original price – reduction = new price
      $x - 0.15x = 8000$

      $0.85x = 8000 \rightarrow x = 9411.76$
The original price of the car was \$9411.76.
The amount of the savings is $\$9411.76 - \$8000.00 = \$1411.76$.

21. Let x represent the price the bookstore pays for the book (publisher price).
     Then $0.35x$ represents the mark up on the book.
     The selling price of the book is $56.00.
       publisher price + mark up = selling price
              $x + 0.35x = 56.00$ The bookstore pays $41.48 for the book.
              $1.35x = 56.00 \rightarrow x = 41.48$

22. Let x represent the dealer's cost of the new car. $x = 0.85(\$12,000) = \$10,200$
     If the dealer accepts $100 over cost, then you will pay $10,200 + $100 = $10,300.

23.

	Number of tickets sold	Price per ticket	Money earned
adults	x	4.75	$4.75x$
children	$5200 - x$	2.5	$(5200 - x)(2.5)$

     money from adult tickets + money from children tickets = total receipts

       $4.75x + (5200 - x)(2.5) = 20,335$
         $4.75x + 13,000 - 2.5x = 20,335$ There were 3260 adult patrons.

              $2.25x = 7335 \rightarrow x = \dfrac{7335}{2.25} = 3260$

24. p = original price for the suit

     $p - 0.30p = 0.70p$ = discounted price for the suit

       $0.70p = 399 \rightarrow p = \dfrac{399}{0.70} = 570$ The suit originally cost $570.

25. l = length, w = width
           $2l + 2w = 60$ Perimeter $= 2l + 2w$
                $l = w + 8$ The length is 8 more than the width.
       $2(w + 8) + 2w = 60$
       $2w + 16 + 2w = 60$
           $4w + 16 = 60 \rightarrow 4w = 44 \rightarrow w = 11$ feet, $l = 19$ feet

26. l = length, w = width
           $2l + 2w = 42$ Perimeter $= 2l + 2w$
                $l = 2w$ The length is 8 more than the width.
       $2(2w) + 2w = 42$
           $4w + 2w = 42 \rightarrow 6w = 42 \rightarrow w = 7$ feet, $l = 14$ feet

27. Let x represent the amount of money invested in bonds.
    Then $50,000 - x$ represents the amount of money invested in CD's.

	Principle	Rate	Time (yrs)	Interest
Bonds	x	0.15	1	$0.15x$
CD's	$50,000 - x$	0.07	1	$0.07(50,000 - x)$

Since the total interest is to be $6,000, we have:
$$0.15x + 0.07(50,000 - x) = 6,000$$

$$(100)(0.15x + 0.07(50,000 - x)) = (6,000)(100)$$

$$15x + 7(50,000 - x) = 600,000$$

$$15x + 350,000 - 7x = 600,000$$

$$8x + 350,000 = 600,000 \rightarrow 8x = 250,000 \rightarrow x = 31,250$$

$31,250 should be invested in bonds at 15% and $18,750 should be invested in CD's at 7%.

28. Let x represent the amount of money invested in bonds.
    Then $50,000 - x$ represents the amount of money invested in CD's.

	Principle	Rate	Time (yrs)	Interest
Bonds	x	0.15	1	$0.15x$
CD's	$50,000 - x$	0.07	1	$0.07(50,000 - x)$

Since the total interest is to be $7,000, we have:
$$0.15x + 0.07(50,000 - x) = 7,000$$

$$(100)(0.15x + 0.07(50,000 - x)) = (7,000)(100)$$

$$15x + 7(50,000 - x) = 700,000$$

$$15x + 350,000 - 7x = 700,000$$

$$8x + 350,000 = 700,000 \rightarrow 8x = 350,000 \rightarrow x = 43,750$$

$43,750 should be invested in bonds at 15% and $6,250 should be invested in CD's at 7%.

29. Let x represent the amount of money loaned at 8%.
    Then $12,000 - x$ represents the amount of money loaned at 18%.

	Principle	Rate	Time (yrs)	Interest
Loan at 8%	x	0.08	1	$0.08x$
Loan at 18%	$12,000 - x$	0.18	1	$0.18(12,000 - x)$

Since the total interest is to be $1,000, we have:
$$0.08x + 0.18(12,000 - x) = 1,000$$

$$(100)(0.08x + 0.18(12,000 - x)) = (1,000)(100)$$

$$8x + 18(12,000 - x) = 100,000$$

$$8x + 216,000 - 18x = 100,000$$

$$-10x + 216,000 = 100,000 \rightarrow -10x = -116,000 \rightarrow x = 11,600$$

$11,600 is loaned at 8% and $400 is loaned at 18%.

30.   Let x represent the amount of money loaned at 16%.
Then $1,000,000 - x$ represents the amount of money loaned at 19%.

	Principle	Rate	Time (yrs)	Interest
Loan at 16%	x	0.16	1	$0.16x$
Loan at 19%	$1,000,000 - x$	0.19	1	$0.19(1,000,000 - x)$

Since the total interest is to be $1,000,000(0.18), we have:

$$0.16x + 0.19(1,000,000 - x) = 1,000,000(0.18)$$

$$(100)(0.16x + 0.19(1,000,000 - x)) = 1,000,000(0.18)(100)$$

$$16x + 19(1,000,000 - x) = 1,000,000(18)$$

$$16x + 19,000,000 - 19x = 18,000,000$$

$$-3x + 19,000,000 = 18,000,000$$

$$-3x = -1,000,000 \rightarrow x = \$333,333.33$$

The loan officer should lend $333,333.33 at 16%.

31.   Let x represent the number of pounds of Earl Gray tea.
Then $100 - x$ represents the number of pounds of Orange Pekoe tea.

	No. of pounds	Price per pound	Total Value
Earl Gray	x	$5.00	$5x$
Orange Pekoe	$100 - x$	$3.00	$3(100 - x)$
Blend	100	$4.50	$4.50(100)$

$$5x + 3(100 - x) = 4.50(100)$$

$$5x + 300 - 3x = 450$$

$$2x + 300 = 450 \rightarrow 2x = 150 \rightarrow x = 75$$

75 pounds of Earl Gray tea must be blended with 25 pounds of Orange Pekoe.

32.   Let x represent the number of pounds of the first kind of coffee.
Then $100 - x$ represents the number of pounds of the second kind of coffee.

	No. of Pounds	Price per Pound	Total Value
First kind	x	$2.75	$2.75x$
Second kind	$100 - x$	$5.00	$5(100 - x)$
Blend	100	$3.90	$3.90(100)$

$$2.75x + 5(100 - x) = 3.90(100)$$

$$2.75x + 500 - 5x = 390$$

$$-2.25x + 500 = 390 \rightarrow -2.25x = -110 \rightarrow x \approx 48.9$$

48.9 pounds of the first kind of coffee must be blended with 51.1 pounds of the second kind of coffee.

33. Let x represent the number of pounds of cashews.
     Then $x+60$ represents the number of pounds in the mixture.

	No. of pounds	Price per pound	Total Value
cashews	x	$4.00	$4x$
peanuts	60	$1.50	$1.50(60)$
mixture	$x+60$	$2.50	$2.50(x+60)$

$$4x + 1.50(60) = 2.50(x+60)$$

$$4x + 90 = 2.50x + 150 \rightarrow 1.5x = 60 \rightarrow x = 40$$

40 pounds of cashews must be added to the 60 pounds of peanuts.

34. Let x represent the number of caramels in the box.
     Then $30 - x$ represents the number of cremes in the box.

	No. of Pieces	Price per Piece	Total Value
caramels	x	$0.25	$0.25x$
cremes	$30 - x$	$0.45	$0.45(30-x)$

Profit = Revenue – Cost

$$12.50 - (0.25x + 0.45(30-x)) = 3.00$$

$$9.50 = 0.25x + 13.50 - 0.45x$$

$$-4.00 = -0.20x \rightarrow x = 20$$

The box should contain 20 caramels and 10 cremes.

35. Let r represent the speed of the current.

	Rate	Time	Distance
Upstream	$16 - r$	$\dfrac{20}{60} = \dfrac{1}{3}$	$\dfrac{16-r}{3}$
Downstream	$16 + r$	$\dfrac{15}{60} = \dfrac{1}{4}$	$\dfrac{16+r}{4}$

Since the distance is the same in each direction:

$$\frac{16-r}{3} = \frac{16+r}{4}$$

$$4(16-r) = 3(16+r)$$

$$64 - 4r = 48 + 3r \rightarrow 16 = 7r \rightarrow r = \frac{16}{7} \approx 2.286$$

The speed of the current is approximately 2.286 miles per hour.

36. Let r represent the speed of the motorboat.

	Rate	Time	Distance
Upstream	$r - 3$	5	$5(r-3)$
Downstream	$r + 3$	2.5	$2.5(r+3)$

The distance is the same in each direction:

$$5(r-3) = 2.5(r+3)$$

$$5r - 15 = 2.5r + 7.5 \rightarrow 2.5r = 22.5 \rightarrow r = 9$$

The speed of the motorboat is 9 miles per hour.

37.   Let r represent the rate of the Metra commuter train.
        Then $r + 50$ represents the rate of the Amtrak train.

	Rate	Time	Distance
Metra train	r	3	$3r$
Amtrak train	$r + 50$	1	$r + 50$

        Amtrak distance = Metra distance $- 10$

$$r + 50 = 3r - 10$$

$$60 = 2r \rightarrow r = 30$$

        The Metra commuter train travels at a rate of 30 miles per hour.
        The Amtrak train travels at a rate of 80 miles per hour.

38.   Let r represent the rate of the slower car.
        Then $r + 10$ represents the rate of the faster car.

	Rate	Time	Distance
Slower Car	r	3.5	$3.5r$
Faster Car	$r + 10$	3	$3(r + 10)$

$$3.5r = 3(r + 10)$$

$$3.5r = 3r + 30 \rightarrow 0.5r = 30 \rightarrow r = 60$$

        The slower car travels at a rate of 60 miles per hour. The faster car travels at a rate of 70
        miles per hour. The distance is $(70)(3) = 210$ miles.

39.   Let t represent the time it takes to do the job together.

	Time to do job	Part of job done in one minute
Trent	30	$\dfrac{1}{30}$
Lois	20	$\dfrac{1}{20}$
Together	t	$\dfrac{1}{t}$

$$\frac{1}{30} + \frac{1}{20} = \frac{1}{t} \rightarrow 2t + 3t = 60 \rightarrow 5t = 60 \rightarrow t = 12$$

        Working together, the job can be done in 12 minutes.

40.   Let t represent the time it takes April to do the job working alone.

	Time to do job	Part of job done in one hour
Patrice	10	$\dfrac{1}{10}$
April	t	$\dfrac{1}{t}$
Together	6	$\dfrac{1}{6}$

$$\frac{1}{10} + \frac{1}{t} = \frac{1}{6} \rightarrow 3t + 30 = 5t \rightarrow 2t = 30 \rightarrow t = 15$$

        It will take April 15 hours to paint the four rooms.

41. l = length of the garden
      w = width of the garden
   (a)   The length of the garden is to be twice its width. Thus, $l = 2w$.
         The dimensions of the fence are $l + 4$ and $w + 4$.
         The perimeter is 46 feet, so:
$$2(l + 4) + 2(w + 4) = 46$$
$$2(2w + 4) + 2(w + 4) = 46$$
$$4w + 8 + 2w + 8 = 46$$
$$6w + 16 = 46 \rightarrow 6w = 30 \rightarrow w = 5$$
         The dimensions of the garden are 5 feet by 10 feet.

   (b)   Area $= l \cdot w = 5 \cdot 10 = 50$ square feet.

   (c)   If the dimensions of the garden are the same, then the length and width of the fence
         are also the same $(l + 4)$. The perimeter is 46 feet, so:
$$2(l + 4) + 2(l + 4) = 46$$
$$2l + 8 + 2l + 8 = 46$$
$$4l + 16 = 46 \rightarrow 4l = 30 \rightarrow l = 7.5$$
         The dimensions of the garden are 7.5 feet by 7.5 feet.
   (d)   Area $= l \cdot w = 7.5(7.5) = 56.25$ square feet.

42. l = length of the pond
      w = width of the pond
   (a)   The pond is to be a square. Thus, $l = w$.
         The dimensions of the fenced area are $w + 6$ on each side.
         The perimeter is 100 feet, so:
$$4(w + 6) = 100$$
$$4w + 24 = 100 \rightarrow 4w = 76 \rightarrow w = 19$$
         The dimensions of the pond are 19 feet by 19 feet.
   (b)   The length of the pond is to be three times the width. Thus, $l = 3w$.
         The dimensions of the fenced area are $w + 6$ and $l + 6$.
         The perimeter is 100 feet, so:
$$2(w + 6) + 2(l + 6) = 100$$
$$2(w + 6) + 2(3w + 6) = 100$$
$$2w + 12 + 6w + 12 = 100$$
$$8w + 24 = 100 \rightarrow 8w = 76 \rightarrow w = 9.5 \rightarrow l = 3(9.5) = 28.5$$
         The dimensions of the pond are 9.5 feet by 28.5 feet.
   (c)   If the pond is circular, the diameter is d and the diameter of the circle with the pond
         and the deck is $d + 6$. The perimeter is 100 feet, so:
$$\pi(d + 6) = 100$$
$$\pi d + 6\pi = 100 \rightarrow \pi d = 100 - 6\pi \rightarrow d = \frac{100}{\pi} - 6 \approx 25.83$$
         The diameter of the pond is 25.83 feet.

(d)   Area of the square = $l \cdot w = 19(19) = 361$ ft^2.
Area of the rectangle = $l \cdot w = 28.5(9.5) = 270.75$ ft^2.

Area of the circle = $\pi r^2 = \pi\left(\dfrac{25.83}{2}\right)^2 \approx 524$ ft^2.

The circular pond has the largest area.

43.   Let t represent the time it takes for the defensive back to catch the tight end.

	Time to run 100 yards	Time	Rate	Distance
Tight End	12 sec	t	$\dfrac{100}{12} = \dfrac{25}{3}$	$\dfrac{25}{3}t$
Defensive Back	10 sec	t	$\dfrac{100}{10} = 10$	$10t$

Since the defensive back has to run 5 yards farther, we have:

$$\dfrac{25}{3}t + 5 = 10t$$

$$25t + 15 = 30t$$

$$15 = 5t$$

$$t = 3 \quad \longrightarrow \quad 10t = 30$$

The defensive back will catch the tight end at the 45 yard line.

44.   Let x represent the number of highway miles.
Then $30,000 - x$ represents the number of city miles.

	No. of miles	Gallons per mile	Gallons used
highway	x	1/40	$\dfrac{1}{40}x$
city	$30,000 - x$	1/25	$(30,000 - x)\left(\dfrac{1}{25}\right)$

$$\dfrac{1}{40}x + (30,000 - x)\left(\dfrac{1}{25}\right) = 900$$

$$\dfrac{1}{40}x + 1200 - \dfrac{1}{25}x = 900$$

$$\dfrac{1}{40}x - \dfrac{1}{25}x = -300$$

$$\dfrac{25 - 40}{(40)(25)}x = -300 \rightarrow \dfrac{-15}{1000}x = -300$$

$$x = -300\left(\dfrac{1000}{-15}\right) = 20000$$

Therese can allow for 20,000 miles as a business expense.

45. Let x represent the number of ounces of pure water.
    Then $x + 1$ represents the number of gallons in the 60% solution.

	No. of gallons	Conc. of Antifreeze	Pure Antifreeze
water	x	0	0
100% antifreeze	1	1.00	1(1)
60% antifreeze	$x + 1$	0.60	$0.60(x + 1)$

$0 + 1(1) = 0.60(x + 1)$

$$1 = 0.6x + 0.6 \rightarrow 0.4 = 0.6x \rightarrow x = \frac{4}{6} = \frac{2}{3}$$

$\frac{2}{3}$ gallon of pure water should be added.

46. Let x represent the number of liters to be drained and replaced with pure antifreeze.

	No. of Liters	Conc. of Antifreeze	Pure Antifreeze
Pure Antifreeze	x	1.00	x
Original Solution	$15 - x$	0.40	$0.40(15 - x)$
New Solution	15	0.60	0.60(15)

$x + 0.40(15 - x) = 0.60(15)$

$$x + 6 - 0.40x = 9 \rightarrow 0.60x = 3 \rightarrow x = 5$$

5 liters should be drained and replaced with pure antifreeze.

47. Let x represent the number of ounces of water to be evaporated.

	No. of ounces	Conc. of Salt	Pure Salt
Water	x	0.00	0
4% Salt	32	0.04	0.04(32)
6% Salt	$32 - x$	0.06	$0.06(32 - x)$

$0 + 0.04(32) = 0.06(32 - x)$

$$1.28 = 1.92 - 0.06x \rightarrow 0.06x = 0.64 \rightarrow x = \frac{0.64}{0.06} = \frac{32}{3}$$

32/3 ounces of water need to be evaporated.

48. Let x represent the number of gallons of water to be evaporated.

	No. of Gallons	Conc. of Salt	Pure Salt
Water	x	0.00	0
3% Salt	240	0.03	0.03(240)
5% Salt	$240 - x$	0.05	$0.05(240 - x)$

$0 + 0.03(240) = 0.05(240 - x)$

$$7.2 = 12 - 0.05x \rightarrow 0.05x = 4.8 \rightarrow x = \frac{4.8}{0.05} = 96$$

96 gallons of water need to be evaporated.

49. Let x represent the number of grams of pure gold.
     Then $60 - x$ represents the number of grams of 12 karat gold to be used.

	No. of grams	Conc. of gold	Pure gold
Pure gold	x	1.00	x
12 karat gold	$60 - x$	$\dfrac{1}{2}$	$\dfrac{1}{2}(60 - x)$
16 karat gold	60	$\dfrac{2}{3}$	$\dfrac{2}{3}(60)$

$$x + \frac{1}{2}(60 - x) = \frac{2}{3}(60)$$

$$x + 30 - 0.5x = 40 \rightarrow 0.5x = 10 \rightarrow x = 20$$

20 grams of pure gold should be mixed with 40 grams of 12 karat gold.

50. Let x represent the number of atoms of oxygen.
     $2x$ represents the number of atoms of hydrogen.
     $x + 1$ represents the number of atoms of carbon.

$$x + 2x + x + 1 = 45 \rightarrow 4x = 44 \rightarrow x = 11$$

There are 11 atoms of oxygen and 22 atoms of hydrogen in the sugar molecule.

51. Let t represent the time it takes for Mike to catch up with Dan.

	Time to run mile	Time	Part of mile run in one minute	Distance
Mike	6	t	$\dfrac{1}{6}$	$\dfrac{1}{6}t$
Dan	9	$t + 1$	$\dfrac{1}{9}$	$\dfrac{1}{9}(t + 1)$

Since the distances are the same, we have:

$$\frac{1}{6}t = \frac{1}{9}(t + 1) \rightarrow 3t = 2t + 2 \rightarrow t = 2$$

Mike will pass Dan after 2 minutes, which is a distance of $\frac{1}{3}$ mile.

52. Let t represent the time of flight with the wind.

	Rate	Time	Distance
With Wind	$300 + 30$	t	$330t$
Against Wind	$300 - 30$	$5 - t$	$270(5 - t)$

The distance is the same in each direction:

$$330t = 270(5 - t)$$

$$330t = 1350 - 270t \rightarrow 600t = 1350 \rightarrow t = 2.25$$

The distance the plane can fly and still return safely is $330(2.25) = 742.5$ miles.

53. Let t represent the time the auxiliary pump needs to run.

	Time to do job alone	Part of job done in one hour	Time on Job	Part of total job done by each pump
Main Pump	4	$\dfrac{1}{4}$	3	$\dfrac{3}{4}$
Auxiliary Pump	9	$\dfrac{1}{9}$	t	$\dfrac{1}{9}t$

Since the two pumps are emptying one tanker, we have:

$$\frac{3}{4} + \frac{1}{9}t = 1 \to 27 + 4t = 36 \to 4t = 9 \to t = \frac{9}{4} = 2.25$$

The auxiliary pump must run for 2.25 hours. It must be started at 9:45 a.m.

54. Let x represent the number of pounds of pure cement.
Then $x + 20$ represents the number of pounds in the 40% mixture.

	No. of pounds	Conc. of Cement	Pure Cement
Pure Cement	x	1.00	x
25% Cement	20	0.25	0.25(20)
40% Cement	$x + 20$	0.40	0.40$(x + 20)$

$$x + 0.25(20) = 0.40(x + 20)$$

$$x + 5 = 0.4x + 8 \to 0.6x = 3 \to x = \frac{30}{6} = 5$$

5 pounds of pure cement should be added.

55. Let t represent the time for the tub to fill with the faucets on and the stopper removed.

	Time to do job alone	Part of job done in one minute	Time on Job	Part of total job done by each
Faucets open	15	$\dfrac{1}{15}$	t	$\dfrac{t}{15}$
Stopper removed	20	$-\dfrac{1}{20}$	t	$-\dfrac{t}{20}$

Since one tub is being filled, we have:

$$\frac{t}{15} + \left(-\frac{t}{20}\right) = 1 \to 4t - 3t = 60 \to t = 60 \qquad \therefore \ 60 \text{ minutes is required to fill the tub.}$$

56. Let t be the time the 5 horsepower pump needs to run to finish emptying the pool.

	Time to do job alone	Part of job done in one hour	Time on Job	Part of total job done by each pump
5 hp Pump	5	$\dfrac{1}{5}$	$2 + t$	$\dfrac{1}{5}(2 + t)$
2 hp Pump	8	$\dfrac{1}{8}$	2	$\dfrac{1}{8} \cdot 2 = \dfrac{1}{4}$

Since the two pumps are emptying one pool, we have:

$$\frac{1}{5}(2+t)+\frac{1}{4}=1 \rightarrow 4(2+t)+5=20 \rightarrow 8+4t+5=20 \rightarrow 4t=7 \rightarrow t=1.75$$

The 5 horsepower pump must run for an additional 1.75 hours or 1 hour and 45 minutes to empty the pool.

57.   Burke's rate is $\frac{100}{12}$ meters/sec.

In 9.99 seconds, Burke will run $\frac{100}{12}(9.99)=83.25$ meters.

Lewis would win by 16.75 meters.

58.   Let x be the original selling price of the shirt.
$$\text{Profit} = \text{Revenue} - \text{Cost}$$
$$4 = x - 0.40x - 20 \rightarrow 24 = 0.60x \rightarrow x = 40$$
The original price should be $40 to ensure a profit of $4 after the sale.

If the sale is 50% off, the profit is:
$$40 - 0.50(40) - 20 = 40 - 20 - 20 = 0$$
At 50% off there will be no profit.

59.   Answers will vary.

60.   It is impossible to mix two solutions with a lower concentration and end up with a new solution with a higher concentration.

Equations and Inequalities

1.3 Quadratic Equations

1. $x^2 - 9x = 0$
   $x(x - 9) = 0 \rightarrow x = 0$ or $x = 9$
   The solution set is $\{0, 9\}$.

2. $x^2 + 4x = 0$
   $x(x + 4) = 0 \rightarrow x = 0$ or $x = -4$
   The solution set is $\{-4, 0\}$.

3. $x^2 - 25 = 0$
   $(x + 5)(x - 5) = 0 \rightarrow x = -5$ or $x = 5$
   The solution set is $\{-5, 5\}$.

4. $x^2 - 9 = 0$
   $(x + 3)(x - 3) = 0 \rightarrow x = -3$ or $x = 3$
   The solution set is $\{-3, 3\}$.

5. $z^2 + z - 6 = 0$
   $(z + 3)(z - 2) = 0 \rightarrow z = -3$ or $z = 2$
   The solution set is $\{-3, 2\}$.

6. $v^2 + 7v + 6 = 0$
   $(v + 6)(v + 1) = 0 \rightarrow v = -6$ or $v = -1$
   The solution set is $\{-6, -1\}$.

7. $2x^2 - 5x - 3 = 0$
   $(2x + 1)(x - 3) = 0 \rightarrow x = -\dfrac{1}{2}$ or $x = 3$
   The solution set is $\left\{-\dfrac{1}{2}, 3\right\}$.

8. $3x^2 + 5x + 2 = 0$
   $(3x + 2)(x + 1) = 0 \rightarrow x = -\dfrac{2}{3}$ or $x = -1$
   The solution set is $\left\{-\dfrac{2}{3}, -1\right\}$.

9. $3t^2 - 48 = 0$
   $3(t^2 - 16) = 0 \rightarrow 3(t + 4)(t - 4) = 0$
   $t = -4$ or $t = 4$
   The solution set is $\{-4, 4\}$.

10. $2y^2 - 50 = 0$
    $2(y^2 - 25) = 0$
    $2(y + 5)(y - 5) = 0 \rightarrow y = -5$ or $y = 5$
    The solution set is $\{-5, 5\}$.

11. $x(x - 8) + 12 = 0$
    $x^2 - 8x + 12 = 0$
    $(x - 6)(x - 2) = 0 \rightarrow x = 6$ or $x = 2$
    The solution set is $\{2, 6\}$.

12. $x(x + 4) = 12$
    $x^2 + 4x = 12 \rightarrow x^2 + 4x - 12 = 0$
    $(x + 6)(x - 2) = 0 \rightarrow x = -6$ or $x = 2$
    The solution set is $\{-6, 2\}$.

13.
$$4x^2 + 9 = 12x$$
$$4x^2 - 12x + 9 = 0$$

$$(2x-3)^2 = 0 \rightarrow x = \frac{3}{2}$$

The solution set is $\left\{\frac{3}{2}\right\}$.

14.
$$25x^2 + 16 = 40x$$
$$25x^2 - 40x + 16 = 0$$

$$(5x-4)^2 = 0 \rightarrow x = \frac{4}{5}$$

The solution set is $\left\{\frac{4}{5}\right\}$.

15.
$$6(p^2 - 1) = 5p$$
$$6p^2 - 6 = 5p$$
$$6p^2 - 5p - 6 = 0$$

$$(3p+2)(2p-3) = 0 \rightarrow p = -\frac{2}{3} \text{ or } p = \frac{3}{2}$$

The solution set is $\left\{-\frac{2}{3}, \frac{3}{2}\right\}$.

16.
$$2(2u^2 - 4u) + 3 = 0$$
$$4u^2 - 8u + 3 = 0$$

$$(2u-1)(2u-3) = 0 \rightarrow u = \frac{1}{2} \text{ or } u = \frac{3}{2}$$

The solution set is $\left\{\frac{1}{2}, \frac{3}{2}\right\}$.

17.
$$6x - 5 = \frac{6}{x}$$
$$6x^2 - 5x = 6 \rightarrow 6x^2 - 5x - 6 = 0$$

$$(3x+2)(2x-3) = 0 \rightarrow x = -\frac{2}{3} \text{ or } x = \frac{3}{2}$$

Since neither of these values causes a denominator to equal zero, the solution set is $\left\{-\frac{2}{3}, \frac{3}{2}\right\}$.

18.
$$x + \frac{12}{x} = 7$$
$$x^2 + 12 = 7x \rightarrow x^2 - 7x + 12 = 0$$

$$(x-3)(x-4) = 0 \rightarrow x = 3 \text{ or } x = 4$$

Since neither of these values causes a denominator to equal zero, the solution set is $\{3, 4\}$.

19.
$$\frac{4(x-2)}{x-3} + \frac{3}{x} = \frac{-3}{x(x-3)}$$

$$x(x-3)\left(\frac{4(x-2)}{x-3} + \frac{3}{x}\right) = \left(\frac{-3}{x(x-3)}\right)x(x-3)$$

$$x(x-3)\left(\frac{4(x-2)}{x-3}\right) + x(x-3)\left(\frac{3}{x}\right) = -3$$

$$x(4(x-2)) + (x-3)(3) = -3$$

$$4x^2 - 8x + 3x - 9 = -3$$

$$4x^2 - 5x - 6 = 0$$

$$(4x+3)(x-2) = 0$$

$$x = -\frac{3}{4} \text{ or } x = 2$$

Since neither of these values causes a denominator to equal zero, the solution set is $\left\{-\frac{3}{4}, 2\right\}$.

20.
$$\frac{5}{x+4} = 4 + \frac{3}{x-2}$$

$$(x+4)(x-2)\left(\frac{5}{x+4}\right) = \left(4 + \frac{3}{x-2}\right)(x+4)(x-2)$$

$$(x-2)(5) = 4(x+4)(x-2) + (3)(x+4)$$

$$5x - 10 = 4(x^2 + 2x - 8) + 3x + 12$$

$$5x - 10 = 4x^2 + 8x - 32 + 3x + 12$$

$$0 = 4x^2 + 6x - 10$$

$$0 = 2(2x^2 + 3x - 5)$$

$$0 = 2(2x+5)(x-1)$$

$$x = -\frac{5}{2} \text{ or } x = 1$$

Since neither of these values causes a denominator to equal zero, the solution set is $\left\{-\frac{5}{2}, 1\right\}$.

21.
$$x^2 = 25 \rightarrow x = \pm\sqrt{25} \rightarrow x = \pm 5$$
The solution set is $\{-5, 5\}$.

22.
$$x^2 = 36 \rightarrow x = \pm\sqrt{36} \rightarrow x = \pm 6$$
The solution set is $\{-6, 6\}$.

23.
$$(x-1)^2 = 4$$
$$x - 1 = \pm\sqrt{4}$$
$$x - 1 = \pm 2$$
$$x - 1 = 2 \text{ or } x - 1 = -2$$
$$\rightarrow x = 3 \text{ or } x = -1$$
The solution set is $\{-1, 3\}$.

24.
$$(x+2)^2 = 1$$
$$x + 2 = \pm\sqrt{1}$$
$$x + 2 = \pm 1$$
$$x + 2 = 1 \text{ or } x + 2 = -1$$
$$\rightarrow x = -1 \text{ or } x = -3$$
The solution set is $\{-3, -1\}$.

25.
$$(2x+3)^2 = 9$$
$$2x + 3 = \pm\sqrt{9}$$
$$2x + 3 = \pm 3$$
$$2x + 3 = 3 \text{ or } 2x + 3 = -3$$
$$\rightarrow x = 0 \text{ or } x = -3$$
The solution set is $\{-3, 0\}$.

26.
$$(3x-2)^2 = 4$$
$$3x - 2 = \pm\sqrt{4}$$
$$3x - 2 = \pm 2$$
$$3x - 2 = 2 \text{ or } 3x - 2 = -2$$
$$\rightarrow x = \frac{4}{3} \text{ or } x = 0$$
The solution set is $\left\{0, \frac{4}{3}\right\}$.

27.
$$\left(\frac{8}{2}\right)^2 = 4^2 = 16$$

28.
$$\left(\frac{-4}{2}\right)^2 = (-2)^2 = 4$$

29.
$$\left(\frac{\left(\frac{1}{2}\right)}{2}\right)^2 = \left(\frac{1}{4}\right)^2 = \frac{1}{16}$$

30.
$$\left(\frac{\left(-\frac{1}{3}\right)}{2}\right)^2 = \left(-\frac{1}{6}\right)^2 = \frac{1}{36}$$

31.
$$\left(\frac{\left(-\frac{2}{3}\right)}{2}\right)^2 = \left(-\frac{1}{3}\right)^2 = \frac{1}{9}$$

32.
$$\left(\frac{\left(-\frac{2}{5}\right)}{2}\right)^2 = \left(-\frac{1}{5}\right)^2 = \frac{1}{25}$$

33.
$$x^2 + 4x = 21$$
$$x^2 + 4x + 4 = 21 + 4$$
$$(x+2)^2 = 25$$
$$x + 2 = \pm\sqrt{25} \rightarrow x + 2 = \pm 5$$
$$x = -2 \pm 5 \rightarrow x = 3 \text{ or } x = -7$$
The solution set is $\{-7, 3\}$.

34.
$$x^2 - 6x = 13$$
$$x^2 - 6x + 9 = 13 + 9$$
$$(x-3)^2 = 22 \rightarrow x - 3 = \pm\sqrt{22}$$
$$x = 3 \pm \sqrt{22}$$
The solution set is $\left\{3 + \sqrt{22}, 3 - \sqrt{22}\right\}$.

35. $x^2 - \dfrac{1}{2}x - \dfrac{3}{16} = 0$

$x^2 - \dfrac{1}{2}x = \dfrac{3}{16}$

$x^2 - \dfrac{1}{2}x + \dfrac{1}{16} = \dfrac{3}{16} + \dfrac{1}{16}$

$\left(x - \dfrac{1}{4}\right)^2 = \dfrac{1}{4}$

$x - \dfrac{1}{4} = \pm\sqrt{\dfrac{1}{4}}$

$x - \dfrac{1}{4} = \pm\dfrac{1}{2}$

$x = \dfrac{1}{4} \pm \dfrac{1}{2} \rightarrow x = \dfrac{3}{4}$

or $x = -\dfrac{1}{4}$

The solution set is $\left\{-\dfrac{1}{4}, \dfrac{3}{4}\right\}$.

36. $x^2 + \dfrac{2}{3}x - \dfrac{1}{3} = 0$

$x^2 + \dfrac{2}{3}x = \dfrac{1}{3}$

$x^2 + \dfrac{2}{3}x + \dfrac{1}{9} = \dfrac{1}{3} + \dfrac{1}{9}$

$\left(x + \dfrac{1}{3}\right)^2 = \dfrac{4}{9}$

$x + \dfrac{1}{3} = \pm\sqrt{\dfrac{4}{9}}$

$x + \dfrac{1}{3} = \pm\dfrac{2}{3}$

$x = -\dfrac{1}{3} \pm \dfrac{2}{3} \rightarrow x = \dfrac{1}{3}$

or $x = -1$

The solution set is $\left\{-1, \dfrac{1}{3}\right\}$.

37. $3x^2 + x - \dfrac{1}{2} = 0$

$x^2 + \dfrac{1}{3}x - \dfrac{1}{6} = 0$

$x^2 + \dfrac{1}{3}x = \dfrac{1}{6}$

$x^2 + \dfrac{1}{3}x + \dfrac{1}{36} = \dfrac{1}{6} + \dfrac{1}{36}$

$\left(x + \dfrac{1}{6}\right)^2 = \dfrac{7}{36}$

$x + \dfrac{1}{6} = \pm\sqrt{\dfrac{7}{36}}$

$x + \dfrac{1}{6} = \pm\dfrac{\sqrt{7}}{6}$

$x = -\dfrac{1}{6} \pm \dfrac{\sqrt{7}}{6}$

The solution set is $\left\{-\dfrac{1}{6} + \dfrac{\sqrt{7}}{6}, -\dfrac{1}{6} - \dfrac{\sqrt{7}}{6}\right\}$.

38. $2x^2 - 3x - 1 = 0$

$x^2 - \dfrac{3}{2}x - \dfrac{1}{2} = 0$

$x^2 - \dfrac{3}{2}x = \dfrac{1}{2}$

$x^2 - \dfrac{3}{2}x + \dfrac{9}{16} = \dfrac{1}{2} + \dfrac{9}{16}$

$\left(x - \dfrac{3}{4}\right)^2 = \dfrac{17}{16}$

$x - \dfrac{3}{4} = \pm\sqrt{\dfrac{17}{16}}$

$x - \dfrac{3}{4} = \pm\dfrac{\sqrt{17}}{4}$

$x = \dfrac{3}{4} \pm \dfrac{\sqrt{17}}{4}$

The solution set is $\left\{\dfrac{3}{4} + \dfrac{\sqrt{17}}{4}, \dfrac{3}{4} - \dfrac{\sqrt{17}}{4}\right\}$.

39. $x^2 - 4x + 2 = 0$
    $a = 1, \quad b = -4, \quad c = 2$

$$x = \frac{-(-4) \pm \sqrt{(-4)^2 - 4(1)(2)}}{2(1)}$$

$$= \frac{4 \pm \sqrt{16 - 8}}{2} = \frac{4 \pm \sqrt{8}}{2}$$

$$= \frac{4 \pm 2\sqrt{2}}{2} = 2 \pm \sqrt{2}$$

$$\left\{ 2 - \sqrt{2}, 2 + \sqrt{2} \right\}$$

40. $x^2 + 4x + 2 = 0$
    $a = 1, \quad b = 4, \quad c = 2$

$$x = \frac{-4 \pm \sqrt{4^2 - 4(1)(2)}}{2(1)}$$

$$= \frac{-4 \pm \sqrt{16 - 8}}{2} = \frac{-4 \pm \sqrt{8}}{2}$$

$$= \frac{-4 \pm 2\sqrt{2}}{2} = -2 \pm \sqrt{2}$$

$$\left\{ -2 - \sqrt{2}, -2 + \sqrt{2} \right\}$$

41. $x^2 - 4x - 1 = 0$
    $a = 1, \quad b = -4, \quad c = -1$

$$x = \frac{-(-4) \pm \sqrt{(-4)^2 - 4(1)(-1)}}{2(1)}$$

$$= \frac{4 \pm \sqrt{16 + 4}}{2} = \frac{4 \pm \sqrt{20}}{2}$$

$$= \frac{4 \pm 2\sqrt{5}}{2} = 2 \pm \sqrt{5}$$

$$\left\{ 2 - \sqrt{5}, 2 + \sqrt{5} \right\}$$

42. $x^2 + 6x + 1 = 0$
    $a = 1, \quad b = 6, \quad c = 1$

$$x = \frac{-6 \pm \sqrt{6^2 - 4(1)(1)}}{2(1)}$$

$$= \frac{-6 \pm \sqrt{36 - 4}}{2} = \frac{-6 \pm \sqrt{32}}{2}$$

$$= \frac{-6 \pm 4\sqrt{2}}{2} = -3 \pm 2\sqrt{2}$$

$$\left\{ -3 - 2\sqrt{2}, -3 + 2\sqrt{2} \right\}$$

43. $2x^2 - 5x + 3 = 0$
    $a = 2, \quad b = -5, \quad c = 3$

$$x = \frac{-(-5) \pm \sqrt{(-5)^2 - 4(2)(3)}}{2(2)}$$

$$= \frac{5 \pm \sqrt{25 - 24}}{4} = \frac{5 \pm 1}{4}$$

$$\left\{ 1, \ \frac{3}{2} \right\}$$

44. $2x^2 + 5x + 3 = 0$
    $a = 2, \quad b = 5, \quad c = 3$

$$x = \frac{-5 \pm \sqrt{5^2 - 4(2)(3)}}{2(2)}$$

$$= \frac{-5 \pm \sqrt{25 - 24}}{4} = \frac{-5 \pm 1}{4}$$

$$\left\{ -1, -\frac{3}{2} \right\}$$

45. $4y^2 - y + 2 = 0$
    $a = 4, \quad b = -1, \quad c = 2$

$$y = \frac{-(-1) \pm \sqrt{(-1)^2 - 4(4)(2)}}{2(4)}$$

$$= \frac{1 \pm \sqrt{1 - 32}}{8} = \frac{1 \pm \sqrt{-31}}{8}$$

No real solution.

46. $4t^2 + t + 1 = 0$
    $a = 4, \quad b = 1, \quad c = 1$

$$t = \frac{-1 \pm \sqrt{1^2 - 4(4)(1)}}{2(4)}$$

$$= \frac{-1 \pm \sqrt{1 - 16}}{8} = \frac{-1 \pm \sqrt{-15}}{8}$$

No real solution.

47. $4x^2 = 1 - 2x$

$4x^2 + 2x - 1 = 0$

$a = 4, \quad b = 2, \quad c = -1$

$$x = \frac{-2 \pm \sqrt{2^2 - 4(4)(-1)}}{2(4)}$$

$$= \frac{-2 \pm \sqrt{4 + 16}}{8} = \frac{-2 \pm \sqrt{20}}{8}$$

$$= \frac{-2 \pm 2\sqrt{5}}{8} = \frac{-1 \pm \sqrt{5}}{4}$$

$$\left\{ \frac{-1 - \sqrt{5}}{4}, \frac{-1 + \sqrt{5}}{4} \right\}$$

48. $2x^2 = 1 - 2x$

$2x^2 + 2x - 1 = 0$

$a = 2, \quad b = 2, \quad c = -1$

$$x = \frac{-2 \pm \sqrt{2^2 - 4(2)(-1)}}{2(2)}$$

$$= \frac{-2 \pm \sqrt{4 + 8}}{4} = \frac{-2 \pm \sqrt{12}}{4}$$

$$= \frac{-2 \pm 2\sqrt{3}}{4} = \frac{-1 \pm \sqrt{3}}{2}$$

$$\left\{ \frac{-1 - \sqrt{3}}{2}, \frac{-1 + \sqrt{3}}{2} \right\}$$

49. $4x^2 = 9x$

$4x^2 - 9x = 0$

$a = 4, \quad b = -9, \quad c = 0$

$$x = \frac{-(-9) \pm \sqrt{(-9)^2 - 4(4)(0)}}{2(4)}$$

$$= \frac{9 \pm \sqrt{81}}{8}$$

$$= \frac{9 \pm 9}{8}$$

$$\rightarrow x = \frac{9 + 9}{8} \quad \text{or} \quad x = \frac{9 - 9}{8}$$

$$x = \frac{18}{8} = \frac{9}{4} \quad \text{or} \quad x = 0$$

$$\left\{ 0, \frac{9}{4} \right\}$$

50. $5x = 4x^2$

$0 = 4x^2 - 5x$

$a = 4, \quad b = -5, \quad c = 0$

$$x = \frac{-(-5) \pm \sqrt{(-5)^2 - 4(4)(0)}}{2(4)}$$

$$= \frac{5 \pm \sqrt{25}}{8}$$

$$= \frac{5 \pm 5}{8}$$

$$\rightarrow x = \frac{5 + 5}{8} \quad \text{or} \quad x = \frac{5 - 5}{8}$$

$$x = \frac{10}{8} = \frac{5}{4} \quad \text{or} \quad x = 0$$

$$\left\{ 0, \frac{5}{4} \right\}$$

51. $9t^2 - 6t + 1 = 0$

$a = 9, \quad b = -6, \quad c = 1$

$$t = \frac{-(-6) \pm \sqrt{(-6)^2 - 4(9)(1)}}{2(9)}$$

$$= \frac{6 \pm \sqrt{36 - 36}}{18}$$

$$= \frac{6 \pm 0}{18} = \frac{1}{3}$$

$$\left\{ \frac{1}{3} \right\}$$

52. $4u^2 - 6u + 9 = 0$

$a = 4, \quad b = -6, \quad c = 9$

$$u = \frac{-(-6) \pm \sqrt{(-6)^2 - 4(4)(9)}}{2(4)}$$

$$= \frac{6 \pm \sqrt{36 - 144}}{8}$$

$$= \frac{6 \pm \sqrt{-108}}{8}$$

No real solution.

53.
$$\frac{3}{4}x^2 - \frac{1}{4}x - \frac{1}{2} = 0$$

$$4\left(\frac{3}{4}x^2 - \frac{1}{4}x - \frac{1}{2}\right) = (0)(4)$$

$$3x^2 - x - 2 = 0$$

$$a = 3, \quad b = -1, \quad c = -2$$

$$x = \frac{-(-1) \pm \sqrt{(-1)^2 - 4(3)(-2)}}{2(3)}$$

$$= \frac{1 \pm \sqrt{1+24}}{6}$$

$$= \frac{1 \pm \sqrt{25}}{6} = \frac{1 \pm 5}{6}$$

$$\rightarrow x = \frac{1+5}{6} \quad \text{or} \quad x = \frac{1-5}{6}$$

$$x = \frac{6}{6} = 1 \quad \text{or} \quad x = \frac{-4}{6} = -\frac{2}{3}$$

$$\left\{-\frac{2}{3}, 1\right\}$$

54.
$$\frac{2}{3}x^2 - x - 3 = 0$$

$$3\left(\frac{2}{3}x^2 - x - 3\right) = (0)(3)$$

$$2x^2 - 3x - 9 = 0$$

$$a = 2, \quad b = -3, \quad c = -9$$

$$x = \frac{-(-3) \pm \sqrt{(-3)^2 - 4(2)(-9)}}{2(2)}$$

$$= \frac{3 \pm \sqrt{9+72}}{4}$$

$$= \frac{3 \pm \sqrt{81}}{4} = \frac{3 \pm 9}{4} \rightarrow x = \frac{3+9}{4} \quad \text{or} \quad x = \frac{3-9}{4}$$

$$x = \frac{12}{4} = 3 \quad \text{or} \quad x = \frac{-6}{4} = -\frac{3}{2}$$

$$\left\{-\frac{3}{2}, 3\right\}$$

55.
$$4 - \frac{1}{x} - \frac{2}{x^2} = 0$$

$$\left(x^2\right)\left(4 - \frac{1}{x} - \frac{2}{x^2}\right) = (0)\left(x^2\right)$$

$$4x^2 - x - 2 = 0$$

$$a = 4, \quad b = -1, \quad c = -2$$

$$x = \frac{-(-1) \pm \sqrt{(-1)^2 - 4(4)(-2)}}{2(4)}$$

$$= \frac{1 \pm \sqrt{1+32}}{8}$$

$$= \frac{1 \pm \sqrt{33}}{8}$$

Since neither of these values causes a denominator to equal zero, the solution set is
$$\left\{\frac{1+\sqrt{33}}{8}, \frac{1-\sqrt{33}}{8}\right\}.$$

56.
$$4 + \frac{1}{x} - \frac{1}{x^2} = 0$$

$$\left(x^2\right)\left(4 + \frac{1}{x} - \frac{1}{x^2}\right) = (0)\left(x^2\right)$$

$$4x^2 + x - 1 = 0$$

$$a = 4, \quad b = 1, \quad c = -1$$

$$x = \frac{-1 \pm \sqrt{1^2 - 4(4)(-1)}}{2(4)}$$

$$= \frac{-1 \pm \sqrt{1+16}}{8}$$

$$= \frac{-1 \pm \sqrt{17}}{8}$$

Since neither of these values causes a denominator to equal zero, the solution set is
$$\left\{\frac{-1+\sqrt{17}}{8}, \frac{-1-\sqrt{17}}{8}\right\}.$$

57.

$$3x = 1 - \frac{1}{x}$$

$$x(3x) = \left(1 - \frac{1}{x}\right)(x)$$

$$3x^2 = x - 1$$

$$3x^2 - x + 1 = 0$$

$$a = 3, \quad b = -1 \quad c = 1$$

$$x = \frac{-(-1) \pm \sqrt{(-1)^2 - 4(3)(1)}}{2(4)}$$

$$= \frac{1 \pm \sqrt{1 - 12}}{8} = \frac{1 \pm \sqrt{-11}}{8}$$

No real solutions.

58.

$$x = 1 - \frac{4}{x}$$

$$x(x) = \left(1 - \frac{4}{x}\right)(x)$$

$$x^2 = x - 4$$

$$x^2 - x + 4 = 0$$

$$a = 1, \quad b = -1 \quad c = 4$$

$$x = \frac{-(-1) \pm \sqrt{(-1)^2 - 4(1)(4)}}{2(1)}$$

$$= \frac{1 \pm \sqrt{1 - 16}}{2} = \frac{1 \pm \sqrt{-15}}{2}$$

No real solutions.

59. $x^2 - 4.1x + 2.2 = 0$

$$a = 1, \quad b = -4.1, \quad c = 2.2$$

$$x = \frac{-(-4.1) \pm \sqrt{(-4.1)^2 - 4(1)(2.2)}}{2(1)}$$

$$= \frac{4.1 \pm \sqrt{16.81 - 8.8}}{2} = \frac{4.1 \pm \sqrt{8.01}}{2}$$

$$x \approx 3.47, x \approx 0.64$$

$$\{3.47, 0.64\}$$

60. $x^2 + 3.9x + 1.8 = 0$

$$a = 1, \quad b = 3.9, \quad c = 1.8$$

$$x = \frac{-(3.9) \pm \sqrt{(3.9)^2 - 4(1)(1.8)}}{2(1)}$$

$$= \frac{-3.9 \pm \sqrt{15.21 - 7.2}}{2} = \frac{-3.9 \pm \sqrt{8.01}}{2}$$

$$x \approx -0.54, x \approx -3.37$$

$$\{-0.54, -3.37\}$$

61. $x^2 + \sqrt{3}x - 3 = 0$

$$a = 1, \quad b = \sqrt{3}, \quad c = -3$$

$$x = \frac{-(\sqrt{3}) \pm \sqrt{(\sqrt{3})^2 - 4(1)(-3)}}{2(1)}$$

$$= \frac{-\sqrt{3} \pm \sqrt{3 + 12}}{2} = \frac{-\sqrt{3} \pm \sqrt{15}}{2}$$

$$x \approx 1.07, x \approx -2.80$$

$$\{1.07, -2.80\}$$

62. $x^2 + \sqrt{2}x - 2 = 0$

$$a = 1, \quad b = \sqrt{2}, \quad c = -2$$

$$x = \frac{-(\sqrt{2}) \pm \sqrt{(\sqrt{2})^2 - 4(1)(-2)}}{2(1)}$$

$$= \frac{-\sqrt{2} \pm \sqrt{2 + 8}}{2} = \frac{-\sqrt{2} \pm \sqrt{10}}{2}$$

$$x \approx 0.87, x \approx -2.29$$

$$\{0.87, -2.29\}$$

63. $\pi x^2 - x - \pi = 0$
$a = \pi, \quad b = -1, \quad c = -\pi$

$$x = \frac{-(-1) \pm \sqrt{(-1)^2 - 4(\pi)(-\pi)}}{2(\pi)}$$

$$= \frac{1 \pm \sqrt{1 + 4\pi^2}}{2\pi}$$

$x \approx 1.17, x \approx -0.83$

$\{1.17, -0.83\}$

64. $\pi x^2 + \pi x - 2 = 0$
$a = \pi, \quad b = \pi, \quad c = -2$

$$x = \frac{-(\pi) \pm \sqrt{(\pi)^2 - 4(\pi)(-2)}}{2(\pi)}$$

$$= \frac{-\pi \pm \sqrt{\pi^2 + 8\pi}}{2\pi}$$

$x \approx 0.44, x \approx -1.44$

$\{0.44, -1.44\}$

65. $3x^2 + 8\pi x + \sqrt{29} = 0$
$a = 3, \quad b = 8\pi, \quad c = \sqrt{29}$

$$x = \frac{-(8\pi) \pm \sqrt{(8\pi)^2 - 4(3)\sqrt{29}}}{2(3)}$$

$$= \frac{-8\pi \pm \sqrt{64\pi^2 - 12\sqrt{29}}}{6}$$

$x \approx -0.22, x \approx -8.16$

$\{-0.22, -8.16\}$

66. $\pi x^2 - 15\sqrt{2}x + 20 = 0$
$a = \pi, \quad b = -15\sqrt{2}, \quad c = 20$

$$x = \frac{-(-15\sqrt{2}) \pm \sqrt{(-15\sqrt{2})^2 - 4(\pi)20}}{2(\pi)}$$

$$= \frac{15\sqrt{2} \pm \sqrt{450 - 80\pi}}{2\pi}$$

$x \approx 5.62, x \approx 1.13$

$\{5.62, 1.13\}$

67. $x^2 - 5 = 0$
$x^2 = 5 \rightarrow x = \pm\sqrt{5}$

$\left\{\sqrt{5}, -\sqrt{5}\right\}$

68. $x^2 - 6 = 0$
$x^2 = 6 \rightarrow x = \pm\sqrt{6}$

$\left\{\sqrt{6}, -\sqrt{6}\right\}$

69. $16x^2 - 8x + 1 = 0$
$(4x - 1)(4x - 1) = 0$

$4x - 1 = 0 \rightarrow x = \dfrac{1}{4}$

$\left\{\dfrac{1}{4}\right\}$

70. $9x^2 - 6x + 1 = 0$
$(3x - 1)(3x - 1) = 0$

$3x - 1 = 0 \rightarrow x = \dfrac{1}{3}$

$\left\{\dfrac{1}{3}\right\}$

71. $10x^2 - 19x - 15 = 0$
$(5x + 3)(2x - 5) = 0$

$5x + 3 = 0 \text{ or } 2x - 5 = 0$

$\rightarrow x = -\dfrac{3}{5} \text{ or } x = \dfrac{5}{2}$

$\left\{-\dfrac{3}{5}, \dfrac{5}{2}\right\}$

72. $6x^2 + 7x - 20 = 0$
$(3x - 4)(2x + 5) = 0$

$3x - 4 = 0 \text{ or } 2x + 5 = 0$

$\rightarrow x = \dfrac{4}{3} \text{ or } x = -\dfrac{5}{2}$

$\left\{-\dfrac{5}{2}, \dfrac{4}{3}\right\}$

73.
$$2 + z = 6z^2$$
$$0 = 6z^2 - z - 2$$
$$0 = (3z - 2)(2z + 1)$$
$$3z - 2 = 0 \text{ or } 2z + 1 = 0$$
$$\rightarrow z = \frac{2}{3} \text{ or } x = -\frac{1}{2}$$
$$\left\{ -\frac{1}{2}, \frac{2}{3} \right\}$$

74.
$$2 = y + 6y^2$$
$$0 = 6y^2 + y - 2$$
$$0 = (3y + 2)(2y - 1)$$
$$3y + 2 = 0 \text{ or } 2y - 1 = 0$$
$$\rightarrow y = -\frac{2}{3} \text{ or } y = \frac{1}{2}$$
$$\left\{ -\frac{2}{3}, \frac{1}{2} \right\}$$

75.
$$x^2 + \sqrt{2}x = \frac{1}{2}$$
$$x^2 + \sqrt{2}x - \frac{1}{2} = 0$$
$$2\left(x^2 + \sqrt{2}x - \frac{1}{2} \right) = (0)(2)$$
$$2x^2 + 2\sqrt{2}x - 1 = 0$$
$$a = 2, \quad b = 2\sqrt{2}, \quad c = -1$$
$$x = \frac{-(2\sqrt{2}) \pm \sqrt{(2\sqrt{2})^2 - 4(2)(-1)}}{2(2)}$$
$$= \frac{-2\sqrt{2} \pm \sqrt{8 + 8}}{4} = \frac{-2\sqrt{2} \pm \sqrt{16}}{4}$$
$$= \frac{-2\sqrt{2} \pm 4}{4} = \frac{-\sqrt{2} \pm 2}{2}$$
$$\left\{ \frac{-\sqrt{2} + 2}{2}, \frac{-\sqrt{2} - 2}{2} \right\}$$

76.
$$\frac{1}{2}x^2 = \sqrt{2}x + 1$$
$$\frac{1}{2}x^2 - \sqrt{2}x - 1 = 0$$
$$2\left(\frac{1}{2}x^2 - \sqrt{2}x - 1 \right) = (0)(2)$$
$$x^2 - 2\sqrt{2}x - 2 = 0$$
$$a = 1, \quad b = -2\sqrt{2}, \quad c = -2$$
$$x = \frac{-(-2\sqrt{2}) \pm \sqrt{(-2\sqrt{2})^2 - 4(1)(-2)}}{2(1)}$$
$$= \frac{2\sqrt{2} \pm \sqrt{8 + 8}}{2} = \frac{2\sqrt{2} \pm \sqrt{16}}{2}$$
$$= \frac{2\sqrt{2} \pm 4}{2} = \frac{\sqrt{2} \pm 2}{1}$$
$$\left\{ \sqrt{2} + 2, \sqrt{2} - 2 \right\}$$

77.
$$x^2 + x = 4$$
$$x^2 + x - 4 = 0$$
$$a = 1, \quad b = 1, \quad c = -4$$
$$x = \frac{-(1) \pm \sqrt{(1)^2 - 4(1)(-4)}}{2(1)}$$
$$= \frac{-1 \pm \sqrt{1 + 16}}{2} = \frac{-1 \pm \sqrt{17}}{2}$$
$$\left\{ \frac{-1 + \sqrt{17}}{2}, \frac{-1 - \sqrt{17}}{2} \right\}$$

78.
$$x^2 + x = 1$$
$$x^2 + x - 1 = 0$$
$$a = 1, \quad b = 1, \quad c = -1$$
$$x = \frac{-(1) \pm \sqrt{(1)^2 - 4(1)(-1)}}{2(1)}$$
$$= \frac{-1 \pm \sqrt{1 + 4}}{2} = \frac{-1 \pm \sqrt{5}}{2}$$
$$\left\{ \frac{-1 + \sqrt{5}}{2}, \frac{-1 - \sqrt{5}}{2} \right\}$$

79. $2x^2 - 6x + 7 = 0$
        $a = 2, \quad b = -6, \quad c = 7$

    $b^2 - 4ac = (-6)^2 - 4(2)(7)$
            $= 36 - 56 = -20$
Since the discriminant < 0, we have no real solutions

80. $x^2 + 4x + 7 = 0$
        $a = 1, \quad b = 4, \quad c = 7$

    $b^2 - 4ac = (4)^2 - 4(1)(7)$
            $= 16 - 28 = -12$
since the discriminant < 0, we have no real solutions

81. $9x^2 - 30x + 25 = 0$
        $a = 9, \quad b = -30, \quad c = 25$

    $b^2 - 4ac = (-30)^2 - 4(9)(25)$
            $= 900 - 900 = 0$
since the discriminant $= 0$, we have one repeated real solution

82. $25x^2 - 20x + 4 = 0$
        $a = 25, \quad b = -20, \quad c = 4$

    $b^2 - 4ac = (-20)^2 - 4(25)(4)$
            $= 400 - 400 = 0$
since the discriminant $= 0$, we have one repeated real solution

83. $3x^2 + 5x - 8 = 0$
        $a = 3, \quad b = 5, \quad c = -8$

    $b^2 - 4ac = (5)^2 - 4(3)(-8)$
            $= 25 + 96 = 121$
since the discriminant > 0, we have two unequal real solutions

84. $2x^2 - 3x - 7 = 0$
        $a = 2, \quad b = -3, \quad c = -7$

    $b^2 - 4ac = (-3)^2 - 4(2)(-7)$
            $= 9 + 56 = 65$
since the discriminant > 0, we have two unequal real solutions

85.   Let w represent the width of window.
      Then $l = w + 2$ represents the length of the window.
      Since the area is 143 square feet, we have: $w(w + 2) = 143$
        $w^2 + 2w - 143 = 0 \rightarrow (w + 13)(w - 11) = 0 \rightarrow w = -13$ which is not practical
            or $w = 11$
      The width of the rectangular window is 11 feet and the length is 13 feet.

86.   Let w represent the width of window.
      Then $l = w + 1$ represents the length of the window.
      Since the area is 306 square centimeters, we have: $w(w + 1) = 306$
        $w^2 + w - 306 = 0 \rightarrow (w + 18)(w - 17) = 0 \rightarrow w = -18$ which is not practical
            or $w = 17$
      The width of the rectangular window is 17 centimeters and the length is 18 centimeters.

87.   Let l represent the length of the rectangle.
      Let w represent the width of the rectangle.
      The perimeter is 26 meters and the area is 40 square meters.
            $2l + 2w = 26 \quad \rightarrow \quad l + w = 13 \quad \rightarrow \quad w = 13 - l$

            $lw = 40$

        $l(13 - l) = 40 \rightarrow 13l - l^2 = 40 \rightarrow l^2 - 13l + 40 = 0 \rightarrow (l - 8)(l - 5) = 0$

            $l = 8$ or $l = 5$

            $w = 5 \qquad w = 8$

      The dimensions are 5 meters by 8 meters.

88.   Let r represent the radius of the circle.
Since the field is a square with area 1250 square feet, the length of a side of the square is
$\sqrt{1250} = 25\sqrt{2}$ feet. The length of the diagonal is $2r$.
Use the Pythagorean Theorem to solve for r:

$$(2r)^2 = \left(25\sqrt{2}\right)^2 + \left(25\sqrt{2}\right)^2 \rightarrow 4r^2 = 1250 + 1250 \rightarrow 4r^2 = 2500 \rightarrow r^2 = 625 \rightarrow r = 25$$

The shortest radius setting for the sprinkler is 25 feet.

89.   Let x represent the length of the side of the sheet metal.

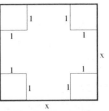

$$(x-2)(x-2)(1) = 4$$
$$x^2 - 4x + 4 = 4$$
$$x^2 - 4x = 0$$
$$x(x-4) = 0 \rightarrow x = 0 \text{ or } x = 4$$

Since the side cannot be 0 feet long, the length of a side of the sheet metal is 4 feet.
Hence, the dimensions of the sheet metal before the cut are 4 feet by 4 feet.

90.   Let x represent the width of the side of the sheet metal. Then the length is $2x$.

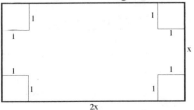

$$(x-2)(2x-2)(1) = 4$$
$$2x^2 - 6x + 4 = 4$$
$$2x^2 - 6x = 0$$
$$2x(x-3) = 0$$
$$x = 0 \text{ or } x = 3$$

Since the side cannot be 0 feet long, the width of the sheet metal is 3 feet and the length is
6 feet. The dimensions of the box are 1 foot by 4 feet by 1 foot.

91.   (a) $s = 96 + 80t - 16t^2$. The ball strikes the ground when the height = 0.

So we solve $0 = 96 + 80t - 16t^2.$

$$0 = -16t^2 + 80t + 96 \rightarrow \frac{0}{-16} = \frac{-16t^2 + 80t + 96}{-16}$$

$0 = t^2 - 5t - 6 \rightarrow 0 = (t-6)(t+1) \rightarrow t = 6$ or $t = -1$, we discard the negative value
since t represents elapsed time. Therefore, the ball hits the ground after 6 seconds.

(b) $s = 96 + 80t - 16t^2$. The ball passes the top of the building when the
height = 96.

So we solve $96 = 96 + 80t - 16t^2.$

$96 = 96 + 80t - 16t^2 \rightarrow 0 = 80t - 16t^2 \rightarrow 0 = 16t(5-t) \rightarrow t = 0$ or $t = 5$
We know that the ball starts ($t = 0$) at a height of 96 feet. Therefore, the ball hits the
ground after 6 seconds.

92. $A = 2\pi r^2 + 2\pi r h$. Since $A = 188.5$ square inches and $h = 7$ inches,
$$2\pi r^2 + 2\pi r(7) = 188.5 \rightarrow 2\pi r^2 + 14\pi r - 188.5 = 0$$
$$r = \frac{-14\pi \pm \sqrt{(14\pi)^2 - 4(2\pi)(-188.5)}}{2(2\pi)} = \frac{-14\pi \pm \sqrt{6671.9642}}{4\pi}$$

$r \approx 3$ or $r \approx -10$, which is not practical
The radius of the coffee can is approximately 3 inches.

93.   Let x = number of boxes in excess of 150.
The total number of boxes ordered $= 150 + x$
The price per box $= 200 - x$
The customer's total bill $=$ (# boxes ordered)(price per box)
$$= (150 + x)(200 - x)$$
So we need to solve the equation $(150 + x)(200 - x) = 30{,}625$.
$$30{,}000 + 50x - x^2 = 30{,}625$$
$$0 = x^2 - 50x + 625 \rightarrow 0 = (x - 25)(x - 25) \rightarrow x = 25$$
So the customer ordered a total of $150 + 25 = 175$ boxes.

94.   Let x be the width and $2x$ be the length of the patio. The height is $\frac{1}{3}$ foot.
$$V = l w h = x(2x) \cdot \frac{1}{3} = 216$$
$$\frac{2}{3}x^2 = 216 \rightarrow x^2 = 324 \rightarrow x = \pm 18$$
The dimensions of the patio are 18 feet by 36 feet.

95.   Let x represent the width of the border measured in feet.
The total area is $A_T = (6 + 2x)(10 + 2x)$.
The area of the garden is $A_G = 6 \cdot 10 = 60$.
The area of the border is $A_B = A_T - A_G = (6 + 2x)(10 + 2x) - 60$.
Since the concrete is 3 inches or 0.25 feet thick, the volume of the concrete in the border is
$$0.25 A_B = 0.25\big((6 + 2x)(10 + 2x) - 60\big)$$
Solving the volume equation:
$$0.25\big((6 + 2x)(10 + 2x) - 60\big) = 27$$
$$60 + 32x + 4x^2 - 60 = 108$$
$$4x^2 + 32x - 108 = 0 \rightarrow x^2 + 8x - 27 = 0$$
$$x = \frac{-8 \pm \sqrt{8^2 - 4(1)(-27)}}{2(1)} = \frac{-8 \pm \sqrt{172}}{2}$$
$$= \frac{-8 \pm 13.11}{2} = 2.56 \text{ or } -10.56 \text{ which is not practical.}$$
The width of the border is approximately 2.56 feet.

96.   (a) $s = -4.9t^2 + 20t$

we solve

$15 = -4.9t^2 + 20t$

$4.9t^2 - 20t + 15 = 0$

$t = \dfrac{-(-20) \pm \sqrt{(-20)^2 - 4(4.9)(15)}}{2(4.9)} = \dfrac{20 \pm \sqrt{106}}{9.8} \approx \dfrac{20 \pm 10.296}{9.8} = 3.09 \text{ or } 0.99$

Therefore, after 0.99 seconds the object passes a height of 15 meters on its way up, and after 3.09 seconds the object passes a height of 15 meters on its way down.

(b) $s = -4.9t^2 + 20t$

we solve

$0 = -4.9t^2 + 20t \rightarrow 0 = t(-4.9t + 20) \rightarrow t = 0 \text{ or } t = \dfrac{20}{4.9} \approx 4.08$

We know that the object starts ($t = 0$) at ground level. Therefore, the object hits the ground after 4.08 seconds.

(c) $s = -4.9t^2 + 20t$

we solve

$100 = -4.9t^2 + 20t \rightarrow 4.9t^2 - 20t + 100 = 0$

$t = \dfrac{-(-20) \pm \sqrt{(-20)^2 - 4(4.9)(100)}}{2(4.9)} = \dfrac{20 \pm \sqrt{-1560}}{9.8}$

The equation has no real solution. Therefore the object never attains a height of 100 meters.

97.   Let x represent the number of centimeters the length and width should be reduced.
$12 - x =$ the new length, $7 - x =$ the new width.
The new volume is 90% of the old volume.
$(12 - x)(7 - x)(3) = 0.9(12)(7)(3)$

$3x^2 - 57x + 252 = 226.8 \rightarrow 3x^2 - 57x + 25.2 = 0 \rightarrow x^2 - 19x + 8.4 = 0$

$x = \dfrac{-(-19) \pm \sqrt{(-19)^2 - 4(1)(8.4)}}{2(1)} = \dfrac{19 \pm \sqrt{327.4}}{2}$

$= \dfrac{19 \pm 18.09}{2} = 0.45 \text{ or } 18.55$

Since 18.55 exceeds the dimensions, it is discarded.
The dimensions of the new chocolate bar are: 11.55 cm by 6.55 cm by 3 cm.

98. Let x represent the number of centimeters the length and width should be reduced.
$12 - x =$ the new length, $7 - x =$ the new width.
The new volume is 80% of the old volume.
$$(12 - x)(7 - x)(3) = 0.8(12)(7)(3)$$
$$3x^2 - 57x + 252 = 201.6$$
$$3x^2 - 57x + 50.4 = 0$$
$$x^2 - 19x + 16.8 = 0$$
$$x = \frac{-(-19) \pm \sqrt{(-19)^2 - 4(1)(16.8)}}{2(1)} = \frac{19 \pm \sqrt{293.8}}{2}$$
$$= \frac{19 \pm 17.1406}{2} = 0.93 \text{ or } 18.07$$
Since 18.07 exceeds the dimensions, it is discarded.
The dimensions of the new chocolate bar are: 11.07 cm by 6.07 cm by 3 cm.

99. Let x represent the width of the border measured in feet.
The radius of the pool is 5 feet.
Then $x + 5$ represents the radius of the circle, including both the pool and the border.
The total area of the pool and border is $A_T = \pi(x + 5)^2$.
The area of the pool is $A_P = \pi(5)^2 = 25\pi$.
The area of the border is $A_B = A_T - A_P = \pi(x + 5)^2 - 25\pi$.
Since the concrete is 3 inches or 0.25 feet thick, the volume of the concrete in the border is
$$0.25A_B = 0.25\left(\pi(x + 5)^2 - 25\pi\right)$$
Solving the volume equation:
$$0.25\left(\pi(x + 5)^2 - 25\pi\right) = 27 \to \pi\left(x^2 + 10x + 25 - 25\right) = 108 \to \pi x^2 + 10\pi x - 108 = 0$$
$$x = \frac{-10\pi \pm \sqrt{(10\pi)^2 - 4(\pi)(-108)}}{2(\pi)}$$
$$= \frac{-31.42 \pm \sqrt{2344.1285}}{6.28} = \frac{-31.42 \pm 48.42}{6.28} = 2.71 \text{ or } -12.71$$
The width of the border is approximately 2.71 feet.

100. Let x represent the width of the border measured in feet.
The radius of the pool is 5 feet.
Then $x + 5$ represents the radius of the circle, including both the pool and the border.
The total area of the pool and border is $A_T = \pi(x + 5)^2$.
The area of the pool is $A_P = \pi(5)^2 = 25\pi$.
The area of the border is $A_B = A_T - A_P = \pi(x + 5)^2 - 25\pi$.
Since the concrete is 4 inches or $\frac{1}{3}$ foot thick, the volume of the concrete in the border is
$$\frac{1}{3}A_B = \frac{1}{3}\left(\pi(x + 5)^2 - 25\pi\right)$$
Solving the volume equation:
$$\frac{1}{3}\left(\pi(x + 5)^2 - 25\pi\right) = 27 \to \pi\left(x^2 + 10x + 25 - 25\right) = 81 \to \pi x^2 + 10\pi x - 81 = 0$$

$$x = \frac{-10\pi \pm \sqrt{(10\pi)^2 - 4(\pi)(-81)}}{2(\pi)} = \frac{-31.42 \pm \sqrt{2004.8365}}{6.28}$$

$$= \frac{-31.42 \pm 44.78}{6.28} = 2.13 \text{ or } -12.13, \text{which is not practical}$$

The width of the border is approximately 2.13 feet.

101. Let r represent the speed of the current.

	Rate	Time	Distance
Upstream	$15 - r$	$\dfrac{10}{15 - r}$	10
Downstream	$15 + r$	$\dfrac{10}{15 + r}$	10

Since the total time is 1.5 hours, we have:

$$\frac{10}{15 - r} + \frac{10}{15 + r} = 1.5$$

$$10(15 + r) + 10(15 - r) = 1.5(15 - r)(15 + r)$$

$$150 + 10r + 150 - 10r = 1.5(225 - r^2) \rightarrow 300 = 1.5(225 - r^2)$$

$$200 = 225 - r^2 \rightarrow r^2 - 25 = 0 \rightarrow (r - 5)(r + 5) = 0 \rightarrow r = 5 \text{ or } r = -5$$

The speed of the current is 5 miles per hour.

102. (a) $s = 1280 - 32t - 16t^2$. The object strikes the ground when the height $= 0$.

So we solve $0 = 1280 - 32t - 16t^2$.

$$0 = -16t^2 - 32t + 1280 \rightarrow \frac{0}{-16} = \frac{-16t^2 - 32t + 1280}{-16}$$

$$0 = t^2 + 2t - 80 \rightarrow 0 = (t - 8)(t + 10) \rightarrow t = 8 \text{ or } t = -10, \text{ we discard the negative}$$

value since t represents elapsed time. Therefore, the object hits the ground after 8 seconds.

(b)   we compute the height when $t = 4$.

$s = 96 + 80(4) - 16(4)^2 = 160$.

The object reaches a height of 160 feet after 4 seconds.

103.   given a quadratic equation $ax^2 + bx + c = 0$

the solutions are given by $x = \dfrac{-b + \sqrt{b^2 - 4ac}}{2a}$ and $x = \dfrac{-b - \sqrt{b^2 - 4ac}}{2a}$

adding these two values we get

$$\frac{-b + \sqrt{b^2 - 4ac}}{2a} + \frac{-b - \sqrt{b^2 - 4ac}}{2a} = \frac{-b + \sqrt{b^2 - 4ac} - b - \sqrt{b^2 - 4ac}}{2a} = \frac{-2b}{2a} = -\frac{b}{a}$$

104.   given a quadratic equation $ax^2 + bx + c = 0$

the solutions are given by $x = \dfrac{-b + \sqrt{b^2 - 4ac}}{2a}$ and $x = \dfrac{-b - \sqrt{b^2 - 4ac}}{2a}$

multiplying these two values we get

$$\left(\dfrac{-b + \sqrt{b^2 - 4ac}}{2a}\right)\left(\dfrac{-b - \sqrt{b^2 - 4ac}}{2a}\right) = \dfrac{\left(-b + \sqrt{b^2 - 4ac}\right)\left(-b - \sqrt{b^2 - 4ac}\right)}{4a^2}$$

$$= \dfrac{b^2 + b\sqrt{b^2 - 4ac} - b\sqrt{b^2 - 4ac} - \left(b^2 - 4ac\right)}{4a^2} = \dfrac{4ac}{4a^2} = \dfrac{c}{a}$$

105.   the quadratic equation $kx^2 + x + k = 0$ will have a repeated solution provided the discriminant $= 0$ that is, we need $b^2 - 4ac = 0$ in the given quadratic equation $b^2 - 4ac = (1)^2 - 4(k)(k) = 1 - 4k^2$
so we solve

$$1 - 4k^2 = 0 \to 1 = 4k^2 \to \dfrac{1}{4} = k^2 \to \pm\sqrt{\dfrac{1}{4}} = k \to \pm\dfrac{1}{2} = k$$

106.   the quadratic equation $x^2 - kx + 4 = 0$ will have a repeated solution provided the discriminant $= 0$ that is, we need $b^2 - 4ac = 0$ in the given quadratic equation
$$b^2 - 4ac = (-k)^2 - 4(1)(4) = k^2 - 16$$
so we solve
$$k^2 - 16 = 0 \to k^2 = 16 \to k = \pm 4$$

107.   the quadratic equation $ax^2 + bx + c = 0$ has solutions given by

$$x_1 = \dfrac{-b + \sqrt{b^2 - 4ac}}{2a} \text{ and } x_2 = \dfrac{-b - \sqrt{b^2 - 4ac}}{2a}$$

the quadratic equation $ax^2 - bx + c = 0$ has solutions given by

$$x_3 = \dfrac{-(-b) + \sqrt{(-b)^2 - 4ac}}{2a} = \dfrac{b + \sqrt{b^2 - 4ac}}{2a} = -x_2$$

and

$$x_4 = \dfrac{-(-b) - \sqrt{(-b)^2 - 4ac}}{2a} = \dfrac{b - \sqrt{b^2 - 4ac}}{2a} = -x_1$$

so we have the negatives of the first pair of solutions.

108.   The quadratic equation $ax^2 + bx + c = 0$ has solutions given by

$$x_1 = \dfrac{-b + \sqrt{b^2 - 4ac}}{2a} \text{ and } x_2 = \dfrac{-b - \sqrt{b^2 - 4ac}}{2a}.$$

The quadratic equation $cx^2 + bx + a = 0$ has solutions given by

$$x_3 = \frac{-b + \sqrt{b^2 - 4ca}}{2c} \quad \text{and} \quad x_4 = \frac{-b - \sqrt{b^2 - 4ca}}{2c}$$

Now notice that

$$(x_1)(x_4) = \left(\frac{-b + \sqrt{b^2 - 4ac}}{2a}\right)\left(\frac{-b - \sqrt{b^2 - 4ca}}{2c}\right)$$

$$= \frac{b^2 + b\sqrt{b^2 - 4ca} - b\sqrt{b^2 - 4ac} - (b^2 - 4ac)}{4ac}$$

$$= \frac{b^2 - b^2 + 4ac}{4ac} = \frac{4ac}{4ac} = 1$$

therefore, x_1 and x_4 are reciprocals of each other. A similar result holds for x_2 and x_3.

109.   We need to solve the equation $\frac{1}{2}n(n+1) = 666$

$$2\left(\frac{1}{2}\right)n(n+1) = (666)(2) \rightarrow n(n+1) = 1332$$

$$n^2 + n = 1332 \rightarrow n^2 + n - 1332 = 0 \rightarrow (n + 37)(n - 36) = 0$$

$$n = -37 \quad \text{or} \quad n = 36$$

since n must be a positive integer (it represents how many numbers we add together), we discard the negative value. Therefore, we conclude that $1 + 2 + 3 + \ldots\ldots + 36 = 666$.

110.   (a) we need to solve the equation $\frac{1}{2}n(n-3) = 65$

$$2\left(\frac{1}{2}\right)n(n-3) = (65)(2)$$

$$n(n-3) = 130 \rightarrow n^2 - 3n = 130 \rightarrow n^2 - 3n - 130 = 0 \rightarrow (n+10)(n-13) = 0$$

$$n = -10 \quad \text{or} \quad n = 13$$

since n must be a positive integer (it represents the number of sides of the polygon), we discard the negative value. Therefore, we conclude that the polygon has 13 sides and 65 diagonals.

(b) we need to solve the equation $\frac{1}{2}n(n-3) = 80$

$$2\left(\frac{1}{2}\right)n(n-3) = (80)(2) \rightarrow n(n-3) = 160 \rightarrow n^2 - 3n = 160 \rightarrow n^2 - 3n - 160 = 0$$

the solutions to this equation are $n = \frac{3 \pm \sqrt{9 + 640}}{2} = \frac{3 \pm \sqrt{649}}{2}$,but neither of these

answers is a whole number. Therefore, there cannot exist a polygon having 80 diagonals.

111.   Let t_1 and t_2 represent the times for the two segments of the trip.

	Rate	Time	Distance
Chicago to Atlanta	45	t_1	$45t_1$
Atlanta to Miami	55	t_2	$55t_2$

Since Atlanta is halfway between Chicago and Miami, the distances are equal.

$$45t_1 = 55t_2 \quad \rightarrow \quad t_1 = \frac{55}{45}t_2 = \frac{11}{9}t_2$$

Computing the average speed:

$$\text{Avg Speed} = \frac{\text{Distance}}{\text{Time}} = \frac{45t_1 + 55t_2}{t_1 + t_2} = \frac{45\left(\frac{11}{9}t_2\right) + 55t_2}{\frac{11}{9}t_2 + t_2}$$

$$= \frac{55t_2 + 55t_2}{\frac{11t_2 + 9t_2}{9}} = \frac{110t_2}{\frac{20t_2}{9}} = \frac{990t_2}{20t_2} = \frac{99}{2} = 49.5 \text{ miles per hour}$$

The average speed for the trip from Chicago to Miami is 49.5 miles per hour.

112.   The time traveled with the tail wind was:

$$919 = 550t$$

$$t = \frac{919}{550} \approx 1.671 \text{ hours}$$

Since they were 20 minutes early, the time in still air would have been:

$$1.671 \text{ hours} + 20 \text{ minutes} = 1.671 + 0.333 \approx 2 \text{ hours}$$

Thus the rate in still air is:

$$919 = r(2)$$

$$r \approx 460 \text{ nautical miles / hour}$$

The tail wind was $550 - 460 = 90$ nautical miles per hour.

113 – 116. Answers will vary.

Chapter 1

Equations and Inequalities

1.4 Radical Equations; Equations Quadratic in Form

1. $\sqrt{2t-1} = 1$
$\left(\sqrt{2t-1}\right)^2 = 1^2$
$\qquad 2t-1 = 1 \rightarrow 2t = 2 \rightarrow t = 1$
Check: $\sqrt{2(1)-1} = \sqrt{1} = 1$
The solution is $t = 1$.

2. $\sqrt{3t+4} = 2$
$\left(\sqrt{3t+4}\right)^2 = 2^2$
$\qquad 3t+4 = 4 \rightarrow 3t = 0 \rightarrow t = 0$
Check: $\sqrt{3(0)+4} = \sqrt{4} = 2$
The solution is $t = 0$.

3. $\sqrt{3t+4} = -6$

Since the principal square root is always a non-negative number, this equation has no real solution.

4. $\sqrt{5t+3} = -2$

Since the principal square root is always a non-negative number, this equation has no real solution.

5. $\sqrt[3]{1-2x} - 3 = 0$
$\qquad \sqrt[3]{1-2x} = 3$
$\qquad \left(\sqrt[3]{1-2x}\right)^3 = 3^3$
$\qquad 1-2x = 27 \rightarrow -2x = 26 \rightarrow x = -13$
Check: $\sqrt[3]{1-2(-13)} - 3$
$\qquad\qquad = \sqrt[3]{27} - 3 = 0$
The solution is $x = -13$.

6. $\sqrt[3]{1-2x} - 1 = 0$
$\qquad \sqrt[3]{1-2x} = 1$
$\qquad \left(\sqrt[3]{1-2x}\right)^3 = 1^3$
$\qquad 1-2x = 1 \rightarrow -2x = 0 \rightarrow x = 0$
Check: $\sqrt[3]{1-2(0)} - 1 = \sqrt[3]{1} - 1 = 0$
The solution is $x = 0$.

7. $x = 8\sqrt{x}$

$$(x)^2 = \left(8\sqrt{x}\right)^2$$

$$x^2 = 64x \rightarrow x^2 - 64x = 0$$

$x(x - 64) = 0 \rightarrow x = 0$ or $x = 64$

Check

$x = 0: \quad 0 = 8\sqrt{0} \rightarrow 0 = 0$

$x = 64: \quad 64 = 8\sqrt{64} \rightarrow 64 = (8)(8) = 64$

The solution set is $\{0, 64\}$.

8. $x = 3\sqrt{x}$

$$(x)^2 = \left(3\sqrt{x}\right)^2$$

$$x^2 = 9x \rightarrow x^2 - 9x = 0$$

$x(x - 9) = 0 \rightarrow x = 0$ or $x = 9$

Check

$x = 0: \quad 0 = 3\sqrt{0} \rightarrow 0 = 0$

$x = 9: \quad 9 = 3\sqrt{9} \rightarrow 9 = (3)(3) = 9$

The solution set is $\{0, 9\}$.

9. $\sqrt{15 - 2x} = x$

$$\left(\sqrt{15 - 2x}\right)^2 = x^2$$

$$15 - 2x = x^2 \rightarrow x^2 + 2x - 15 = 0$$

$(x + 5)(x - 3) = 0 \rightarrow x = -5$ or $x = 3$

Check $-5: \quad \sqrt{15 - 2(-5)} = \sqrt{25}$

$$= 5 \neq -5$$

Check $3: \quad \sqrt{15 - 2(3)} = \sqrt{9} = 3 = 3$

The solution is $x = 3$.

10. $\sqrt{12 - x} = x$

$$\left(\sqrt{12 - x}\right)^2 = x^2$$

$$12 - x = x^2 \rightarrow x^2 + x - 12 = 0$$

$(x + 4)(x - 3) = 0 \rightarrow x = -4$ or $x = 3$

Check $-4: \quad \sqrt{12 - (-4)} = \sqrt{16}$

$$= 4 \neq -4$$

Check $3: \quad \sqrt{12 - 3} = \sqrt{9} = 3 = 3$

The solution is $x = 3$.

11. $x = 2\sqrt{x - 1}$

$$x^2 = \left(2\sqrt{x - 1}\right)^2$$

$$x^2 = 4(x - 1) \rightarrow x^2 = 4x - 4$$

$x^2 - 4x + 4 = 0 \rightarrow (x - 2)^2 = 0 \rightarrow x = 2$

Check: $2 = 2\sqrt{2 - 1} \rightarrow 2 = 2$

The solution is $x = 2$.

12. $x = 2\sqrt{-x - 1}$

$$x^2 = \left(2\sqrt{-x - 1}\right)^2$$

$$x^2 = 4(-x - 1) \rightarrow x^2 = -4x - 4$$

$x^2 + 4x + 4 = 0 \rightarrow (x + 2)^2 = 0 \rightarrow x = -2$

Check: $-2 = 2\sqrt{-(-2) - 1}$

$$\rightarrow -2 \neq 2$$

No real solution.

13. $\sqrt{x^2 - x - 4} = x + 2$

$$\left(\sqrt{x^2 - x - 4}\right)^2 = (x + 2)^2$$

$$x^2 - x - 4 = x^2 + 4x + 4$$

$$-8 = 5x \rightarrow -\frac{8}{5} = x$$

14. $\sqrt{3 - x + x^2} = x - 2$

$$\left(\sqrt{3 - x + x^2}\right)^2 = (x - 2)^2$$

$$3 - x + x^2 = x^2 - 4x + 4$$

$$5x = 1 \rightarrow x = \frac{1}{5}$$

Check

$x = -\dfrac{8}{5} : \sqrt{\left(-\dfrac{8}{5}\right)^2 - \left(-\dfrac{8}{5}\right) - 4} = \left(-\dfrac{8}{5}\right) + 2$

$\sqrt{\dfrac{64}{25} + \dfrac{8}{5} - 4} = \dfrac{2}{5} \rightarrow \sqrt{\dfrac{64 + 40 - 100}{25}} = \dfrac{2}{5}$

$\sqrt{\dfrac{4}{25}} = \dfrac{2}{5} \rightarrow \dfrac{2}{5} = \dfrac{2}{5}$, The solution is $x = -\dfrac{8}{5}$.

Check

$x = \dfrac{1}{5} : \sqrt{3 - \left(\dfrac{1}{5}\right) + \left(\dfrac{1}{5}\right)^2} = \left(\dfrac{1}{5}\right) - 2$

$\sqrt{3 - \dfrac{1}{5} + \dfrac{1}{25}} = -\dfrac{9}{5}$

Since the principal square root is always a non-negative number, x = 1/5 does not check, therefore this equation has no real solution.

15.
$$3 + \sqrt{3x+1} = x$$
$$\sqrt{3x+1} = x - 3$$
$$\left(\sqrt{3x+1}\right)^2 = (x-3)^2$$
$$3x + 1 = x^2 - 6x + 9$$
$$0 = x^2 - 9x + 8$$
$$(x-1)(x-8) = 0$$
$$x = 1 \text{ or } x = 8$$
Check 1: $3 + \sqrt{3(1)+1}$
$$= 3 + \sqrt{4} = 5 \neq 1$$
Check 8: $3 + \sqrt{3(8)+1}$
$$= 3 + \sqrt{25} = 8 = 8$$
The solution is $x = 8$.

16.
$$2 + \sqrt{12 - 2x} = x$$
$$\sqrt{12 - 2x} = x - 2$$
$$\left(\sqrt{12-2x}\right)^2 = (x-2)^2$$
$$12 - 2x = x^2 - 4x + 4$$
$$0 = x^2 - 2x - 8$$
$$(x+2)(x-4) = 0$$
$$x = -2 \text{ or } x = 4$$
Check -2: $2 + \sqrt{12 - 2(-2)}$
$$= 2 + \sqrt{16} = 6 \neq -2$$
Check 4: $2 + \sqrt{12 - 2(4)}$
$$= 2 + \sqrt{4} = 4 = 4$$
The solution is $x = 4$.

17.
$$\sqrt{2x+3} - \sqrt{x+1} = 1$$
$$\sqrt{2x+3} = 1 + \sqrt{x+1}$$
$$\left(\sqrt{2x+3}\right)^2 = \left(1 + \sqrt{x+1}\right)^2$$
$$2x + 3 = 1 + 2\sqrt{x+1} + x + 1$$
$$x + 1 = 2\sqrt{x+1}$$
$$(x+1)^2 = \left(2\sqrt{x+1}\right)^2$$
$$x^2 + 2x + 1 = 4(x+1)$$
$$x^2 + 2x + 1 = 4x + 4$$
$$x^2 - 2x - 3 = 0$$
$$(x+1)(x-3) = 0 \rightarrow x = -1 \text{ or } x = 3$$

18.
$$\sqrt{3x+7} + \sqrt{x+2} = 1$$
$$\sqrt{3x+7} = 1 - \sqrt{x+2}$$
$$\left(\sqrt{3x+7}\right)^2 = \left(1 - \sqrt{x+2}\right)^2$$
$$3x + 7 = 1 - 2\sqrt{x+2} + x + 2$$
$$2x + 4 = -2\sqrt{x+2}$$
$$-x - 2 = \sqrt{x+2}$$
$$(-x-2)^2 = \left(\sqrt{x+2}\right)^2$$
$$x^2 + 4x + 4 = x + 2$$
$$x^2 + 3x + 2 = 0$$
$$(x+1)(x+2) = 0$$
$$x = -1 \text{ or } x = -2$$

Check -1: $\sqrt{2(-1)+3} - \sqrt{-1+1}$

$\qquad = \sqrt{1} - \sqrt{0} = 1 - 0 = 1 = 1$

Check 3: $\sqrt{2(3)+3} - \sqrt{3+1}$

$\qquad = \sqrt{9} - \sqrt{4} = 3 - 2 = 1 = 1$

The solution is $x = -1$ or $x = 3$.

Check -1: $\sqrt{3(-1)+7} + \sqrt{-1+2}$

$\qquad = \sqrt{4} + \sqrt{1} = 2 + 1 = 3 \neq 1$

Check -2: $\sqrt{3(-2)+7} + \sqrt{-2+2}$

$\qquad = \sqrt{1} + \sqrt{0} = 1 + 0 = 1 = 1$

The solution is $x = -2$.

19. $\sqrt{3x+1} - \sqrt{x-1} = 2$

$\qquad \sqrt{3x+1} = 2 + \sqrt{x-1}$

$\qquad \left(\sqrt{3x+1}\right)^2 = \left(2 + \sqrt{x-1}\right)^2$

$\qquad 3x+1 = 4 + 4\sqrt{x-1} + x - 1$

$\qquad 2x - 2 = 4\sqrt{x-1}$

$\qquad (2x-2)^2 = \left(4\sqrt{x-1}\right)^2$

$\qquad 4x^2 - 8x + 4 = 16(x-1)$

$\qquad x^2 - 2x + 1 = 4x - 4$

$\qquad x^2 - 6x + 5 = 0$

$\qquad (x-1)(x-5) = 0 \rightarrow x = 1$ or $x = 5$

Check 1: $\sqrt{3(1)+1} - \sqrt{1-1}$

$\qquad = \sqrt{4} - \sqrt{0} = 2 - 0 = 2 = 2$

Check 5: $\sqrt{3(5)+1} - \sqrt{5-1}$

$\qquad = \sqrt{16} - \sqrt{4} = 4 - 2 = 2 = 2$

The solution is $x = 1$ or $x = 5$.

20. $\sqrt{3x-5} - \sqrt{x+7} = 2$

$\qquad \sqrt{3x-5} = 2 + \sqrt{x+7}$

$\qquad \left(\sqrt{3x-5}\right)^2 = \left(2 + \sqrt{x+7}\right)^2$

$\qquad 3x - 5 = 4 + 4\sqrt{x+7} + x + 7$

$\qquad 2x - 16 = 4\sqrt{x+7}$

$\qquad (2x-16)^2 = \left(4\sqrt{x+7}\right)^2$

$\qquad 4x^2 - 64x + 256 = 16(x+7)$

$\qquad 4x^2 - 64x + 256 = 16x + 112$

$\qquad 4x^2 - 80x + 144 = 0$

$\qquad x^2 - 20x + 36 = 0$

$\qquad (x-2)(x-18) = 0 \rightarrow x = 2$ or $x = 18$

Check 2: $\sqrt{3(2)-5} - \sqrt{2+7}$

$\qquad = \sqrt{1} - \sqrt{9} = 1 - 3 = -2 \neq 2$

Check 18: $\sqrt{3(18)-5} - \sqrt{18+7}$

$\qquad = \sqrt{49} - \sqrt{25} = 7 - 5 = 2 = 2$

The solution is $x = 18$.

21. $\sqrt{3 - 2\sqrt{x}} = \sqrt{x}$

$\qquad \left(\sqrt{3 - 2\sqrt{x}}\right)^2 = \left(\sqrt{x}\right)^2$

$\qquad 3 - 2\sqrt{x} = x$

$\qquad -2\sqrt{x} = x - 3$

$\qquad \left(-2\sqrt{x}\right)^2 = (x-3)^2$

$\qquad 4x = x^2 - 6x + 9 \rightarrow 0 = x^2 - 10x + 9$

$\qquad 0 = (x-9)(x-1) \rightarrow x = 9$ or $x = 1$

22. $\sqrt{10 + 3\sqrt{x}} = \sqrt{x}$

$\qquad \left(\sqrt{10 + 3\sqrt{x}}\right)^2 = \left(\sqrt{x}\right)^2$

$\qquad 10 + 3\sqrt{x} = x$

$\qquad 3\sqrt{x} = x - 10$

$\qquad \left(3\sqrt{x}\right)^2 = (x-10)^2$

$\qquad 9x = x^2 - 20x + 100 \rightarrow 0 = x^2 - 29x + 100$

$\qquad 0 = (x-25)(x-4) \rightarrow x = 25$ or $x = 4$

Check

$x = 9$: $\sqrt{3 - 2\sqrt{9}} = \sqrt{9}$

$\qquad \sqrt{3 - 2(3)} = 3 \rightarrow \sqrt{-3} \neq 3$

Check

$x = 1$: $\sqrt{3 - 2\sqrt{1}} = \sqrt{1}$

$\qquad \sqrt{3 - 2(1)} = 1 \rightarrow \sqrt{1} = 1$

The solution is $x = 1$.

Check

$x = 25$: $\sqrt{10 + 3\sqrt{25}} = \sqrt{25}$

$\qquad \sqrt{10 + (3)(5)} = 5 \rightarrow \sqrt{25} = 5$

Check

$x = 4$: $\sqrt{10 + 3\sqrt{4}} = \sqrt{4}$

$\qquad \sqrt{10 + (3)(2)} = 2 \rightarrow \sqrt{16} \neq 2$

The solution is $x = 25$.

23. $\qquad (3x + 1)^{1/2} = 4$

$\left((3x + 1)^{1/2}\right)^2 = (4)^2$

$\qquad 3x + 1 = 16 \rightarrow 3x = 15 \rightarrow x = 5$

Check

$x = 5$: $(3(5) + 1)^{1/2} = 4$

$\qquad 16^{1/2} = 4 \rightarrow 4 = 4$

The solution is $x = 5$.

24. $\qquad (3x - 5)^{1/2} = 2$

$\left((3x - 5)^{1/2}\right)^2 = (2)^2$

$\qquad 3x - 5 = 4 \rightarrow 3x = 9 \rightarrow x = 3$

Check

$x = 3$: $(3(3) - 5)^{1/2} = 2$

$\qquad 4^{1/2} = 2 \rightarrow 2 = 2$

The solution is $x = 3$.

25. $\qquad (5x - 2)^{1/3} = 2$

$\left((5x - 2)^{1/3}\right)^3 = (2)^3$

$\qquad 5x - 2 = 8 \rightarrow 5x = 10 \rightarrow x = 2$

Check

$x = 2$: $(5(2) - 2)^{1/3} = 2$

$\qquad 8^{1/3} = 2 \rightarrow 2 = 2$

The solution is $x = 2$.

26. $\qquad (2x + 1)^{1/3} = -1$

$\left((2x + 1)^{1/3}\right)^3 = (-1)^3$

$\qquad 2x + 1 = -1 \rightarrow 2x = -2 \rightarrow x = -1$

Check

$x = -1$: $(2(-1) + 1)^{1/3} = -1$

$\qquad (-1)^{1/3} = -1 \rightarrow -1 = -1$

The solution is $x = -1$.

27. $$\left(x^2+9\right)^{1/2}=5$$

$$\left(\left(x^2+9\right)^{1/2}\right)^2=(5)^2$$

$$x^2+9=25 \rightarrow x^2=16$$

$$x=-4 \text{ or } x=4$$

Check

$$x=-4: \quad \left((-4)^2+9\right)^{1/2}=5$$

$$25^{1/2}=5 \rightarrow 5=5$$

$$x=4: \quad \left((4)^2+9\right)^{1/2}=5$$

$$25^{1/2}=5 \rightarrow 5=5$$

The solution set is $\{-4,4\}$.

28. $$\left(x^2-16\right)^{1/2}=9$$

$$\left(\left(x^2-16\right)^{1/2}\right)^2=(9)^2$$

$$x^2-16=81 \rightarrow x^2=97$$

$$x=-\sqrt{97} \text{ or } x=\sqrt{97}$$

Check

$$x=-\sqrt{97}: \quad \left(\left(-\sqrt{97}\right)^2-16\right)^{1/2}=9$$

$$(97-16)^{1/2}=9$$

$$81^{1/2}=9 \rightarrow 9=9$$

$$x=\sqrt{97}: \quad \left(\left(\sqrt{97}\right)^2-16\right)^{1/2}=9$$

$$(97-16)^{1/2}=9$$

$$81^{1/2}=9 \rightarrow 9=9$$

The solution set is $\left\{-\sqrt{97},\sqrt{97}\right\}$.

29. $$x^{3/2}-3x^{1/2}=0$$
$$x^{3/2}=3x^{1/2}$$

$$\left(x^{3/2}\right)^2=\left(3x^{1/2}\right)^2$$

$$x^3=9x \rightarrow x^3-9x=0$$

$$x\left(x^2-9\right)=0 \rightarrow x=0 \text{ or } x=-3 \text{ or } x=3$$

Check

$$x=0: \quad 0^{3/2}-3\left(0^{1/2}\right)=0$$

$$0=0$$

$$x=-3: \quad (-3)^{3/2}-3\left((-3)^{1/2}\right)=0$$

$$\left(\sqrt{-3}\right)^3-3\left(\sqrt{-3}\right)\neq0$$

$$x=3: \quad (3)^{3/2}-3\left((3)^{1/2}\right)=0$$

$$(3)^{3/2}-(3)^{3/2}=0 \rightarrow 0=0$$

The solution set is $\{0,3\}$.

30. $$x^{3/4}-9x^{1/4}=0$$
$$x^{3/4}=9x^{1/4}$$

$$\left(x^{3/4}\right)^4=\left(9x^{1/4}\right)^4$$

$$x^3=6561x \rightarrow x^3-6561x=0$$

$$x\left(x^2-6561\right)=0 \rightarrow x=0 \text{ or } x=-81 \text{ or } x=81$$

Check

$$x=0: \quad 0^{3/4}-9(0)^{1/4}=0$$

$$0=0$$

$$x=-81: \quad (-81)^{3/4}-9\left((-81)^{1/4}\right)=0$$

$$\left(\sqrt[4]{-81}\right)^3-9\left(\sqrt[4]{-81}\right)\neq0$$

$$x=81: \quad (81)^{3/4}-9\left((81)^{1/4}\right)=0$$

$$(81)^{3/4}-9\left((81)^{1/4}\right)=0$$

$$27-27=0 \rightarrow 0=0$$

The solution set is $\{0,81\}$.

31.
$$x^4 - 5x^2 + 4 = 0$$
$$(x^2 - 4)(x^2 - 1) = 0$$
$$x^2 - 4 = 0 \text{ or } x^2 - 1 = 0$$
$$x = \pm 2 \text{ or } x = \pm 1$$

The solution set is $\{-2, -1, 1, 2\}$.

32.
$$x^4 - 10x^2 + 25 = 0$$
$$(x^2 - 5)(x^2 - 5) = 0$$
$$x^2 - 5 = 0 \rightarrow x = \pm\sqrt{5}$$

The solution set is $\{-\sqrt{5}, \sqrt{5}\}$.

33.
$$3x^4 - 2x^2 - 1 = 0$$
$$(3x^2 + 1)(x^2 - 1) = 0$$
$$3x^2 + 1 = 0 \text{ or } x^2 - 1 = 0$$
$$3x^2 = -1 \text{ , which is impossible}$$
or $x = \pm 1$

The solution set is $\{-1, 1\}$.

34.
$$2x^4 - 5x^2 - 12 = 0$$
$$(2x^2 + 3)(x^2 - 4) = 0$$
$$2x^2 + 3 = 0 \text{ or } x^2 - 4 = 0$$
$$2x^2 = -3 \text{ , which is impossible}$$
or $x = \pm 2$

The solution set is $\{-2, 2\}$.

35.
$$x^6 + 7x^3 - 8 = 0$$
$$(x^3 + 8)(x^3 - 1) = 0$$
$$x^3 + 8 = 0 \text{ or } x^3 - 1 = 0$$
$$x^3 = -8 \rightarrow x = -2$$
or $x^3 = 1 \rightarrow x = 1$

The solution set is $\{-2, 1\}$.

36.
$$x^6 - 7x^3 - 8 = 0$$
$$(x^3 - 8)(x^3 + 1) = 0$$
$$x^3 - 8 = 0 \text{ or } x^3 + 1 = 0$$
$$x^3 = 8 \rightarrow x = 2$$
or $x^3 = -1 \rightarrow x = -1$

The solution set is $\{-1, 2\}$.

37.
$$(x + 2)^2 + 7(x + 2) + 12 = 0$$
$let \ p = x + 2 \rightarrow p^2 = (x + 2)^2$
$$p^2 + 7p + 12 = 0$$
$$(p + 3)(p + 4) = 0$$
$$p + 3 = 0 \text{ or } p + 4 = 0$$
$$p = -3 \rightarrow x + 2 = -3 \rightarrow x = -5$$
or $p = -4 \rightarrow x + 2 = -4 \rightarrow x = -6$
The solution set is $\{-6, -5\}$.

38.
$$(2x + 5)^2 - (2x + 5) - 6 = 0$$
$let \ p = 2x + 5 \rightarrow p^2 = (2x + 5)^2$
$$p^2 - p - 6 = 0$$
$$(p - 3)(p + 2) = 0$$
$$p - 3 = 0 \text{ or } p + 2 = 0$$
$$p = 3 \rightarrow 2x + 5 = 3 \rightarrow x = -1$$
or $p = -2 \rightarrow 2x + 5 = -2 \rightarrow x = -\dfrac{7}{2}$

The solution set is $\left\{-\dfrac{7}{2}, -1\right\}$.

39. $(3x+4)^2 - 6(3x+4) + 9 = 0$

    $let\ p = 3x + 4 \rightarrow p^2 = (3x+4)^2$

    $p^2 - 6p + 9 = 0$

    $(p-3)(p-3) = 0$

    $p - 3 = 0$

    $p = 3 \rightarrow 3x + 4 = 3 \rightarrow x = -\dfrac{1}{3}$

    The solution set is $\left\{-\dfrac{1}{3}\right\}$.

40. $(2-x)^2 + (2-x) - 20 = 0$

    $let\ p = 2 - x \rightarrow p^2 = (2-x)^2$

    $p^2 + p - 20 = 0$

    $(p+5)(p-4) = 0$

    $p + 5 = 0\ \text{or}\ p - 4 = 0$

    $p = -5 \rightarrow 2 - x = -5 \rightarrow x = 7$

    $\text{or}\ \ p = 4 \rightarrow 2 - x = 4 \rightarrow x = -2$

    The solution set is $\{-2, 7\}$.

41. $2(s+1)^2 - 5(s+1) = 3$

    $let\ p = s + 1 \rightarrow p^2 = (s+1)^2$

    $2p^2 - 5p = 3$

    $2p^2 - 5p - 3 = 0$

    $(2p+1)(p-3) = 0$

    $2p + 1 = 0\ \text{or}\ p - 3 = 0$

    $p = -\dfrac{1}{2} \rightarrow s + 1 = -\dfrac{1}{2} \rightarrow s = -\dfrac{3}{2}$

    $\text{or}\ p = 3 \rightarrow s + 1 = 3 \rightarrow s = 2$

    The solution set is $\left\{-\dfrac{3}{2}, 2\right\}$.

42. $3(1-y)^2 + 5(1-y) + 2 = 0$

    $let\ p = 1 - y \rightarrow p^2 = (1-y)^2$

    $3p^2 + 5p + 2 = 0$

    $(3p+2)(p+1) = 0$

    $3p + 2 = 0\ \text{or}\ p + 1 = 0$

    $p = -\dfrac{2}{3} \rightarrow 1 - y = -\dfrac{2}{3} \rightarrow y = \dfrac{5}{3}$

    $\text{or}\ p = -1 \rightarrow 1 - y = -1 \rightarrow y = 2$

    The solution set is $\left\{\dfrac{5}{3}, 2\right\}$.

43. $x - 4x\sqrt{x} = 0$
     $x = 4x\sqrt{x}$
     $(x)^2 = \left(4x\sqrt{x}\right)^2$
     $x = 16x^2 x \rightarrow x = 16x^3 \rightarrow 0 = 16x^3 - x$
     $0 = x\left(16x^2 - 1\right) \rightarrow x = 0$
     or $16x^2 - 1 = 0 \rightarrow x = \pm\dfrac{1}{4}$

     Check
     $x = 0:\ \ 0 - 4(0)\sqrt{0} = 0$
     $\qquad\qquad 0 = 0$
     $x = -\dfrac{1}{4}:\ \ \left(-\dfrac{1}{4}\right) - 4\left(-\dfrac{1}{4}\right)\sqrt{-\dfrac{1}{4}} \neq 0$
     $x = \dfrac{1}{4}:\ \ \left(\dfrac{1}{4}\right) - 4\left(\dfrac{1}{4}\right)\sqrt{\dfrac{1}{4}} = 0$
     $\left(\dfrac{1}{4}\right) - 1\left(\dfrac{1}{2}\right) = 0 \rightarrow -\dfrac{1}{4} \neq 0$

     The solution set is $\{0\}$.

44. $x + 8\sqrt{x} = 0$
     $8\sqrt{x} = -x$
     $\left(8\sqrt{x}\right)^2 = (-x)^2$
     $64x = x^2 \rightarrow 0 = x^2 - 64x$
     $0 = x(x - 64) \rightarrow x = 0\ $ or $\ x = 64$

     Check
     $x = 0:\ \ 0 + 8\sqrt{0} = 0$
     $\qquad\qquad 0 = 0$
     $x = 64:\ \ 64 + 8\sqrt{64} = 0$
     $\qquad\qquad 64 + 64 \neq 0$

     The solution set is $\{0\}$.

45. $x + \sqrt{x} = 20$
     let $p = \sqrt{x} \rightarrow p^2 = x$
     $p^2 + p = 20$
     $p^2 + p - 20 = 0$
     $(p + 5)(p - 4) = 0$
     $p + 5 = 0\ $ or $\ p - 4 = 0$
     $p = -5 \rightarrow \sqrt{x} = -5 \rightarrow x = 25$
     or $p = 4 \rightarrow \sqrt{x} = 4 \rightarrow x = 16$

     Check
     $x = 25:\ \ 25 + \sqrt{25} = 20$
     $\qquad\qquad 25 + 5 \neq 20$
     $x = 16:\ \ 16 + \sqrt{16} = 20$
     $\qquad\qquad 16 + 4 = 20$
     The solution set is $\{16\}$.

46. $x + \sqrt{x} = 6$
     let $p = \sqrt{x} \rightarrow p^2 = x$
     $p^2 + p = 6$
     $p^2 + p - 6 = 0$
     $(p + 3)(p - 2) = 0$
     $p + 3 = 0\ $ or $\ p - 2 = 0$
     $p = -3 \rightarrow \sqrt{x} = -3 \rightarrow x = 9$
     or $p = 2 \rightarrow \sqrt{x} = 2 \rightarrow x = 4$

     Check
     $x = 9:\ \ 9 + \sqrt{9} = 6$
     $\qquad\qquad 9 + 3 \neq 6$
     $x = 4:\ \ 4 + \sqrt{4} = 6$
     $\qquad\qquad 4 + 2 = 6$
     The solution set is $\{4\}$.

47. $t^{1/2} - 2t^{1/4} + 1 = 0$
        let $p = t^{1/4} \to p^2 = t^{1/2}$

$p^2 - 2p + 1 = 0$

$(p - 1)(p - 1) = 0$

$p - 1 = 0$

$p = 1 \to t^{1/4} = 1 \to t = 1$

Check

$t = 1: \quad 1^{1/2} - 2(1)^{1/4} + 1 = 0$

$\qquad\qquad 1 - 2 + 1 = 0 \to 0 = 0$

The solution set is $\{1\}$.

48. $z^{1/2} - 4t^{1/4} + 4 = 0$
        let $p = z^{1/4} \to p^2 = z^{1/2}$

$p^2 - 4p + 4 = 0$

$(p - 2)(p - 2) = 0$

$p - 2 = 0$

$p = 2 \to z^{1/4} = 2 \to z = 16$

Check

$z = 16: \quad 16^{1/2} - 4(16)^{1/4} + 4 = 0$

$\qquad\qquad 4 - 8 + 4 = 0 \to 0 = 0$

The solution set is $\{16\}$.

49. $4x^{1/2} - 9x^{1/4} + 4 = 0$
        let $p = x^{1/4} \to p^2 = x^{1/2}$

$$4p^2 - 9p + 4 = 0 \to p = \frac{9 \pm \sqrt{81 - 64}}{8} = \frac{9 \pm \sqrt{17}}{8} \to x^{1/4} = \frac{9 \pm \sqrt{17}}{8} \to x = \left(\frac{9 \pm \sqrt{17}}{8}\right)^4$$

Check

$$x = \left(\frac{9 + \sqrt{17}}{8}\right)^4 : \quad 4\left(\left(\frac{9 + \sqrt{17}}{8}\right)^4\right)^{1/2} - 9\left(\left(\frac{9 + \sqrt{17}}{8}\right)^4\right)^{1/4} + 4 = 0$$

$$4\left(\frac{9 + \sqrt{17}}{8}\right)^2 - 9\left(\frac{9 + \sqrt{17}}{8}\right) + 4 = 0$$

$$4\frac{\left(9 + \sqrt{17}\right)^2}{64} - 9\left(\frac{9 + \sqrt{17}}{8}\right) + 4 = 0$$

$$64\left(4\frac{\left(9 + \sqrt{17}\right)^2}{64} - 9\left(\frac{9 + \sqrt{17}}{8}\right) + 4\right) = (0)(64)$$

$$4\left(9 + \sqrt{17}\right)^2 - 72\left(9 + \sqrt{17}\right) + 256 = 0$$

$$4\left(81 + 18\sqrt{17} + 17\right) - 72\left(9 + \sqrt{17}\right) + 256 = 0$$

$$324 + 72\sqrt{17} + 68 - 648 - 72\sqrt{17} + 256 = 0 \to 0 = 0$$

$$x = \left(\frac{9 - \sqrt{17}}{8}\right)^4 : \quad 4\left(\left(\frac{9 - \sqrt{17}}{8}\right)^4\right)^{1/2} - 9\left(\left(\frac{9 - \sqrt{17}}{8}\right)^4\right)^{1/4} + 4 = 0$$

$$4\left(\frac{9 - \sqrt{17}}{8}\right)^2 - 9\left(\frac{9 - \sqrt{17}}{8}\right) + 4 = 0 \to 4\left(81 - 18\sqrt{17} + 17\right) - 72\left(9 - \sqrt{17}\right) + 256 = 0$$

$324 - 72\sqrt{17} + 68 - 648 + 72\sqrt{17} + 256 = 0$

$0 = 0$

$$4\frac{\left(9-\sqrt{17}\right)^2}{64} - 9\left(\frac{9-\sqrt{17}}{8}\right) + 4 = 0 \Bigg\} \to 64\left(4\frac{\left(9-\sqrt{17}\right)^2}{64} - 9\left(\frac{9-\sqrt{17}}{8}\right) + 4\right) = (0)(64)$$

$$\to 4\left(9-\sqrt{17}\right)^2 - 72\left(9-\sqrt{17}\right) + 256 = 0 \to 0 = 0 \therefore \text{ the solution set is } \left\{\frac{9\pm\sqrt{17}}{8}\right\}$$

50.

$x^{1/2} - 3x^{1/4} + 2 = 0$

$let\ p = x^{1/4} \to p^2 = x^{1/2}$

$p^2 - 3p + 2 = 0$

$(p-2)(p-1) = 0$

$p = 2 \to x^{1/4} = 2 \to x = 16$

$or\ p = 1 \to x^{1/4} = 1 \to x = 1$

Check

$x = 16:\ 16^{1/2} - 3(16)^{1/4} + 2 = 0$

$4 - 6 + 2 = 0 \to 0 = 0$

$x = 1:\ 1^{1/2} - 3(1)^{1/4} + 2 = 0$

$1 - 3 + 2 = 0 \to 0 = 0$

The solution set is $\{1, 16\}$.

51.

$\sqrt[4]{5x^2 - 6} = x$

$\left(\sqrt[4]{5x^2 - 6}\right)^4 = x^4$

$5x^2 - 6 = x^4$

$0 = x^4 - 5x^2 + 6$

$let\ p = x^2 \to p^2 = x^4$

$0 = p^2 - 5p + 6 \to (p-3)(p-2) = 0$

$p = 3 \to x^2 = 3 \to x = \pm\sqrt{3}$

$or\ p = 2 \to x^2 = 2 \to x = \pm\sqrt{2}$

Check

$x = -\sqrt{3}:\ \sqrt[4]{5\left(-\sqrt{3}\right)^2 - 6} = -\sqrt{3}$

$\sqrt[4]{15 - 6} = -\sqrt{3} \to \sqrt[4]{9} \neq -\sqrt{3}$

$x = \sqrt{3}:\ \sqrt[4]{5\left(\sqrt{3}\right)^2 - 6} = \sqrt{3}$

$\sqrt[4]{15 - 6} = \sqrt{3} \to \sqrt[4]{9} = \sqrt{3} \to \sqrt{3} = \sqrt{3}$

$x = -\sqrt{2}:\ \sqrt[4]{5\left(-\sqrt{2}\right)^2 - 6} = -\sqrt{2}$

$\sqrt[4]{10 - 6} = -\sqrt{2} \to \sqrt[4]{4} \neq -\sqrt{2}$

$x = \sqrt{2}:\ \sqrt[4]{5\left(\sqrt{2}\right)^2 - 6} = \sqrt{2}$

$\sqrt[4]{10 - 6} = \sqrt{2}$

$\sqrt[4]{4} = \sqrt{2} \to \sqrt{2} = \sqrt{2}$

The solution set is $\left\{\sqrt{2}, \sqrt{3}\right\}$.

52. $\sqrt[4]{4-5x^2} = x$

$\left(\sqrt[4]{4-5x^2}\right)^4 = x^4$

$4-5x^2 = x^4$

$0 = x^4 + 5x^2 - 4$

let $p = x^2 \rightarrow p^2 = x^4$

$0 = p^2 + 5p - 4$

$p = \dfrac{-5 \pm \sqrt{25+16}}{2} = \dfrac{-5 \pm \sqrt{41}}{2}$

$\rightarrow x^2 = \dfrac{-5 \pm \sqrt{41}}{2} \rightarrow x = \pm\sqrt{\dfrac{-5 \pm \sqrt{41}}{2}}$

but since $-5 - \sqrt{41} < 0$,

$x = \pm\sqrt{\dfrac{-5 - \sqrt{41}}{2}}$ is undefined

Check:

$x = \pm\sqrt{\dfrac{-5+\sqrt{41}}{2}}$:

$\sqrt[4]{4 - 5\left(\pm\sqrt{\dfrac{-5+\sqrt{41}}{2}}\right)^2} = \pm\sqrt{\dfrac{-5+\sqrt{41}}{2}}$

$\sqrt[4]{4 - 5\left(\dfrac{-5+\sqrt{41}}{2}\right)} = \pm\sqrt{\dfrac{-5+\sqrt{41}}{2}}$

$\sqrt[4]{\dfrac{8 - 5\left(-5+\sqrt{41}\right)}{2}} = \pm\sqrt{\dfrac{-5+\sqrt{41}}{2}}$

$\sqrt[4]{\dfrac{33 + \sqrt{41}}{2}} = \pm\sqrt{\dfrac{-5+\sqrt{41}}{2}}$

which is only true when $x = \sqrt{\dfrac{-5+\sqrt{41}}{2}}$

53. $x^2 + 3x + \sqrt{x^2 + 3x} = 6$

let $p = \sqrt{x^2 + 3x} \rightarrow p^2 = x^2 + 3x$

$p^2 + p = 6 \rightarrow p^2 + p - 6 = 0$

$(p + 3)(p - 2) = 0 \rightarrow p = -3$ or $p = 2$

$\rightarrow \sqrt{x^2 + 3x} = -3$ which is impossible

since the principal square root is always
a non-negative number.

or

$\sqrt{x^2 + 3x} = 2 \rightarrow x^2 + 3x = 4$

$x^2 + 3x - 4 = 0 \rightarrow (x + 4)(x - 1) = 0$

$x = -4$ or $x = 1$

Check

$x = -4:\ (-4)^2 + 3(-4) + \sqrt{(-4)^2 + 3(-4)} = 6$

$16 - 12 + \sqrt{16 - 12} = 6$

$16 - 12 + \sqrt{4} = 6 \rightarrow 6 = 6$

$x = 1:\ (1)^2 + 3(1) + \sqrt{(1)^2 + 3(1)} = 6$

$1 + 3 + \sqrt{1 + 3} = 6$

$4 + \sqrt{4} = 6 \rightarrow 6 = 6$

The solution set is $\{-4, 1\}$.

54. $x^2 - 3x - \sqrt{x^2 - 3x} = 2$

let $p = \sqrt{x^2 - 3x} \rightarrow p^2 = x^2 - 3x$

$p^2 - p = 2 \rightarrow p^2 - p - 2 = 0$

$(p + 1)(p - 2) = 0 \rightarrow p = -1$ or $p = 2$

$p = -1 \rightarrow \sqrt{x^2 - 3x} = -1$ which is impossible

since the principal square root is always

a non-negative number.

or

$p = 2 \rightarrow \sqrt{x^2 - 3x} = 2 \rightarrow x^2 - 3x = 4$

$x^2 - 3x - 4 = 0 \rightarrow (x - 4)(x + 1) = 0$

$x = 4$ or $x = -1$

Check

$x = 4 : (4)^2 - 3(4) - \sqrt{(4)^2 - 3(4)} = 2$

$16 - 12 - \sqrt{4} = 2$

$4 - 2 = 2 \rightarrow 2 = 2$

$x = -1 : (-1)^2 - 3(-1) - \sqrt{(-1)^2 - 3(-1)} = 2$

$1 + 3 - \sqrt{4} = 2 \rightarrow 4 - 2 = 2$

The solution set is $\{-1, 4\}$.

55.

$$\frac{1}{(x+1)^2} = \frac{1}{x+1} + 2$$

let $p = \frac{1}{x+1} \rightarrow p^2 = \left(\frac{1}{x+1}\right)^2$

$p^2 = p + 2 \rightarrow p^2 - p - 2 = 0$

$(p + 1)(p - 2) = 0 \rightarrow p = -1$ or $p = 2$

$p = -1 \rightarrow \frac{1}{x+1} = -1 \rightarrow 1 = -x - 1 \rightarrow x = -2$

or

$\frac{1}{x+1} = 2 \rightarrow 1 = 2x + 2 \rightarrow x = -\frac{1}{2}$

Check

$x = -2 : \frac{1}{(-2+1)^2} = \frac{1}{-2+1} + 2$

$1 = -1 + 2 \rightarrow 1 = 1$

$x = -\frac{1}{2} : \frac{1}{\left(-\frac{1}{2}+1\right)^2} = \frac{1}{-\frac{1}{2}+1} + 2$

$4 = 2 + 2 \rightarrow 4 = 4$

The solution set is $\left\{-2, -\frac{1}{2}\right\}$.

56. $\frac{1}{(x-1)^2} + \frac{1}{x-1} = 12$

let $p = \frac{1}{x-1} \rightarrow p^2 = \left(\frac{1}{x-1}\right)^2$

$p^2 + p = 12 \rightarrow p^2 + p - 12 = 0$

$(p + 4)(p - 3) = 0 \rightarrow p = -4$ or $p = 3$

$p = -4 \rightarrow \frac{1}{x-1} = -4$

$\rightarrow 1 = -4x + 1 \rightarrow 4x = 0 \rightarrow x = 0$

or

$\frac{1}{x-1} = 3 \rightarrow 1 = 3x - 3 \rightarrow x = \frac{4}{3}$

Check

$x = 0 : \frac{1}{(0-1)^2} + \frac{1}{0-1} = 12$

$1 - 1 \neq 12$

$x = \frac{4}{3} : \frac{1}{\left(\frac{4}{3}-1\right)^2} + \frac{1}{\frac{4}{3}-1} = 12$

$9 + 3 = 12$

$12 = 12$

The solution set is $\left\{\frac{4}{3}\right\}$.

57. $3x^{-2} - 7x^{-1} - 6 = 0$

$\text{let } p = x^{-1} \to p^2 = x^{-2}$

$3p^2 - 7p - 6 = 0$

$(3p + 2)(p - 3) = 0$

$p = -\dfrac{2}{3} \text{ or } p = 3$

$p = -\dfrac{2}{3} \to x^{-1} = -\dfrac{2}{3} \to \left(x^{-1}\right)^{-1}$

$= \left(-\dfrac{2}{3}\right)^{-1} \to x = -\dfrac{3}{2}$

or

$p = 3 \to x^{-1} = 3 \to \left(x^{-1}\right)^{-1} = (3)^{-1} \to x = \dfrac{1}{3}$

Check

$x = -\dfrac{3}{2}: \;\; 3\left(-\dfrac{3}{2}\right)^{-2} - 7\left(-\dfrac{3}{2}\right)^{-1} - 6 = 0$

$3\left(\dfrac{4}{9}\right) - 7\left(-\dfrac{2}{3}\right) - 6 = 0$

$\dfrac{4}{3} + \dfrac{14}{3} - 6 = 0 \to 6 - 6 = 0 \to 0 = 0$

$x = \dfrac{1}{3}: \;\; 3\left(\dfrac{1}{3}\right)^{-2} - 7\left(\dfrac{1}{3}\right)^{-1} - 6 = 0$

$3(9) - 7(3) - 6 = 0$

$27 - 21 - 6 = 0 \to 6 - 6 = 0 \to 0 = 0$

The solution set is $\left\{ -\dfrac{3}{2}, \dfrac{1}{3} \right\}$.

58. $2x^{-2} - 3x^{-1} - 4 = 0$

$\text{let } p = x^{-1} \to p^2 = x^{-2}$

$2p^2 - 3p - 4 = 0$

$p = \dfrac{3 \pm \sqrt{9 + 32}}{4} = \dfrac{3 \pm \sqrt{41}}{4}$

$p = \dfrac{3 + \sqrt{41}}{4} \to x^{-1} = \dfrac{3 + \sqrt{41}}{4}$

$\to \left(x^{-1}\right)^{-1} = \left(\dfrac{3 + \sqrt{41}}{4}\right)^{-1} \to x = \dfrac{4}{3 + \sqrt{41}}$

or

$p = \dfrac{3 - \sqrt{41}}{4} \to x^{-1} = \dfrac{3 - \sqrt{41}}{4}$

$\to \left(x^{-1}\right)^{-1} = \left(\dfrac{3 - \sqrt{41}}{4}\right)^{-1} \to x = \dfrac{4}{3 - \sqrt{41}}$

Check

$x = \dfrac{4}{3 + \sqrt{41}}:$

$2\left(\dfrac{4}{3 + \sqrt{41}}\right)^{-2} - 3\left(\dfrac{4}{3 + \sqrt{41}}\right)^{-1} - 4 = 0$

$2\dfrac{\left(3 + \sqrt{41}\right)^2}{16} - 3\left(\dfrac{3 + \sqrt{41}}{4}\right) - 4 = 0$

$(16)\left\{ 2\dfrac{\left(9 + 6\sqrt{41} + 41\right)}{16} - 3\left(\dfrac{3 + \sqrt{41}}{4}\right) - 4 \right\} = (0)(16)$

$2\left(9 + 6\sqrt{41} + 41\right) - 12\left(3 + \sqrt{41}\right) - 64 = 0$

$18 + 12\sqrt{41} + 82 - 36 - 12\sqrt{41} - 64 = 0$

$0 = 0$

$x = \dfrac{4}{3-\sqrt{41}}:$

$2\left(\dfrac{4}{3-\sqrt{41}}\right)^{-2} - 3\left(\dfrac{4}{3-\sqrt{41}}\right)^{-1} - 4 = 0$

$2\dfrac{\left(3-\sqrt{41}\right)^2}{16} - 3\left(\dfrac{3-\sqrt{41}}{4}\right) - 4 = 0$

$(16)\left\{2\dfrac{\left(9-6\sqrt{41}+41\right)}{16} - 3\left(\dfrac{3-\sqrt{41}}{4}\right) - 4\right\} = (0)(16)$

$\left. \right\} \rightarrow$

$2\left(9-6\sqrt{41}+41\right) - 12\left(3-\sqrt{41}\right) - 64 = 0$

$18 - 12\sqrt{41} + 82 - 36 + 12\sqrt{41} - 64 = 0$

$0 = 0$

The solution set is $\left\{\dfrac{4}{3-\sqrt{41}}, \dfrac{4}{3+\sqrt{41}}\right\}$

---

59. $2x^{2/3} - 5x^{1/3} - 3 = 0$

$let\ p = x^{1/3} \rightarrow p^2 = x^{2/3}$

$2p^2 - 5p - 3 = 0$

$(2p+1)(p-3) = 0$

$p = -\dfrac{1}{2}\ \text{ or } p = 3$

$p = -\dfrac{1}{2} \rightarrow x^{1/3} = -\dfrac{1}{2}$

$\rightarrow \left(x^{1/3}\right)^3 = \left(-\dfrac{1}{2}\right)^3 \rightarrow x = -\dfrac{1}{8}$

or

$p = 3 \rightarrow x^{1/3} = 3 \rightarrow \left(x^{1/3}\right)^3 = (3)^3$

$\rightarrow x = 27$

Check

$x = -\dfrac{1}{8}:\ 2\left(-\dfrac{1}{8}\right)^{2/3} - 5\left(-\dfrac{1}{8}\right)^{1/3} - 3 = 0$

$2\left(\dfrac{1}{4}\right) - 5\left(-\dfrac{1}{2}\right) - 3 = 0$

$\dfrac{1}{2} + \dfrac{5}{2} - 3 = 0 \rightarrow 3 - 3 = 0 \rightarrow 0 = 0$

$x = 27:\ 2(27)^{2/3} - 5(27)^{1/3} - 3 = 0$

$2(9) - 5(3) - 3 = 0$

$18 - 15 - 3 = 0 \rightarrow 3 - 3 = 0 \rightarrow 0 = 0$

The solution set is $\left\{-\dfrac{1}{8}, 27\right\}$.

---

60. $3x^{4/3} + 5x^{2/3} - 2 = 0$

$let\ p = x^{2/3} \rightarrow p^2 = x^{4/3}$

$3p^2 + 5p^2 - 2 = 0$

$(3p-1)(p+2) = 0$

$p = \dfrac{1}{3}\ \text{ or } p = -2$

$\left. \right\} \rightarrow$

$p = \dfrac{1}{3} \rightarrow x^{2/3} = \dfrac{1}{3} \rightarrow \left(x^{2/3}\right)^{3/2} = \left(\dfrac{1}{3}\right)^{3/2}$

or

$p = -2 \rightarrow x^{2/3} = -2 \rightarrow \left(x^{2/3}\right)^{3/2} = (-2)^{3/2}$

which is impossible

Check

$$x = \left(\frac{1}{3}\right)^{3/2}:$$

$$3\left(\left(\frac{1}{3}\right)^{3/2}\right)^{4/3} + 5\left(\left(\frac{1}{3}\right)^{3/2}\right)^{2/3} - 2 = 0 \left.\begin{array}{c}\\\\\\\\\\\end{array}\right\} \rightarrow$$

$$3\left(\frac{1}{3}\right)^2 + 5\left(\frac{1}{3}\right) - 2 = 0$$

$$\frac{3}{9} + \frac{5}{3} - 2 = 0$$

$$\frac{1}{3} + \frac{5}{3} - 2 = 0$$

$$2 - 2 = 0$$

$$0 = 0$$

The solution set is $\left\{\left(\frac{1}{3}\right)^{3/2}\right\}$.

61. $\left(\dfrac{v}{v+1}\right)^2 + \dfrac{2v}{v+1} = 8$

$\text{let } p = \dfrac{v}{v+1} \rightarrow p^2 = \left(\dfrac{v}{v+1}\right)^2$

$\left(\dfrac{v}{v+1}\right)^2 + \dfrac{2v}{v+1} = 8 \rightarrow \left(\dfrac{v}{v+1}\right)^2 + 2\left(\dfrac{v}{v+1}\right) = 8$

$p^2 + 2p = 8 \rightarrow p^2 + 2p - 8 = 0$

$(p+4)(p-2) = 0 \rightarrow p = -4 \text{ or } p = 2$

$p = -4 \rightarrow \dfrac{v}{v+1} = -4$

$\rightarrow v = -4v - 4 \rightarrow v = -\dfrac{4}{5}$

or

$p = 2 \rightarrow \dfrac{v}{v+1} = 2 \rightarrow v = 2v + 2 \rightarrow v = -2$

Check

$v = -\dfrac{4}{5}: \left(\dfrac{-\dfrac{4}{5}}{-\dfrac{4}{5}+1}\right)^2 + \dfrac{2\left(-\dfrac{4}{5}\right)}{\left(-\dfrac{4}{5}\right)+1} = 8$

$\dfrac{\left(\dfrac{16}{25}\right)}{\left(\dfrac{1}{25}\right)} + \dfrac{\left(-\dfrac{8}{5}\right)}{\left(\dfrac{1}{5}\right)} = 8$

$16 - 8 = 8 \rightarrow 8 = 8$

$v = -2: \left(\dfrac{-2}{-2+1}\right)^2 + \dfrac{2(-2)}{(-2)+1} = 8$

$4 + 4 = 8 \rightarrow 8 = 8$

The solution set is $\left\{-\dfrac{4}{5}, -2\right\}$.

62. $\left(\dfrac{y}{y-1}\right)^2 = 6\left(\dfrac{y}{y-1}\right) + 7$

$\text{let } p = \dfrac{y}{y-1} \rightarrow p^2 = \left(\dfrac{y}{y-1}\right)^2$

$p^2 = 6p + 7 \rightarrow p^2 - 6p - 7 = 0 \left.\begin{array}{c}\\\\\end{array}\right\} \rightarrow$

$(p-7)(p+1) = 0$

$p = -1 \rightarrow \dfrac{y}{y-1} = -1 \rightarrow y = -y + 1 \rightarrow y = \dfrac{1}{2}$

or

$p = 7 \rightarrow \dfrac{y}{y-1} = 7 \rightarrow y = 7y - 7 \rightarrow y = \dfrac{7}{6}$

Check

$$y = \frac{1}{2}: \quad \left(\frac{\frac{1}{2}}{\frac{1}{2}-1}\right)^2 = 6\left(\frac{\frac{1}{2}}{\frac{1}{2}-1}\right)+7$$

$$\frac{\left(\frac{1}{4}\right)}{\left(\frac{1}{4}\right)} = 6\left(\frac{\left(\frac{1}{2}\right)}{\left(-\frac{1}{2}\right)}\right)+7$$

$$1 = 6(-1)+7 \rightarrow 1 = 1$$

$$y = \frac{7}{6}: \quad \left(\frac{\frac{7}{6}}{\frac{7}{6}-1}\right)^2 = 6\left(\frac{\frac{7}{6}}{\frac{7}{6}-1}\right)+7$$

$$\frac{\left(\frac{49}{36}\right)}{\left(\frac{1}{36}\right)} = 6\left(\frac{\left(\frac{7}{6}\right)}{\left(\frac{1}{6}\right)}\right)+7$$

$$49 = 42+7 \rightarrow 49 = 49$$

The solution set is $\left\{\frac{1}{2}, \frac{7}{6}\right\}$.

63. $x - 4x^{1/2} + 2 = 0$

$let\ p = x^{1/2} \rightarrow p^2 = x^2$

$p^2 - 4p + 2 = 0$

$$p = \frac{4 \pm \sqrt{16-8}}{2} = \frac{4 \pm \sqrt{8}}{2}$$

$$p = \frac{4 + \sqrt{8}}{2} \rightarrow x^{1/2} = \frac{4 + \sqrt{8}}{2}$$

$$\rightarrow \left(x^{1/2}\right)^2 = \left(\frac{4+\sqrt{8}}{2}\right)^2 \rightarrow x = \left(\frac{4+\sqrt{8}}{2}\right)^2$$

or

$$p = \frac{4 - \sqrt{8}}{2} \rightarrow x^{1/2} = \frac{4 - \sqrt{8}}{2}$$

$$\rightarrow \left(x^{1/2}\right)^2 = \left(\frac{4-\sqrt{8}}{2}\right)^2 \rightarrow x = \left(\frac{4-\sqrt{8}}{2}\right)^2$$

Check

$$x = \left(\frac{4+\sqrt{8}}{2}\right)^2: \quad \left(\frac{4+\sqrt{8}}{2}\right)^2 - 4\left(\frac{4+\sqrt{8}}{2}\right)+2 = 0$$

$$\frac{16+8\sqrt{8}+8}{4} - 4\left(\frac{4+\sqrt{8}}{2}\right)+2 = 0$$

$$4+2\sqrt{8}+2 - 2\left(4+\sqrt{8}\right)+2 = 0$$

$$4+2\sqrt{8}+2 - 8 - 2\sqrt{8}+2 = 0$$

$$0 = 0$$

$$x = \left(\frac{4-\sqrt{8}}{2}\right)^2: \quad \left(\frac{4-\sqrt{8}}{2}\right)^2 - 4\left(\frac{4-\sqrt{8}}{2}\right)+2 = 0$$

$$\frac{16-8\sqrt{8}+8}{4} - 4\left(\frac{4-\sqrt{8}}{2}\right)+2 = 0$$

$$4-2\sqrt{8}+2 - 2\left(4-\sqrt{8}\right)+2 = 0$$

$$4-2\sqrt{8}+2 - 8 + 2\sqrt{8}+2 = 0 \rightarrow 0 = 0$$

The solution set is

$$\left\{\left(\frac{4+\sqrt{8}}{2}\right)^2, \left(\frac{4-\sqrt{8}}{2}\right)^2\right\} \rightarrow \{11.66, 0.34\}.$$

64. $x^{2/3} + 4x^{1/3} + 2 = 0$

let $p = x^{1/3}$

$p^2 + 4p + 2 = 0$

$p = \dfrac{-4 \pm \sqrt{16 - 8}}{2} = \dfrac{-4 \pm \sqrt{8}}{2}$

$p = \dfrac{-4 + \sqrt{8}}{2} \rightarrow x^{1/3} = \dfrac{-4 + \sqrt{8}}{2}$

$\rightarrow \left(x^{1/3}\right)^3 = \left(\dfrac{-4 + \sqrt{8}}{2}\right)^3 \rightarrow x = \left(\dfrac{-4 + \sqrt{8}}{2}\right)^3$

or

$p = \dfrac{-4 - \sqrt{8}}{2} \rightarrow x^{1/3} = \dfrac{-4 - \sqrt{8}}{2}$

$\rightarrow \left(x^{1/3}\right)^3 = \left(\dfrac{-4 - \sqrt{8}}{2}\right)^3 \rightarrow x = \left(\dfrac{-4 - \sqrt{8}}{2}\right)^3$

Check

$x = \left(\dfrac{-4 + \sqrt{8}}{2}\right)^3 :$

$\left(\left(\dfrac{-4 + \sqrt{8}}{2}\right)^3\right)^{2/3} + 4\left(\left(\dfrac{-4 + \sqrt{8}}{2}\right)^3\right)^{1/3} + 2 = 0$

$\left(\dfrac{-4 + \sqrt{8}}{2}\right)^2 + 4\left(\dfrac{-4 + \sqrt{8}}{2}\right) + 2 = 0$

$\left(\dfrac{16 - 8\sqrt{8} + 8}{4}\right) + 2\left(-4 + \sqrt{8}\right) + 2 = 0$

$4 - 2\sqrt{8} + 2 + 2\left(-4 + \sqrt{8}\right) + 2 = 0$

$4 - 2\sqrt{8} + 2 - 8 + 2\sqrt{8} + 2 = 0 \rightarrow 0 = 0$

$x = \left(\dfrac{-4 - \sqrt{8}}{2}\right)^3 :$

$\left(\left(\dfrac{-4 - \sqrt{8}}{2}\right)^3\right)^{2/3} + 4\left(\left(\dfrac{-4 - \sqrt{8}}{2}\right)^3\right)^{1/3} + 2 = 0$

$\left(\dfrac{-4 - \sqrt{8}}{2}\right)^2 + 4\left(\dfrac{-4 - \sqrt{8}}{2}\right) + 2 = 0$

$\left(\dfrac{16 + 8\sqrt{8} + 8}{4}\right) + 2\left(-4 - \sqrt{8}\right) + 2 = 0$

$4 + 2\sqrt{8} + 2 + 2\left(-4 - \sqrt{8}\right) + 2 = 0$

$4 + 2\sqrt{8} + 2 - 8 - 2\sqrt{8} + 2 = 0 \rightarrow 0 = 0$

The solution set is $\left\{\left(\dfrac{-4 + \sqrt{8}}{2}\right)^3, \left(\dfrac{-4 - \sqrt{8}}{2}\right)^3\right\}$

$\rightarrow \{-0.20, -39.80\}$

65. $x^4 + \sqrt{3}x^2 - 3 = 0$

$\quad$ let $p = x^2 \rightarrow p^2 = x^4$

$\quad p^2 + \sqrt{3}p - 3 = 0$

$\quad p = \dfrac{-\sqrt{3} \pm \sqrt{3 + 12}}{2} = \dfrac{-\sqrt{3} \pm \sqrt{15}}{2}$

$\quad p = \dfrac{-\sqrt{3} + \sqrt{15}}{2}$

$\quad \rightarrow x^2 = \dfrac{-\sqrt{3} + \sqrt{15}}{2} \rightarrow x = \pm\sqrt{\dfrac{-\sqrt{3} + \sqrt{15}}{2}}$

or

$\quad p = \dfrac{-\sqrt{3} - \sqrt{15}}{2}$

$\quad \rightarrow x^2 = \dfrac{-\sqrt{3} - \sqrt{15}}{2} \rightarrow$

$\quad x = \pm\sqrt{\dfrac{-\sqrt{3} - \sqrt{15}}{2}}$

$\quad$ which is impossible since $\dfrac{-\sqrt{3} - \sqrt{15}}{2} < 0$

Check

$x = \sqrt{\dfrac{-\sqrt{3} + \sqrt{15}}{2}}$:

$\left(\sqrt{\dfrac{-\sqrt{3} + \sqrt{15}}{2}}\right)^4 + \sqrt{3}\left(\sqrt{\dfrac{-\sqrt{3} + \sqrt{15}}{2}}\right)^2 - 3 = 0$

$\left(\dfrac{-\sqrt{3} + \sqrt{15}}{2}\right)^2 + \sqrt{3}\left(\dfrac{-\sqrt{3} + \sqrt{15}}{2}\right) - 3 = 0$

$\left(\dfrac{3 - 2\sqrt{3}\sqrt{15} + 15}{4}\right) + \left(\dfrac{\sqrt{3}(-\sqrt{3}) + \sqrt{3}\sqrt{15}}{2}\right) - 3 = 0$

$\left(\dfrac{18 - 2\sqrt{45}}{4}\right) + \left(\dfrac{-3 + \sqrt{45}}{2}\right) - 3 = 0$

$\left(\dfrac{9 - \sqrt{45}}{2}\right) + \left(\dfrac{-3 + \sqrt{45}}{2}\right) - 3 = 0$

$\left(\dfrac{9 - \sqrt{45} - 3 + \sqrt{45}}{2}\right) - 3 = 0$

$3 - 3 = 0 \rightarrow 0 = 0$

$x = -\sqrt{\dfrac{-\sqrt{3} + \sqrt{15}}{2}}$:

$\left(-\sqrt{\dfrac{-\sqrt{3} + \sqrt{15}}{2}}\right)^4 + \sqrt{3}\left(-\sqrt{\dfrac{-\sqrt{3} + \sqrt{15}}{2}}\right)^2 - 3 = 0$

$\left(\dfrac{-\sqrt{3} + \sqrt{15}}{2}\right)^2 + \sqrt{3}\left(\dfrac{-\sqrt{3} + \sqrt{15}}{2}\right) - 3 = 0$

$\left(\dfrac{3 - 2\sqrt{3}\sqrt{15} + 15}{4}\right) + \left(\dfrac{\sqrt{3}(-\sqrt{3}) + \sqrt{3}\sqrt{15}}{2}\right) - 3 = 0$

$\left(\dfrac{18 - 2\sqrt{45}}{4}\right) + \left(\dfrac{-3 + \sqrt{45}}{2}\right) - 3 = 0$

$\left(\dfrac{9 - \sqrt{45}}{2}\right) + \left(\dfrac{-3 + \sqrt{45}}{2}\right) - 3 = 0$

$\left(\dfrac{9 - \sqrt{45} - 3 + \sqrt{45}}{2}\right) - 3 = 0 \rightarrow 3 - 3 = 0 \rightarrow 0 = 0$

The solution set is

$\left\{\sqrt{\dfrac{-\sqrt{3} + \sqrt{15}}{2}}, -\sqrt{\dfrac{-\sqrt{3} + \sqrt{15}}{2}}\right\}$

$\rightarrow \{1.04, -1.04\}$

66. $x^4 + \sqrt{2}x^2 - 2 = 0$

$\quad$ let $p = x^2 \rightarrow p^2 = x^4$

$\quad p^2 + \sqrt{2}p - 2 = 0$

$\quad p = \dfrac{-\sqrt{2} \pm \sqrt{2+8}}{2} = \dfrac{-\sqrt{2} \pm \sqrt{10}}{2}$

$\quad p = \dfrac{-\sqrt{2} + \sqrt{10}}{2}$

$\quad \rightarrow x^2 = \dfrac{-\sqrt{2} + \sqrt{10}}{2} \rightarrow x = \pm\sqrt{\dfrac{-\sqrt{2} + \sqrt{10}}{2}}$

$\quad$ or

$\quad p = \dfrac{-\sqrt{2} - \sqrt{10}}{2} \rightarrow x^2 = \dfrac{-\sqrt{2} - \sqrt{10}}{2}$

$\quad \rightarrow x = \pm\sqrt{\dfrac{-\sqrt{2} - \sqrt{10}}{2}}$

which is impossible since $\dfrac{-\sqrt{2} - \sqrt{10}}{2} < 0$

Check

$x = \sqrt{\dfrac{-\sqrt{2} + \sqrt{10}}{2}}$:

$\left(\sqrt{\dfrac{-\sqrt{2} + \sqrt{10}}{2}}\right)^4 + \sqrt{2}\left(\sqrt{\dfrac{-\sqrt{2} + \sqrt{10}}{2}}\right)^2 - 2 = 0$

$\left(\dfrac{-\sqrt{2} + \sqrt{10}}{2}\right)^2 + \sqrt{2}\left(\dfrac{-\sqrt{2} + \sqrt{10}}{2}\right) - 2 = 0$

$\left(\dfrac{2 - 2\sqrt{2}\sqrt{10} + 10}{4}\right) + \left(\dfrac{\sqrt{2}(-\sqrt{2}) + \sqrt{2}\sqrt{10}}{2}\right) - 2 = 0$

$\left(\dfrac{12 - 2\sqrt{20}}{4}\right) + \left(\dfrac{-2 + \sqrt{20}}{2}\right) - 2 = 0$

$\left(\dfrac{6 - \sqrt{20}}{2}\right) + \left(\dfrac{-2 + \sqrt{20}}{2}\right) - 2 = 0$

$\left(\dfrac{6 - \sqrt{20} - 2 + \sqrt{20}}{2}\right) - 2 = 0 \rightarrow 2 - 2 = 0 \rightarrow 0 = 0$

$x = -\sqrt{\dfrac{-\sqrt{2} + \sqrt{10}}{2}}$:

$\left(-\sqrt{\dfrac{-\sqrt{2} + \sqrt{10}}{2}}\right)^4 + \sqrt{2}\left(-\sqrt{\dfrac{-\sqrt{2} + \sqrt{10}}{2}}\right)^2 - 2 = 0$

$\left(\dfrac{-\sqrt{2} + \sqrt{10}}{2}\right)^2 + \sqrt{2}\left(\dfrac{-\sqrt{2} + \sqrt{10}}{2}\right) - 2 = 0$

$\left(\dfrac{2 - 2\sqrt{2}\sqrt{10} + 10}{4}\right) + \left(\dfrac{\sqrt{2}(-\sqrt{2}) + \sqrt{2}\sqrt{10}}{2}\right) - 2 = 0$

$\left(\dfrac{12 - 2\sqrt{20}}{4}\right) + \left(\dfrac{-2 + \sqrt{20}}{2}\right) - 2 = 0$

$\left(\dfrac{6 - \sqrt{20}}{2}\right) + \left(\dfrac{-2 + \sqrt{20}}{2}\right) - 2 = 0$

$\left(\dfrac{6 - \sqrt{20} - 2 + \sqrt{20}}{2}\right) - 2 = 0 \rightarrow 2 - 2 = 0 \rightarrow 0 = 0$

The solution set is

$$\left\{\sqrt{\dfrac{-\sqrt{2} + \sqrt{10}}{2}}, -\sqrt{\dfrac{-\sqrt{2} + \sqrt{10}}{2}}\right\}$$

$\rightarrow \{0.94, -0.94\}$

67. $\pi(1+t)^2 = \pi + 1 + t$

let $p = 1 + t \rightarrow p^2 = (1+t)^2$

$\pi p^2 = \pi + p \rightarrow \pi p^2 - p - \pi = 0$

$p = \dfrac{1 \pm \sqrt{1 + 4\pi^2}}{2\pi}$

$\rightarrow 1 + t = \dfrac{1 \pm \sqrt{1 + 4\pi^2}}{2\pi}$

$\rightarrow t = -1 + \dfrac{1 \pm \sqrt{1 + 4\pi^2}}{2\pi}$

$t = -1 + \dfrac{1 \pm \sqrt{1 + 4\pi^2}}{2\pi}$

Check

$t = -1 + \dfrac{1 + \sqrt{1 + 4\pi^2}}{2\pi}$:

$\pi\left(\dfrac{1 + \sqrt{1 + 4\pi^2}}{2\pi}\right)^2 = \pi + \dfrac{1 + \sqrt{1 + 4\pi^2}}{2\pi}$

$\pi\left(\dfrac{1 + 2\sqrt{1 + 4\pi^2} + 1 + 4\pi^2}{4\pi^2}\right) = \pi + \dfrac{1 + \sqrt{1 + 4\pi^2}}{2\pi}$

$\dfrac{2 + 2\sqrt{1 + 4\pi^2} + 4\pi^2}{4\pi} = \dfrac{2\pi^2 + 1 + \sqrt{1 + 4\pi^2}}{2\pi}$

$\dfrac{1 + \sqrt{1 + 4\pi^2} + 2\pi^2}{2\pi} = \dfrac{2\pi^2 + 1 + \sqrt{1 + 4\pi^2}}{2\pi}$

$0 = 0$

$t = -1 + \dfrac{1 - \sqrt{1 + 4\pi^2}}{2\pi}$:

$\pi\left(\dfrac{1 - \sqrt{1 + 4\pi^2}}{2\pi}\right)^2 = \pi + \dfrac{1 - \sqrt{1 + 4\pi^2}}{2\pi}$

$\pi\left(\dfrac{1 - 2\sqrt{1 + 4\pi^2} + 1 + 4\pi^2}{4\pi^2}\right) = \pi + \dfrac{1 - \sqrt{1 + 4\pi^2}}{2\pi}$

$\dfrac{2 - 2\sqrt{1 + 4\pi^2} + 4\pi^2}{4\pi} = \dfrac{2\pi^2 + 1 - \sqrt{1 + 4\pi^2}}{2\pi}$

$\dfrac{1 - \sqrt{1 + 4\pi^2} + 2\pi^2}{2\pi} = \dfrac{2\pi^2 + 1 - \sqrt{1 + 4\pi^2}}{2\pi}$

$0 = 0$

The solution set is

$\left\{ -1 + \dfrac{1 + \sqrt{1 + 4\pi^2}}{2\pi}, -1 + \dfrac{1 - \sqrt{1 + 4\pi^2}}{2\pi} \right\}$

$\rightarrow \{0.17, -1.85\}$

68. $\pi(1 + r)^2 = 2 + \pi(1 + r)$

let $p = 1 + r \rightarrow p^2 = (1 + r)^2$

$\pi p^2 = 2 + \pi p \rightarrow \pi p^2 - \pi p - 2 = 0$

$p = \dfrac{\pi \pm \sqrt{\pi^2 + 8\pi}}{2\pi}$ $\Bigg\} \rightarrow$

$p = \dfrac{\pi \pm \sqrt{\pi^2 + 8\pi}}{2\pi} \rightarrow 1 + r = \dfrac{\pi \pm \sqrt{\pi^2 + 8\pi}}{2\pi}$

$r = -1 + \dfrac{\pi \pm \sqrt{\pi^2 + 8\pi}}{2\pi}$

Check

$r = -1 + \dfrac{\pi + \sqrt{\pi^2 + 8\pi}}{2\pi}$:

$\pi\left(\dfrac{\pi + \sqrt{\pi^2 + 8\pi}}{2\pi}\right)^2 = 2 + \pi\left(\dfrac{\pi + \sqrt{\pi^2 + 8\pi}}{2\pi}\right)$

$\pi\left(\dfrac{\pi^2 + 2\pi\sqrt{\pi^2 + 8\pi} + \pi^2 + 8\pi}{4\pi^2}\right)$

$= 2 + \pi\left(\dfrac{\pi + \sqrt{\pi^2 + 8\pi}}{2\pi}\right)$

$\dfrac{2\pi^2 + 2\pi\sqrt{\pi^2 + 8\pi} + 8\pi}{4\pi} = 2 + \dfrac{\pi + \sqrt{\pi^2 + 8\pi}}{2}$

$\dfrac{\pi + \sqrt{\pi^2 + 8\pi} + 4}{2} = \dfrac{4 + \pi + \sqrt{\pi^2 + 8\pi}}{2}$

$0 = 0$

$r = -1 + \dfrac{\pi - \sqrt{\pi^2 + 8\pi}}{2\pi}$:

$\pi\left(\dfrac{\pi - \sqrt{\pi^2 + 8\pi}}{2\pi}\right)^2 = 2 + \pi\left(\dfrac{\pi - \sqrt{\pi^2 + 8\pi}}{2\pi}\right)$

$\pi\left(\dfrac{\pi^2 - 2\pi\sqrt{\pi^2 + 8\pi} + \pi^2 + 8\pi}{4\pi^2}\right) = 2 + \pi\left(\dfrac{\pi - \sqrt{\pi^2 + 8\pi}}{2\pi}\right)$

$\dfrac{2\pi^2 - 2\pi\sqrt{\pi^2 + 8\pi} + 8\pi}{4\pi} = 2 + \dfrac{\pi - \sqrt{\pi^2 + 8\pi}}{2}$

$\dfrac{\pi - \sqrt{\pi^2 + 8\pi} + 4}{2} = \dfrac{4 + \pi - \sqrt{\pi^2 + 8\pi}}{2}$

$0 = 0$

The solution set is

$$\left\{-1 + \dfrac{\pi + \sqrt{\pi^2 + 8\pi}}{2\pi}, -1 + \dfrac{\pi - \sqrt{\pi^2 + 8\pi}}{2\pi}\right\}$$

$\rightarrow \{0.44, -1.44\}$

69. $k^2 - k = 12 \rightarrow k^2 - k - 12 = 0$
$(k - 4)(k + 3) = 0$
$k = 4$ or $k = -3$

$\rightarrow \dfrac{x + 3}{x - 3} = 4$

$\rightarrow x + 3 = 4x - 12 \rightarrow x = 15$

or

$\dfrac{x + 3}{x - 3} = -3$

$\rightarrow x + 3 = -3x + 9 \rightarrow x = \dfrac{3}{2}$

and since neither of these x values causes a denominator to equal zero, the solution set is $\left\{\dfrac{3}{2}, 15\right\}$.

70. $k^2 - 3k = 28 \rightarrow k^2 - 3k - 28 = 0$

$(k + 4)(k - 7) = 0$
$k = -4$ or $k = 7$

$\rightarrow \dfrac{x + 3}{x - 4} = -4$

$\rightarrow x + 3 = -4x + 16 \rightarrow x = \dfrac{13}{5}$

or

$\dfrac{x + 3}{x - 4} = 7$

$\rightarrow x + 3 = 7x - 28 \rightarrow x = \dfrac{31}{6}$

and since neither of these x values causes a denominator to equal zero, the solution set is $\left\{\dfrac{13}{5}, \dfrac{31}{6}\right\}$.

71.   Graph the equations and to find the x-coordinate of the points of intersection:

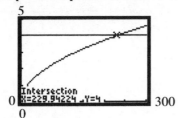

The distance to the water's surface is approximately 229.94 feet.

72.   Answers will vary, one example is $\sqrt{x+1} = -1$

73.   Answers will vary, one example is $x - \sqrt{x} - 2 = 0$

74.   Answers will vary.

Equations and Inequalities

1.5   Solving Inequalities

1. $[0, 2]$ $0 \le x \le 2$

2. $[2, \infty)$ $2 \le x < \infty$

3. $(-1, 2)$ $-1 < x < 2$

4. $(-\infty, 0]$ $-\infty < x \le 0$

5. $[0, 3)$ $0 \le x < 3$

6. $(-1, 1]$ $-1 < x \le 1$

(a) $6 < 8$
(b) $-2 < 0$
(c) $9 < 15$
(d) $-6 > -10$

(a) $5 > 4$
(b) $-3 > -4$
(c) $6 > 3$
(d) $-4 < -2$

9.   (a) $7 > 0$
      (b) $-1 > -8$
      (c) $12 > -9$
      (d) $-8 < 6$

10.   (a) $0 > -2$
      (b) $-8 > -10$
      (c) $-9 > -15$
      (d) $6 < 10$

11.   (a) $2x + 4 < 5$
      (b) $2x - 4 < -3$
      (c) $6x + 3 < 6$
      (d) $-4x - 2 > -4$

12.   (a) $4 - 2x > 8$
      (b) $-4 - 2x > 0$
      (c) $3 - 6x > 15$
      (d) $-2 + 4x < -10$

13. $[0, 4]$

14. $(-1, 5)$

15. $[4, 6)$

16. $(-2, 0)$

17. $[4, \infty)$

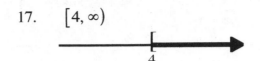

18. $(-\infty, 5]$

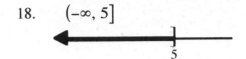

19. $(-\infty, -4)$

20. $(1, \infty)$

21. $2 \le x \le 5$

22. $1 < x < 2$

23. $-3 < x < -2$

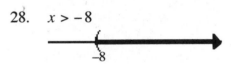

24. $0 \le x < 1$

25. $x \ge 4$

26. $x \le 2$

27. $x < -3$

28. $x > -8$

29.   If $x < 5$, then $x - 5 < 0$.

30.   If $x < -4$, then $x + 4 < 0$.

31.   If $x > -4$, then $x + 4 > 0$.

32.   If $x > 6$, then $x - 6 > 0$.

33.   If $x \ge -4$, then $3x \ge -12$.

34.   If $x \le 3$, then $2x \le 6$.

35.   If $x > 6$, then $-2x < -12$.

36.   If $x > -2$, then $-4x < 8$.

37.   If $x \ge 5$, then $-4x \le -20$.

38.   If $x \le -4$, then $-3x \ge 12$.

39.   If $2x > 6$, then $x > 3$.

40.   If $3x \le 12$, then $x \le 4$.

41.   If $-\dfrac{1}{2}x \le 3$, then $x \ge -6$.

42.   If $-\dfrac{1}{4}x > 1$, then $x < -4$.

43. $x + 1 < 5$

  $x + 1 - 1 < 5 - 1 \rightarrow x < 4$

  $\{x \mid x < 4\}$ or $(-\infty, 4)$

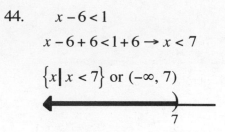

44. $x - 6 < 1$

  $x - 6 + 6 < 1 + 6 \rightarrow x < 7$

  $\{x \mid x < 7\}$ or $(-\infty, 7)$

45. $1 - 2x \leq 3$

  $-2x \leq 2 \rightarrow x \geq -1$

  $\{x \mid x \geq -1\}$ or $[-1, +\infty)$

46. $2 - 3x \leq 5$

  $-3x \leq 3 \rightarrow x \geq -1$

  $\{x \mid x \geq -1\}$ or $[-1, +\infty)$

47. $3x - 7 > 2$

  $3x > 9 \rightarrow x > 3$

  $\{x \mid x > 3\}$ or $(3, +\infty)$

48. $2x + 5 > 1$

  $2x > -4 \rightarrow x > -2$

  $\{x \mid x > -2\}$ or $(-2, +\infty)$

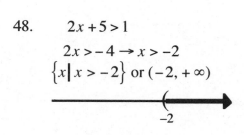

49. $3x - 1 \geq 3 + x$

  $2x \geq 4 \rightarrow x \geq 2$

  $\{x \mid x \geq 2\}$ or $[2, +\infty)$

50. $2x - 2 \geq 3 + x$

  $x \geq 5$

  $x \geq 5$

  $\{x \mid x \geq 5\}$ or $[5, +\infty)$

51. $-2(x + 3) < 8$

  $-2x - 6 < 8$

  $-2x < 14$

  $x > -7$

  $\{x \mid x > -7\}$ or $(-7, +\infty)$

52. $-3(1 - x) < 12$

  $-3 + 3x < 12$

  $3x < 15$

  $x < 5$

  $\{x \mid x < 5\}$ or $(-\infty, 5)$

53.

$$4 - 3(1 - x) \le 3$$
$$4 - 3 + 3x \le 3$$
$$3x + 1 \le 3$$
$$3x \le 2$$
$$x \le \frac{2}{3}$$
$$\left\{ x \,\middle|\, x \le \frac{2}{3} \right\} \text{ or } \left(-\infty, \frac{2}{3} \right]$$

54.

$$8 - 4(2 - x) \le -2x$$
$$8 - 8 + 4x \le -2x$$
$$4x \le -2x$$
$$6x \le 0$$
$$x \le 0$$
$$\left\{ x \,\middle|\, x \le 0 \right\} \text{ or } (-\infty, 0]$$

55.

$$\frac{1}{2}(x - 4) > x + 8$$
$$\frac{1}{2}x - 2 > x + 8$$
$$-\frac{1}{2}x > 10$$
$$x < -20$$
$$\left\{ x \,\middle|\, x < -20 \right\} \text{ or } (-\infty, -20)$$

56.

$$3x + 4 > \frac{1}{3}(x - 2)$$
$$3x + 4 > \frac{1}{3}x - \frac{2}{3}$$
$$9x + 12 > x - 2$$
$$8x > -14$$
$$x > -\frac{7}{4}$$
$$\left\{ x \,\middle|\, x > -\frac{7}{4} \right\} \text{ or } \left(-\frac{7}{4}, \infty \right)$$

57.

$$\frac{x}{2} \ge 1 - \frac{x}{4}$$
$$2x \ge 4 - x$$
$$3x \ge 4$$
$$x \ge \frac{4}{3}$$
$$\left\{ x \,\middle|\, x \ge \frac{4}{3} \right\} \text{ or } \left[\frac{4}{3}, +\infty \right)$$

58.

$$\frac{x}{3} \ge 2 + \frac{x}{6}$$
$$2x \ge 12 + x$$
$$x \ge 12$$
$$\left\{ x \,\middle|\, x \ge 12 \right\} \text{ or } \left[12, +\infty \right)$$

59.

$$0 \leq 2x - 6 \leq 4$$
$$6 \leq 2x \leq 10$$
$$3 \leq x \leq 5$$
$$\{x \mid 3 \leq x \leq 5\} \text{ or } [3, 5]$$

60.

$$4 \leq 2x + 2 \leq 10$$
$$2 \leq 2x \leq 8$$
$$1 \leq x \leq 4$$
$$\{x \mid 1 \leq x \leq 4\} \text{ or } [1, 4]$$

61.

$$-5 \leq 4 - 3x \leq 2$$
$$-9 \leq -3x \leq -2$$
$$3 \geq x \geq \frac{2}{3}$$
$$\left\{x \mid \frac{2}{3} \leq x \leq 3\right\} \text{ or } \left[\frac{2}{3}, 3\right]$$

62.

$$-3 \leq 3 - 2x \leq 9$$
$$-6 \leq -2x \leq 6$$
$$3 \geq x \geq -3$$
$$\{x \mid -3 \leq x \leq 3\} \text{ or } [-3, 3]$$

63.

$$-3 < \frac{2x - 1}{4} < 0$$
$$-12 < 2x - 1 < 0$$
$$-11 < 2x < 1$$
$$\frac{-11}{2} < x < \frac{1}{2}$$
$$\left\{x \mid -\frac{11}{2} < x < \frac{1}{2}\right\} \text{ or } \left(-\frac{11}{2}, \frac{1}{2}\right)$$

64.

$$0 < \frac{3x + 2}{2} < 4$$
$$0 < 3x + 2 < 8$$
$$-2 < 3x < 6$$
$$-\frac{2}{3} < x < 2$$
$$\left\{x \mid -\frac{2}{3} < x < 2\right\} \text{ or } \left(-\frac{2}{3}, 2\right)$$

65.

$$1 < 1 - \frac{1}{2}x < 4$$
$$0 < -\frac{1}{2}x < 3$$
$$0 > x > -6$$
$$\{x \mid -6 < x < 0\} \text{ or } (-6, 0)$$

66.

$$0 < 1 - \frac{1}{3}x < 1$$
$$-1 < -\frac{1}{3}x < 0$$
$$3 > x > 0$$
$$\{x \mid 0 < x < 3\} \text{ or } (0, 3)$$

67.
$$(x+2)(x-3) > (x-1)(x+1)$$
$$x^2 - x - 6 > x^2 - 1$$
$$-x - 6 > -1$$
$$-x > 5$$
$$x < -5$$
$$\{x \mid x < -5\} \text{ or } (-\infty, -5)$$

68.
$$(x-1)(x+1) > (x-3)(x+4)$$
$$x^2 - 1 > x^2 + x - 12$$
$$-1 > x - 12$$
$$-x > -11$$
$$x < 11$$
$$\{x \mid x < 11\} \text{ or } (-\infty, 11)$$

69.
$$x(4x+3) \le (2x+1)^2$$
$$4x^2 + 3x \le 4x^2 + 4x + 1$$
$$3x \le 4x + 1$$
$$-x \le 1$$
$$x \ge -1$$
$$\{x \mid x \ge -1\} \text{ or } [-1, +\infty)$$

70.
$$x(9x-5) \le (3x-1)^2$$
$$9x^2 - 5x \le 9x^2 - 6x + 1$$
$$-5x \le -6x + 1$$
$$x \le 1$$
$$\{x \mid x \le 1\} \text{ or } (-\infty, 1)$$

71.
$$\frac{1}{2} \le \frac{x+1}{3} < \frac{3}{4}$$
$$6 \le 4x + 4 < 9$$
$$2 \le 4x < 5$$
$$\frac{1}{2} \le x < \frac{5}{4}$$
$$\left\{x \mid \frac{1}{2} \le x < \frac{5}{4}\right\} \text{ or } \left[\frac{1}{2}, \frac{5}{4}\right)$$

72.
$$\frac{1}{3} < \frac{x+1}{2} \le \frac{2}{3}$$
$$2 < 3x + 3 \le 4$$
$$-1 < 3x \le 1$$
$$-\frac{1}{3} < x \le \frac{1}{3}$$
$$\left\{x \mid -\frac{1}{3} < x \le \frac{1}{3}\right\} \text{ or } \left(-\frac{1}{3}, \frac{1}{3}\right]$$

73.
$$(4x+2)^{-1} < 0$$
$$\frac{1}{4x+2} < 0 \rightarrow 4x + 2 < 0$$
$$x < -\frac{1}{2}$$
$$\left\{x \mid x < -\frac{1}{2}\right\} \text{ or } \left(-\infty, -\frac{1}{2}\right)$$

74.
$$(2x+1)^{-1} > 0$$
$$\frac{1}{2x+1} > 0 \rightarrow 2x + 1 > 0$$
$$x > -\frac{1}{2}$$
$$\left\{x \mid x > -\frac{1}{2}\right\} \text{ or } \left(-\frac{1}{2}, +\infty\right)$$

149

75.

$$0 < \frac{2}{x} < \frac{3}{5} \rightarrow 0 < \frac{2}{x} \quad \text{and} \quad \frac{2}{x} < \frac{3}{5}$$

$$0 < \frac{2}{x} \rightarrow x > 0 \quad \text{therefore} \quad \frac{2}{x} < \frac{3}{5} \rightarrow 10 < 3x \rightarrow \frac{10}{3} < x$$

$$\left\{ x \,\middle|\, \frac{10}{3} < x \right\} \text{ or } \left(\frac{10}{3}, +\infty \right)$$

10/3

76.

$$0 < \frac{4}{x} < \frac{2}{3} \rightarrow 0 < \frac{4}{x} \quad \text{and} \quad \frac{4}{x} < \frac{2}{3}$$

$$0 < \frac{4}{x} \rightarrow x > 0 \quad \text{therefore} \quad \frac{4}{x} < \frac{2}{3} \rightarrow 12 < 2x \rightarrow 6 < x$$

$$\left\{ x \,\middle|\, 6 < x \right\} \text{ or } (6, +\infty)$$

6

77.

$$0 < (2x - 4)^{-1} < \frac{1}{2} \rightarrow 0 < \frac{1}{2x - 4} \quad \text{and} \quad \frac{1}{2x - 4} < \frac{1}{2}$$

$$0 < \frac{1}{2x - 4} \rightarrow 2x - 4 > 0 \quad \text{therefore} \quad \frac{1}{2x - 4} < \frac{1}{2} \rightarrow 2 < 2x - 4 \rightarrow 3 < x$$

$$\left\{ x \,\middle|\, 3 < x \right\} \text{ or } (3, +\infty)$$
3

78.

$$0 < (3x + 6)^{-1} < \frac{1}{3} \rightarrow 0 < \frac{1}{3x + 6} < \frac{1}{3} \rightarrow 0 < \frac{1}{3x + 6} \quad \text{and} \quad \frac{1}{3x + 6} < \frac{1}{3}$$

$$0 < \frac{1}{3x + 6} \rightarrow 3x + 6 > 0 \quad \text{therefore} \quad \frac{1}{3x + 6} < \frac{1}{3} \rightarrow 3 < 3x + 6 \rightarrow -1 < x$$

$$\left\{ x \,\middle|\, -1 < x \right\} \text{ or } (-1, +\infty)$$

-1

79.   If $-1 < x < 1$, then $3 < x + 4 < 5 \rightarrow a = 3, b = 5$

80.   If $-3 < x < 2$, then $-9 < x - 6 < -4 \rightarrow a = -9, b = -4$

81.   If $2 < x < 3$, then $-12 < -4x < -8 \rightarrow a = -12, b = -8$

82.   If $-4 < x < 0$, then $-2 < \dfrac{1}{2}x < 0 \rightarrow a = -2, b = 0$

83.   If $0 < x < 4$, then $0 < 2x < 8 \rightarrow 3 < 2x + 3 < 11 \rightarrow a = 3, b = 11$

84.
If $-3 < x < 3$, then $6 > -2x > -6 \rightarrow 7 > 1 - 2x > -5$
$\rightarrow -5 < 1 - 2x < 7 \rightarrow a = -5, b = 7$

85.
If $-3 < x < 0$, then $1 < x + 4 < 4$
$\rightarrow 1 > \dfrac{1}{x+4} > \dfrac{1}{4} \rightarrow \dfrac{1}{4} < \dfrac{1}{x+4} < 1 \rightarrow a = \dfrac{1}{4}, b = 1$

86.
If $2 < x < 4$, then $-4 < x - 6 < -2$
$\rightarrow -\dfrac{1}{4} > \dfrac{1}{x-6} > -\dfrac{1}{2} \rightarrow -\dfrac{1}{2} < \dfrac{1}{x-6} < -\dfrac{1}{4} \rightarrow a = -\dfrac{1}{2}, b = -\dfrac{1}{4}$

87.   If $6 < 3x < 12$, then $2 < x < 4 \rightarrow 4 < x^2 < 16 \rightarrow a = 4, b = 16$

88.   If $0 < 2x < 6$, then $0 < x < 3 \rightarrow 0 < x^2 < 9 \rightarrow a = 0, b = 9$

89.   We need $3x + 6 \geq 0 \rightarrow 3x \geq -6 \rightarrow x \geq -2$, so the domain is $\{x | x \geq -2\}$.

90.   We need $8 + 2x \geq 0 \rightarrow 2x \geq -8 \rightarrow x \geq -4$, so the domain is $\{x | x \geq -4\}$

91. $21 <$ young adult's age < 30

92. $40 \leq$ middle-aged < 60

93.   (a)   An average 25-year-old male can expect to live at least 48.4 more years.
            $25 + 48.4 = 73.4$. Therefore, the average age of a 25-year-old male will be
            ≥ 73.4.
      (b)   An average 25-year-old female can expect to live at least 54.7 more years.
            $25 + 54.7 = 79.7$. Therefore, the average age of a 25-year-old female will be
            ≥ 79.7.
      (c)   By the given information, a female can expect to live 6.3 years longer.

94. $V = 20T$

$$80° \le T \le 120° \rightarrow 80° \le \frac{V}{20} \le 120°$$

$1600 \le V \le 2400$

The volume ranges from 1600 to 2400 cubic centimeters.

95.   Let P represent the selling price and C represent the commission.
Calculating the commission:
$C = 45,000 + 0.25(P - 900,000) = 45,000 + 0.25P - 225,000 = 0.25P - 180,000$
Calculate the commission range, given the price range:

$$900,000 \le \qquad P \qquad \le 1,100,000$$
$$0.25(900,000) \le \quad 0.25P \quad \le 0.25(1,100,000)$$
$$225,000 \le \quad 0.25P \quad \le 275,000$$
$$225,000 - 180,000 \le 0.25P - 180,000 \le 275,000 - 180,000$$
$$45,000 \le \qquad C \qquad \le 95,000$$

The agent's commission ranges from $45,000 to $95,000, inclusive.

$$\frac{45,000}{900,000} = 0.05 = 5\% \quad \text{to} \quad \frac{95,000}{1,100,000} = 0.086 = 8.6\%, \text{ inclusive.}$$

As a percent of selling price, the commission ranges from 5% to 8.6%.

96.   Let C represent the commission.
Calculate the commission range:

$$25 + 0.4(70) \le C \le 25 + 0.4(300)$$
$$53 \le C \le 145$$

The commission varies between $53 and $145.

97.   Let W represent the weekly wage and T represent the withholding tax.
Calculating the tax:
$T = 69.90 + 0.28(W - 517) = 69.90 + 0.28W - 144.76 = 0.28W - 74.86$
Calculating the withholding tax range, given the range of weekly wages:

$$525 \le \qquad W \qquad \le 600$$
$$0.28(525) \le \quad 0.28W \quad \le 0.28(600)$$
$$147 \le \quad 0.28W \quad \le 168$$
$$147 - 74.86 \le 0.28W - 74.86 \le 168 - 74.86$$
$$72.14 \le \qquad T \qquad \le 93.14$$

The amount of withholding tax ranges from $72.14 to $93.14, inclusive.

98.   Let W represent the weekly wage and T represent the withholding tax.
Calculating the tax:
$T = 69.90 + 0.28(W - 517) = 69.90 + 0.28W - 144.76 = 0.28W - 74.86$
Calculating the withholding tax range, given the range of weekly wages:

$$600 \le \qquad W \qquad \le 700$$
$$0.28(600) \le \quad 0.28W \quad \le 0.28(700)$$
$$168 \le \quad 0.28W \quad \le 196$$
$$168 - 74.86 \le 0.28W - 74.86 \le 196 - 74.86$$
$$93.14 \le \qquad T \qquad \le 121.14$$

The amount of withholding tax ranges from $93.14 to $121.14, inclusive.

99.   Let K represent the monthly usage in kilowatt-hours.
      Let C represent the monthly customer bill.
      Calculating the bill:
$$C = 0.10494K + 9.36$$
      Calculating the range of kilowatt-hours, given the range of bills:
$$80.24 \leq \quad\quad C \quad\quad \leq 271.80$$
$$80.24 \leq 0.10494K + 9.36 \leq 271.80$$
$$70.88 \leq \quad 0.10494K \quad \leq 262.44$$
$$675.43 \leq \quad\quad K \quad\quad \leq 2500.86$$
      The range of usage in kilowatt-hours varied from 675.43 to 2500.86.

100. Let W represent the amount of water used.
      Let C represent the customer charge.
      Calculating the charge:
$$C = 21.60 + 1.70(W - 12) = 21.60 + 1.70W - 20.40 = 1.70W + 1.20$$
      Calculating the range of water usage, given the range of charges:
$$28.40 \leq \quad C \quad \leq 65.75$$
$$28.40 \leq 1.70W + 1.20 \leq 65.75$$
$$27.20 \leq \quad 1.70W \quad \leq 64.55$$
$$16 \leq \quad\quad W \quad\quad \leq 37.97$$
      The range of water usage varied from 16,000 to 38,000 gallons.

101. Let C represent the dealer's cost and M represent the markup over dealer's cost.
      If the price is $8800, then $8800 = C + MC = C(1 + M)$
      Solving for C: $C = \dfrac{8800}{1 + M}$
      Calculating the range of dealer costs, given the range of markups:
$$0.12 \leq \quad M \quad \leq 0.18$$
$$1.12 \leq 1 + M \leq 1.18$$
$$\frac{1}{1.12} \geq \frac{1}{1 + M} \geq \frac{1}{1.18}$$
$$\frac{8800}{1.12} \geq \frac{8800}{1 + M} \geq \frac{8800}{1.18}$$
$$7857.14 \geq \quad C \quad \geq 7457.63$$
      The dealer's cost ranged from $7457.63 to $7857.14, inclusive.

102. Let T represent the test scores of the people in the top 2.5%.
$$T > 1.96(12) + 100 = 123.52$$
      People in the top 2.5% will have test scores greater than 123.52.

103. Let T represent the score on the last test and G represent the course grade.
      Calculating the course grade and solving for the last test:
$$G = \frac{68 + 82 + 87 + 89 + T}{5} = \frac{326 + T}{5} \rightarrow T = 5G - 326$$
      Calculating the range of scores on the last test, given the grade range:

$$80 \le \quad G \quad < 90$$
$$400 \le \quad 5G \quad < 450$$
$$74 \le 5G - 326 < 124$$
$$74 \le \quad T \quad < 124$$

The fifth test must be greater than or equal to 74.

104. Let T represent the score on the last test and G represent the course grade.
Calculating the course grade and solving for the last test:
$$G = \frac{68 + 82 + 87 + 89 + 2T}{6} = \frac{326 + 2T}{6} = \frac{163 + T}{3}$$
$$T = 3G - 163$$
Calculating the range of scores on the last test, given the grade range:
$$80 \le \quad G \quad < 90$$
$$240 \le \quad 3G \quad < 270$$
$$77 \le 3G - 163 < 107$$
$$77 \le \quad T \quad < 107$$

The fifth test must be greater than or equal to 77 to get a B.

105. Since $a < b$

$$\frac{a}{2} < \frac{b}{2} \qquad\qquad \frac{a}{2} < \frac{b}{2}$$
$$\frac{a}{2} + \frac{a}{2} < \frac{a}{2} + \frac{b}{2} \qquad \frac{a}{2} + \frac{b}{2} < \frac{b}{2} + \frac{b}{2} \qquad \text{Thus, } a < \frac{a+b}{2} < b$$
$$a < \frac{a+b}{2} \qquad\qquad \frac{a+b}{2} < b$$

106. $$\frac{a+b}{2} - a = \frac{a+b-2a}{2} = \frac{b-a}{2}$$
$$b - \frac{a+b}{2} = \frac{2b-a-b}{2} = \frac{b-a}{2}$$
$$\therefore \ \frac{a+b}{2} \text{ is equidistant from } a \text{ and } b.$$

107. If $0 < a < b$, then $0 < a^2 < ab$ and $0 < ab < b^2$
$$ab - a^2 > 0 \qquad\qquad b^2 - ab > 0$$
$$ab > a^2 > 0 \qquad\qquad b^2 > ab > 0$$
$$\left(\sqrt{ab}\right)^2 > a^2 \qquad\qquad b^2 > \left(\sqrt{ab}\right)^2$$
$$\sqrt{ab} > a \qquad\qquad b > \sqrt{ab}$$
Thus, $a < \sqrt{ab} < b$

108. Show that $\sqrt{ab} < \frac{a+b}{2}$.
$$\frac{a+b}{2} - \sqrt{ab} = \frac{1}{2}\left(a - 2\sqrt{ab} + b\right) = \frac{1}{2}\left(\sqrt{a} - \sqrt{b}\right)^2 > 0 \quad \text{Therefore, } \sqrt{ab} < \frac{a+b}{2}.$$

109. For $0 < a < b$, $\dfrac{1}{h} = \dfrac{1}{2}\left(\dfrac{1}{a} + \dfrac{1}{b}\right)$

$$h \cdot \dfrac{1}{h} = \dfrac{1}{2}\left(\dfrac{b+a}{ab}\right) \cdot h \quad \rightarrow \quad 1 = \dfrac{1}{2}\left(\dfrac{b+a}{ab}\right) \cdot h \quad \rightarrow \quad \dfrac{2ab}{a+b} = h$$

$$
\begin{aligned}
h - a &= \dfrac{2ab}{a+b} - a \\
&= \dfrac{2ab - a(a+b)}{a+b} \\
&= \dfrac{2ab - a^2 - ab}{a+b} \\
&= \dfrac{ab - a^2}{a+b} \\
&= \dfrac{a(b-a)}{a+b} > 0
\end{aligned}
\qquad
\begin{aligned}
b - h &= b - \dfrac{2ab}{a+b} \\
&= \dfrac{b(a+b) - 2ab}{a+b} \\
&= \dfrac{ab + b^2 - 2ab}{a+b} \\
&= \dfrac{b^2 - ab}{a+b} \\
&= \dfrac{b(b-a)}{a+b} > 0
\end{aligned}
$$

Therefore, $h > a$. \qquad Therefore, $h < b$. \qquad Thus, $a < h < b$.

110. Show that $h = \dfrac{(\text{geometric mean})^2}{\text{arithmetic mean}} = \dfrac{\left(\sqrt{ab}\right)^2}{\left(\dfrac{1}{2}(a+b)\right)}$

From Problem 109 we know:

$$\dfrac{1}{h} = \dfrac{1}{2}\left(\dfrac{1}{a} + \dfrac{1}{b}\right)$$

$$\dfrac{2}{h} = \dfrac{1}{a} + \dfrac{1}{b} = \dfrac{b+a}{ab}$$

$$\dfrac{h}{2} = \dfrac{ab}{a+b}$$

$$h = 2 \cdot \dfrac{ab}{a+b} = \dfrac{\left(\sqrt{ab}\right)^2}{\left(\dfrac{1}{2}(a+b)\right)}$$

111. Answers will vary.

112. $x^2 + 1$ is a positive number. Therefore it cannot be less than a negative number.

Equations and Inequalities

1.6   Equations and Inequalities Involving Absolute Value

1. $|2x| = 6$
  $2x = 6$ or $2x = -6$
  $x = 3$ or $x = -3$
  The solution set is $\{-3, 3\}$.

2. $|3x| = 12$
  $3x = 12$ or $3x = -12$
  $x = 4$ or $x = -4$
  The solution set is $\{-4, 4\}$.

3. $|2x + 3| = 5$
  $2x + 3 = 5$ or $2x + 3 = -5$
  $2x = 2$ or $2x = -8$
  $x = 1$ or $x = -4$
  The solution set is $\{-4, 1\}$.

4. $|3x - 1| = 2$
  $3x - 1 = 2$ or $3x - 1 = -2$
  $3x = 3$ or $3x = -1$
  $x = 1$ or $x = -\dfrac{1}{3}$
  The solution set is $\left\{-\dfrac{1}{3}, 1\right\}$.

5. $|1 - 4t| + 8 = 13 \rightarrow |1 - 4t| = 5$
  $1 - 4t = 5$ or $1 - 4t = -5$
  $-4t = 4$ or $-4t = -6$
  $t = -1$ or $t = \dfrac{3}{2}$
  The solution set is $\left\{-1, \dfrac{3}{2}\right\}$.

6. $|1 - 2z| + 6 = 9 \rightarrow |1 - 2z| = 3$
  $1 - 2z = 3$ or $1 - 2z = -3$
  $-2z = 2$ or $-2z = -4$
  $z = -1$ or $z = 2$
  The solution set is $\{-1, 2\}$.

7. $|-2x| = 8$
  $-2x = 8$ or $-2x = -8$
  $x = -4$ or $x = 4$
  The solution set is $\{-4, 4\}$.

8. $|-x| = |1|$
  $-x = 1$ or $-x = -1$
  The solution set is $\{-1, 1\}$.

9. $|-2|x = 4$
  $2x = 4 \rightarrow x = 2$
  The solution set is $\{2\}$.

10. $|3|x = 9$
  $3x = 9 \rightarrow x = 3$
  The solution set is $\{3\}$.

11. $\dfrac{2}{3}|x| = 9$
  $|x| = \dfrac{27}{2} \rightarrow x = \dfrac{27}{2}$ or $x = -\dfrac{27}{2}$
  The solution set is $\left\{-\dfrac{27}{2}, \dfrac{27}{2}\right\}$.

12. $\dfrac{3}{4}|x| = 9$
  $|x| = 12 \rightarrow x = 12$ or $x = -12$
  The solution set is $\{-12, 12\}$.

13. $\left|\dfrac{x}{3} + \dfrac{2}{5}\right| = 2$

$\dfrac{x}{3} + \dfrac{2}{5} = 2$ or $\dfrac{x}{3} + \dfrac{2}{5} = -2$

$5x + 6 = 30$ or $5x + 6 = -30$

$5x = 24$ or $5x = -36$

$x = \dfrac{24}{5}$ or $x = -\dfrac{36}{5}$

The solution set is $\left\{-\dfrac{36}{5}, \dfrac{24}{5}\right\}$.

14. $\left|\dfrac{x}{2} - \dfrac{1}{3}\right| = 1$

$\dfrac{x}{2} - \dfrac{1}{3} = 1$ or $\dfrac{x}{2} - \dfrac{1}{3} = -1$

$3x - 2 = 6$ or $3x - 2 = -6$

$3x = 8$ or $3x = -4$

$x = \dfrac{8}{3}$ or $x = -\dfrac{4}{3}$

The solution set is $\left\{-\dfrac{4}{3}, \dfrac{8}{3}\right\}$.

15. $\left|u - 2\right| = -\dfrac{1}{2}$

impossible, since absolute value always yields a non-negative number.

16. $\left|2 - v\right| = -1$

impossible, since absolute value always yields a non-negative number.

17. $4 - \left|2x\right| = 3 \rightarrow -\left|2x\right| = -1$

$\rightarrow \left|2x\right| = 1$

$2x = 1$ or $2x = -1$

$x = \dfrac{1}{2}$ or $x = -\dfrac{1}{2}$

The solution set is $\left\{-\dfrac{1}{2}, \dfrac{1}{2}\right\}$.

18. $5 - \left|\dfrac{1}{2}x\right| = 3 \rightarrow -\left|\dfrac{1}{2}x\right| = -2$

$\rightarrow \left|\dfrac{1}{2}x\right| = 2$

$\dfrac{1}{2}x = 2$ or $\dfrac{1}{2}x = -2$

$x = 4$ or $x = -4$

The solution set is $\{-4, 4\}$.

19. $\left|x^2 - 9\right| = 0$

$x^2 - 9 = 0$

$x^2 = 9$

$x = \pm 3$

The solution set is $\{-3, 3\}$.

20. $\left|x^2 - 16\right| = 0$

$x^2 - 16 = 0$

$x^2 = 16$

$x = \pm 4$

The solution set is $\{-4, 4\}$.

21. $\left|x^2 - 2x\right| = 3$

$x^2 - 2x = 3$ or $x^2 - 2x = -3$

$x^2 - 2x - 3 = 0$ or $x^2 - 2x + 3 = 0$

$(x - 3)(x + 1) = 0$

or $x = \dfrac{2 \pm \sqrt{4 - 12}}{2} = \dfrac{2 \pm \sqrt{-8}}{2}$

$x = 3, x = -1$ or $\rightarrow$ no real solution

The solution set is $\{-1, 3\}$.

22. $\left|x^2 + x\right| = 12$

$x^2 + x = 12$ or $x^2 + x = -12$

$x^2 + x - 12 = 0$ or $x^2 + x + 12 = 0$

$(x - 3)(x + 4) = 0$ or $x = \dfrac{-1 \pm \sqrt{1 - 48}}{2} = \dfrac{1 \pm \sqrt{-47}}{2}$

$x = 3, x = -4$ or no real solution

The solution set is $\{-4, 3\}$.

23. $\left|x^2 + x - 1\right| = 1$

$x^2 + x - 1 = 1$ or $x^2 + x - 1 = -1$

$x^2 + x - 2 = 0$ or $x^2 + x = 0$

$(x - 1)(x + 2) = 0$ or $x(x + 1) = 0$

$x = 1, x = -2$ or $x = 0, x = -1$

The solution set is $\{-2, -1, 0, 1\}$.

24. $\left|x^2 + 3x - 2\right| = 2$

$x^2 + 3x - 2 = 2$ or $x^2 + 3x - 2 = -2$

$x^2 + 3x = 4$ or $x^2 + 3x = 0$

$x^2 + 3x - 4 = 0$ or $x(x + 3) = 0$

$(x + 4)(x - 1) = 0$ or $x = 0, x = -3$

$x = -4, x = 1$

The solution set is $\{-4, -3, 0, 1\}$.

25. $|2x| < 8$

$-8 < 2x < 8$

$-4 < x < 4$

$\{x | -4 < x < 4\}$ or $(-4, 4)$

26. $|3x| < 15$

$-15 < 3x < 15$

$-5 < x < 5$

$\{x | -5 < x < 5\}$ or $(-5, 5)$

27. $|3x| > 12$

$3x < -12$ or $3x > 12$

$x < -4$ or $x > 4$

$\{x | x < -4 \text{ or } x > 4\}$ or

$(-\infty, -4) \cup (4, +\infty)$

28. $|2x| > 6$

$2x < -6$ or $2x > 6$

$x < -3$ or $x > 3$

$\{x | x < -3 \text{ or } x > 3\}$ or

$(-\infty, -3) \cup (3, +\infty)$

158

29. $|x-2|+2<3$
$|x-2|<1$
$-1<x-2<1$
$1<x<3$
$\{x|1<x<3\}$ or $(1,3)$

30. $|x+4|+3<5$
$|x+4|<2$
$-2<x+4<2$
$-6<x<-2$
$\{x|-6<x<-2\}$ or $(-6,-2)$

31. $|3t-2|\le 4$
$-4\le 3t-2\le 4$
$-2\le \ 3t \ \le 6$
$-\dfrac{2}{3}\le \ t \ \le 2$
$\left\{t\left|-\dfrac{2}{3}\le t\le 2\right.\right\}$ or $\left[-\dfrac{2}{3},2\right]$

32. $|2u+5|\le 7$
$-7\le 2u+5\le 7$
$-12\le \ 2u \ \le 2$
$-6\le \ u \ \le 1$
$\{u|-6\le u\le 1\}$ or $[-6,1]$

33. $|x-3|\ge 2$
$x-3\le -2$ or $x-3\ge 2$
$x\le 1$ or $x\ge 5$
$\{x|x\le 1 \text{ or } x\ge 5\}$
or $(-\infty,1]\cup[5,\infty)$

34. $|x+4|\ge 2$
$x+4\le -2$ or $x+4\ge 2$
$x\le -6$ or $x\ge -2$
$\{x|x\le -6 \text{ or } x\ge -2\}$
or $(-\infty,-6]\cup[-2,\infty)$

35. $|1-4x|-7<-2$
$|1-4x|<5$
$-5<1-4x<5$
$-6<-4x<4$
$-1<x<\dfrac{3}{2}$
$\left\{x\left|-1<x<\dfrac{3}{2}\right.\right\}$ or $\left(-1,\dfrac{3}{2}\right)$

36. $|1-2x|-4<-1$
$|1-2x|<3$
$-3<1-2x<3$
$-4<-2x<2$
$-1<x<2$
$\{x|-1<x<2\}$ or $(-1,2)$

37. $|1 - 2x| > 3$

    $1 - 2x < -3$ or $1 - 2x > 3$

    $-2x < -4$ or $-2x > 2$

    $x > 2$ or $x < -1$

  $\{x \mid x < -1 \text{ or } x > 2\}$ or $(-\infty, -1) \cup (2, \infty)$

38. $|2 - 3x| > 1$

    $2 - 3x < -1$ or $2 - 3x > 1$

    $-3x < -3$ or $-3x > -1$

    $x > 1$ or $x < \dfrac{1}{3}$

  $\left\{x \mid x < \dfrac{1}{3} \text{ or } x > 1\right\}$ or $\left(-\infty, \tfrac{1}{3}\right) \cup (1, \infty)$

39. $|-4x| + |-5| \le 1$

  $|4x| + 5 \le 1$

  $|4x| \le -4$

but this is impossible since absolute value always yields a non-negative number.

40. $|-x| - |4| \le 2$

  $|x| - 4 \le 2$

  $|x| \le 6$

  $-6 \le x \le 6$

  $\{x \mid -6 \le x \le 6\}$ or $[-6, 6]$

41. $|-2x| > |-3|$

  $|2x| > 3$

    $2x < -3$ or $2x > 3$

    $x < -\dfrac{3}{2}$ or $x > \dfrac{3}{2}$

  $\left\{x \mid x < -\dfrac{3}{2} \text{ or } x > \dfrac{3}{2}\right\}$

or $\left(-\infty, -\dfrac{3}{2}\right) \cup \left(\dfrac{3}{2}, +\infty\right)$

42. $|-x - 2| \ge 1$

    $-x - 2 \le -1$ or $-x - 2 \ge 1$

    $-x \le 1$ or $-x \ge 3$

    $x \ge -1$ or $x \le -3$

  $\{x \mid x \le -3 \text{ or } x \ge -1\}$ or

  $(-\infty, -3] \cup [-1, +\infty)$

43. $-|2x - 1| \ge -3$

    $|2x - 1| \le 3$

  $-3 \le 2x - 1 \le 3$

  $-2 \le 2x \le 4$

  $-1 \le x \le 2$

  $\{x \mid -1 \le x \le 2\}$ or $[-1, 2]$

44. $-|1 - 2x| \ge -3$

    $|1 - 2x| \le 3$

  $-3 \le 1 - 2x \le 3$

  $-4 \le -2x \le 2$

  $-1 \le x \le 2$

  $\{x \mid -1 \le x \le 2\}$ or $[-1, 2]$

45.
$$|x-1| < 3 \rightarrow -3 < x-1 < 3$$
$$\rightarrow -2 < x < 4$$
$$\rightarrow 2 < x+4 < 8$$
$$\rightarrow a = 2, b = 8$$

46
$$|x+2| < 5 \rightarrow -5 < x+2 < 5$$
$$\rightarrow -7 < x < 3$$
$$\rightarrow -9 < x-2 < 1$$
$$\rightarrow a = -9, b = 1$$

47.
$$|x+4| \le 2 \rightarrow -2 \le x+4 \le 2$$
$$\rightarrow -6 \le x \le -2$$
$$\rightarrow -12 \le 2x \le -4$$
$$\rightarrow -15 \le 2x-3 \le -7$$
$$\rightarrow a = -15, b = -7$$

48.
$$|x-3| \le 1 \rightarrow -1 \le x-3 \le 1$$
$$\rightarrow 2 \le x \le 4$$
$$\rightarrow 6 \le 3x \le 12$$
$$\rightarrow 7 \le 3x+1 \le 13$$
$$\rightarrow a = 7, b = 13$$

49.
$$|x-2| \le 7 \rightarrow -7 \le x-2 \le 7$$
$$\rightarrow -5 \le x \le 9$$
$$\rightarrow -15 \le x-10 \le -1$$
$$\rightarrow -\frac{1}{15} \ge \frac{1}{x-10} \ge -1$$
$$\rightarrow -1 \le \frac{1}{x-10} \le -\frac{1}{15}$$
$$\rightarrow a = -1, b = -\frac{1}{15}$$

50.
$$|x+1| \le 3 \rightarrow -3 \le x+1 \le 3$$
$$\rightarrow -4 \le x \le 2$$
$$\rightarrow 1 \le x+5 \le 7$$
$$\rightarrow 1 \ge \frac{1}{x+5} \ge \frac{1}{7}$$
$$\rightarrow \frac{1}{7} \le \frac{1}{x+5} \le 1$$
$$\rightarrow a = \frac{1}{7}, b = 1$$

51. If $b \ne 0$, prove $\left|\dfrac{a}{b}\right| = \dfrac{|a|}{|b|}$.

Case1: $\dfrac{a}{b} \ge 0 \rightarrow a \ge 0$ and $b > 0$ or $a \le 0$ and $b < 0$.

if $a \ge 0$ and $b > 0$ then $|a| = a$ and $|b| = b$.

so, $\dfrac{a}{b} \ge 0 \rightarrow \left|\dfrac{a}{b}\right| = \dfrac{a}{b} = \dfrac{|a|}{|b|}$.

if $a \le 0$ and $b < 0$ then $|a| = -a$ and $|b| = -b$.

so, $\dfrac{a}{b} \ge 0 \rightarrow \left|\dfrac{a}{b}\right| = \dfrac{a}{b} = \dfrac{-|a|}{-|b|} = \dfrac{|a|}{|b|}$.

Case2: $\dfrac{a}{b} < 0 \rightarrow a > 0$ and $b < 0$ or $a < 0$ and $b > 0$.

if $a > 0$ and $b < 0$ then $|a| = a$ and $|b| = -b$.

now, $\dfrac{a}{b} < 0 \rightarrow \left|\dfrac{a}{b}\right| = -\left(\dfrac{a}{b}\right) = -\left(\dfrac{a}{-b}\right) = \dfrac{a}{b}$.

if $a < 0$ and $b > 0$ then $|a| = -a$ and $|b| = b$.

now, $\dfrac{a}{b} < 0 \rightarrow \left|\dfrac{a}{b}\right| = -\left(\dfrac{a}{b}\right) = -\left(\dfrac{-a}{b}\right) = \dfrac{a}{b}$.

52.   Show that $a \leq |a|$.

We know that $0 \leq |a|$. So if $a < 0$, then we have $a < 0 \leq |a| \rightarrow a \leq |a|$

Now, if $a \geq 0$, then $|a| = a$. So $a \leq |a|$.

53. $|a+b|^2 = |a+b| \cdot |a+b|$

Case 1: $a + b \geq 0 \rightarrow |a+b| = a+b$
so $|a+b| \cdot |a+b| = (a+b)(a+b) = a^2 + 2ab + b^2$
$\leq |a|^2 + 2|a| \cdot |b| + |b|^2$ by problem 52
$= (|a| + |b|)^2$
$\therefore (|a+b|)^2 \leq (|a| + |b|)^2 \rightarrow |a+b| \leq |a| + |b|$

Case 2: $a + b < 0 \rightarrow |a+b| = -(a+b)$
so $|a+b| \cdot |a+b| = (-(a+b))(-(a+b))$
$= (a+b)(a+b) = a^2 + 2ab + b^2$
$\leq |a|^2 + 2|a| \cdot |b| + |b|^2$ by problem 52
$= (|a| + |b|)^2$
$\therefore (|a+b|)^2 \leq (|a| + |b|)^2 \rightarrow |a+b| \leq |a| + |b|$

54. To prove $|a-b| \geq a - b$, consider the following:

$|a| = |(a-b) + b| \leq |a-b| + |b|$ by the Triangle Inequality

so $|a| \leq |a-b| + |b| \rightarrow |a| - |b| \leq |a-b|$
therefore $|a-b| \geq |a| - |b|$.

55. x differs from 3 by less than $\dfrac{1}{2}$

$|x - 3| < \dfrac{1}{2}$

$\dfrac{-1}{2} < x - 3 < \dfrac{7}{2}$

$\dfrac{5}{2} < x < \dfrac{7}{2}$

$\left\{ x \mid \dfrac{3}{2} < x < \dfrac{5}{2} \right\}$

56   x differs from -1 by less than 1

$|x - (-4)| < 1$

$|x + 4| < 1$

$-1 < x + 4 < 1$

$-5 < x < -3$

$\{ x \mid -5 < x < -3 \}$

57. x differs from -3 by more than 2

$|x - (-3)| > 2$

$x + 3 < -2$ or $x + 3 > 2$

$x < -5$ or $x > -1$

$\{x | x < -5 \text{ or } x > -1\}$

58. x differs from 2 by more than 3

$|x - 2| > 3$

$x - 2 < -3$ or $x - 2 > 3$

$x < -1$ or $x > 5$

$\{x | x < -1 \text{ or } x > 5\}$

59. A temperature x that differs from $98.6°$ F by at least $1.5°$

$|x - 98.6°| \geq 1.5°$

$x - 98.6° \leq -1.5°$ or $x - 98.6° \geq 1.5°$

$x \leq 97.1°$ or $x \geq 100.1°$

The temperatures that are considered unhealthy are those that are less than $97.1°$F or greater than $100.1°$F, inclusive.

60. A voltage x that differs from 115 volts by at most 5 volts

$|x - 115| \leq 5$

$-5 \leq x - 115 \leq 5$

$110 \leq x \leq 120$

The actual voltage is between 110 and 120 volts, inclusive.

61. given that $a > 0$

$$x^2 < a \rightarrow x^2 - a < 0$$

$$\left(x + \sqrt{a}\right)\left(x - \sqrt{a}\right) < 0$$

if $x < -\sqrt{a}$, then $x + \sqrt{a} < 0$ and $x - \sqrt{a} < -2\sqrt{a} < 0$

therefore $\left(x + \sqrt{a}\right)\left(x - \sqrt{a}\right) > 0$

if $-\sqrt{a} < x < \sqrt{a}$, then $0 < x + \sqrt{a} < 2\sqrt{a}$ and $-2\sqrt{a} < x - \sqrt{a} < 0$

therefore $\left(x + \sqrt{a}\right)\left(x - \sqrt{a}\right) < 0$

if $x > \sqrt{a}$, then $x + \sqrt{a} > 2\sqrt{a} > 0$ and $x - \sqrt{a} > 0$

therefore $\left(x + \sqrt{a}\right)\left(x - \sqrt{a}\right) > 0$

So the solution set for $x^2 < a$ is $\{\text{real numbers } x | -\sqrt{a} < x < \sqrt{a}\}$

62.   given that $a > 0$

$$x^2 > a \rightarrow x^2 - a > 0$$
$$\left(x + \sqrt{a}\right)\left(x - \sqrt{a}\right) > 0$$

if $x < -\sqrt{a}$, then $x + \sqrt{a} < 0$ and $x - \sqrt{a} < -2\sqrt{a} < 0$
therefore
$$\left(x + \sqrt{a}\right)\left(x - \sqrt{a}\right) > 0$$

if $-\sqrt{a} < x < \sqrt{a}$, then $0 < x + \sqrt{a} < 2\sqrt{a}$ and $-2\sqrt{a} < x - \sqrt{a} < 0$
therefore
$$\left(x + \sqrt{a}\right)\left(x - \sqrt{a}\right) < 0$$

if $x > \sqrt{a}$, then $x + \sqrt{a} > 2\sqrt{a} > 0$ and $x - \sqrt{a} > 0$
therefore
$$\left(x + \sqrt{a}\right)\left(x - \sqrt{a}\right) > 0$$

So the solution set for
$x^2 > a$ is $\left\{\text{real numbers } x \middle| x < -\sqrt{a} \text{ or } x > \sqrt{a}\right\}$

63.
$\left\{\text{real numbers } x \middle| -1 < x < 1\right\}$

64.
$\left\{\text{real numbers } x \middle| -2 < x < 2\right\}$

65.
$\left\{\text{real numbers } x \middle| x \leq -3 \text{ or } x \geq 3\right\}$

66.
$\left\{\text{real numbers } x \middle| x \leq -1 \text{ or } x \geq 1\right\}$

67.
$\left\{\text{real numbers } x \middle| -4 \leq x \leq 4\right\}$

68.
$\left\{\text{real numbers } x \middle| -3 \leq x \leq 3\right\}$

69.
$\left\{\text{real numbers } x \middle| x < -2 \text{ or } x > 2\right\}$

70.
$\left\{\text{real numbers } x \middle| x < -4 \text{ or } x > 4\right\}$

71. $\left| 3x - \left|2x + 1\right|\right| = 4$

$\rightarrow 3x - \left|2x + 1\right| = 4$ or $3x - \left|2x + 1\right| = -4$
$3x - \left|2x + 1\right| = 4 \rightarrow 3x - 4 = \left|2x + 1\right|$
$\rightarrow 2x + 1 = 3x - 4 \rightarrow 2x + 1 = 3x - 4 \rightarrow 5 = x$

or $2x + 1 = -(3x - 4) \rightarrow 2x + 1 = -3x + 4 \rightarrow 5x = 3 \rightarrow x = \dfrac{3}{5}$

$3x - |2x + 1| = -4 \rightarrow 3x + 4 = |2x + 1|$

$\rightarrow 2x + 1 = 3x + 4 \rightarrow 2x + 1 = 3x + 4 \rightarrow -3 = x$

or $2x + 1 = -(3x + 4) \rightarrow 2x + 1 = -3x - 4 \rightarrow 5x = -5 \rightarrow x = -1$

however, the only values that check in the original equation are $x = 5$ and $x = -1$.

72. $\left| x + |3x - 2| \right| = 2$

$\rightarrow x + |3x - 2| = 2$ or $x + |3x - 2| = -2$

$x + |3x - 2| = 2 \rightarrow |3x - 2| = 2 - x$

$\rightarrow 3x - 2 = 2 - x \rightarrow 3x - 2 = 2 - x \rightarrow 4x = 4 \rightarrow x = 1$

or $3x - 2 = -(2 - x) \rightarrow 3x - 2 = -2x + 1 \rightarrow 5x = -3 \rightarrow x = -\dfrac{3}{5}$

$x + |3x - 2| = -2 \rightarrow |3x - 2| = -2 - x$

$\rightarrow 3x - 2 = -2 - x$ or $3x - 2 = -(-2 - x)$

$3x - 2 = -2 - x \rightarrow 4x = 0 \rightarrow x = 0$

$3x - 2 = -(-2 - x) \rightarrow 3x - 2 = 2 + x \rightarrow 2x = 4 \rightarrow x = 2$

however, the only values that check in the original equation are $x = 0$ and $x = 1$.

73.   The absolute value of a real number is always greater than or equal to zero.

74.   The absolute value of a real number is always greater than or equal to zero, and zero is greater than -0.5.

75.   if $x > 0$, then $|x| = x$, therefore $|x| > 0$.

if $x < 0$, then $|x| = -x$. So $x < 0 \rightarrow -x > 0 \rightarrow |x| > 0$.

Chapter 1

Equations and Inequalities

1.R   Chapter Review

1. $2 - \dfrac{x}{3} = 8$

    $6 - x = 24 \rightarrow x = -18$

2. $\dfrac{x}{4} - 2 = 4$

    $x - 8 = 16 \rightarrow x = 24$

3. $-2(5 - 3x) + 8 = 4 + 5x$

    $-10 + 6x + 8 = 4 + 5x$

    $6x - 2 = 4 + 5x$

    $x = 6$

4. $(6 - 3x) - 2(1 + x) = 6x$

    $6 - 3x - 2 - 2x = 6x$

    $-5x + 4 = 6x$

    $-11x = -4 \rightarrow x = \dfrac{4}{11}$

5. $\dfrac{3x}{4} - \dfrac{x}{3} = \dfrac{1}{12}$

    $9x - 4x = 1$

    $5x = 1 \rightarrow x = \dfrac{1}{5}$

6. $\dfrac{4 - 2x}{3} + \dfrac{1}{6} = 2x$

    $2(4 - 2x) + 1 = 12x$

    $8 - 4x + 1 = 12x$

    $9 = 16x \rightarrow x = \dfrac{9}{16}$

7. $\dfrac{x}{x - 1} = \dfrac{6}{5}$

    $5x = 6x - 6$

    $6 = x$

    and since $x = 6$ does not cause a denominator to equal zero, the solution set is $\{6\}$.

8. $\dfrac{4x - 5}{3 - 7x} = 2$

    $4x - 5 = 6 - 14x$

    $18x = 11$

    $x = \dfrac{11}{18}$

    and since $x = \dfrac{11}{18}$ does not cause a denominator to equal zero, the solution set is $\left\{\dfrac{11}{18}\right\}$.

9. $x(1-x)=6$
$$x-x^2=6$$
$$0=x^2-x+6$$
$$0=(x-3)(x+2)$$
$$x=3 \text{ or } x=-2$$

10. $x(1+x)=6$
$$x+x^2=6$$
$$x^2+x-6=0$$
$$(x+3)(x-2)=0$$
$$x=-3 \text{ or } x=2$$

11. $\frac{1}{2}\left(x-\frac{1}{3}\right)=\frac{3}{4}-\frac{x}{6}$
$$\frac{x}{2}-\frac{1}{6}=\frac{3}{4}-\frac{x}{6}$$
$$6x-2=9-2x$$
$$8x=11$$
$$x=\frac{11}{8}$$

12. $\frac{1-3x}{4}=\frac{x+6}{3}+\frac{1}{2}$
$$3(1-3x)=4(x+6)+6$$
$$3-9x=4x+24+6$$
$$-13x=27$$
$$x=-\frac{27}{13}$$

13. $(x-1)(2x+3)=3$
$$2x^2+x-3=3$$
$$2x^2+x-6=0$$
$$(2x-3)(x+2)=0$$
$$x=\frac{3}{2} \text{ or } x=-2$$

14. $x(2-x)=3(x-4)$
$$2x-x^2=3x-12$$
$$x^2+x-12=0$$
$$(x+4)(x-3)=0$$
$$x=-4 \text{ or } x=3$$

15. $2x+3=4x^2$
$$0=4x^2-2x-3$$
$$x=\frac{2\pm\sqrt{4+48}}{8}=\frac{2\pm\sqrt{52}}{8}$$
$$=\frac{2\pm2\sqrt{13}}{8}=\frac{1\pm\sqrt{13}}{4}$$

16. $1+6x=4x^2$
$$0=4x^2-6x-1$$
$$x=\frac{6\pm\sqrt{36+16}}{8}=\frac{6\pm\sqrt{52}}{8}$$
$$=\frac{6\pm2\sqrt{13}}{8}=\frac{3\pm\sqrt{13}}{4}$$

17. $\sqrt[3]{x^2-1}=2$
$$\left(\sqrt[3]{x^2-1}\right)^3=(2)^3$$
$$x^2-1=8$$
$$x^2=9$$
$$x=\pm3$$

18. $\sqrt{1+x^3}=3$
$$\left(\sqrt{1+x^3}\right)^2=(3)^2$$
$$1+x^3=9$$
$$x^3=8$$
$$x=2$$

Check:

$$x = -3$$

$$\sqrt[3]{(-3)^2 - 1} = 2$$

$$\sqrt[3]{9 - 1} = 2$$

$$\sqrt[3]{8} = 2$$

$$2 = 2$$

$$x = 3$$

$$\sqrt[3]{(3)^2 - 1} = 2$$

$$\sqrt[3]{9 - 1} = 2$$

$$\sqrt[3]{8} = 2$$

$$2 = 2$$

so the solution set is $\{-3, 3\}$.

Check:

$$x = 2$$

$$\sqrt{1 + (2)^3} = 3$$

$$\sqrt{9} = 3$$

$$3 = 3$$

so the solution set is $\{2\}$.

19. $x(x + 1) + 2 = 0$

$\quad\quad x^2 + x + 2 = 0$

$$x = \frac{-1 \pm \sqrt{1 - 8}}{2} = \frac{-1 \pm \sqrt{-7}}{2}$$

no real solutions

20. $3x^2 - x + 1 = 0$

$$x = \frac{1 \pm \sqrt{1 - 12}}{6} = \frac{1 \pm \sqrt{-11}}{6}$$

no real solutions

21. $x^4 - 5x^2 + 4 = 0$

$\quad\quad (x^2 - 4)(x^2 - 1) = 0$

$\quad\quad x^2 - 4 = 0$ or $x^2 - 1 = 0$

$\quad\quad\quad x = \pm 2$ or $x = \pm 1$

22. $3x^4 + 4x^2 + 1 = 0$

$\quad\quad (3x^2 + 1)(x^2 + 1) = 0$

$\quad\quad 3x^2 + 1 = 0$ or $x^2 + 1 = 0$

$\quad\quad 3x^2 = -13$ or $x^2 = -1$

but this is impossible, so there are no real solutions.

23. $\quad \sqrt{2x - 3} + x = 3$

$\quad\quad\quad \sqrt{2x - 3} = 3 - x$

$\quad\quad\quad 2x - 3 = 9 - 6x + x^2$

$\quad x^2 - 8x + 12 = 0$

$\quad (x - 2)(x - 6) = 0$

$\quad\quad\quad\quad\quad x = 2$ or $x = 6$

Check 2: $\sqrt{2(2) - 3} + 2 = \sqrt{1} + 2 = 3$

Check 6: $\sqrt{2(6) - 3} + 6 = \sqrt{9} + 6$

$\quad\quad\quad\quad\quad\quad = 9 \neq 3$

The solution is $x = 2$.

24. $\sqrt{2x - 1} = x - 2$

$\quad\quad\quad 2x - 1 = x^2 - 4x + 4$

$\quad\quad x^2 - 6x + 5 = 0$

$\quad (x - 1)(x - 5) = 0$

$\quad\quad\quad\quad\quad x = 1$ or $x = 5$

Check 1: $\sqrt{2(1) - 1} = 1 - 2 \rightarrow 1 \neq -1$

Check 5: $\sqrt{2(5) - 1} = 5 - 2 \rightarrow 3 = 3$

The solution is $x = 5$.

25. $x^{3/2} + 5x^{1/2} = 0$

$x^{3/2} = -5x^{1/2}$

$\left(x^{3/2}\right)^2 = \left(-5x^{1/2}\right)^2$

$x^3 = 25x$

$x^3 - 25x = 0$

$x\left(x^2 - 25\right) = 0$

$x(x-5)(x+5) = 0$

$x = 0$

$x - 5 = 0 \rightarrow x = 5$

$x + 5 = 0 \rightarrow x = -5$

Check $x = 0$:

$0^{3/2} + 5(0)^{1/2} = 0$

$0 + 0 = 0$

$0 = 0$

Check $x = 5$:

$5^{3/2} + 5(5)^{1/2} = 0$

$5^{3/2} + 5^{3/2} = 0$

$2\left(5^{3/2}\right) \neq 0$

Check $x = -5$:

$(-5)^{3/2} + 5(-5)^{1/2} = 0$

$\left(\sqrt{-5}\right)^3 + 5\sqrt{-5} = 0$

but $\sqrt{-5}$ is undefined.

The solution set is $\{0\}$.

26. $x^{2/3} + x = 0$

$x^{2/3} = -x$

$\left(x^{2/3}\right)^3 = (-x)^3$

$x^2 = -x^3$

$x^2 + x^3 = 0$

$x^2(1 + x) = 0$

$x^2 = 0 \rightarrow x = 0$

$1 + x = 0 \rightarrow x = -1$

Check $x = 0$:

$0^{2/3} + 0 = 0$

$0 + 0 = 0$

$0 = 0$

Check $x = -1$:

$(-1)^{2/3} + (-1) = 0$

$1 - 1 = 0$

$0 = 0$

The solutions are $x = 0$ or $x = -1$.

27.

$$\sqrt{x+1} + \sqrt{x-1} = \sqrt{2x+1}$$

$$\left(\sqrt{x+1} + \sqrt{x-1}\right)^2 = \left(\sqrt{2x+1}\right)^2$$

$$x+1+2\sqrt{x+1}\sqrt{x-1} + x - 1 = 2x+1$$

$$2x + 2\sqrt{x+1}\sqrt{x-1} = 2x+1$$

Check:

$$2\sqrt{x+1}\sqrt{x-1} = 1$$

$$\left(2\sqrt{x+1}\sqrt{x-1}\right)^2 = (1)^2$$

$$x = \frac{\sqrt{5}}{2} \rightarrow \sqrt{\frac{\sqrt{5}}{2}+1} + \sqrt{\frac{\sqrt{5}}{2}-1} = \sqrt{2\left(\frac{\sqrt{5}}{2}\right)+1}$$

$$4(x+1)(x-1) = 1$$

$$1.79890743995 = 1.79890743995$$

$$4x^2 - 4 = 1$$

$$4x^2 = 5 \rightarrow x^2 = \frac{5}{4}$$

$$x = -\frac{\sqrt{5}}{2} \rightarrow \sqrt{-\frac{\sqrt{5}}{2}+1} + \sqrt{-\frac{\sqrt{5}}{2}-1} = \sqrt{2\left(-\frac{\sqrt{5}}{2}\right)+1}$$

$$x = \pm\frac{\sqrt{5}}{2}$$

impossible since $-\frac{\sqrt{5}}{2} - 1 < 0$

The solution set is $\left\{\frac{\sqrt{5}}{2}\right\}$.

28.

$$\sqrt{2x-1} - \sqrt{x-5} = 3$$

$$\sqrt{2x-1} = 3 + \sqrt{x-5}$$

$$\left(\sqrt{2x-1}\right)^2 = \left(3+\sqrt{x-5}\right)^2$$

Check:

$$2x-1 = 9 + 6\sqrt{x-5} + x - 5$$

$$x - 5 = 6\sqrt{x-5}$$

$$x = 41 \rightarrow \sqrt{2(41)-1} - \sqrt{41-5} = 3$$

$$\left(x-5\right)^2 = \left(6\sqrt{x-5}\right)^2$$

$$\sqrt{81} - \sqrt{36} = 3$$

$$x^2 - 10x + 25 = 36(x-5)$$

$$9 - 6 = 3$$

$$x^2 - 10x + 25 = 36x - 180$$

$$3 = 3$$

$$x^2 - 46x + 205 = 0$$

$$(x-41)(x-5) = 0$$

$$x = 5 \rightarrow \sqrt{2(5)-1} - \sqrt{5-5} = 3 -$$

$$x = 41 \text{ or } x = 5$$

$$\sqrt{9} - \sqrt{0} = 3$$

$$3 - 0 = 3$$

$$3 = 3$$

The solution set is $\{5, 41\}$.

29. $2\sqrt[3]{x^2} - \sqrt[3]{x} = 1$

$2\sqrt[3]{x^2} - \sqrt[3]{x} - 1 = 0 \rightarrow 2x^{2/3} - x^{1/3} - 1 = 0$

$\qquad p = x^{1/3} \rightarrow p^2 = x^{2/3}$

$2p^2 - p - 1 = 0 \rightarrow (2p+1)(p-1) = 0$

$\qquad p = -\dfrac{1}{2} \quad \text{or} \quad p = 1$

$\qquad p = -\dfrac{1}{2} \rightarrow x^{1/3} = -\dfrac{1}{2}$

$\qquad \rightarrow \left(x^{1/3}\right)^3 = \left(-\dfrac{1}{2}\right)^3 \rightarrow x = -\dfrac{1}{8}$

$\qquad p = 1 \rightarrow x^{1/3} = 1$

$\qquad \rightarrow \left(x^{1/3}\right)^3 = (1)^3 \rightarrow x = 1$

Check

$x = -\dfrac{1}{8}: 2\sqrt[3]{\left(-\dfrac{1}{8}\right)^2} - \sqrt[3]{-\dfrac{1}{8}} - 1 = 0$

$2\left(\dfrac{1}{4}\right) - \left(-\dfrac{1}{2}\right) - 1 = 0 \rightarrow \dfrac{1}{2} + \dfrac{1}{2} - 1 = 0 \rightarrow 0 = 0$

$x = 1: 2\sqrt[3]{1^2} - \sqrt[3]{1} - 1 = 0$

$2 - 1 - 1 = 0 \rightarrow 2 - 2 = 0 \rightarrow 0 = 0$

the solution set is $\left\{-\dfrac{1}{8}, 1\right\}$

30. $4\sqrt[3]{x^2} = 1$

$\qquad \left(4x^2\right)^3 = (1)^3$

$\qquad 64x^2 = 1$

$\qquad 64x^2 - 1 = 0$

$\qquad (8x+1)(8x-1) = 0$

$\qquad x = -\dfrac{1}{8} \quad \text{or} \quad x = \dfrac{1}{8}$

Check

$x = -\dfrac{1}{8}: 4\sqrt[3]{\left(-\dfrac{1}{8}\right)^2} = 1 \qquad x = \dfrac{1}{8}: 4\sqrt[3]{\left(\dfrac{1}{8}\right)^2} = 1$

$4\left(\dfrac{1}{4}\right) = 1 \qquad\qquad\qquad 4\left(\dfrac{1}{4}\right) = 1$

$1 = 1 \qquad\qquad\qquad\qquad 1 = 1$

the solution set is $\left\{-\dfrac{1}{8}, \dfrac{1}{8}\right\}$

31. $x^{-6} - 7x^{-3} - 8 = 0$

$\qquad p = x^{-3} \rightarrow p^2 = x^{-6}$

$p^2 - 7p - 8 = 0 \rightarrow (p-8)(p+1) = 0$

$\qquad p = 8 \quad \text{or} \quad p = -1$

$\qquad p = 8 \rightarrow x^{-3} = 8 \rightarrow \left(x^{-3}\right)^{-1/3} = (8)^{-1/3} \rightarrow x = \dfrac{1}{2}$

$\qquad p = -1 \rightarrow x^{-3} = -1 \rightarrow \left(x^{-3}\right)^{-1/3} = (-1)^{-1/3} \rightarrow x = -1$

Check:

$$x = \frac{1}{2} : \left(\frac{1}{2}\right)^{-6} - 7(p)^{-3} - 8 = 0 \rightarrow 64 - 56 - 8 = 0 \rightarrow 0 = 0 \qquad \text{the solution set is } \left\{\frac{1}{2}, -1\right\}$$

$$x = -1 : (-1)^{-6} - 7(-1)^{-3} - 8 = 0 \rightarrow 1 + 7 - 8 = 0 \rightarrow 0 = 0$$

32. $6x^{-1} - 5x^{-1/2} + 1 = 0$

$$p = x^{-1/2} \rightarrow p^2 = x^{-1}$$

$$6p^2 - 5p + 1 = 0 \rightarrow (3p - 1)(2p - 1) = 0$$

$$p = \frac{1}{3} \quad \text{or} \quad p = \frac{1}{2}$$

$$p = \frac{1}{3} \rightarrow x^{-1/2} = \frac{1}{3} \rightarrow \left(x^{-1/2}\right)^{-2} = \left(\frac{1}{3}\right)^{-2} \rightarrow x = 9$$

$$p = \frac{1}{2} \rightarrow x^{-1/2} = \frac{1}{2} \rightarrow \left(x^{-1/2}\right)^{-2} = \left(\frac{1}{2}\right)^{-2} \rightarrow x = 4$$

Check:

$$x = 9 : (9)^{-1} - 5(9)^{-1/2} + 1 = 0 \rightarrow \frac{1}{9} - 5\left(\frac{1}{3}\right) + 1 = 0$$

$$\frac{1}{9} - \frac{5}{3} + 1 = 0 \rightarrow 1 - 15 + 9 = 0 \rightarrow 0 = 0 \qquad \text{the solution set is } \{4, 9\}$$

$$x = 4 : (4)^{-1} - 5(4)^{-1/2} + 1 = 0 \rightarrow \frac{1}{4} - 5\left(\frac{1}{2}\right) + 1 = 0$$

$$\frac{1}{4} - \frac{5}{2} + 1 = 0 \rightarrow 1 - 10 + 9 = 0 \rightarrow 0 = 0$$

33. $x^2 + m^2 = 2mx + (nx)^2$

$$x^2 + m^2 = 2mx + n^2 x^2 \rightarrow x^2 - n^2 x^2 - 2mx + m^2 = 0$$

$$(1 - n^2)x^2 - 2mx + m^2 = 0$$

$$x = \frac{2m \pm \sqrt{4m^2 - 4m^2(1 - n^2)}}{2(1 - n^2)} = \frac{2m \pm \sqrt{4m^2(1 - (1 - n^2))}}{2(1 - n^2)}$$

$$= \frac{2m \pm 2m\sqrt{1 - (1 - n^2)}}{2(1 - n^2)} = \frac{m \pm m\sqrt{n^2}}{1 - n^2} = \frac{m \pm mn}{1 - n^2} = \frac{m(1 \pm n)}{1 - n^2}$$

$$x = \frac{m(1 + n)}{1 - n^2} = \frac{m(1 + n)}{(1 + n)(1 - n)} = \frac{m}{1 - n}$$

or   the solution set is $\left\{\dfrac{m}{1 - n}, \dfrac{m}{1 + n}\right\}$.

$$x = \frac{m(1 - n)}{1 - n^2} = \frac{m(1 - n)}{(1 + n)(1 - n)} = \frac{m}{1 + n}$$

34. $b^2x^2 + 2ax = x^2 + a^2$

$b^2x^2 + 2ax - x^2 - a^2 = 0 \rightarrow b^2x^2 - x^2 + 2ax - a^2 = 0$

$\left(b^2 - 1\right)x^2 + 2ax - a^2 = 0$

$x = \dfrac{-2a \pm \sqrt{4a^2 - 4\left(b^2 - 1\right)\left(-a^2\right)}}{2\left(b^2 - 1\right)} = \dfrac{-2a \pm \sqrt{4a^2 + 4\left(b^2 - 1\right)\left(a^2\right)}}{2\left(b^2 - 1\right)}$

$= \dfrac{-2a \pm \sqrt{4a^2\left(1 + b^2 - 1\right)}}{2\left(b^2 - 1\right)} = \dfrac{-2a \pm \sqrt{4a^2\left(b^2\right)}}{2\left(b^2 - 1\right)} = \dfrac{-2a \pm 2ab}{2\left(b^2 - 1\right)} = \dfrac{a(-1 \pm b)}{b^2 - 1}$

$x = \dfrac{a(-1 + b)}{b^2 - 1} = \dfrac{a(b - 1)}{(b+1)(b-1)} = \dfrac{a}{b+1}$

or   the solution set is $\left\{\dfrac{a}{b+1}, \dfrac{-a}{b-1}\right\}.$

$x = \dfrac{a(-1 - b)}{b^2 - 1} = \dfrac{-a(b+1)}{(b+1)(b-1)} = \dfrac{-a}{b-1}$

35. $10a^2x^2 - 2abx - 36b^2 = 0$

$5a^2x^2 - abx - 18b^2 = 0$

$(5ax + 9b)(ax - 2b) = 0$ the solution set is $\left\{-\dfrac{9b}{5a}, \dfrac{2b}{a}\right\}.$

$x = -\dfrac{9b}{5a} \ \text{ or } \ x = \dfrac{2b}{a}$

36. $\dfrac{1}{x - m} + \dfrac{1}{x - n} = \dfrac{2}{x}$

$x(x - m)(x - n)\left(\dfrac{1}{x - m} + \dfrac{1}{x - n}\right) = \left(\dfrac{2}{x}\right)x(x - m)(x - n)$

$x(x - n) + x(x - m) = 2(x - m)(x - n)$

$x^2 - xn + x^2 - xm = 2x^2 - 2xn - 2xm + 2mn$

$x^2 - xn + x^2 - xm - 2x^2 + 2xn + 2xm - 2mn = 0$

$xn + xm - 2mn = 0$

$xn + xm = 2mn$

$x(n + m) = 2mn$

$x = \dfrac{2mn}{n + m}$

the solution set is $\left\{\dfrac{2mn}{n + m}\right\}, n \neq -m, x \neq m, x \neq n, x \neq 0$

37. $\sqrt{x^2 + 3x + 7} - \sqrt{x^2 - 3x + 9} + 2 = 0$

$$\sqrt{x^2 + 3x + 7} = \sqrt{x^2 - 3x + 9} - 2$$

$$\left(\sqrt{x^2 + 3x + 7}\right)^2 = \left(\sqrt{x^2 - 3x + 9} - 2\right)^2$$

$$x^2 + 3x + 7 = x^2 - 3x + 9 - 4\sqrt{x^2 - 3x + 9} + 4$$

$$6x - 6 = -4\sqrt{x^2 - 3x + 9}$$

$$\left(6(x - 1)\right)^2 = \left(-4\sqrt{x^2 - 3x + 9}\right)^2$$

$$36\left(x^2 - 2x + 1\right) = 16\left(x^2 - 3x + 9\right)$$

$$36x^2 - 72x + 36 = 16x^2 - 48x + 144$$

$$20x^2 - 24x - 108 = 0 \rightarrow 5x^2 - 6x - 27 = 0$$

$$(5x + 9)(x - 3) = 0$$

$$x = -\frac{9}{5} \text{ or } x = 3$$

Check $x = -\dfrac{9}{5}$:

$$\sqrt{\left(-\frac{9}{5}\right)^2 + 3\left(-\frac{9}{5}\right) + 7} - \sqrt{\left(-\frac{9}{5}\right)^2 - 3\left(-\frac{9}{5}\right) + 9} + 2 = 0$$

$$\sqrt{\frac{81}{25} - \frac{27}{5} + 7} - \sqrt{\frac{81}{25} + \frac{27}{5} + 9} + 2 = 0$$

$$\sqrt{\frac{81 - 135 + 175}{25}} - \sqrt{\frac{81 + 135 + 225}{25}} + 2 = 0$$

$$\sqrt{\frac{121}{25}} - \sqrt{\frac{441}{25}} + 2 = 0$$

$$\frac{11}{5} - \frac{21}{5} + 2 = 0$$

$$0 = 0$$

Check:

$$x = 3 : \sqrt{(3)^2 + 3(3) + 7} - \sqrt{(3)^2 - 3(3) + 9} + 2 = 0$$

$$\sqrt{9 + 9 + 7} - \sqrt{9 - 9 + 9} + 2 = 0$$

$$\sqrt{25} - \sqrt{9} + 2 = 0$$

$$2 + 2 = 0$$

$$4 \neq 0$$

the solution set is $\left\{-\dfrac{9}{5}\right\}$.

38. $\sqrt{x^2 + 3x + 7} - \sqrt{x^2 + 3x + 9} = 2$

$$\sqrt{x^2 + 3x + 7} = \sqrt{x^2 + 3x + 9} + 2$$

$$\left(\sqrt{x^2 + 3x + 7}\right)^2 = \left(\sqrt{x^2 + 3x + 9} + 2\right)^2$$

$$x^2 + 3x + 7 = x^2 + 3x + 9 + 4\sqrt{x^2 + 3x + 9} + 4$$

$$-6 = 4\sqrt{x^2 + 3x + 9}$$

but this is impossible since the principal square root always yields a non-negative number. Therefore, there is no real solution.

39. $|2x + 3| = 7$

$2x + 3 = 7$ or $2x + 3 = -7$

$2x = 4$ or $\quad 2x = -10$

$x = 2$ or $\quad\quad x = -5$

The solution set is $\{-5, 2\}$.

40. $|3x - 1| = 5$

$3x - 1 = 5$ or $3x - 1 = -5$

$3x = 6$ or $\quad 3x = -4$

$x = 2$ or $\quad\quad x = -\dfrac{4}{3}$

The solution set is $\left\{-\dfrac{4}{3}, 2\right\}$.

41. $|2 - 3x| + 2 = 9 \rightarrow |2 - 3x| = 7$

$2 - 3x = 7$ or $2 - 3x = -7$

$3x = -5$ or $\quad 3x = 9$

$x = -\dfrac{5}{2}$ or $\quad\quad x = 3$

The solution set is $\left\{-\dfrac{5}{2}, 3\right\}$

42. $|1 - 2x| + 1 = 4 \rightarrow |1 - 2x| = 3$

$1 - 2x = 3$ or $1 - 2x = -3$

$2x = -2$ or $\quad 2x = 4$

$x = -1$ or $\quad\quad x = 2$

The solution set is $\{-1, 2\}$.

43. $\dfrac{2x - 3}{5} + 2 \le \dfrac{x}{2}$

$2(2x - 3) + 10(2) \le 5x$

$4x - 6 + 20 \le 5x$

$14 \le x$

$x \ge 14$

$\{x \mid x \ge 14\}$ or $[14, +\infty)$

44. $\dfrac{5 - x}{3} \le 6x - 4$

$5 - x \le 3(6x - 4)$

$5 - x \le 18x - 12$

$-19x \le -17$

$x \ge \dfrac{17}{19}$

$\left\{x \mid x \ge \dfrac{17}{19}\right\}$ or $\left[\dfrac{17}{19}, +\infty\right)$

45. $-9 \le \dfrac{2x+3}{-4} \le 7$

$36 \ge 2x + 3 \ge -28$

$33 \ge \quad 2x \quad \ge -31$

$\dfrac{33}{2} \ge \quad x \quad \ge -\dfrac{31}{2}$

$-\dfrac{31}{2} \le \quad x \quad \le \dfrac{33}{2}$

$\left\{ x \,\middle|\, -\dfrac{31}{2} \le x \le \dfrac{33}{2} \right\}$ or $\left[-\dfrac{31}{2}, \dfrac{33}{2} \right]$

46. $-4 < \dfrac{2x-2}{3} < 6$

$-12 < 2x - 2 < 18$

$-10 < \quad 2x \quad < 20$

$-5 < \quad x \quad < 10$

$\left\{ x \,\middle|\, -5 < x < 10 \right\}$ or $(-5, 10)$

47. $6 > \dfrac{3-3x}{12} > 2$

$72 > 3 - 3x > 24$

$69 > \ -3x \ > 21$

$-23 < \quad x \quad < -7$

$\left\{ x \,\middle|\, -23 < x < -7 \right\}$ or $(-23, -7)$

48. $6 > \dfrac{5-3x}{2} \ge -3$

$12 > 5 - 3x \ge -6$

$7 > \ -3x \ \ge -11$

$-\dfrac{7}{3} < \quad x \quad \le \dfrac{11}{3}$

$\left\{ x \,\middle|\, -\dfrac{7}{3} < x \le \dfrac{11}{3} \right\}$ or $\left(-\dfrac{7}{3}, \dfrac{11}{3} \right]$

49. $|3x + 4| < \dfrac{1}{2}$

$\dfrac{-1}{2} < 3x + 4 < \dfrac{1}{2}$

$-\dfrac{9}{2} < \quad 3x \quad < -\dfrac{7}{2}$

$-\dfrac{3}{2} < \quad x \quad < -\dfrac{7}{6}$

$\left\{ x \,\middle|\, -\dfrac{3}{2} < x < -\dfrac{7}{6} \right\}$ or $\left(-\dfrac{3}{2}, -\dfrac{7}{6} \right)$

50. $|1 - 2x| < \dfrac{1}{3}$

$-\dfrac{1}{3} < 1 - 2x < \dfrac{1}{3}$

$-\dfrac{4}{3} < -2x < -\dfrac{2}{3}$

$\dfrac{2}{3} > \quad x \quad > \dfrac{1}{3}$

$\left\{ x \,\middle|\, \dfrac{1}{3} < x < \dfrac{2}{3} \right\}$ or $\left(\dfrac{1}{3}, \dfrac{2}{3} \right)$

51. $|2x-5| \geq 9$

$2x - 5 \leq -9$ or $2x - 5 \geq 9$

$2x \leq -4$ or $\quad 2x \geq 14$

$x \leq -2$ or $\quad\quad x \geq 7$

$\{x \mid x \leq -2 \text{ or } x \geq 7\}$

$\text{or } (-\infty, -2] \cup [7, +\infty)$

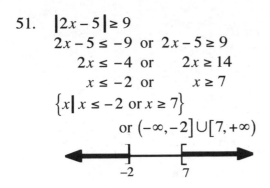

52. $|3x+1| \geq 10$

$3x + 1 \leq -10$ or $3x + 1 \geq 10$

$3x \leq -11$ or $\quad 3x \geq 9$

$x \leq -\dfrac{11}{3}$ or $\quad x \geq 3$

$\left\{x \mid x \leq -\dfrac{11}{3} \text{ or } x \geq 3\right\}$

$\text{or } \left(-\infty, -\dfrac{11}{3}\right] \cup [3, +\infty)$

53. $2 + |2 - 3x| \leq 4$

$|2 - 3x| \leq 2$

$-2 \leq 2 - 3x \leq 2$

$-4 \leq -3x \leq 0 \rightarrow \dfrac{4}{3} \geq x \geq 0$

$0 \leq x \leq \dfrac{4}{3}$

$\left\{x \mid 0 \leq x \leq \dfrac{4}{3}\right\} \text{ or } \left[0, \dfrac{4}{3}\right]$

54. $\dfrac{1}{2} + \left|\dfrac{2x-1}{3}\right| \leq 1$

$\left|\dfrac{2x-1}{3}\right| \leq \dfrac{1}{2}$

$-\dfrac{1}{2} \leq \dfrac{2x-1}{3} \leq \dfrac{1}{2}$

$-\dfrac{3}{2} \leq 2x - 1 \leq \dfrac{3}{2}$

$-\dfrac{1}{2} \leq 2x \leq \dfrac{5}{2}$

$-\dfrac{1}{4} \leq x \leq \dfrac{5}{4}$

$\left\{x \mid -\dfrac{1}{4} \leq x \leq \dfrac{5}{4}\right\} \text{ or } \left[-\dfrac{1}{4}, \dfrac{5}{4}\right]$

55.
$$1 - |2 - 3x| < -4$$
$$-|2 - 3x| < -5 \rightarrow |2 - 3x| > 5$$
$$2 - 3x < -5 \ \text{or} \ 2 - 3x > 5$$
$$7 < 3x \ \text{or} \ -3 > 3x$$
$$\frac{7}{3} < x \ \text{or} \ -1 > x$$
$$\rightarrow x < -1 \ \text{or} \ x > \frac{7}{3}$$
$$\left\{ x \middle| x < -1 \ \text{or} \ x > \frac{7}{3} \right\}$$
$$\text{or} \ (-\infty, -1) \cup \left(\frac{7}{3}, +\infty \right)$$

−1   7/3

56.
$$1 - \left| \frac{2x - 1}{3} \right| < -2$$
$$-\left| \frac{2x - 1}{3} \right| < -3 \rightarrow \left| \frac{2x - 1}{3} \right| > 3$$
$$\frac{2x - 1}{3} < -3 \ \text{or} \ \frac{2x - 1}{3} > 3$$
$$2x < -6 \ \text{or} \ 2x > 9$$
$$x < -3 \ \text{or} \ x > \frac{9}{2}$$
$$\left\{ x \middle| x < -3 \ \text{or} \ x > \frac{9}{2} \right\}$$
$$\text{or} \ (-\infty, -3) \cup \left(\frac{9}{2}, +\infty \right)$$

−3   9/2

57. $\left(\dfrac{6}{2} \right)^2 = 9$

58. $\left(-\dfrac{10}{2} \right)^2 = 25$

59. $\left(\dfrac{\left(-\dfrac{4}{3} \right)}{2} \right)^2 = \dfrac{4}{9}$

60. $\left(\dfrac{\left(\dfrac{4}{5} \right)}{2} \right)^2 = \dfrac{4}{25}$

61. Using $s = vt$, we have $t = 3$ and $v = 1100$. Finding the distance s in feet:
$$s = 1100(3)$$
$$s = 3300$$
The storm is 3300 feet away.

62. $1600 \leq I \leq 3600$
$$1600 \leq \frac{900}{x^2} \leq 3600$$
$$\frac{1}{1600} \geq \frac{x^2}{900} \geq \frac{1}{3600}$$
$$\frac{9}{16} \geq x^2 \geq \frac{1}{4}$$
$$\frac{3}{4} \geq x \geq \frac{1}{2}$$
The range of distances is from 0.5 meters to 0.75 meters, inclusive.

63. Let s represent the distance the plane can travel.

	Rate	Time	Distance
With wind	250+30=280	$\dfrac{\left(\dfrac{s}{2}\right)}{280}$	$\dfrac{s}{2}$
Against wind	250–30=220	$\dfrac{\left(\dfrac{s}{2}\right)}{220}$	$\dfrac{s}{2}$

Since the total time is at most 5 hours, we have:

$$\frac{\left(\dfrac{s}{2}\right)}{280}+\frac{\left(\dfrac{s}{2}\right)}{220}\le 5 \rightarrow \frac{s}{560}+\frac{s}{440}\le 5$$

$$11s+14s\le 5(6160)\rightarrow 25s\le 30800\rightarrow s\le 1232$$

The plane can travel at most 1232 miles or 616 miles one way and return 616 miles.

64. Let s represent the distance the plane can travel.

	Rate	Time	Distance
With wind	250+30=280	$\dfrac{\left(\dfrac{s}{2}\right)}{280}$	$\dfrac{s}{2}$
Against wind	250–30=220	$\dfrac{\left(\dfrac{s}{2}\right)}{220}$	$\dfrac{s}{2}$

Since the total time is at most 7 hours, we have:

$$\frac{\left(\dfrac{s}{2}\right)}{280}+\frac{\left(\dfrac{s}{2}\right)}{220}\le 7 \rightarrow \frac{s}{560}+\frac{s}{440}\le 7$$

$$11s+14s\le 7(6160)\rightarrow 25s\le 43120\rightarrow s\le 1724.8$$

The plane can travel at most 1724.8 miles or 862.4 miles one way. This is 246.4 miles further than in Problem 63.

65. Let t represent the time it takes the helicopter to reach the raft.

	Rate	Time	Distance
Raft	5	t	$5t$
Helicopter	90	t	$90t$

Since the total distance is 150 miles, we have:

$$5t+90t=150\rightarrow 95t=150\rightarrow t=1.58 \text{ hours } = 1 \text{ hour and } 35 \text{ minutes}$$
The helicopter will reach the raft in 1 hour and 35 minutes.

66.   Let d represent the distance flown by the bee traveling at 3 meters per second.

$$\frac{d}{3} = \frac{150 - d}{5}$$ (Times needed to meet are equal.)

$$5d = 450 - 3d \rightarrow 8d = 450 \rightarrow d = 56.25 \text{ meters}$$

$$t = \frac{56.25}{3} = 18.75 \text{ seconds}$$

The bees meet for the first time after 18.75 seconds.

The bees will meet a second time on the second lap. The first bee will have traveled 150 + x meters and the second bee will have traveled 150 + (150 – x) meters.
Solving for time, we have:

$$\frac{150 + x}{3} = \frac{150 + (150 - x)}{5} \rightarrow \frac{150 + x}{3} = \frac{300 - x}{5}$$

$$750 + 5x = 900 - 3x \rightarrow 8x = 150$$

$$x = 18.75 \text{ meters into the second lap}$$

$$t = \frac{168.75}{3} = 56.25 \text{ seconds}$$

The bees meet the second time after 56.25 seconds.

67.   Let t represent the time it takes Clarissa to complete the job by herself.

	Time to do job alone	Part of job done in one day	Time on Job	Part of total job done by each person
Clarissa	t	$\frac{1}{t}$	6	$\frac{6}{t}$
Shawna	$t + 5$	$\frac{1}{t+5}$	6	$\frac{6}{t+5}$

Since the two people paint one house, we have:

$$\frac{6}{t} + \frac{6}{t+5} = 1 \rightarrow 6(t + 5) + 6t = t(t + 5) \rightarrow 6t + 30 + 6t = t^2 + 5t$$

$$t^2 - 7t - 30 = 0 \rightarrow (t - 10)(t + 3) = 0$$

$$t = 10 \text{ or } t = -3$$

It takes Clarissa 10 days to paint the house when working by herself.

68.   Let t represent the time it takes the smaller pump to empty the tank.

	Time to do job alone	Part of job done in one hour	Time on Job	Part of total job done by each pump
Small Pump	t	$\frac{1}{t}$	5	$\frac{5}{t}$
Large Pump	$t - 4$	$\frac{1}{t-4}$	5	$\frac{5}{t-4}$

Since the two pumps empty one tank, we have:

$$\frac{5}{t} + \frac{5}{t-4} = 1$$

$$5(t - 4) + 5t = t(t - 4) \rightarrow 5t - 20 + 5t = t^2 - 4t \rightarrow t^2 - 14t + 20 = 0$$

$$t = \frac{-(-14) \pm \sqrt{(-14)^2 - 4(1)(20)}}{2(1)} = \frac{14 \pm \sqrt{196 - 80}}{2} = \frac{14 \pm \sqrt{116}}{2}$$

$$= \frac{14 \pm 2\sqrt{29}}{2} = 7 \pm \sqrt{29} \approx 7 \pm 5.385$$

$t = 12.385$ or $t = 1.615$(extraneous)

It takes the small pump approximately 12.385 hours to empty the tank.

69.

% acid	amount	amount of acid
40%	60	$(0.40)(60)$
15%	x	$(0.15)(x)$
25%	$60 + x$	$(0.25)(60 + x)$

$(0.40)(60) + (0.15)(x) = (0.25)(60 + x)$

$24 + .15x = 15 + .25x \rightarrow 9 = 0.1x \rightarrow x = 90$

90 cubic centimeters of the 15% solution must be added, producing 150 cubic centimeters of the 25% solution.

70.

Amount of coffee (lbs)	Price (dollars)	Total money
20	4	$(20)(4)$
x	8	$(8)(x)$
$20 + x$	5	$(5)(20 + x)$

$80 + 8x = (5)(20 + x)$

$80 + 8x = 100 + 5x$

$3x = 20$ Add $6\frac{2}{3}$ pounds of $8/lb coffee to get $26\frac{2}{3}$ pounds of $5/lb coffee.

$x = \dfrac{20}{3} = 6\frac{2}{3}$

71.

% salt	amount	amount of salt
10%	64	$(0.10)(64)$
0%	x	$(0.00)(x)$
2%	$64 + x$	$(0.02)(64 + x)$

$(0.10)(64) + (0.00)(x) = (0.02)(64 + x)$

$6.4 = 1.28 + .02x$ 256 ounces of water must be added.

$5.12 = 0.2x$

$x = 256$

72.

% salt	amount	amount of salt
2%	64	$(0.02)(64)$
0%	x	$(0.00)(x)$
10%	$64 - x$	$(0.10)(64 - x)$

$(0.02)(64) - (0.00)(x) = (0.10)(64 - x)$

$1.28 = 6.4 - .10x$ 51.2 ounces of water must be evaporated

$.10x = 5.12 \rightarrow x = 51.2$

73. length of $\text{leg}_1 = x$, length of $\text{leg}_2 = 17 - x$, by the Pythagorean Theorem we have

$x^2 + (17 - x)^2 = (13)^2$

$x^2 + x^2 - 34x + 289 = 169 \quad 2x^2 - 34x + 120 = 0$

$x^2 - 17x + 60 = 0 \rightarrow (x - 12)(x - 5) = 0 \rightarrow x = 12 \quad \text{or} \quad x = 5$

the legs are 5 inches and 12 inches long.

74.

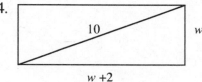

by the Pythagorean Theorem we have

$w^2 + (w + 2)^2 = (10)^2$

$w^2 + w^2 + 4w + 4 = 100$

$2w^2 + 4w - 96 = 0 \rightarrow w^2 + 2w - 48 = 0$

$(w + 8)(w - 6) = 0$

$w = -8 \quad \text{or} \quad w = 6$

the width is 6 inches and the length is 8 inches.

75. The effective speed of the train (i.e., relative to the man) is $30 - 4 = 26$ miles per hour. The

time is 5 seconds $= \dfrac{5}{60}$ minutes $= \dfrac{5}{3600}$ hours $= \dfrac{1}{720}$ hours.

$s = vt = 26\left(\dfrac{1}{720}\right) = \dfrac{26}{720}$ miles $= \dfrac{26}{720} \cdot 5280 = 190.67$ feet

The freight train is 190.67 feet long.

76. (a) $4(s + 6) = 50$

$4s + 24 = 50$

$4s = 26$

$s = 6.5$

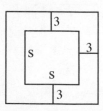

The painting is 6.5 inches by 6.5 inches.

$s + 6 = 12.5$ So the frame is 12.5 inches by 12.5 inches.

(b) $2(2w+6)+2(w+6)=50$

$4w+12+2w+12=50$

$6w=26$

$w=\dfrac{26}{6}=4\tfrac{1}{3} \rightarrow l=2w=8\tfrac{2}{3}$

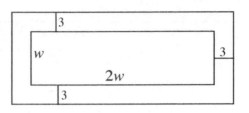

The painting is $8\tfrac{2}{3}$ inches by $4\tfrac{1}{3}$ inches.

The frame is $14\tfrac{2}{3}$ inches by $10\tfrac{1}{3}$ inches.

77.   Let t represent the time it takes the smaller pump to fill the tank.

	Time to do job alone	Part of job done in one hour	Time on Job	Part of total job done by each pump
3hp Pump	12	$\dfrac{1}{12}$	$t+4$	$\dfrac{t+4}{12}$
8hp Pump	8	$\dfrac{1}{8}$	4	$\dfrac{4}{8}$

Since the two pumps fill one tank, we have:

$$\frac{t+4}{12}+\frac{4}{8}=1 \rightarrow \frac{t+4}{12}=\frac{1}{2}$$

$$2t+8=12 \rightarrow 2t=4 \rightarrow t=2$$

It takes the small pump a total of 2 more hours to fill the tank.

78.   Let $w=4$. Solve for the length:

$$l^2=4(l+4) \rightarrow l^2=4l+16$$

$$l^2-4l-16=0 \rightarrow l=\frac{-(-4)\pm\sqrt{(-4)^2-4(1)(-16)}}{2(1)}=\frac{4\pm\sqrt{80}}{2}=2\pm2\sqrt{5}\approx6.47$$

The length of the plasterboard should be 6.47 feet.

79.   Let x represent the number of passengers over 20.

Then $20+x$ represents the total number of passengers.

$15-0.1x$ represents the fare for each passenger.

Solving the equation for total cost ($482.40), we have:

$(20+x)(15-0.1x)=482.40$

$$300+13x-0.1x^2=482.40 \rightarrow -0.1x^2+13x-182.40=0$$

$$x^2-130x+1824=0 \rightarrow (x-114)(x-16)=0 \rightarrow x=114 \text{ or } x=16$$

Since the capacity of the bus is 44, we discard the 114. The total number of passengers is $20+16=36$, and the ticket price per passenger is $15-0.1(16)=\$13.40$.

So 36 people went on the trip; each person paid $13.40.

80. Let t represent the time it takes the older machine to complete the job by itself.

	Time to do job alone	Part of job done in one hour	Time on Job	Part of total job done by each machine
Old Copier	t	$\dfrac{1}{t}$	1.2	$\dfrac{12}{t}$
New Copier	$t-1$	$\dfrac{1}{t-1}$	1.2	$\dfrac{12}{t-1}$

Since the two copiers complete one job, we have:

$$\frac{1.2}{t}+\frac{1.2}{t-1}=1 \rightarrow 1.2(t-1)+1.2t=t(t-1)$$

$$1.2t-1.2+1.2t=t^2-t \rightarrow t^2-3.4t+1.2=0$$

$$5t^2-17t+6=0 \rightarrow (5t-2)(t-3)=0 \rightarrow t=0.4 \ \text{ or } \ t=3$$

It takes the old copier 3 hours to do the job by itself. (0.4 hours is impossible since together it takes 1.2 hours.)

81. Let r_S represent Scott's rate and let r_T represent Todd's rate.

The time for Scott to run 95 meters is the same as for Todd to run 100 meters.

$$\frac{95}{r_S}=\frac{100}{r_T}$$

$$r_S=0.95r_T$$

$$d_S=0.95d_T$$

If Todd starts from 5 meters behind the start: $d_T=105$

$d_S=0.95d_T=0.95(105)=99.75$

(a)   The race does not end in a tie.

(b)   Todd wins the race.

(c)   Todd wins by 0.25 meters.

(d)   To end in a tie:

$$100=0.95(100+x)$$

$$100=95+0.95x$$

$$5=0.95x$$

$$x=5.263 \text{ meters}$$

(e) $95=0.95(100)$ Therefore, the race ends in a tie.

Chapter 2

Graphs

2.1 Rectangular Coordinates

1. (a) Quadrant II
   (b) Positive x-axis
   (c) Quadrant III
   (d) Quadrant I
   (e) Negative y-axis
   (f) Quadrant IV

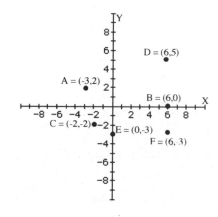

2. (a) Quadrant I
   (b) Quadrant III
   (c) Quadrant II
   (d) Quadrant I
   (e) Positive y-axis
   (f) Negative x-axis

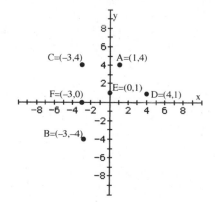

3. The points will be on a vertical line that is two units to the right of the y-axis.

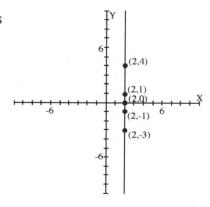

185

4.   The points will be on a horizontal line
      that is three units above the x-axis.

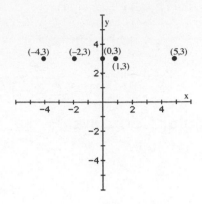

5. $d(P_1, P_2) = \sqrt{(2-0)^2 + (1-0)^2} = \sqrt{4+1} = \sqrt{5}$

6. $d(P_1, P_2) = \sqrt{(-2-0)^2 + (1-0)^2} = \sqrt{4+1} = \sqrt{5}$

7. $d(P_1, P_2) = \sqrt{(-2-1)^2 + (2-1)^2} = \sqrt{9+1} = \sqrt{10}$

8. $d(P_1, P_2) = \sqrt{(2-(-1))^2 + (2-1)^2} = \sqrt{9+1} = \sqrt{10}$

9. $d(P_1, P_2) = \sqrt{(5-3)^2 + (4-(-4))^2} = \sqrt{2^2+8^2} = \sqrt{4+64} = \sqrt{68} = 2\sqrt{17}$

10. $d(P_1, P_2) = \sqrt{(2-(-1))^2 + (4-0)^2} = \sqrt{3^2+4^2} = \sqrt{9+16} = \sqrt{25} = 5$

11. $d(P_1, P_2) = \sqrt{(6-(-3))^2 + (0-2)^2} = \sqrt{9^2+(-2)^2} = \sqrt{81+4} = \sqrt{85}$

12. $d(P_1, P_2) = \sqrt{(4-2)^2 + (2-(-3))^2} = \sqrt{2^2+5^2} = \sqrt{4+25} = \sqrt{29}$

13. $d(P_1, P_2) = \sqrt{(6-4)^2 + (4-(-3))^2} = \sqrt{2^2+7^2} = \sqrt{4+49} = \sqrt{53}$

14. $d(P_1, P_2) = \sqrt{(6-(-4))^2 + (2-(-3))^2} = \sqrt{10^2+5^2} = \sqrt{100+25} = \sqrt{125} = 5\sqrt{5}$

15. $d(P_1, P_2) = \sqrt{(2.3-(-0.2))^2 + (1.1-0.3)^2} = \sqrt{(2.5)^2+(0.8)^2}$
      $= \sqrt{6.25+0.64} = \sqrt{6.89} \approx 2.625$

16. $d(P_1, P_2) = \sqrt{(-0.3-1.2)^2 + (1.1-2.3)^2} = \sqrt{(-1.5)^2+(-1.2)^2}$
      $= \sqrt{2.25+1.44} = \sqrt{3.69}$

17. $d(P_1, P_2) = \sqrt{(0-a)^2 + (0-b)^2} = \sqrt{a^2+b^2}$

18. $d(P_1, P_2) = \sqrt{(0-a)^2 + (0-a)^2} = \sqrt{a^2+a^2} = \sqrt{2a^2} = \sqrt{2}\,|a|$

19. $A = (-2, 5)$, $B = (1, 3)$, $C = (-1, 0)$

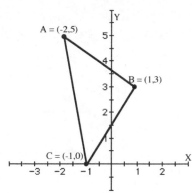

$$d(A,B) = \sqrt{(1-(-2))^2 + (3-5)^2} = \sqrt{3^2 + (-2)^2}$$
$$= \sqrt{9+4} = \sqrt{13}$$
$$d(B,C) = \sqrt{(-1-1)^2 + (0-3)^2} = \sqrt{(-2)^2 + (-3)^2}$$
$$= \sqrt{4+9} = \sqrt{13}$$
$$d(A,C) = \sqrt{(-1-(-2))^2 + (0-5)^2} = \sqrt{1^2 + (-5)^2}$$
$$= \sqrt{1+25} = \sqrt{26}$$

Verifying that $\triangle$ ABC is a right triangle by the Pythagorean Theorem:
$$[d(A,B)]^2 + [d(B,C)]^2 = [d(A,C)]^2$$
$$\left(\sqrt{13}\right)^2 + \left(\sqrt{13}\right)^2 = \left(\sqrt{26}\right)^2$$
$$13 + 13 = 26$$
$$26 = 26$$

The area of a triangle is $A = \tfrac{1}{2}bh$. In this problem,
$$A = \tfrac{1}{2}[d(A,B)] \cdot [d(B,C)] = \tfrac{1}{2}\sqrt{13} \cdot \sqrt{13} = \tfrac{1}{2} \cdot 13 = \frac{13}{2} \text{ square units}$$

20. $A = (-2, 5)$, $B = (12, 3)$, $C = (10, -11)$

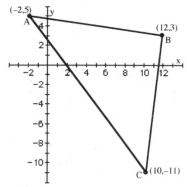

$$d(A,B) = \sqrt{(12-(-2))^2 + (3-5)^2} = \sqrt{14^2 + (-2)^2}$$
$$= \sqrt{196+4} = \sqrt{200} = 10\sqrt{2}$$
$$d(B,C) = \sqrt{(10-12)^2 + (-11-3)^2} = \sqrt{(-2)^2 + (-14)^2}$$
$$= \sqrt{4+196} = \sqrt{200} = 10\sqrt{2}$$
$$d(A,C) = \sqrt{(10-(-2))^2 + (-11-5)^2} = \sqrt{12^2 + (-16)^2}$$
$$= \sqrt{144+256} = \sqrt{400} = 20$$

Verifying that $\triangle$ ABC is a right triangle by the Pythagorean Theorem:
$$[d(A,B)]^2 + [d(B,C)]^2 = [d(A,C)]^2$$
$$\left(10\sqrt{2}\right)^2 + \left(10\sqrt{2}\right)^2 = (20)^2$$
$$200 + 200 = 400$$
$$400 = 400$$

The area of a triangle is $A = \dfrac{1}{2} \cdot bh$. In this problem,
$$A = \frac{1}{2} \cdot [d(A,B)] \cdot [d(B,C)] = \frac{1}{2} \cdot 10\sqrt{2} \cdot 10\sqrt{2} = \frac{1}{2} \cdot 100 \cdot 2 = 100 \text{ square units}$$

21. $A = (-5,3)$, $B = (6,0)$, $C = (5,5)$

$$d(A,B) = \sqrt{(6-(-5))^2 + (0-3)^2} = \sqrt{11^2 + (-3)^2}$$
$$= \sqrt{121 + 9} = \sqrt{130}$$
$$d(B,C) = \sqrt{(5-6)^2 + (5-0)^2} = \sqrt{(-1)^2 + 5^2}$$
$$= \sqrt{1 + 25} = \sqrt{26}$$
$$d(A,C) = \sqrt{(5-(-5))^2 + (5-3)^2} = \sqrt{10^2 + 2^2}$$
$$= \sqrt{100 + 4} = \sqrt{104}$$

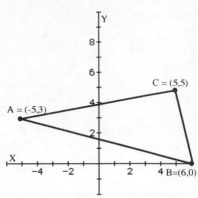

Verifying that Δ ABC is a right triangle by the Pythagorean Theorem:
$$[d(A,C)]^2 + [d(B,C)]^2 = [d(A,B)]^2$$
$$\left(\sqrt{104}\right)^2 + \left(\sqrt{26}\right)^2 = \left(\sqrt{130}\right)^2$$
$$104 + 26 = 130$$
$$130 = 130$$

The area of a triangle is $A = \dfrac{1}{2} \cdot bh$. In this problem,

$$A = \frac{1}{2} \cdot [d(A,C)] \cdot [d(B,C)] = \frac{1}{2} \cdot \sqrt{104} \cdot \sqrt{26} = \frac{1}{2} \cdot \sqrt{2704} = \frac{1}{2} \cdot 52 = 26 \text{ square units}$$

22. $A = (-6, 3)$, $B = (3, -5)$, $C = (-1, 5)$

$$d(A,B) = \sqrt{(3-(-6))^2 + (-5-3)^2} = \sqrt{9^2 + (-8)^2}$$
$$= \sqrt{81 + 64} = \sqrt{145}$$
$$d(B,C) = \sqrt{(-1-3)^2 + (5-(-5))^2} = \sqrt{(-4)^2 + 10^2}$$
$$= \sqrt{16 + 100} = \sqrt{116}$$
$$d(A,C) = \sqrt{(-1-(-6))^2 + (5-3)^2} = \sqrt{5^2 + 2^2}$$
$$= \sqrt{25 + 4} = \sqrt{29}$$

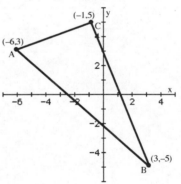

Verifying that Δ ABC is a right triangle by the Pythagorean Theorem:
$$[d(A,C)]^2 + [d(B,C)]^2 = [d(A,B)]^2$$
$$\left(\sqrt{29}\right)^2 + \left(\sqrt{116}\right)^2 = \left(\sqrt{145}\right)^2$$
$$29 + 116 = 145$$
$$145 = 145$$

The area of a triangle is $A = \dfrac{1}{2} \cdot bh$. In this problem,

$$A = \frac{1}{2} \cdot [d(A,C)] \cdot [d(B,C)] = \frac{1}{2} \cdot \sqrt{29} \cdot \sqrt{116} = \frac{1}{2} \cdot \sqrt{3364} = \frac{1}{2} \cdot 58 = 29 \text{ square units}$$

23. $A = (4,-3)$, $B = (0,-3)$, $C = (4,2)$

$$d(A,B) = \sqrt{(0-4)^2 + (-3-(-3))^2} = \sqrt{(-4)^2 + 0^2}$$
$$= \sqrt{16+0} = \sqrt{16} = 4$$
$$d(B,C) = \sqrt{(4-0)^2 + (2-(-3))^2} = \sqrt{4^2 + 5^2}$$
$$= \sqrt{16+25} = \sqrt{41}$$
$$d(A,C) = \sqrt{(4-4)^2 + (2-(-3))^2} = \sqrt{0^2 + 5^2}$$
$$= \sqrt{0+25} = \sqrt{25} = 5$$

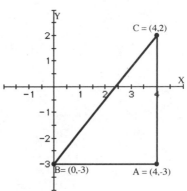

Verifying that Δ ABC is a right triangle by the Pythagorean Theorem:

$$\left[d(A,B)\right]^2 + \left[d(A,C)\right]^2 = \left[d(B,C)\right]^2$$

$$4^2 + 5^2 = \left(\sqrt{41}\right)^2 \rightarrow 16+25 = 41 \rightarrow 41 = 41$$

The area of a triangle is $A = \frac{1}{2}\cdot bh$. In this problem,

$$A = \frac{1}{2}\cdot\left[d(A,B)\right]\cdot\left[d(A,C)\right] = \frac{1}{2}\cdot 4\cdot 5 = 10 \text{ square units}$$

24. $A = (4,-3)$, $B = (4,1)$, $C = (2,1)$

$$d(A,B) = \sqrt{(4-4)^2 + (1-(-3))^2} = \sqrt{0^2 + 4^2}$$
$$= \sqrt{0+16} = \sqrt{16} = 4$$
$$d(B,C) = \sqrt{(2-4)^2 + (1-1)^2} = \sqrt{(-2)^2 + 0^2}$$
$$= \sqrt{4+0} = \sqrt{4} = 2$$
$$d(A,C) = \sqrt{(2-4)^2 + (1-(-3))^2} = \sqrt{(-2)^2 + 4^2}$$
$$= \sqrt{4+16} = \sqrt{20} = 2\sqrt{5}$$

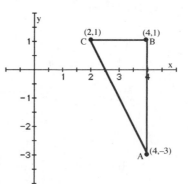

Verifying that Δ ABC is a right triangle by the Pythagorean Theorem:

$$\left[d(A,B)\right]^2 + \left[d(B,C)\right]^2 = \left[d(A,C)\right]^2$$

$$4^2 + 2^2 = \left(2\sqrt{5}\right)^2 \rightarrow 16+4 = 20 \rightarrow 20 = 20$$

The area of a triangle is $A = \frac{1}{2}\cdot bh$. In this problem,

$$A = \frac{1}{2}\cdot\left[d(A,B)\right]\cdot\left[d(B,C)\right] = \frac{1}{2}\cdot 4\cdot 2 = 4 \text{ square units}$$

25.   All points having an x-coordinate of 2 are of the form (2, y). Those which are 5 units from (–2, –1) are:

$$\sqrt{(2-(-2))^2 + (y-(-1))^2} = 5 \rightarrow \sqrt{4^2 + (y+1)^2} = 5$$

Squaring both sides: $4^2 + (y+1)^2 = 25$

$$16 + y^2 + 2y + 1 = 25$$

$$y^2 + 2y - 8 = 0$$
$$(y + 4)(y - 2) = 0$$
$$y = -4 \text{ or } y = 2$$

Therefore, the points are (2, –4) or (2, 2).

26. All points having a y-coordinate of –3 are of the form (x, –3). Those which are 13 units from (1, 2) are:

$$\sqrt{(x-1)^2 + (-3-2)^2} = 13 \rightarrow \sqrt{(x-1)^2 + (-5)^2} = 13$$

Squaring both sides: $(x-1)^2 + 25 = 169$

$$x^2 - 2x + 1 + 25 = 169 \rightarrow x^2 - 2x - 143 = 0$$

$$(x - 13)(x + 11) = 0 \rightarrow x = 13 \text{ or } x = -11$$

Therefore, the points are (–11, –3) or (13, –3).

27. All points on the x-axis are of the form (x, 0). Those which are 5 units from (4, –3) are:

$$\sqrt{(x-4)^2 + (0-(-3))^2} = 5 \rightarrow \sqrt{(x-4)^2 + 3^2} = 5$$

Squaring both sides: $(x-4)^2 + 9 = 25$

$$x^2 - 8x + 16 + 9 = 25 \rightarrow x^2 - 8x = 0$$

$$x(x - 8) = 0 \rightarrow x = 0 \text{ or } x = 8$$

Therefore, the points are (0, 0) or (8, 0).

28. All points on the y-axis are of the form (0, y). Those which are 5 units from (4, 4) are:

$$\sqrt{(0-4)^2 + (y-4)^2} = 5 \rightarrow \sqrt{(-4)^2 + (y-4)^2} = 5$$

Squaring both sides: $(-4)^2 + (y-4)^2 = 25$

$$16 + y^2 - 8y + 16 = 25$$

$$y^2 - 8y + 7 = 0 \rightarrow (y-1)(y-7) = 0 \rightarrow y = 1 \text{ or } y = 7$$

Therefore, the points are (0, 1) or (0, 7).

29. The coordinates of the midpoint are:

$$(x, y) = \left(\frac{x_1 + x_2}{2}, \frac{y_1 + y_2}{2} \right) = \left(\frac{5+3}{2}, \frac{-4+2}{2} \right) = \left(\frac{8}{2}, \frac{-2}{2} \right) = (4, -1)$$

30. The coordinates of the midpoint are:

$$(x, y) = \left(\frac{x_1 + x_2}{2}, \frac{y_1 + y_2}{2} \right) = \left(\frac{-1+2}{2}, \frac{0+4}{2} \right) = \left(\frac{1}{2}, \frac{4}{2} \right) = \left(\frac{1}{2}, 2 \right)$$

31. The coordinates of the midpoint are:

$$(x, y) = \left(\frac{x_1 + x_2}{2}, \frac{y_1 + y_2}{2} \right) = \left(\frac{-3+6}{2}, \frac{2+0}{2} \right) = \left(\frac{3}{2}, \frac{2}{2} \right) = \left(\frac{3}{2}, 1 \right)$$

32. The coordinates of the midpoint are:

$$(x, y) = \left(\frac{x_1 + x_2}{2}, \frac{y_1 + y_2}{2} \right) = \left(\frac{2+4}{2}, \frac{-3+2}{2} \right) = \left(\frac{6}{2}, \frac{-1}{2} \right) = \left(3, -\frac{1}{2} \right)$$

33. The coordinates of the midpoint are:

$$(x,y) = \left(\frac{x_1 + x_2}{2}, \frac{y_1 + y_2}{2}\right) = \left(\frac{4+6}{2}, \frac{-3+1}{2}\right) = \left(\frac{10}{2}, \frac{-2}{2}\right) = (5, -1)$$

34. The coordinates of the midpoint are:

$$(x,y) = \left(\frac{x_1 + x_2}{2}, \frac{y_1 + y_2}{2}\right) = \left(\frac{-4+2}{2}, \frac{-3+2}{2}\right) = \left(\frac{-2}{2}, \frac{-1}{2}\right) = \left(-1, -\frac{1}{2}\right)$$

35. The coordinates of the midpoint are:

$$(x,y) = \left(\frac{x_1 + x_2}{2}, \frac{y_1 + y_2}{2}\right) = \left(\frac{-0.2+2.3}{2}, \frac{0.3+1.1}{2}\right) = \left(\frac{2.1}{2}, \frac{1.4}{2}\right) = (1.05, 0.7)$$

36. The coordinates of the midpoint are:

$$(x,y) = \left(\frac{x_1 + x_2}{2}, \frac{y_1 + y_2}{2}\right) = \left(\frac{1.2+(-0.3)}{2}, \frac{2.3+1.1}{2}\right) = \left(\frac{0.9}{2}, \frac{3.4}{2}\right) = (0.45, 1.7)$$

37. The coordinates of the midpoint are:

$$(x,y) = \left(\frac{x_1 + x_2}{2}, \frac{y_1 + y_2}{2}\right) = \left(\frac{a+0}{2}, \frac{b+0}{2}\right) = \left(\frac{a}{2}, \frac{b}{2}\right)$$

38. The coordinates of the midpoint are:

$$(x,y) = \left(\frac{x_1 + x_2}{2}, \frac{y_1 + y_2}{2}\right) = \left(\frac{a+0}{2}, \frac{a+0}{2}\right) = \left(\frac{a}{2}, \frac{a}{2}\right)$$

39. The midpoint of AB is: $D = \left(\frac{0+0}{2}, \frac{0+6}{2}\right) = (0, 3)$

    The midpoint of AC is: $E = \left(\frac{0+4}{2}, \frac{0+4}{2}\right) = (2, 2)$

    The midpoint of BC is: $F = \left(\frac{0+4}{2}, \frac{6+4}{2}\right) = (2, 5)$

$$d(C, D) = \sqrt{(0-4)^2 + (3-4)^2} = \sqrt{(-4)^2 + (-1)^2} = \sqrt{16+1} = \sqrt{17}$$

$$d(B, E) = \sqrt{(2-0)^2 + (2-6)^2} = \sqrt{2^2 + (-4)^2} = \sqrt{4+16} = \sqrt{20} = 2\sqrt{5}$$

$$d(A, F) = \sqrt{(2-0)^2 + (5-0)^2} = \sqrt{2^2 + 5^2} = \sqrt{4+25} = \sqrt{29}$$

40. Let $P_1 = (0, 0)$, $P_2 = (0, 4)$, $P = (x, y)$

$$d(P_1, P_2) = \sqrt{(0-0)^2 + (4-0)^2} = \sqrt{16} = 4$$

$$d(P_1, P) = \sqrt{(x-0)^2 + (y-0)^2} = \sqrt{x^2 + y^2} = 4 \rightarrow x^2 + y^2 = 16$$

$$d(P_2, P) = \sqrt{(x-0)^2 + (y-4)^2} = \sqrt{x^2 + (y-4)^2} = 4 \rightarrow x^2 + (y-4)^2 = 16$$

$$x^2 + y^2 - 8y + 16 = 16$$

$$16 - 8y + 16 = 16$$

$$-8y = -16 \rightarrow y = 2 \rightarrow x^2 + 2^2 = 16 \rightarrow x^2 = 12 \rightarrow x = \pm 2\sqrt{3}$$

Two triangles are possible. The third vertex is $\left(-2\sqrt{3}, 2\right)$ or $\left(2\sqrt{3}, 2\right)$.

41. $d(P_1, P_2) = \sqrt{(-4-2)^2 + (1-1)^2} = \sqrt{(-6)^2 + 0^2} = \sqrt{36} = 6$

  $d(P_2, P_3) = \sqrt{(-4-(-4))^2 + (-3-1)^2} = \sqrt{0^2 + (-4)^2} = \sqrt{16} = 4$

  $d(P_1, P_3) = \sqrt{(-4-2)^2 + (-3-1)^2} = \sqrt{(-6)^2 + (-4)^2} = \sqrt{36+16} = \sqrt{52} = 2\sqrt{13}$

  Since $\left[d(P_1, P_2)\right]^2 + \left[d(P_2, P_3)\right]^2 = \left[d(P_1, P_3)\right]^2$, the triangle is a right triangle.

42. $d(P_1, P_2) = \sqrt{(6-(-1))^2 + (2-4)^2} = \sqrt{7^2 + (-2)^2} = \sqrt{49+4} = \sqrt{53}$

  $d(P_2, P_3) = \sqrt{(4-6)^2 + (-5-2)^2} = \sqrt{(-2)^2 + (-7)^2} = \sqrt{4+49} = \sqrt{53}$

  $d(P_1, P_3) = \sqrt{(4-(-1))^2 + (-5-4)^2} = \sqrt{5^2 + (-9)^2} = \sqrt{25+81} = \sqrt{106}$

  Since $\left[d(P_1, P_2)\right]^2 + \left[d(P_2, P_3)\right]^2 = \left[d(P_1, P_3)\right]^2$, the triangle is a right triangle.

  Since $d(P_1, P_2) = d(P_2, P_3)$, the triangle is isosceles.

  Therefore, the triangle is an isosceles right triangle.

43. $d(P_1, P_2) = \sqrt{(0-(-2))^2 + (7-(-1))^2} = \sqrt{2^2 + 8^2} = \sqrt{4+64} = \sqrt{68} = 2\sqrt{17}$

  $d(P_2, P_3) = \sqrt{(3-0)^2 + (2-7)^2} = \sqrt{3^2 + (-5)^2} = \sqrt{9+25} = \sqrt{34}$

  $d(P_1, P_3) = \sqrt{(3-(-2))^2 + (2-(-1))^2} = \sqrt{5^2 + 3^2} = \sqrt{25+9} = \sqrt{34}$

  Since $d(P_2, P_3) = d(P_1, P_3)$, the triangle is isosceles.

  Since $\left[d(P_1, P_3)\right]^2 + \left[d(P_2, P_3)\right]^2 = \left[d(P_1, P_2)\right]^2$, the triangle is also a right triangle.

  Therefore, the triangle is an isosceles right triangle.

44. $d(P_1, P_2) = \sqrt{(-4-7)^2 + (0-2)^2} = \sqrt{(-11)^2 + (-2)^2} = \sqrt{121+4} = \sqrt{125} = 5\sqrt{5}$

  $d(P_2, P_3) = \sqrt{(4-(-4))^2 + (6-0)^2} = \sqrt{8^2 + 6^2} = \sqrt{64+36} = \sqrt{100} = 10$

  $d(P_1, P_3) = \sqrt{(4-7)^2 + (6-2)^2} = \sqrt{(-3)^2 + 4^2} = \sqrt{9+16} = \sqrt{25} = 5$

  Since $\left[d(P_1, P_3)\right]^2 + \left[d(P_2, P_3)\right]^2 = \left[d(P_1, P_2)\right]^2$, the triangle is a right triangle.

45. $P_1 = (1,3), \quad P_2 = (5,15)$

  $d(P_1, P_2) = \sqrt{(5-1)^2 + (15-3)^2} = \sqrt{4^2 + 12^2} = \sqrt{16+144} = \sqrt{160} = 4\sqrt{10}$

46. $P_1 = (-8, -4), \quad P_2 = (2, 3)$

  $d(P_1, P_2) = \sqrt{(2-(-8))^2 + (3-(-4))^2} = \sqrt{10^2 + 7^2} = \sqrt{100+49} = \sqrt{149}$

47. $P_1 = (-4,6), \quad P_2 = (4,-8)$

  $d(P_1, P_2) = \sqrt{(4-(-4))^2 + (-8-6)^2} = \sqrt{8^2 + (-14)^2} = \sqrt{64+196} = \sqrt{260} = 2\sqrt{65}$

48. $P_1 = (0, 6), \quad P_2 = (3, -8)$

  $d(P_1, P_2) = \sqrt{(3-0)^2 + (-8-6)^2} = \sqrt{3^2 + (-14)^2} = \sqrt{9+196} = \sqrt{205}$

49.   Plot the vertices of the square at
      (0, 0), (0, s), (s, s), and (s, 0).

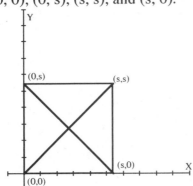

Find the midpoints of the diagonals.

$$M_1 = \left(\frac{0+s}{2}, \frac{0+s}{2}\right) = \left(\frac{s}{2}, \frac{s}{2}\right)$$

$$M_2 = \left(\frac{0+s}{2}, \frac{s+0}{2}\right) = \left(\frac{s}{2}, \frac{s}{2}\right)$$

Since the coordinates of the midpoints are the same, the diagonals of a square intersect at their midpoints.

50.   Let $A = (0, 0)$, $B = (a, 0)$, $C = \left(\frac{a}{2}, \frac{\sqrt{3}\,a}{2}\right)$

$$d(A, B) = \sqrt{(a-0)^2 + (0-0)^2} = \sqrt{a^2} = a$$

$$d(B, C) = \sqrt{\left(\frac{a}{2}-a\right)^2 + \left(\frac{\sqrt{3}\,a}{2}-0\right)^2} = \sqrt{\left(-\frac{a}{2}\right)^2 + \left(\frac{\sqrt{3}\,a}{2}\right)^2} = \sqrt{\frac{a^2}{4}+\frac{3a^2}{4}} = \sqrt{a^2} = a$$

$$d(A, C) = \sqrt{\left(\frac{a}{2}-0\right)^2 + \left(\frac{\sqrt{3}\,a}{2}-0\right)^2} = \sqrt{\left(\frac{a}{2}\right)^2 + \left(\frac{\sqrt{3}\,a}{2}\right)^2} = \sqrt{\frac{a^2}{4}+\frac{3a^2}{4}} = \sqrt{a^2} = a$$

Since the sides are the same length, the triangle is equilateral.

Find the midpoints of the sides:

$$D = M_{AB} = \left(\frac{0+a}{2}, \frac{0+0}{2}\right) = \left(\frac{a}{2}, 0\right) \qquad E = M_{BC} = \left(\frac{a+\frac{a}{2}}{2}, \frac{0+\frac{\sqrt{3}\,a}{2}}{2}\right) = \left(\frac{3a}{4}, \frac{\sqrt{3}\,a}{4}\right)$$

$$F = M_{AC} = \left(\frac{0+\frac{a}{2}}{2}, \frac{0+\frac{\sqrt{3}\,a}{2}}{2}\right) = \left(\frac{a}{4}, \frac{\sqrt{3}\,a}{4}\right)$$

$$d(D, E) = \sqrt{\left(\frac{3a}{4}-\frac{a}{2}\right)^2 + \left(\frac{\sqrt{3}\,a}{4}-0\right)^2} = \sqrt{\left(\frac{a}{4}\right)^2 + \left(\frac{\sqrt{3}\,a}{4}\right)^2} = \sqrt{\frac{a^2}{16}+\frac{3a^2}{16}} = \frac{a}{2}$$

$$d(D, F) = \sqrt{\left(\frac{a}{4}-\frac{a}{2}\right)^2 + \left(\frac{\sqrt{3}\,a}{4}-0\right)^2} = \sqrt{\left(-\frac{a}{4}\right)^2 + \left(\frac{\sqrt{3}\,a}{4}\right)^2} = \sqrt{\frac{a^2}{16}+\frac{3a^2}{16}} = \frac{a}{2}$$

$$d(E, F) = \sqrt{\left(\frac{3a}{4}-\frac{a}{4}\right)^2 + \left(\frac{\sqrt{3}\,a}{4}-\frac{\sqrt{3}\,a}{4}\right)^2} = \sqrt{\left(\frac{a}{2}\right)^2 + 0^2} = \sqrt{\frac{a^2}{4}} = \frac{a}{2}$$

Since the sides are the same length, the triangle is equilateral.

51. Using the Pythagorean Theorem:

$$90^2 + 90^2 = d^2$$
$$8100 + 8100 = d^2$$
$$16200 = d^2$$
$$d = \sqrt{16200}$$
$$d = 90\sqrt{2} \approx 127.28 \text{ feet}$$

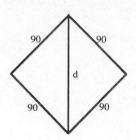

52. Using the Pythagorean Theorem:

$$60^2 + 60^2 = d^2$$
$$3600 + 3600 = d^2$$
$$7200 = d^2$$
$$d = \sqrt{7200}$$
$$d = 60\sqrt{2} \approx 84.85 \text{ feet}$$

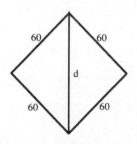

53. (a) First: (90, 0), Second: (90, 90)
     Third: (0, 90)

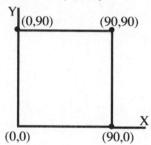

(b) Using the distance formula:
$$d = \sqrt{(310 - 90)^2 + (15 - 90)^2}$$
$$= \sqrt{220^2 + (-75)^2}$$
$$= \sqrt{54025} \approx 232.4 \text{ feet}$$

(c) Using the distance formula:
$$d = \sqrt{(300 - 0)^2 + (300 - 90)^2}$$
$$= \sqrt{300^2 + 210^2}$$
$$= \sqrt{134100} \approx 366.2 \text{ feet}$$

54. (a) First: (60, 0), Second: (60, 60)
     Third: (0, 60)

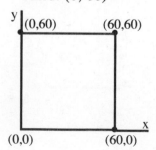

(b) Using the distance formula:
$$d = \sqrt{(180 - 60)^2 + (20 - 60)^2}$$
$$= \sqrt{120^2 + (-40)^2}$$
$$= \sqrt{16000} \approx 126.5 \text{ feet}$$

(c) Using the distance formula:
$$d = \sqrt{(220 - 0)^2 + (220 - 60)^2}$$
$$= \sqrt{220^2 + 160^2}$$
$$= \sqrt{74000} \approx 272.0 \text{ feet}$$

55. The Intrepid heading east moves a distance $30t$ after t hours. The truck heading south moves a distance $40t$ after t hours. Their distance apart after t hours is:

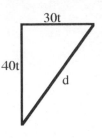

$$d = \sqrt{(30t)^2 + (40t)^2}$$
$$= \sqrt{900t^2 + 1600t^2}$$
$$= \sqrt{2500t^2}$$
$$= 50t$$

56. $d = \sqrt{100^2 + \left(15 \cdot \dfrac{5280}{1} \cdot \dfrac{1}{3600} t\right)^2} = \sqrt{100^2 + (22t)^2} = \sqrt{10000 + 484t^2}$

Graphs

2.2 Graphs of Equations

1.
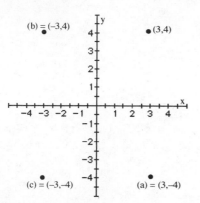

2.
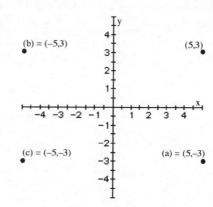

3.
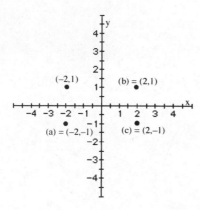

4.
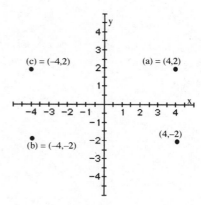

5.
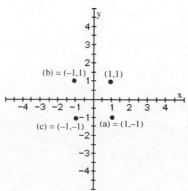

6.
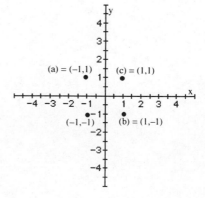

7.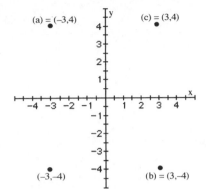

8.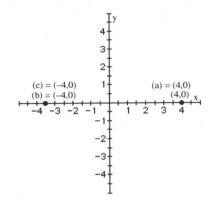

9.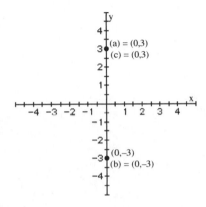

10.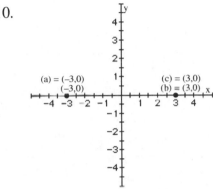

11. (a) $(-1, 0), (1, 0)$ (b) symmetric to the x-axis, y-axis and origin

12. (a) $(0, 1)$ (b) not symmetric to x-axis, y-axis, or origin

13. (a) $\left(-\frac{\pi}{2}, 0\right), \left(\frac{\pi}{2}, 0\right), (0, 1)$ (b) symmetric to the y-axis

14. (a) $(-2, 0), (2, 0), (0, -3)$ (b) symmetric to the y-axis

15. (a) $(0, 0)$ (b) symmetric to the x-axis

16. (a) $(2, 0), (0, 2), (-2, 0), (0, -2)$ (b) symmetric to the x-axis, y-axis, and origin

17. (a) $(1, 0)$ (b) not symmetric to x-axis, y-axis, or origin

18. (a) $(0, 0)$ (b) not symmetric to x-axis, y-axis, or origin

19. (a) $(-1.5, 0), (1.5, 0), (0, -2)$ (b) symmetric to the y-axis

20. (a) $(0, 0)$ (b) symmetric to the origin

21. (a) none   (b) symmetric to the origin

22. (a) none   (b) symmetric to the x-axis

23. $y = x^4 - \sqrt{x}$

       $0 = 0^4 - \sqrt{0}$ $1 = 1^4 - \sqrt{1}$ $0 = (-1)^4 - \sqrt{-1}$

       $0 = 0$ $1 \neq 0$ $0 \neq 1 - \sqrt{-1}$

       $(0, 0)$ is on the graph of the equation.

24. $y = x^3 - 2\sqrt{x}$

       $0 = 0^3 - 2\sqrt{0}$ $1 = 1^3 - 2\sqrt{1}$ $-1 = 1^3 - 2\sqrt{1}$

       $0 = 0$ $1 \neq -1$ $-1 = -1$

       $(0, 0)$ and $(1, -1)$ are on the graph of the equation.

25. $y^2 = x^2 + 9$

       $3^2 = 0^2 + 9$ $0^2 = 3^2 + 9$ $0^2 = (-3)^2 + 9$

       $9 = 9$ $0 \neq 18$ $0 \neq 18$

       $(0, 3)$ is on the graph of the equation.

26. $y^3 = x + 1$

       $2^3 = 1 + 1$ $1^3 = 0 + 1$ $0^3 = -1 + 1$

       $8 \neq 2$ $1 = 1$ $0 = 0$

       $(0, 1)$ and $(-1, 0)$ are on the graph of the equation.

27. $x^2 + y^2 = 4$

       $0^2 + 2^2 = 4$ $(-2)^2 + 2^2 = 4$ $\left(\sqrt{2}\right)^2 + \left(\sqrt{2}\right)^2 = 4$

           $4 = 4$ $8 \neq 4$ $4 = 4$

       $(0, 2)$ and $\left(\sqrt{2}, \sqrt{2}\right)$ are on the graph of the equation.

28. $x^2 + 4y^2 = 4$

                                              $2^2 + 4\left(\dfrac{1}{2}\right)^2 = 4$

       $0^2 + 4 \cdot 1^2 = 4$ $2^2 + 4 \cdot 0^2 = 4$

           $4 = 4$ $4 = 4$ $5 \neq 4$

       $(0, 1)$ and $(2, 0)$ are on the graph of the equation.

29. $x^2 = y$

       y - intercept: Let $x = 0$, then $y = 0$ $(0,0)$

       x - intercept: Let $y = 0$, then $x = 0$ $(0,0)$

       Test for symmetry:

       x - axis: Replace y by $-y$ so $x^2 = -y$, which is not equivalent to $x^2 = y$.

       y - axis: Replace x by $-x$ so $(-x)^2 = y$ or $x^2 = y$, which is equivalent to $x^2 = y$.

       Origin: Replace x by $-x$ and y by $-y$ so $(-x)^2 = -y$ or $x^2 = -y$,

                        which is not equivalent to $x^2 = y$.

       Therefore, the graph is symmetric with respect to the y - axis.

30. $y^2 = x$

y- intercept: Let $x = 0$, then $y = 0$ $(0,0)$

x - intercept: Let $y = 0$, then $x = 0$ $(0,0)$

Test for symmetry:

x - axis: Replace y by $-y$ so $(-y)^2 = x$ or $y^2 = x$,

which is equivalent to $y^2 = x$.

y - axis: Replace x by $-x$ so $y^2 = -x$,

which is not equivalent to $y^2 = x$.

Origin :   Replace x by $-x$ and y by $-y$ so $(-y)^2 = -x$ or $y^2 = -x$,

which is not equivalent to $y^2 = x$.

Therefore, the graph is symmetric with respect to the x-axis.

31. $y = 3x$

y - intercept: Let $x = 0$, then $y = 0$ $(0,0)$

x - intercept: Let $y = 0$, then $x = 0$ $(0,0)$

Test for symmetry:

x - axis: Replace y by $-y$ so $-y = 3x$, which is not equivalent to $y = 3x$.

y - axis: Replace x by $-x$ so $y = 3(-x)$ or $y = -3x$,

which is not equivalent to $y = 3x$.

Origin :   Replace x by $-x$ and y by $-y$ so $-y = 3(-x)$ or $y = 3x$,

which is equivalent to $y = 3x$.

Therefore, the graph is symmetric with respect to the origin.

32. $y = -5x$

y- intercept: Let $x = 0$, then $y = 0$ $(0,0)$

x - intercept: Let $y = 0$, then $x = 0$ $(0,0)$

Test for symmetry:

x - axis: Replace y by $-y$ so $-y = -5x$ or $y = 5x$,

which is not equivalent to $y = -5x$.

y - axis: Replace x by $-x$ so $y = -5(-x)$ or $y = 5x$,

which is not equivalent to $y = -5x$.

Origin :   Replace x by $-x$ and y by $-y$ so $-y = -5(-x)$ or $y = -5x$,

which is equivalent to $y = -5x$.

Therefore, the graph is symmetric with respect to the origin.

33. $x^2 + y - 9 = 0$

y - intercept : Let $x = 0$, then $y = 9$ $(0,9)$

x - intercept : Let $y = 0$, then $x = \pm 3$ $(-3,0),(3,0)$

Test for symmetry:

x - axis: Replace y by $-y$ so $x^2 + (-y) - 9 = 0$ or $x^2 - y - 9 = 0$,

which is not equivalent to $x^2 + y - 9 = 0$.

y - axis: Replace x by $-x$ so $(-x)^2 + y - 9 = 0$ or $x^2 + y - 9 = 0$,

which is equivalent to $x^2 + y - 9 = 0$.

Origin: Replace x by $-x$ and y by $-y$ so $(-x)^2 + (-y) - 9 = 0$ or $x^2 - y - 9 = 0$,

which is not equivalent to $x^2 + y - 9 = 0$.

Therefore, the graph is symmetric with respect to the y-axis.

34. $y^2 - x - 4 = 0$

y - intercept : Let $x = 0$, then $y = \pm 2$ $(0,2), (0,-2)$

x - intercept : Let $y = 0$, then $x = -4$ $(-4,0)$

Test for symmetry:

x - axis: Replace y by $-y$ so $(-y)^2 - x - 4 = 0$ or $y^2 - x - 4 = 0$,

which is equivalent to $y^2 - x - 4 = 0$.

y - axis: Replace x by $-x$ so $y^2 - (-x) - 4 = 0$ or $y^2 + x - 4 = 0$,

which is not equivalent to $y^2 - x - 4 = 0$.

Origin: Replace x by $-x$ and y by $-y$ so $(-y)^2 - (-x) - 4 = 0$ or $y^2 + x - 4 = 0$,

which is not equivalent to $y^2 - x - 4 = 0$

Therefore, the graph is symmetric with respect to the x-axis.

35. $9x^2 + 4y^2 = 36$

y - intercept : Let $x = 0$, then $y = \pm 3$ $(0,-3), (0,3)$

x - intercept : Let $y = 0$, then $x = \pm 2$ $(-2,0), (2,0)$

Test for symmetry:

x - axis: Replace y by $-y$ so $9x^2 + 4(-y)^2 = 36$ or $9x^2 + 4y^2 = 36$,

which is equivalent to $9x^2 + 4y^2 = 36$.

y - axis: Replace x by $-x$ so $9(-x)^2 + 4y^2 = 36$ or $9x^2 + 4y^2 = 36$,

which is equivalent to $9x^2 + 4y^2 = 36$.

Origin: Replace x by $-x$ and y by $-y$ so $9(-x)^2 + 4(-y)^2 = 36$ or $9x^2 + 4y^2 = 36$,

which is equivalent to $9x^2 + 4y^2 = 36$.

Therefore, the graph is symmetric with respect to the x-axis, the y-axis and the origin.

36. $4x^2 + y^2 = 4$

y - intercept : Let $x = 0$, then $y = \pm 2$ $(0,-2), (0,2)$

x - intercept : Let $y = 0$, then $x = \pm 1$ $(-1,0), (1,0)$

Test for symmetry:

x - axis: Replace y by $-y$ so $4x^2 + (-y)^2 = 4$ or $4x^2 + y^2 = 4$,

which is equivalent to $4x^2 + y^2 = 4$.

y-axis: Replace x by $-x$ so $4(-x)^2 + y^2 = 4$ or $4x^2 + y^2 = 4$,

which is equivalent to $4x^2 + y^2 = 4$.

Origin: Replace x by $-x$ and y by $-y$ so $4(-x)^2 + (-y)^2 = 4$ or $4x^2 + y^2 = 4$,

which is equivalent to $4x^2 + y^2 = 4$.

Therefore, the graph is symmetric with respect to the x-axis, the y-axis and the origin.

37. $y = x^3 - 27$

    y-intercept: Let $x = 0$, then $y = 0^3 - 27$

                            $y = -27$ $(0, -27)$

    x-intercept: Let $y = 0$, then $0 = x^3 - 27$

                                $x^3 = 27$

                              $x = 3$ $(3, 0)$

Test for symmetry:

   x-axis: Replace y by $-y$ so $-y = x^3 - 27$, which is not

                equivalent to $y = x^3 - 27$.

   y-axis: Replace x by $-x$ so $y = (-x)^3 - 27$ or $y = -x^3 - 27$,

                which is not equivalent to $y = x^3 - 27$.

   Origin: Replace x by $-x$ and y by $-y$ so $-y = (-x)^3 - 27$ or

                $y = x^3 + 27$, which is not equivalent to $y = x^3 - 27$.

Therefore, the graph is not symmetric to the x-axis, the y-axis, or the origin.

38. $y = x^4 - 1$

    y-intercept: Let $x = 0$, then $y = 0^4 - 1$

                            $y = -1$ $(0, -1)$

    x-intercept: Let $y = 0$, then $0 = x^4 - 1$

                              $x^4 = 1$

                            $x = \pm 1$ $(1, 0), (-1, 0)$

Test for symmetry:

   x-axis: Replace y by $-y$ so $-y = x^4 - 1$, which is not

                equivalent to $y = x^4 - 1$.

   y-axis: Replace x by $-x$ so $y = (-x)^4 - 1$ or $y = x^4 - 1$,

                which is equivalent to $y = x^4 - 1$.

   Origin: Replace x by $-x$ and y by $-y$ so $-y = (-x)^4 - 1$ or

                $-y = x^4 - 1$, which is not equivalent to $y = x^4 - 1$.

Therefore, the graph is symmetric with respect to the y-axis.

39. $y = x^2 - 3x - 4$

  y - intercept: Let $x = 0$, then $y = 0^2 - 3(0) - 4$
  $$y = -4 \qquad (0, -4)$$

  x - intercept: Let $y = 0$, then $0 = x^2 - 3x - 4$
  $$(x - 4)(x + 1) = 0$$
  $$x = 4 \quad x = -1 \quad (4, 0), (-1, 0)$$

Test for symmetry:

  x - axis: Replace y by $-y$ so $-y = x^2 - 3x - 4$, which is not

  equivalent to $y = x^2 - 3x - 4$.

  y - axis: Replace x by $-x$ so $y = (-x)^2 - 3(-x) - 4$ or $y = x^2 + 3x - 4$,

  which is not equivalent to $y = x^2 - 3x - 4$.

  Origin: Replace x by $-x$ and y by $-y$ so $-y = (-x)^2 - 3(-x) - 4$ or

  $y = -x^2 - 3x + 4$, which is not equivalent to $y = x^2 - 3x - 4$.

Therefore, the graph is not symmetric to the x-axis, the y-axis, or the origin.

40. $y = x^2 + 4$

  y - intercept: Let $x = 0$, then $y = 0^2 + 4$
  $$y = 4 \qquad (0, 4)$$

  x - intercept: Let $y = 0$, then $0 = x^2 + 4$
  $$x^2 = -4$$
  no solution - no x - intercept

Test for symmetry:

  x - axis: Replace y by $-y$ so $-y = x^2 + 4$, which is not

  equivalent to $y = x^2 + 4$.

  y - axis: Replace x by $-x$ so $y = (-x)^2 + 4$ or $y = x^2 + 4$,

  which is equivalent to $y = x^2 + 4$.

  Origin: Replace x by $-x$ and y by $-y$ so $-y = (-x)^2 + 4$ or

  $y = -x^2 - 4$, which is not equivalent to $y = x^2 + 4$.

Therefore, the graph is symmetric with respect to the y-axis.

41. $y = \dfrac{3x}{x^2 + 9}$

  y - intercept : Let $x = 0$, then $y = \dfrac{0}{0 + 9}$
  $$y = 0 \qquad (0, 0)$$

  x - intercept : Let $y = 0$, then $0 = \dfrac{3x}{x^2 + 9}$
  $$3x = 0 \rightarrow x = 0 \quad (0, 0)$$

Test for symmetry:

x - axis: Replace y by $-y$ so $-y = \dfrac{3x}{x^2+9}$, which is not

equivalent to $y = \dfrac{3x}{x^2+9}$.

y - axis: Replace x by $-x$ so $y = \dfrac{3(-x)}{(-x)^2+9}$ or $y = \dfrac{-3x}{x^2+9}$,

which is not equivalent to $y = \dfrac{3x}{x^2+9}$.

Origin :   Replace x by $-x$ and y by $-y$ so $-y = \dfrac{-3x}{(-x)^2+9}$ or

$y = \dfrac{3x}{x^2+9}$, which is equivalent to $y = \dfrac{3x}{x^2+9}$.

Therefore, the graph is symmetric with respect to the origin.

42. $y = \dfrac{x^2-4}{2x}$

y - intercept :   Let $x = 0$, then $y = \dfrac{-4}{0}$

$undefined \rightarrow$ no y – intercept

x - intercept :   Let $y = 0$, then $0 = \dfrac{x^2-4}{2x} \rightarrow x^2 - 4 = 0$

$x = \pm 2$ $(-2,0),(2,0)$

Test for symmetry:

x - axis: Replace y by $-y$ so $-y = \dfrac{x^2-4}{2x}$, which is not

equivalent to $y = \dfrac{x^2-4}{2x}$.

y - axis: Replace x by $-x$ so $y = \dfrac{(-x)^2-4}{2(-x)}$ or $y = \dfrac{x^2-4}{-2x}$,

which is not equivalent to $y = \dfrac{x^2-4}{2x}$.

Origin :   Replace x by $-x$ and y by $-y$ so $-y = \dfrac{(-x)^2-4}{2(-x)}$ or

$-y = \dfrac{x^2-4}{-2x}$, which is equivalent to $y = \dfrac{x^2-4}{2x}$.

Therefore, the graph is symmetric with respect to the origin.

43. $y = \dfrac{-x^3}{x^2 - 9}$

y - intercept : Let $x = 0$, then $y = \dfrac{0}{-9} = 0$

$(0,0)$

x - intercept : Let $y = 0$, then $0 = \dfrac{-x^3}{x^2 - 9} \rightarrow -x^3 = 0$

$x = 0$ $(0,0)$

Test for symmetry:

  x - axis: Replace y by $-y$ so $-y = \dfrac{-x^3}{x^2 - 9}$, which is not

equivalent to $y = \dfrac{-x^3}{x^2 - 9}$.

  y - axis: Replace x by $-x$ so $y = \dfrac{-(-x)^3}{(-x)^2 - 9}$ or $y = \dfrac{x^3}{x^2 - 9}$,

which is not equivalent to $y = \dfrac{-x^3}{x^2 - 9}$.

  Origin :   Replace x by $-x$ and y by $-y$ so $-y = \dfrac{-(-x)^3}{(-x)^2 - 9}$ or

$-y = \dfrac{x^3}{x^2 - 9}$, which is equivalent to $y = \dfrac{-x^3}{x^2 - 9}$.

Therefore, the graph is symmetric with respect to the origin.

44. $y = \dfrac{x^4 + 1}{2x^5}$

y - intercept : Let $x = 0$, then $y = \dfrac{1}{0}$

undefined $\rightarrow$ no y – intercept

x - intercept : Let $y = 0$, then $0 = \dfrac{x^4 + 1}{2x^5} \rightarrow x^4 + 1 = 0$

no solution $\rightarrow$ no x – intercept

Test for symmetry:

  x - axis: Replace y by $-y$ so $-y = \dfrac{x^4 + 1}{2x^5}$, which is not equivalent to $y = \dfrac{x^4 + 1}{2x^5}$.

  y - axis: Replace x by $-x$ so $y = \dfrac{(-x)^4 + 1}{2(-x)^5}$ or $y = \dfrac{x^4 + 1}{-2x^5}$, which is

not equivalent to $y = \dfrac{x^4 + 1}{2x^5}$.

Origin :   Replace x by $-x$ and y by $-y$ so $-y = \dfrac{(-x)^4 + 1}{2(-x)^5}$ or $-y = \dfrac{x^4 + 1}{-2x^5}$,

which is equivalent to $y = \dfrac{x^4 + 1}{2x^5}$.

Therefore, the graph is symmetric with respect to the origin.

45. $y = x^3$

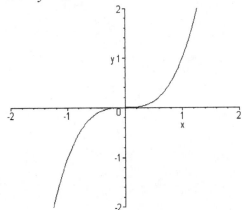

46. $x = y^2$

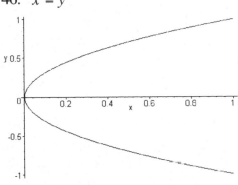

47. $y = \sqrt{x}$

48. $y = \dfrac{1}{x}$

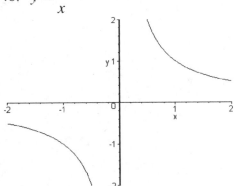

49. $y = 3x + 5$

$2 = 3a + 5$

$3a = -3$

$a = -1$

50. $y = x^2 + 4x$

$b = 2^2 + 4(2) = 4 + 8 = 12$

51. $2x + 3y = 6$

$2a + 3b = 6 \rightarrow b = 2 - \dfrac{2}{3}a$

52. $y = mx + b$

$0 = m(2) + b$

$5 = m(0) + b \rightarrow 5 = b$

$0 = 2m + 5$

$-2m = 5 \rightarrow m = -\dfrac{5}{2}$

53.   (a)

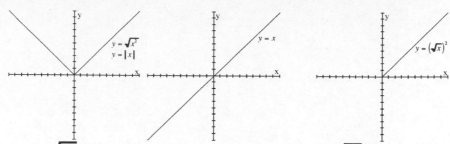

(b)   Since $\sqrt{x^2} = |x|$, then for all x, the graphs of $y = \sqrt{x^2}$ and $y = |x|$ are the same.

(c)   For $y = \left(\sqrt{x}\right)^2$, the domain of the variable x is $x \geq 0$; for $y = x$, the domain of the variable x is all real numbers. Thus, $\left(\sqrt{x}\right)^2 = x$ only for $x \geq 0$.

(d)   For $y = \sqrt{x^2}$, the range of the variable y is $y \geq 0$; for $y = x$, the range of the variable y is all real numbers. Also, $\sqrt{x^2} = x$ only if $x \geq 0$.

54.   Answers will vary

55.   If the equation has x-axis and y-axis symmetry, then we have the following:

x – axis symmetry means $(x, y) \leftrightarrow (x, -y)$

y – axis symmetry means $(x, y) \leftrightarrow (-x, y)$

$\therefore (x, -y) \leftrightarrow (-x, y)$

but the third statement is equivalent to origin symmetry.

If the equation has x-axis and origin symmetry, then we have the following:

x – axis symmetry means $(x, y) \leftrightarrow (x, -y)$

origin symmetry means $(x, y) \leftrightarrow (-x, -y)$

$\therefore (x, -y) \leftrightarrow (-x, -y)$

but the third statement is equivalent to y-axis symmetry.

If the equation has y-axis and origin symmetry, then we have the following:

y – axis symmetry means $(x, y) \leftrightarrow (-x, y)$

origin symmetry means $(x, y) \leftrightarrow (-x, -y)$

$\therefore (-x, y) \leftrightarrow (-x, -y)$

but the third statement is equivalent to x-axis symmetry.

56.   Answers will vary.

Chapter 2

Graphs

2.3 Lines

1. (a) Slope $= \dfrac{1-0}{2-0} = \dfrac{1}{2}$

   (b) If x increases by 2 units, y will increase by 1 unit.

2. (a) Slope $= \dfrac{1-0}{-2-0} = -\dfrac{1}{2}$

   (b) If x increases by 2 units, y will decrease by 1 unit.

3. (a) Slope $= \dfrac{1-2}{1-(-2)} = -\dfrac{1}{3}$

   (b) If x increases by 3 units, y will decrease by 1 unit.

4. (a) Slope $= \dfrac{2-1}{2-(-1)} = \dfrac{1}{3}$

   (b) If x increases by 3 units, y will increase by 1 unit.

5. (x_1, y_1) (x_2, y_2)
   $(2,3)$ $(4,0)$

   Slope $= \dfrac{y_2 - y_1}{x_2 - x_1} = \dfrac{0-3}{4-2} = \dfrac{-3}{2}$

   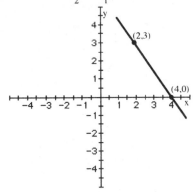

6. (x_1, y_1) (x_2, y_2)
   $(4,2)$ $(3,4)$

   Slope $= \dfrac{y_2 - y_1}{x_2 - x_1} = \dfrac{4-2}{3-4} = \dfrac{2}{-1} = -2$

   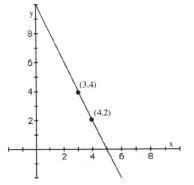

7. (x_1, y_1) (x_2, y_2)
$(-2,3)$ $(2,1)$

Slope $= \dfrac{y_2 - y_1}{x_2 - x_1} = \dfrac{1 - 3}{2 - (-2)} = \dfrac{-2}{4} = -\dfrac{1}{2}$

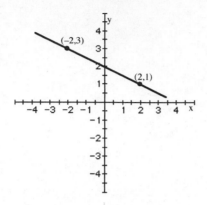

8. (x_1, y_1) (x_2, y_2)
$(-1, 1)$ $(2, 3)$

Slope $= \dfrac{y_2 - y_1}{x_2 - x_1} = \dfrac{3 - 1}{2 - (-1)} = \dfrac{2}{3}$

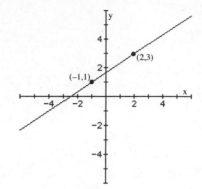

9. (x_1, y_1) (x_2, y_2)
$(-3, -1)$ $(2, -1)$

Slope $= \dfrac{y_2 - y_1}{x_2 - x_1} = \dfrac{-1 - (-1)}{2 - (-3)} = \dfrac{0}{5} = 0$

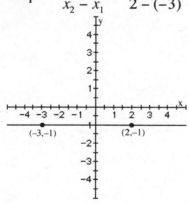

10. (x_1, y_1) (x_2, y_2)
$(4, 2)$ $(-5, 2)$

Slope $= \dfrac{y_2 - y_1}{x_2 - x_1} = \dfrac{2 - 2}{-5 - 4} = \dfrac{0}{-9} = 0$

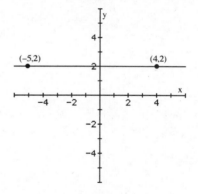

11. (x_1, y_1) (x_2, y_2)
$(-1, 2)$ $(-1, -2)$

Slope $= \dfrac{y_2 - y_1}{x_2 - x_1} = \dfrac{-2 - 2}{-1 - (-1)} = \dfrac{-4}{0}$
Slope is undefined.

12. (x_1, y_1) (x_2, y_2)
$(2, 0)$ $(2, 2)$

Slope $= \dfrac{y_2 - y_1}{x_2 - x_1} = \dfrac{2 - 0}{2 - 2} = \dfrac{2}{0}$
Slope is undefined.

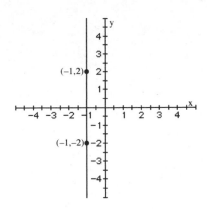

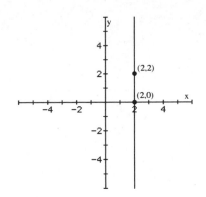

13.

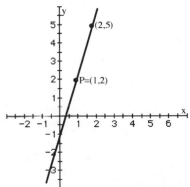

14.

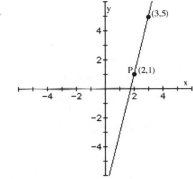

15.

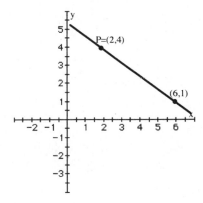

16.

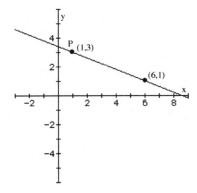

17.

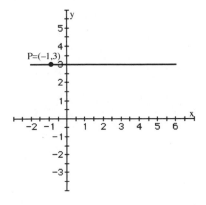

18.

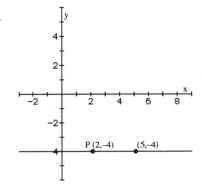

19.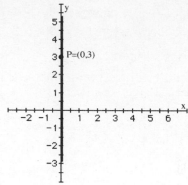

20.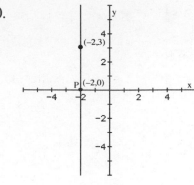

21. Slope = 4 → if x increases by 1,
    y increases by 4

    original point $(1,2)$

    Answers will vary. Three possible points are:
    $x = 1 + 1 = 2$ and $y = 2 + 4 = 6$

    $(2,6)$

    $x = 2 + 1 = 3$ and $y = 6 + 4 = 10$

    $(3,10)$

    $x = 3 + 1 = 4$ and $y = 10 + 4 = 14$

    $(4,14)$

22. Slope = 2 → if x increases by 1,
    y increases by 2

    original point $(-2,3)$

    Answers will vary. Three possible points are:
    $x = -2 + 1 = -1$ and $y = 3 + 2 = 5$

    $(-1,5)$

    $x = -1 + 1 = 0$ and $y = 5 + 2 = 7$

    $(0,7)$

    $x = 0 + 1 = 1$ and $y = 7 + 2 = 9$

    $(1,9)$

23. Slope $= -\dfrac{3}{2}$ → if x increases by 2,
    y decreases by 3

    original point $(2,-4)$

    Answers will vary. Three possible points are:
    $x = 2 + 2 = 4$ and $y = -4 - 3 = -7$

    $(4,-7)$

    $x = 4 + 2 = 6$ and $y = -7 - 3 = -10$

    $(6,-10)$

    $x = 6 + 2 = 8$ and $y = -10 - 3 = -13$

    $(8,-13)$

24. Slope $= \dfrac{4}{3}$ → if x increases by 3,
    y increases by 4

    original point $(-3,2)$

    Answers will vary. Three possible points are:
    $x = -3 + 3 = 0$ and $y = 2 + 4 = 6$

    $(0,6)$

    $x = 0 + 3 = 3$ and $y = 6 + 4 = 10$

    $(3,10)$

    $x = 3 + 3 = 6$ and $y = 10 + 4 = 14$

    $(6,14)$

25.   Slope $= -2 \rightarrow$ if x increases by 1,
       y decreases by 2
       original point $(-2,-3)$
Answers will vary. Three possible points are:
$x = -2 + 1 = -1$ and $y = -3 - 2 = -5$
   $(-1,-5)$
$x = -1 + 1 = 0$ and $y = -5 - 2 = -7$
   $(0,-7)$
$x = 0 + 1 = 1$ and $y = -7 - 2 = -9$
   $(1,-9)$

26.   Slope $= -1 \rightarrow$ if x increases by 1,
       y decreases by 1
       original point $(4,1)$
Answers will vary. Three possible points are:
$x = 4 + 1 = 5$ and $y = 1 - 1 = 0$
   $(5,0)$
$x = 5 + 1 = 6$ and $y = 0 - 1 = -1$
   $(6,-1)$
$x = 6 + 1 = 7$ and $y = -1 - 1 = -2$
   $(7,-2)$

27. $(0,0)$ and $(2,1)$ are points on the line.
       Slope $= \dfrac{1-0}{2-0} = \dfrac{1}{2}$
       y- intercept is 0; using $y = mx + b$:
$$y = \frac{1}{2}x + 0$$
$$2y = x$$
$$0 = x - 2y$$
$$x - 2y = 0 \text{ or } y = \frac{1}{2}x$$

28. $(0,0)$ and $(-2,1)$ are points on the line.
       Slope $= \dfrac{1-0}{-2-0} = \dfrac{1}{-2} = -\dfrac{1}{2}$
       y- intercept is 0; using $y = mx + b$:
$$y = -\frac{1}{2}x + 0$$
$$2y = -x$$
$$x + 2y = 0$$
$$x + 2y = 0 \text{ or } y = -\frac{1}{2}x$$

29. $(-2,2)$ and $(1,1)$ are points on the line.
       Slope $= \dfrac{1-2}{1-(-2)} = -\dfrac{1}{3}$
       Using $y - y_1 = m(x - x_1)$
$$y - 1 = -\frac{1}{3}(x - 1)$$
$$y - 1 = -\frac{1}{3}x + \frac{1}{3}$$
$$y = -\frac{1}{3}x + \frac{4}{3}$$
$$x + 3y = 4 \text{ or } y = -\frac{1}{3}x + \frac{4}{3}$$

30. $(-1,1)$ and $(2,2)$ are points on the line.
       Slope $= \dfrac{2-1}{2-(-1)} = \dfrac{1}{3}$
       Using $y - y_1 = m(x - x_1)$
$$y - 1 = \frac{1}{3}[x - (-1)]$$
$$y - 1 = \frac{1}{3}(x + 1)$$
$$y - 1 = \frac{1}{3}x + \frac{1}{3}$$
$$y = \frac{1}{3}x + \frac{4}{3}$$
$$x - 3y = -4 \text{ or } y = \frac{1}{3}x + \frac{4}{3}$$

31.   Slope $= 3$; containing $(-2,3)$
$$y - y_1 = m(x - x_1)$$
$$y - 3 = 3(x - (-2))$$
$$y - 3 = 3x + 6$$
$$y = 3x + 9$$
$$3x - y = -9 \text{ or } y = 3x + 9$$

32.   Slope $= 2$; containing the point $(4,-3)$
$$y - y_1 = m(x - x_1)$$
$$y - (-3) = 2(x - 4)$$
$$y + 3 = 2x - 8$$
$$y = 2x - 11$$
$$2x - y = 11 \text{ or } y = 2x - 11$$

33. Slope $= -\dfrac{2}{3}$; containing $(1,-1)$

$$y - y_1 = m(x - x_1)$$

$$y - (-1) = -\dfrac{2}{3}(x - 1)$$

$$y + 1 = -\dfrac{2}{3}x + \dfrac{2}{3}$$

$$y = -\dfrac{2}{3}x - \dfrac{1}{3}$$

$$2x + 3y = -1 \ \text{ or } \ y = -\dfrac{2}{3}x - \dfrac{1}{3}$$

34. Slope $= \dfrac{1}{2}$; containing the point $(3, 1)$

$$y - y_1 = m(x - x_1)$$

$$y - 1 = \dfrac{1}{2}(x - 3)$$

$$y - 1 = \dfrac{1}{2}x - \dfrac{3}{2}$$

$$y = \dfrac{1}{2}x - \dfrac{1}{2}$$

$$x - 2y = 1 \ \text{ or } \ y = \dfrac{1}{2}x - \dfrac{1}{2}$$

35. Containing $(1,3)$ and $(-1,2)$

$$m = \dfrac{2 - 3}{-1 - 1} = \dfrac{-1}{-2} = \dfrac{1}{2}$$

$$y - y_1 = m(x - x_1)$$

$$y - 3 = \dfrac{1}{2}(x - 1)$$

$$y - 3 = \dfrac{1}{2}x - \dfrac{1}{2}$$

$$y = \dfrac{1}{2}x + \dfrac{5}{2}$$

$$x - 2y = -5 \ \text{ or } \ y = \dfrac{1}{2}x + \dfrac{5}{2}$$

36. Containing the points $(-3,4)$ and $(2,5)$

$$m = \dfrac{5 - 4}{2 - (-3)} = \dfrac{1}{5}$$

$$y - y_1 = m(x - x_1)$$

$$y - 5 = \dfrac{1}{5}(x - 2)$$

$$y - 5 = \dfrac{1}{5}x - \dfrac{2}{5}$$

$$y = \dfrac{1}{5}x + \dfrac{23}{5}$$

$$x - 5y = -23 \ \text{ or } \ y = \dfrac{1}{5}x + \dfrac{23}{5}$$

37. Slope $= -3$; y-intercept $=3$

$$y = mx + b$$

$$y = -3x + 3$$

$$3x + y = 3 \ \text{ or } \ y = -3x + 3$$

38. Slope $= -2$; y-intercept $=-2$

$$y = mx + b$$

$$y = -2x + (-2)$$

$$y = -2x - 2$$

$$2x + y = -2 \ \text{ or } \ y = -2x - 2$$

39. x-intercept $= 2$; y-intercept $= -1$
Points are $(2,0)$ and $(0,-1)$

$$m = \dfrac{-1 - 0}{0 - 2} = \dfrac{-1}{-2} = \dfrac{1}{2}$$

$$y = mx + b$$

$$y = \dfrac{1}{2}x - 1$$

$$x - 2y = 2 \ \text{ or } \ y = \dfrac{1}{2}x - 1$$

40. x-intercept $= -4$; y-intercept $= 4$
Points are $(-4, 0)$ and $(0, 4)$

$$m = \dfrac{4 - 0}{0 - (-4)} = \dfrac{4}{4} = 1$$

$$y = mx + b$$

$$y = 1x + 4$$

$$y = x + 4$$

$$x - y = -4 \ \text{ or } \ y = x + 4$$

41. Slope undefined; passing through $(2,4)$
This is a vertical line.
$x = 2$
No slope intercept form.

42. Slope undefined; containing the point $(3, 8)$
This is a vertical line.
$x = 3$
No slope intercept form.

43. $y = 2x + 3$
Slope = 2; y-intercept = 3

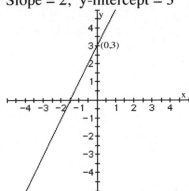

44. $y = -3x + 4$
Slope = -3; y-intercept = 4

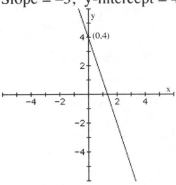

45. $\dfrac{1}{2}y = x - 1$
$y = 2x - 2$; Slope = 2; y-intercept = -2

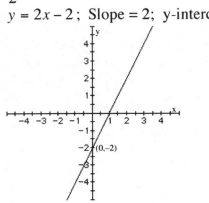

46. $\dfrac{1}{3}x + y = 2$
$y = -\dfrac{1}{3}x + 2$; Slope = $-\dfrac{1}{3}$; y-intercept = 2

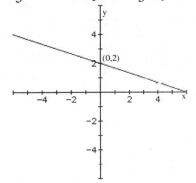

47. $y = \dfrac{1}{2}x + 2$
Slope = $\dfrac{1}{2}$; y-intercept = 2

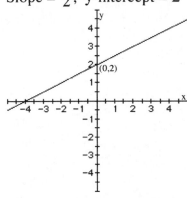

48. $y = 2x + \dfrac{1}{2}$
Slope = 2; y-intercept = $\dfrac{1}{2}$

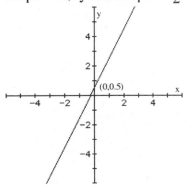

49. $x + 2y = 4$
$2y = -x + 4$

$y = -\dfrac{1}{2}x + 2$; Slope $= -\dfrac{1}{2}$; y-intercept $= 2$

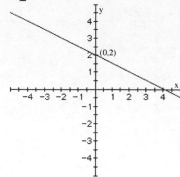

50. $-x + 3y = 6$
$3y = x + 6$

$y = \dfrac{1}{3}x + 2$; Slope $= \dfrac{1}{3}$; y-intercept $= 2$

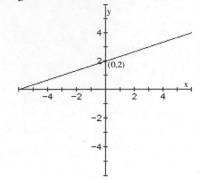

51. $2x - 3y = 6$
$-3y = -2x + 6$

$y = \dfrac{2}{3}x - 2$; Slope $= \dfrac{2}{3}$; y-intercept $= -2$

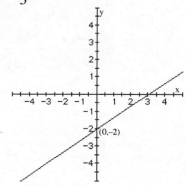

52. $3x + 2y = 6$
$2y = -3x + 6$

$y = -\dfrac{3}{2}x + 3$; Slope $= -\dfrac{3}{2}$; y-intercept $= 3$

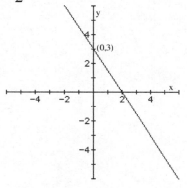

53. $x + y = 1$

$y = -x + 1$; Slope $= -1$; y-intercept $= 1$

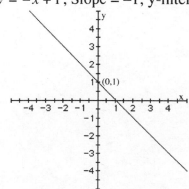

54. $x - y = 2$

$y = x - 2$; Slope $= 1$; y-intercept $= -2$

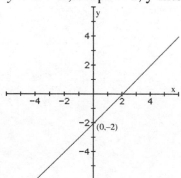

55. $x = -4$
Slope is undefined; y-intercept - none

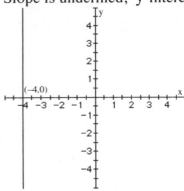

56. $y = -1$
Slope = 0; y-intercept $= -1$

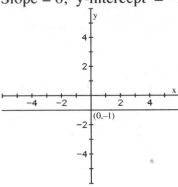

57. $y = 5$
Slope = 0; y-intercept = 5

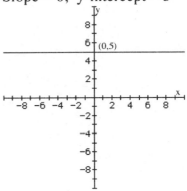

58. $x = 2$
Slope is undefined; y-intercept - none

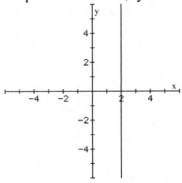

59. $y - x = 0$
$y = x$; Slope = 1; y-intercept $= 0$

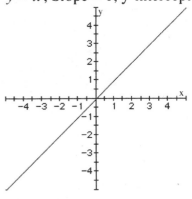

60. $x + y = 0$
$y = -x$; Slope $= -1$; y-intercept $= 0$

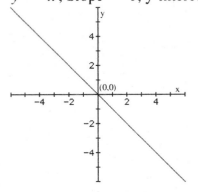

61. $2y - 3x = 0$
     $2y = 3x$

$y = \dfrac{3}{2}x$; Slope $= \dfrac{3}{2}$; y-intercept $= 0$

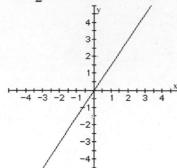

62. $3x + 2y = 0$
     $2y = -3x$

$y = -\dfrac{3}{2}x$; Slope $= -\dfrac{3}{2}$; y-intercept $= 0$

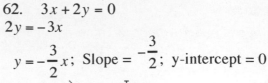
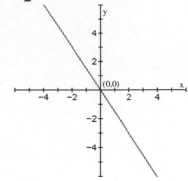

63. The equation of the x-axis is $y = 0$. (The slope is 0 and the y-intercept is 0.)

64. The equation of the y-axis is $x = 0$. (The slope is undefined.)

65. $(^\circ C, ^\circ F) = (0, 32);\quad (^\circ C, ^\circ F) = (100, 212)$

$\text{slope } = \dfrac{212 - 32}{100 - 0} = \dfrac{180}{100} = \dfrac{9}{5}$

$^\circ F - 32 = \dfrac{9}{5}(^\circ C - 0)$

$^\circ F - 32 = \dfrac{9}{5}(^\circ C)$

$^\circ C = \dfrac{5}{9}(^\circ F - 32)$

If $^\circ F = 70,$ then

$^\circ C = \dfrac{5}{9}(70 - 32) = \dfrac{5}{9}(38)$

$^\circ C \approx 21^\circ$

66. (a) $K = ^\circ C + 273$

     (b) $^\circ C = \dfrac{5}{9}(^\circ F - 32)$

$K = \dfrac{5}{9}(^\circ F - 32) + 273 \rightarrow K = \dfrac{5}{9}{}^\circ F - \dfrac{160}{9} + 273 \rightarrow K = \dfrac{5}{9}{}^\circ F + \dfrac{2297}{9}$

67. (a) Since there is only a profit of
          $0.50 per copy and the expense
          of $100 must be deducted, the
          profit is: $P = 0.50x - 100$

     (b) $P = 0.50(1000) - 100$

          $= 500 - 100 = \$400$

     (c) $P = 0.50(5000) - 100$

          $= 2500 - 100 = \$2400$

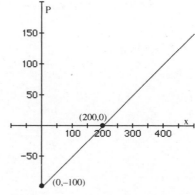

68. (a) Since there is only a profit of
          $0.55 per copy and the expense
          of $125 must be deducted, the
          profit is: $P = 0.55x - 125$
     (b) $P = 0.55(1000) - 125$
          $= 550 - 125 = \$425$
     (c) $P = 0.55(5000) - 125$
          $= 2750 - 125 = \$2625$

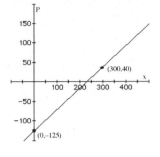

69. $C = 0.06543x + 5.65$
     For 300 kWh,
     $C = 0.06543(300) + 5.65 = \$25.28$
     For 750 kWh,
     $C = 0.06543(750) + 5.65 = \$54.72$

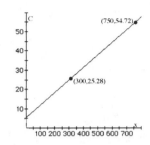

70. given x-intercept $(a,0)$ and y-intercept $(0,b)$,

$$slope = \frac{b-0}{0-a} = -\frac{b}{a}$$

$$y - y_1 = m(x - x_1) \rightarrow y - 0 = -\frac{b}{a}(x - a) \rightarrow y = -\frac{b}{a}x + b$$

$$ay = -x + ba \rightarrow bx + ay = ba$$

now divide each term by ab to get $\dfrac{bx}{ab} + \dfrac{ay}{ab} = \dfrac{ba}{ab} \rightarrow \dfrac{x}{a} + \dfrac{y}{b} = 1$

71. (b)   72. (c)   73. (d)   74. (a)

75. Slope $= 1$; y-intercept $= 2$
     $y = x + 2$ or $x - y = -2$

76.   Slope $= -1$; y-intercept $= 1$
         $y = -x + 1$ or $x + y = 1$

77. Slope $= -\dfrac{1}{3}$; y-intercept $= 1$
     $y = -\dfrac{1}{3}x + 1$ or $x + 3y = 3$

78.   Slope $= -\dfrac{1}{2}$; y-intercept $= -1$
         $y = -\dfrac{1}{2}x - 1$ or $x + 2y = -2$

79. (b), (c), (e) and (g)   80. (a), (c), (f) and (g)

81. Answers will vary.

82. A vertical line cannot be written in slope-intercept form since the slope is undefined.

83. Not every line has two distinct intercepts since a horizontal line might not touch the x-axis
     and a vertical line might not touch the y-axis.
     A line must have at least one intercept since a vertical line always crosses the x-axis, a
     horizontal line always crosses the y-axis and a non-vertical, non-horizontal line always
     crosses both axes.

84.   Two lines that have equal slopes and equal y-intercepts must be represented by equivalent equations.

85.   Two lines with the same non-zero x-intercept and the same y-intercept must have the same slope and therefore must be represented by equivalent equations.

86.   Two lines that have the same slope but different x-intercepts cannot have the same y-intercept.

Assume Line 1 has equation $y = mx + b_1$ and Line 2 has equation $y = mx + b_2$,

Line 1 has x-intercept $-\dfrac{b_1}{m}$ and y-intercept b_1.

Line 2 has x-intercept $-\dfrac{b_2}{m}$ and y-intercept b_2.

Assume also that Line 1 and Line 2 have unequal x-intercepts.

If the lines have the same y-intercept, then $b_1 = b_2$.

$$b_1 = b_2 \Rightarrow \frac{b_1}{m} = \frac{b_2}{m} \Rightarrow -\frac{b_1}{m} = -\frac{b_2}{m}$$

But $-\dfrac{b_1}{m} = -\dfrac{b_2}{m} \Rightarrow$ Line 1 and Line 2 have the same x-intercept, which contradicts the

original assumption that the lines have unequal x-intercepts.

Therefore, Line 1 and Line 2 cannot have the same y-intercept.

87.   Two lines that have the same y-intercept but different slopes can only have the same x-intercept if the y-intercept is zero.

Assume Line 1 has equation $y = m_1 x + b$ and Line 2 has equation $y = m_2 x + b$,

Line 1 has x-intercept $-\dfrac{b}{m_1}$ and y-intercept b.

Line 2 has x-intercept $-\dfrac{b}{m_2}$ and y-intercept b.

Assume also that Line 1 and Line 2 have unequal slopes, that is $m_1 \neq m_2$.

If the lines have the same x-intercept, then $-\dfrac{b}{m_1} = -\dfrac{b}{m_2}$.

$$-\frac{b}{m_1} = -\frac{b}{m_2} \Rightarrow -m_2 b = -m_1 b \Rightarrow -m_2 b + m_1 b = 0$$

$$\text{But} \quad -m_2 b + m_1 b = 0 \Rightarrow b(m_1 - m_2) = 0$$

$$\Rightarrow b = 0$$

$$\text{or } m_1 - m_2 = 0 \Rightarrow m_1 = m_2$$

Since we are assuming that $m_1 \neq m_2$, the only way that the two lines can have the same x-intercept is if $b = 0$.

88 – 90.   Answers will vary.

Chapter 2

Graphs

2.4 Parallel and Perpendicular Lines; Circles

1. parallel line: slope = 6

    perpendicular line: slope = $-\dfrac{1}{6}$

2. parallel line: slope = -3

    perpendicular line: slope = $\dfrac{1}{3}$

3. parallel line: slope = $-\dfrac{1}{2}$

    perpendicular line: slope = 2

4. parallel line: slope = $\dfrac{2}{3}$

    perpendicular line: slope = $-\dfrac{3}{2}$

5. $2x - 4y + 5 = 0 \rightarrow y = \dfrac{1}{2}x + \dfrac{5}{4}$

    parallel line: slope = $\dfrac{1}{2}$

    perpendicular line: slope = - 2

6. $3x + y = 4 \rightarrow y = -3x + 4$

    parallel line: slope = - 3

    perpendicular line: slope = $\dfrac{1}{3}$

7. $3x + 5y - 10 = 0 \rightarrow y = -\dfrac{3}{5}x + 2$

    parallel line: slope = $-\dfrac{3}{5}$

    perpendicular line: slope = $\dfrac{5}{3}$

8. $4x - 3y + 7 = 0 \rightarrow y = \dfrac{4}{3}x + \dfrac{7}{3}$

    parallel line: slope = $\dfrac{4}{3}$

    perpendicular line: slope = $-\dfrac{3}{4}$

9. parallel line: slope is undefined
    perpendicular line: slope = 0

10. parallel line: slope = 0
    perpendicular line: slope is undefined

11. $y - y_1 = m(x - x_1), \ \ m = 2$
    $\quad y - 3 = 2(x - 3)$
    $\quad y - 3 = 2x - 6$
    $\qquad y = 2x - 3$
    $\ 2x - y = 3 \ \text{ or } \ y = 2x - 3$

12. $y - y_1 = m(x - x_1), \ \ m = -1$
    $\quad y - 2 = -1(x - 1)$
    $\quad y - 2 = -x + 1$
    $\qquad y = -x + 3$
    $\ x + y = 3 \ \text{ or } \ y = -x + 3$

13. $y - y_1 = m(x - x_1),\ m = -\dfrac{1}{2}$

$$y - 2 = -\frac{1}{2}(x - 1)$$

$$y - 2 = -\frac{1}{2}x + \frac{1}{2}$$

$$y = \frac{1}{-2}x + \frac{5}{2}$$

$$x + 2y = 5 \ \text{ or } \ y = -\frac{1}{2}x + \frac{5}{2}$$

14. $y - y_1 = m(x - x_1),\ m = 1$

$$y - 1 = 1(x - (-1))$$

$$y - 1 = x + 1$$

$$y = x + 2$$

$$x - y = -2 \ \text{ or } \ y = x + 2$$

15.   Parallel to $y = 2x$; Slope $= 2$
Containing $(-1, 2)$

$$y - y_1 = m(x - x_1)$$

$$y - 2 = 2(x - (-1))$$

$$y - 2 = 2x + 2$$

$$y = 2x + 4$$

$$2x - y = -4 \ \text{ or } \ y = 2x + 4$$

16.   Parallel to $y = -3x$; Slope $= -3$;
Containing the point $(-1, 2)$

$$y - y_1 = m(x - x_1)$$

$$y - 2 = -3(x - (-1))$$

$$y - 2 = -3x - 3$$

$$y = -3x - 1$$

$$3x + y = -1 \ \text{ or } \ y = -3x - 1$$

17.   Parallel to $2x - y = -2$; Slope $= 2$
Containing $(0, 0)$

$$y - y_1 = m(x - x_1)$$

$$y - 0 = 2(x - 0)$$

$$y = 2x$$

$$2x - y = 0 \ \text{ or } \ y = 2x$$

18.   Parallel to $x - 2y = -5$; Slope $= \dfrac{1}{2}$;
Containing the point $(0, 0)$

$$y - y_1 = m(x - x_1)$$

$$y - 0 = \frac{1}{2}(x - 0)$$

$$y = \frac{1}{2}x$$

$$x - 2y = 0 \ \text{ or } \ y = \frac{1}{2}x$$

19.   Parallel to $x = 5$;
Containing $(4, 2)$
This is a vertical line.
$x = 4$
    No slope intercept form.

20.   Parallel to $y = 5$;
Containing the point $(4, 2)$
This is a horizontal line. Slope $= 0$
$y = 2$

21. Perpendicular to $y = \frac{1}{2}x + 4$;
Slope of perpendicular $= -2$
Containing $(1,-2)$
$$y - y_1 = m(x - x_1)$$
$$y - (-2) = -2(x - 1)$$
$$y + 2 = -2x + 2$$
$$y = -2x$$
$$2x + y = 0 \ \text{ or } \ y = -2x$$

22. Perpendicular to $y = 2x - 3$;
Slope of perpendicular $= -\frac{1}{2}$
Containing the point $(1,-2)$
$$y - y_1 = m(x - x_1)$$
$$y - (-2) = -\frac{1}{2}(x - 1)$$
$$y + 2 = -\frac{1}{2}x + \frac{1}{2} \rightarrow y = -\frac{1}{2}x - \frac{3}{2}$$
$$x + 2y = -3 \ \text{ or } \ y = -\frac{1}{2}x - \frac{3}{2}$$

23. Perpendicular to $2x + y = 2$;
Containing $(-3,0)$
Slope of perpendicular $= \frac{1}{2}$
$$y - y_1 = m(x - x_1)$$
$$y - 0 = \frac{1}{2}(x - (-3)) \rightarrow y = \frac{1}{2}x + \frac{3}{2}$$
$$x - 2y = -3 \ \text{ or } \ y = \frac{1}{2}x + \frac{3}{2}$$

24. Perpendicular to $x - 2y = -5$;
Slope of perpendicular $= -2$
Containing the point $(0, 4)$
$$y = mx + b$$
$$y = -2x + 4$$
$$2x + y = 4 \ \text{ or } \ y = -2x + 4$$

25. Perpendicular to $x = 8$;
Slope of perpendicular $= 0$
Containing $(3,4)$
$$y - y_1 = m(x - x_1)$$
$$y - 4 = 0(x - 3)$$
$$y - 4 = 0 \rightarrow y = 4 \ \text{ or } \ y = 0x + 4$$

26. Perpendicular to $y = 8$;
Slope of perpendicular is undefined.
Containing the point $(3,4)$
$x = 3$ No slope-intercept form.

27. Center $= (2, 1)$
Radius $=$ distance from $(0,1)$ to $(2,1)$
$$= \sqrt{(2-0)^2 + (1-1)^2} = \sqrt{4} = 2$$
$$(x-2)^2 + (y-1)^2 = 4$$

28. Center $= (1, 2)$
Radius $=$ distance from $(1,0)$ to $(1,2)$
$$= \sqrt{(1-1)^2 + (2-0)^2} = \sqrt{4} = 2$$
$$(x-1)^2 + (y-2)^2 = 4$$

29. Center $=$ midpoint of $(1,2)$ and $(4,2)$
$$= \left(\frac{1+4}{2}, \frac{2+2}{2}\right) = \left(\frac{5}{2}, 2\right)$$
Radius $=$ distance from $\left(\frac{5}{2},2\right)$ to $(4,2)$
$$= \sqrt{\left(4 - \frac{5}{2}\right)^2 + (2-2)^2} = \sqrt{\frac{9}{4}} = \frac{3}{2}$$
$$\left(x - \frac{5}{2}\right)^2 + (y-2)^2 = \frac{9}{4}$$

30. Center $=$ midpoint of $(0,1)$ and $(2,3)$
$$= \left(\frac{0+2}{2}, \frac{1+3}{2}\right) = (1, 2)$$
Radius $=$ distance from $(1,2)$ to $(2,3)$
$$= \sqrt{(2-1)^2 + (3-2)^2} = \sqrt{2}$$
$$(x-1)^2 + (y-2)^2 = 2$$

31. $(x-h)^2 + (y-k)^2 = r^2$
      $(x-0)^2 + (y-0)^2 = 2^2$
      $\qquad x^2 + y^2 = 4$
      General form:
      $x^2 + y^2 - 4 = 0$

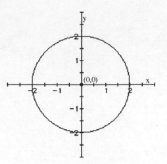

32. $(x-h)^2 + (y-k)^2 = r^2$
      $(x-0)^2 + (y-0)^2 = 3^2$
      $\qquad x^2 + y^2 = 9$
      General form:
      $x^2 + y^2 - 9 = 0$

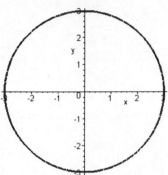

33. $(x-h)^2 + (y-k)^2 = r^2$
      $(x-1)^2 + (y-(-1))^2 = 1^2$
      $\qquad (x-1)^2 + (y+1)^2 = 1$
      General form:
      $x^2 - 2x + 1 + y^2 + 2y + 1 = 1$
      $\qquad x^2 + y^2 - 2x + 2y + 1 = 0$

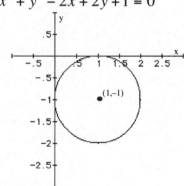

34. $(x-h)^2 + (y-k)^2 = r^2$
      $(x-(-2))^2 + (y-1)^2 = 2^2$
      $\qquad (x+2)^2 + (y-1)^2 = 4$
      General form:
      $x^2 + 4x + 4 + y^2 - 2y + 1 = 4$
      $\qquad x^2 + y^2 + 4x - 2y + 1 = 0$

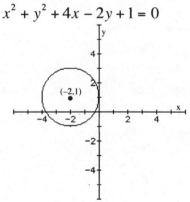

222

35.
$(x-h)^2 + (y-k)^2 = r^2$
$(x-0)^2 + (y-2)^2 = 2^2$
$x^2 + (y-2)^2 = 4$
General form:
$x^2 + y^2 - 4y + 4 = 4$
$x^2 + y^2 - 4y = 0$

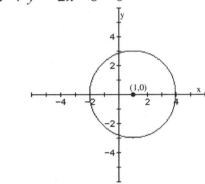

36.
$(x-h)^2 + (y-k)^2 = r^2$
$(x-1)^2 + (y-0)^2 = 3^2$
$(x-1)^2 + y^2 = 9$
General form:
$x^2 - 2x + 1 + y^2 = 9$
$x^2 + y^2 - 2x - 8 = 0$

37.
$(x-h)^2 + (y-k)^2 = r^2$
$(x-4)^2 + (y-(-3))^2 = 5^2$
$(x-4)^2 + (y+3)^2 = 25$
General form:
$x^2 - 8x + 16 + y^2 + 6y + 9 = 25$
$x^2 + y^2 - 8x + 6y = 0$

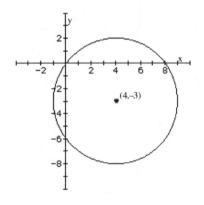

38.
$(x-h)^2 + (y-k)^2 = r^2$
$(x-2)^2 + (y-(-3))^2 = 4^2$
$(x-2)^2 + (y+3)^2 = 16$
General form:
$x^2 - 4x + 4 + y^2 + 6y + 9 = 16$
$x^2 + y^2 - 4x + 6y - 3 = 0$

39.
$x^2 + y^2 = 4$
$x^2 + y^2 = 2^2$
Center: $(0,0)$
Radius $= 2$

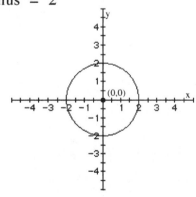

40. $x^2 + (y-1)^2 = 1$
      $x^2 + (y-1)^2 = 1^2$
      Center: $(0, 1)$
      Radius = 1

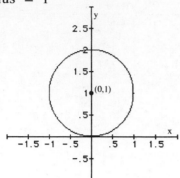

41. $2(x-3)^2 + 2y^2 = 8$
      $(x-3)^2 + y^2 = 4$
      Center: $(3,0)$
      Radius = 2

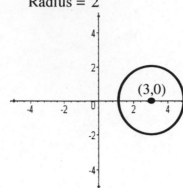

42. $3(x+1)^2 + 3(y-1)^2 = 6$
      $(x+1)^2 + (y-1)^2 = 2$
      Center: $(-1,1)$
      Radius = $\sqrt{2}$

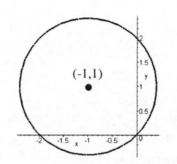

43. $x^2 + y^2 + 4x - 4y - 1 = 0$
      $\qquad x^2 + 4x + y^2 - 4y = 1$
      $(x^2 + 4x + 4) + (y^2 - 4y + 4) = 1 + 4 + 4$
      $\qquad (x+2)^2 + (y-2)^2 = 3^2$
      Center: $(-2,2)$
      Radius = 3

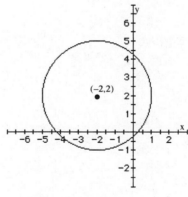

44. $x^2 + y^2 - 6x + 2y + 9 = 0$
      $\qquad x^2 - 6x + y^2 + 2y = -9$
      $(x^2 - 6x + 9) + (y^2 + 2y + 1) = -9 + 9 + 1$
      $\qquad (x-3)^2 + (y+1)^2 = 1^2$
      Center: $(3, -1)$
      Radius = 1

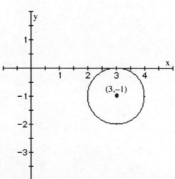

224

45. $x^2 + y^2 - x + 2y + 1 = 0$

$$x^2 - x + y^2 + 2y = -1$$

$$\left(x^2 - x + \frac{1}{4}\right) + (y^2 + 2y + 1) = -1 + \frac{1}{4} + 1$$

$$\left(x - \frac{1}{2}\right)^2 + (y + 1)^2 = \left(\frac{1}{2}\right)^2$$

Center: $\left(\frac{1}{2}, -1\right)$

Radius $= \dfrac{1}{2}$

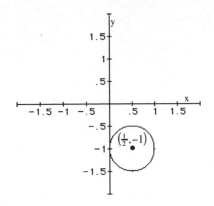

46. $x^2 + y^2 + x + y - \dfrac{1}{2} = 0$

$$x^2 + x + y^2 + y = \frac{1}{2}$$

$$\left(x^2 + x + \frac{1}{4}\right) + \left(y^2 + y + \frac{1}{4}\right) = \frac{1}{2} + \frac{1}{4} + \frac{1}{4}$$

$$\left(x + \frac{1}{2}\right)^2 + \left(y + \frac{1}{2}\right)^2 = 1^2$$

Center: $\left(-\frac{1}{2}, -\frac{1}{2}\right)$

Radius $= 1$

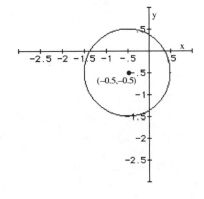

47. $2x^2 + 2y^2 - 12x + 8y - 24 = 0$

$$x^2 + y^2 - 6x + 4y = 12$$

$$x^2 - 6x + y^2 + 4y = 12$$

$$(x^2 - 6x + 9) + (y^2 + 4y + 4) = 12 + 9 + 4$$

$$(x - 3)^2 + (y + 2)^2 = 5^2$$

Center: $(3, -2)$

Radius $= 5$

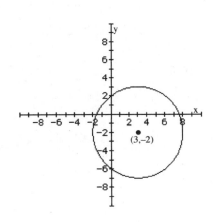

48. $2x^2 + 2y^2 + 8x + 7 = 0$

$$x^2 + y^2 + 4x = -\frac{7}{2}$$

$$x^2 + 4x + y^2 = -\frac{7}{2}$$

$$(x^2 + 4x + 4) + y^2 = -\frac{7}{2} + 4$$

$$(x + 2)^2 + y^2 = \frac{1}{2}$$

$$(x + 2)^2 + y^2 = \left(\frac{\sqrt{2}}{2}\right)^2$$

Center: $(-2, 0)$

Radius $= \dfrac{\sqrt{2}}{2}$

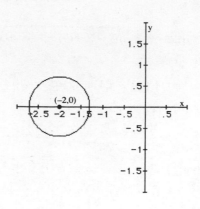

49.   Center at (0,0); containing point (- 3, 2).

$$r = \sqrt{(-3-0)^2 + (2-0)^2} = \sqrt{9+4} = \sqrt{13}$$

Equation:

$$(x-0)^2 + (y-0)^2 = \left(\sqrt{13}\right)^2 \rightarrow x^2 + y^2 = 13 \rightarrow x^2 + y^2 - 13 = 0$$

50.   Center at (1,0); containing point (- 2, 3).

$$r = \sqrt{(-2-1)^2 + (3-0)^2} = \sqrt{9+9} = \sqrt{18} = 3\sqrt{2}$$

Equation:

$$(x-1)^2 + (y-0)^2 = \left(\sqrt{18}\right)^2 \rightarrow x^2 - 2x + 1 + y^2 = 18 \rightarrow x^2 + y^2 - 2x - 17 = 0$$

51.   Center at (2,3); tangent to the x-axis.

$r = 3$

Equation:

$$(x-2)^2 + (y-3)^2 = 3^2$$

$$x^2 - 4x + 4 + y^2 - 6y + 9 = 9 \rightarrow x^2 + y^2 - 4x - 6y + 4 = 0$$

52.   Center at (–3, 1); tangent to the y-axis.

$r = 3$

Equation:

$$(x+3)^2 + (y-1)^2 = 3^2$$

$$x^2 + 6x + 9 + y^2 - 2y + 1 = 9 \rightarrow x^2 + y^2 + 6x - 2y + 1 = 0$$

53.   Endpoints of a diameter are (1,4) and (–3,2).
The center is at the midpoint of that diameter:

Center: $\left(\dfrac{1 + (-3)}{2}, \dfrac{4+2}{2}\right) = (-1, 3)$

Radius: $r = \sqrt{(1-(-1))^2 + (4-3)^2} = \sqrt{4+1} = \sqrt{5}$

Equation:

$$(x-(-1))^2 + (y-3)^2 = \left(\sqrt{5}\right)^2$$
$$x^2 + 2x + 1 + y^2 - 6y + 9 = 5$$
$$x^2 + y^2 + 2x - 6y + 5 = 0$$

54. Endpoints of a diameter are (4, 3) and (0, 1).
The center is at the midpoint of that diameter:

Center: $\left(\dfrac{4+0}{2}, \dfrac{3+1}{2}\right) = (2, 2)$

Radius: $r = \sqrt{(4-2)^2 + (3-2)^2} = \sqrt{4+1} = \sqrt{5}$

Equation:

$$(x-2)^2 + (y-2)^2 = \left(\sqrt{5}\right)^2$$
$$x^2 - 4x + 4 + y^2 - 4y + 4 = 5$$
$$x^2 + y^2 - 4x - 4y + 3 = 0$$

55. Consider the points $A(-2,5)$, $B(1,3)$ and $C(-1,0)$

slope of $\overline{AB} = \dfrac{3-5}{1-(-2)} = -\dfrac{2}{3}$;   slope of $\overline{AC} = \dfrac{0-5}{-1-(-2)} = -\dfrac{5}{3}$;   slope of $\overline{BC} = \dfrac{0-3}{-1-1} = \dfrac{3}{2}$

Therefore, $\triangle ABC$ has a right angle at vertex B since

slope $\overline{AB} = -\dfrac{2}{3}$ and slope $\overline{BC} = \dfrac{3}{2} \to \overline{AB} \perp \overline{BC}$

56. Consider the points $A(1,-1)$, $B(4,1)$, $C(2,2)$ and $D(5,4)$

slope of $\overline{AB} = \dfrac{1-(-1)}{4-1} = \dfrac{2}{3}$;   slope of $\overline{CD} = \dfrac{4-2}{5-2} = \dfrac{2}{3}$

slope of $\overline{AC} = \dfrac{2-(-1)}{2-1} = 3$;   slope of $\overline{BD} = \dfrac{4-1}{5-4} = 3$

Therefore, the quadrilateral $ACDB$ is a parallelogram since

slope $\overline{AB} = \dfrac{2}{3}$ and slope $\overline{CD} = \dfrac{2}{3} \to \overline{AB}$ is parallel to $\overline{CD}$

slope $\overline{AC} = 3$ and slope $\overline{BD} = 3 \to \overline{AC}$ is parallel to $\overline{BD}$

57.   Consider the points $A(-1,0)$, $B(2,3)$, $C(1,-2)$ and $D(4,1)$

slope of $\overline{AB} = \dfrac{3-0}{2-(-1)} = 1$;   slope of $\overline{CD} = \dfrac{1-(-2)}{4-1} = 1$

slope of $\overline{AC} = \dfrac{-2-0}{1-(-1)} = -1$;   slope of $\overline{BD} = \dfrac{1-3}{4-2} = -1$

Therefore, the quadrilateral $ACDB$ is a parallelogram since

slope $\overline{AB} = 1$ and slope $\overline{CD} = 1 \rightarrow \overline{AB}$ is parallel to $\overline{CD}$

slope $\overline{AC} = -1$ and slope $\overline{BD} = -1 \rightarrow \overline{AC}$ is parallel to $\overline{BD}$

Furthermore,

slope $\overline{AB} = 1$ and slope $\overline{BD} = -1 \rightarrow \overline{AB} \perp \overline{BD}$

slope $\overline{AC} = -1$ and slope $\overline{CD} = 1 \rightarrow \overline{AC} \perp \overline{CD}$

So the quadrilateral $ACDB$ is a rectangle.

58.   Consider the points $A(0,0)$, $B(1,3)$, $C(4,2)$ and $D(3,-1)$

slope of $\overline{AB} = \dfrac{3-0}{1-0} = 3$;   slope of $\overline{CD} = \dfrac{-1-2}{3-4} = 3$

slope of $\overline{AD} = \dfrac{-1-0}{3-0} = -\dfrac{1}{3}$;   slope of $\overline{BC} = \dfrac{2-3}{4-1} = -\dfrac{1}{3}$

Therefore, the quadrilateral $ABCD$ is a parallelogram since

slope $\overline{AB} = 3$ and slope $\overline{CD} = 3 \rightarrow \overline{AB}$ is parallel to $\overline{CD}$

slope $\overline{AD} = -\dfrac{1}{3}$ and slope $\overline{BC} = -\dfrac{1}{3} \rightarrow \overline{BC}$ is parallel to $\overline{AD}$

Furthermore,

slope $\overline{AB} = 3$ and slope $\overline{BC} = -\dfrac{1}{3} \rightarrow \overline{AB} \perp \overline{BC}$

slope $\overline{AD} = -\dfrac{1}{3}$ and slope $\overline{CD} = 3 \rightarrow \overline{AD} \perp \overline{CD}$

So the quadrilateral $ABCD$ is a rectangle.

Finally, the quadrilateral is a square since

$$d(A,B) = \sqrt{(1-0)^2 + (3-0)^2} = \sqrt{10}$$

$$d(A,D) = \sqrt{(-1-0)^2 + (3-0)^2} = \sqrt{10}$$

$$d(B,C) = \sqrt{(4-1)^2 + (2-3)^2} = \sqrt{10}$$

$$d(C,D) = \sqrt{(3-4)^2 + (-1-2)^2} = \sqrt{10}$$

59. (c)   60. (d)   61.   (b)   62.   (a)

63. $(x+3)^2 + (y-1)^2 = 16$ 64. $(x-4)^2 + (y+2)^2 = 9$

65. $(x-2)^2 + (y-2)^2 = 9$ 66. $(x-1)^2 + (y-3)^2 = 4$

67. (b), (c), (e) and (g)   68. (b), (e) and (g)

69. (c)   70. (d)

71. Consider the diagram

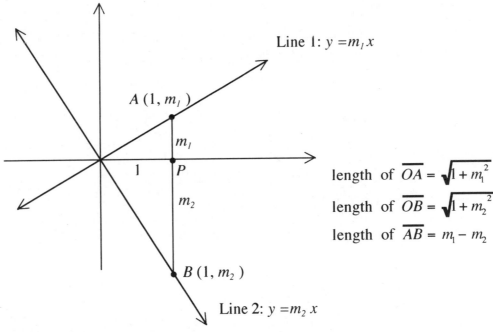

Line 1: $y = m_1 x$

$A(1, m_1)$

m_1

1 P

length of $\overline{OA} = \sqrt{1 + m_1^2}$

m_2

length of $\overline{OB} = \sqrt{1 + m_2^2}$

length of $\overline{AB} = m_1 - m_2$

$B(1, m_2)$

Line 2: $y = m_2 x$

Now consider the equation

$$\left(\sqrt{1 + m_1^2}\right)^2 + \left(\sqrt{1 + m_2^2}\right)^2 = (m_1 - m_2)^2$$

If this equation is valid, then $\triangle AOB$ is a right triangle with right angle at vertex O.

$$\left(\sqrt{1 + m_1^2}\right)^2 + \left(\sqrt{1 + m_2^2}\right)^2 = (m_1 - m_2)^2$$

$$1 + m_1^2 + 1 + m_2^2 = m_1^2 - 2m_1 m_2 + m_2^2$$

$$2 + m_1^2 + m_2^2 = m_1^2 - 2m_1 m_2 + m_2^2$$

but we are assuming that $m_1 m_2 = -1$, so we have

$$2 + m_1^2 + m_2^2 = m_1^2 - 2(-1) + m_2^2$$

$$2 + m_1^2 + m_2^2 = m_1^2 + 2 + m_2^2$$

$$0 = 0$$

Therefore, by the converse of the Pythagorean Theorem, $\triangle AOB$ is a right triangle with right angle at vertex O. Thus Line1 $\perp$ Line2.

72. $x^2 + y^2 + 2x + 4y - 4091 = 0$
       $x^2 + 2x + y^2 + 4y - 4091 = 0$

   $x^2 + 2x + 1 + y^2 + 4y + 4 = 4091 + 5 \rightarrow (x + 2)^2 + (y + 2)^2 = 4096$

   The circle representing Earth has center $(-2, -2)$ and radius $= \sqrt{4096} = 64$
   So the radius of the satellite's orbit is $64 + 0.6 = 64.06$ units.

   The equation of the orbit is $(x + 2)^2 + (y + 2)^2 = (64.06)^2$.

73.   (a) $x^2 + (mx + b)^2 = r^2$

       $x^2 + m^2 x^2 + 2bmx + b^2 = r^2 \rightarrow (1 + m^2)x^2 + 2bmx + b^2 - r^2 = 0$
       There is one solution if and only if the discriminant is zero.
       $$(2bm)^2 - 4(1 + m^2)(b^2 - r^2) = 0$$
       $$4b^2 m^2 - 4b^2 + 4r^2 - 4b^2 m^2 + 4m^2 r^2 = 0 \rightarrow -4b^2 + 4r^2 + 4m^2 r^2 = 0$$
       $$-b^2 + r^2 + m^2 r^2 = 0 \rightarrow r^2(1 + m^2) = b^2$$

       (b)   Using the quadratic formula, knowing that the discriminant is zero:
       $$x = \frac{-2bm}{2(1 + m^2)} = \frac{-bm}{\left(\dfrac{b^2}{r^2}\right)} = \frac{-bmr^2}{b^2} = \frac{-mr^2}{b}$$

       $$y = m\left(\frac{-mr^2}{b}\right) + b = \frac{-m^2 r^2}{b} + b = \frac{-m^2 r^2 + b^2}{b} = \frac{r^2}{b}$$

       (c)   The slope of the tangent line is m.
       The slope of the line joining the point of tangency and the center is:
       $$\frac{\left(\dfrac{r^2}{b} - 0\right)}{\left(\dfrac{-mr^2}{b} - 0\right)} = \frac{r^2}{b} \cdot \frac{b}{-mr^2} = -\frac{1}{m}$$

74. $x^2 + y^2 = 9$
       Center: $(0, 0)$

   Slope from center to $\left(1, 2\sqrt{2}\right)$ is $\dfrac{2\sqrt{2} - 0}{1 - 0} = \dfrac{2\sqrt{2}}{1} = 2\sqrt{2}$.

   Slope of the tangent line is $\dfrac{-1}{2\sqrt{2}} = -\dfrac{\sqrt{2}}{4}$.

Equation of the tangent line is:

$$y - 2\sqrt{2} = -\frac{\sqrt{2}}{4}(x-1) \rightarrow y - 2\sqrt{2} = -\frac{\sqrt{2}}{4}x + \frac{\sqrt{2}}{4}$$

$$4y - 8\sqrt{2} = -\sqrt{2}\,x + \sqrt{2} \rightarrow \sqrt{2}\,x + 4y = 9\sqrt{2}$$

75. $x^2 + y^2 - 4x + 6y + 4 = 0$

$(x^2 - 4x + 4) + (y^2 + 6y + 9) = -4 + 4 + 9$

$(x-2)^2 + (y+3)^2 = 9$

Center: $(2, -3)$

Slope from center to $\left(3, 2\sqrt{2} - 3\right)$ is $\dfrac{2\sqrt{2} - 3 - (-3)}{3 - 2} = \dfrac{2\sqrt{2}}{1} = 2\sqrt{2}$

Slope of the tangent line is: $\dfrac{-1}{2\sqrt{2}} = -\dfrac{\sqrt{2}}{4}$

Equation of the tangent line:

$$y - \left(2\sqrt{2} - 3\right) = -\frac{\sqrt{2}}{4}(x-3) \rightarrow y - 2\sqrt{2} + 3 = -\frac{\sqrt{2}}{4}x + \frac{3\sqrt{2}}{4}$$

$$4y - 8\sqrt{2} + 12 = -\sqrt{2}x + 3\sqrt{2} \rightarrow \sqrt{2}x + 4y = 11\sqrt{2} - 12$$

76. Let (h, k) be the center of the circle.

$$x - 2y + 4 = 0 \rightarrow 2y - x + 4 \rightarrow y = \frac{1}{2}x + 2$$

The slope of the tangent line is $\dfrac{1}{2}$. The slope from (h, k) to $(0, 2)$ is -2.

$\dfrac{2-k}{0-h} = -2 \rightarrow 2 - k = 2h$

The other tangent line is $y = 2x - 7$. Its slope is 2.

The slope from (h, k) to $(3, -1)$ is $-\dfrac{1}{2}$.

$\dfrac{-1-k}{3-h} = -\dfrac{1}{2} \rightarrow 2 + 2k = 3 - h \rightarrow 2k = 1 - h \rightarrow h = 1 - 2k$

Solve the two equations in h and k:

$2 - k = 2(1 - 2k) \rightarrow 2 - k = 2 - 4k \rightarrow 3k = 0 \rightarrow k = 0$

$h = 1 - 2(0) = 1$

The center of the circle is $(1, 0)$.

77. Find the centers of the two circles:

$$x^2 + y^2 - 4x + 6y + 4 = 0$$

$$(x^2 - 4x + 4) + (y^2 + 6y + 9) = -4 + 4 + 9$$

$$(x-2)^2 + (y+3)^2 = 9 \qquad \text{Center: } (2, -3)$$

$$x^2 + y^2 + 6x + 4y + 9 = 0$$

$$(x^2 + 6x + 9) + (y^2 + 4y + 4) = -9 + 9 + 4$$

$$(x+3)^2 + (y+2)^2 = 4 \qquad \text{Center: } (-3, -2)$$

Find the slope of the line containing the centers:

$$m = \frac{-2 - (-3)}{-3 - 2} = -\frac{1}{5}$$

Find the equation of the line containing the centers:

$$y + 3 = -\frac{1}{5}(x - 2) \rightarrow 5y + 15 = -x + 2 \rightarrow x + 5y = -13$$

78. Find the slope of the line containing (a,b) and (b, a): $\dfrac{a - b}{b - a} = -1$

The slope of the line $y = x$ is 1.

Since $-1 \cdot 1 = -1$, the line containing the points (a,b) and (b, a) is perpendicular to the line $y = x$.

The midpoint of (a,b) and (b, a) = $\left(\dfrac{a + b}{2}, \dfrac{b + a}{2} \right)$.

Since the coordinates are the same, the midpoint lies on the line $y = x$.

79. $2x - y = C$
Graph the lines:
$$2x - y = -2$$
$$2x - y = 0$$
$$2x - y = 4$$
All the lines have the same slope, 2.
The lines are parallel.

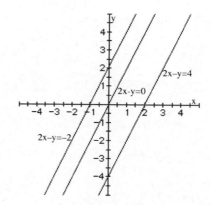

80. $Cx + y = -4$
Graph the lines:
$$-2x + y = -4$$
$$0x + y = -4$$
$$4x + y = -4$$
All the lines have the same y-intercept, –4.

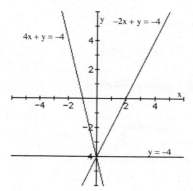

81. $y = 2$

Graphs

2.5   Scatter Diagrams; Linear Curve Fitting

1.   Linear, $m > 0$ 2.   Nonlinear   3.   Linear, $m < 0$

4.   Nonlinear   5.   Nonlinear   6.   Linear, $m > 0$

7.   (a)

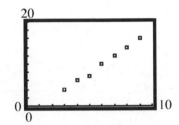

(b)   Answers will vary. We select (4,6) and (8,14). The slope of the line containing these points is:
$$m = \frac{14 - 6}{8 - 4} = \frac{8}{4} = 2$$
The equation of the line is:
$$y - y_1 = m(x - x_1)$$
$$y - 6 = 2(x - 4)$$
$$y - 6 = 2x - 8$$
$$y = 2x - 2$$

(c)

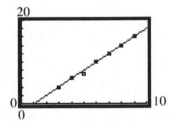

(d)   Using the LINear REGresssion program, the line of best fit is:
$$y = 2.0357x - 2.3571$$

(e)

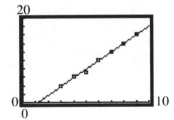

8.   (a)
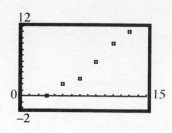

(b)   Selection of points will vary. We select (5,2) and (11,9). The slope of the line containing these points is:

$$m = \frac{9-2}{11-5} = \frac{7}{6}$$

The equation of the line is:

$$y - y_1 = m(x - x_1)$$

$$y - 2 = \frac{7}{6}(x - 5)$$

$$y - 2 = \frac{7}{6}x - \frac{35}{6}$$

$$y = \frac{7}{6}x - \frac{23}{6}$$

(c)
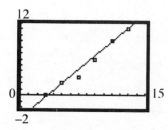

(d)   Using the LINear REGression program, the line of best fit is:

$$y = 1.1286x - 3.8619$$

(e)
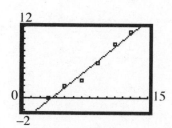

9.   (a)
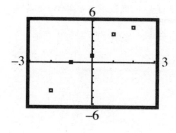

(b)   Answers will vary. We select $(-2,-4)$ and $(1,4)$. The slope of the line containing these points is:

$$m = \frac{4-(-4)}{1-(-2)} = \frac{8}{3}$$

The equation of the line is:

$$y - y_1 = m(x - x_1)$$

$$y - (-4) = \frac{8}{3}(x - (-2))$$

$$y + 4 = \frac{8}{3}x + \frac{16}{3}$$

$$y = \frac{8}{3}x + \frac{4}{3}$$

(c)

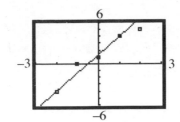

(d) Using the LINear REGresssion
program, the line of best fit is:
$$y = 2.2x + 1.2$$

(e)

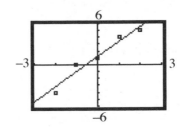

10. (a)

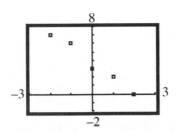

(b) Selection of points will vary. We select
$(-1,6)$ and $(1,2)$. The slope of the line
containing these points is:
$$m = \frac{2-6}{1-(-1)} = \frac{-4}{2} = -2$$
The equation of the line is:
$$y - y_1 = m(x - x_1)$$
$$y - 6 = -2(x - (-1))$$
$$y - 6 = -2x - 2$$
$$y = -2x + 4$$

(c)

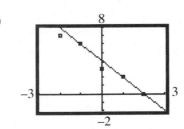

(d) Using the LINear REGression
program, the line of best fit is:
$$y = -1.8x + 3.6$$

(e)

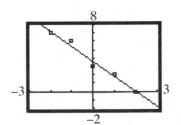

11. (a)

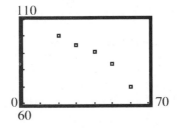

(b) Answers will vary. We select $(30,95)$
and $(60,70)$. The slope of the line
containing these points is:
$$m = \frac{70-95}{60-30} = \frac{-25}{30} = -\frac{5}{6}$$
The equation of the line is:
$$y - y_1 = m(x - x_1)$$
$$y - 95 = -\frac{5}{6}(x - 30)$$
$$y - 95 = -\frac{5}{6}x + 25$$
$$y = -\frac{5}{6}x + 120$$

(c)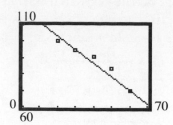

(d) Using the LINear REGresssion program, the line of best fit is:
$$y = -0.72x + 116.6$$

(e)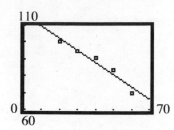

12. (a)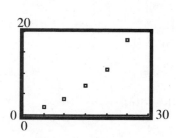

(b) Selection of points will vary. We select (10,4) and (20,11). The slope of the line containing these points is:
$$m = \frac{11-4}{20-10} = \frac{7}{10}$$
The equation of the line is:
$$y - y_1 = m(x - x_1)$$
$$y - 4 = \frac{7}{10}(x - 10)$$
$$y - 4 = \frac{7}{10}x - 7$$
$$y = \frac{7}{10}x - 3$$

(c)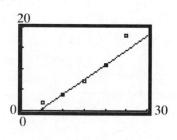

(d) Using the LINear REGression program, the line of best fit is:
$$y = 0.78x - 3.3$$

(e)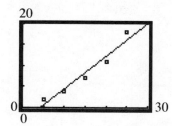

13. (a)

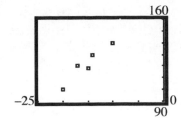

(b) Answers will vary. We select
(−20,100) and (−15,118). The slope
of the line containing these points is:
$$m = \frac{118 - 100}{-15 - (-20)} = \frac{18}{5}$$
The equation of the line is:
$$y - y_1 = m(x - x_1)$$
$$y - 100 = \frac{18}{5}(x - (-20))$$
$$y - 100 = \frac{18}{5}x + 72$$
$$y = \frac{18}{5}x + 172$$

(c)

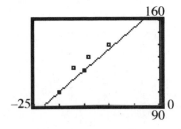

(d) Using the LINear REGresssion
program, the line of best fit is:
$$y = 3.8613x + 180.2920$$

(e)

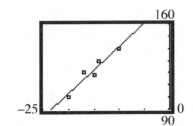

14. (a)

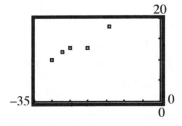

(b) Selection of points will vary. We select
(−27,12) and (−20,13). The slope of the
line containing these
points is:
$$m = \frac{13 - 12}{-20 - (-27)} = \frac{1}{7}$$
The equation of the line is:
$$y - y_1 = m(x - x_1)$$
$$y - 12 = \frac{1}{7}(x - (-27))$$
$$y - 12 = \frac{1}{7}x + \frac{27}{7}$$
$$y = \frac{1}{7}x + \frac{111}{7}$$

(c)

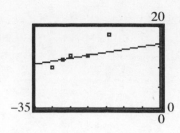

(d) Using the LINear REGression program, the line of best fit is:
$$y = 0.4421x + 23.4559$$

(e)

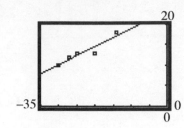

15. (a)

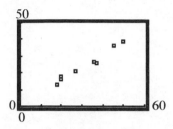

(b) using points $(20,16)$ and $(50,39)$,
$$slope = \frac{39-16}{50-20} = \frac{23}{30}$$
the point slope formula yields
$$C - 16 = \frac{23}{30}(I - 20)$$
$$C = \left(\frac{23}{30}\right)I - \frac{460}{30} + 16$$
$$C = 0.76I + 0.67$$

(c) As disposable income increases by $1, consumption increases by $0.76.

(d) $C = 0.77(42) + 0.67 = \$33.01$
A family with disposable income of $42,000 consumes about $33,010.

(e) $C = 0.7549I + 0.6266$

16. (a)

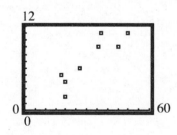

(b) using points $(20,4)$ and $(50,11)$,
$$slope = \frac{11-4}{50-20} = \frac{7}{30} \approx 0.23$$
the point slope formula yields
$$S - 4 = 0.23(I - 20)$$
$$S = 0.23L - 0.6$$

(c) As disposable income increases by $1, savings increases by $0.23.

(d) $S = 0.23(42) - 0.6 = 9.06$
A family with disposable income of $42,000 saves about $9,060.

(e) $S = 0.2451I - 0.6266$

238

17. (a) (Data used in graphs is in thousands.)

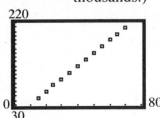

(b) $L = 2.9814I - 0.0761$

(c)

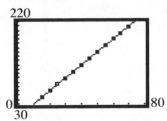

(d) As annual income increases by $1, the loan amount increases by $2.9814.

(e) $L = 2.9814(42) - 0.0761 = 125.143$
A person with an annual income of $42,000 would qualify for a loan of about $125,143.

18. (a) (All amounts are in thousands.)

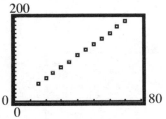

(b) $L = 2.7098I - 0.0661$

(c)

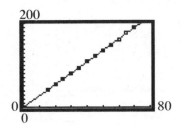

(d) As annual income increases by $1, the loan amount increases by $2.7098.

(e) $L = 2.7098(42) - 0.0661 = 113.746$
A person with an annual income of $42,000 would qualify for a loan of about $113,746.

19. (a)

(b) $T = 0.0782h + 59.0909$

(c)

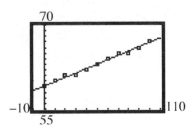

(d) As relative humidity increases by 1%, the apparent temperature increases by 0.0782°.

(e) $T = 0.0782(75) + 59.0909 = 64.96$
A relative humidity of 75% would give an apparent temperature of 65°.

20. (a)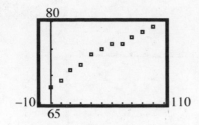

(b) $T = 0.1082h + 68.6818$
(c)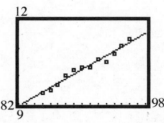

(d) As relative humidity increases
by 1%, the apparent temperature
increases by 0.1082°.

(e) $T = 0.1082(75) + 68.6818 \approx 76.80$
A relative humidity of 75% would
give an apparent temperature of 77°.

21. (a)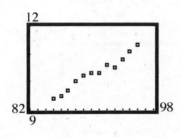

(b) $M = 0.1633x - 4.4691$
(c)

(d) As the year increases by 1, the
average miles per car (in thousands)
increases by 0.1633.

(e) $M = 0.1633(97) - 4.4691 = 11.371$
In 1997, the average number of miles
driven per car is 11,371.

Graphs

2.6 Variation

1. $y = kx$

   $2 = 10k \rightarrow k = \dfrac{1}{5}$

   $y = \dfrac{1}{5}x$

2. $v = kt$

   $16 = 2k \rightarrow k = 8$

   $v = 8t$

3. $A = kx^2$

   $4\pi = 4k \rightarrow k = \pi$

   $A = \pi x^2$

4. $V = kx^3$

   $36\pi = 27k \rightarrow k = \dfrac{4}{3}\pi$

   $V = \dfrac{4}{3}\pi x^3$

5. $F = \dfrac{k}{d^2}$

   $10 = \dfrac{k}{25} \rightarrow k = 250$

   $F = \dfrac{250}{d^2}$

6. $y = \dfrac{k}{\sqrt{x}}$

   $4 = \dfrac{k}{3} \rightarrow k = 12$

   $y = \dfrac{12}{\sqrt{x}}$

7. $z = k\left(x^2 + y^2\right)$

   $5 = k\left(3^2 + 4^2\right) \rightarrow k = \dfrac{1}{5}$

   $z = \dfrac{1}{5}\left(x^2 + y^2\right)$

8. $T = k\left(\sqrt[3]{x}\right)\left(d^2\right)$

   $18 = k\left(\sqrt[3]{8}\right)\left(3^2\right) \rightarrow 18 = k\,(18)$

   $\rightarrow k = 1$

   $T = \left(\sqrt[3]{x}\right)\left(d^2\right)$

9. $M = \dfrac{kd^2}{\sqrt{x}}$

   $24 = \dfrac{k\left(4^2\right)}{\sqrt{9}} \rightarrow 24 = \dfrac{16k}{3} \rightarrow k = 4.5$

   $M = \dfrac{4.5\left(d^2\right)}{\sqrt{x}}$

10. $z = k\left(x^3 + y^2\right)$

    $1 = k\left(2^3 + 3^2\right) \rightarrow 1 = k\,(17)$

    $\rightarrow k = \dfrac{1}{17}$

    $z = \dfrac{1}{17}\left(x^3 + y^2\right)$

11. $T^2 = \dfrac{ka^3}{d^2}$

$2^2 = \dfrac{k(2^3)}{4^2} \rightarrow k = 8$

$T^2 = \dfrac{8a^3}{d^2}$

12. $z^3 = k\left(x^2 + y^2\right)$

$2^3 = k\left(9^2 + 4^2\right) \rightarrow 8 = k\,(97) \rightarrow k = \dfrac{8}{97}$

$z^3 = \dfrac{8}{97}\left(x^2 + y^2\right)$

13. $V = \dfrac{4}{3}\pi r^3$

14. $c^2 = a^2 + b^2$

15. $A = \dfrac{1}{2}bh$

16. $p = 2\,(l + w)$

17. $V = \pi r^2 h$

18. $V = \dfrac{\pi}{3}r^2 h$

19. $F = \dfrac{\left(6.67 \times 10^{-11}\right)mM}{d^2}$

20. $T = \dfrac{2\pi}{\sqrt{32}}\sqrt{l}$

21. $s = kt^2$

$16 = k(1)^2 \rightarrow k = 16$

in 3 seconds $s = (16)(9) = 144\ feet$

$64 = 16t^2 \rightarrow t^2 = 4 \rightarrow t = \pm 2$

so it takes 2 seconds to fall 64 feet.

22. $v = kt$

$64 = k(2) \rightarrow k = 32$

in 3 seconds

$v = (32)(3) = 96$ feet per second

23. $E = kw$

$3 = k(20) \rightarrow k = \dfrac{3}{20}$

when $w = 15,\quad E = \left(\dfrac{3}{20}\right)(15) = 2.25$

24. $R = \dfrac{k}{l}$

$256 = \dfrac{k}{48} \rightarrow k = 12288$

when $R = 576,$

$576 = \dfrac{12288}{l} \rightarrow l = 21.\overline{33}$ inches

25. $W = \dfrac{k}{d^2}$

$55 = \dfrac{k}{3960^2} \rightarrow k = 862488000$

when $d = 3965,$

$W = \dfrac{862488000}{3965^2} = 54.86$ pounds

26. $F = kAv^2$

$11 = k(20)(22)^2 \rightarrow k = \dfrac{11}{9680}$

when $A = 47.125$ and $v = 36.5$

$F = \left(\dfrac{11}{9680}\right)(47.125)(36.5\ )^2 \approx 70.37$ pounds

27. $h = ksd^3$

$36 = k(75)(2)^3 \rightarrow k = 0.06$

when $h = 45$ and $s = 125$,

$45 = (0.06)(125)(d)^3$

$\rightarrow d = \sqrt[3]{\dfrac{45}{7.5}} \approx 0.84$ inches

28. $W = \dfrac{k}{d^2}$

$200 = \dfrac{k}{3960^2} \rightarrow k = 3136320000$

when $d = 3961$,

$W = \dfrac{3136320000}{3961^2} \approx 199.89$ pounds

29. $K = kmv^2$

$400 = k(25)(100)^2 \rightarrow k = 0.0016$

when $v = 150$,

$K = (0.0016)(25)(150)^2 = 900$ foot $-$ pounds

30. $R = \dfrac{kl}{d^2}$

$1.24 = \dfrac{k(432)}{(4)^2} \rightarrow k = \dfrac{(1.24)(16)}{432} \approx 0.0459$

when $R = 1.44$ and $d = 3$,

$1.44 = \dfrac{\left(\dfrac{(1.24)(16)}{432}\right)(l)}{(3)^2}$

$\rightarrow l = (9)(1.44)\left(\dfrac{432}{(1.24)(16)}\right) \approx 282.19$ feet

31. $S = \dfrac{kpd}{t}$

$100 = \dfrac{k(25)(5)}{(0.75)} \rightarrow k = 0.6$

when $p = 40, d = 8$ and $t = 0.50$

$S = \dfrac{(0.6)(40)(8)}{(0.50)} = 320$ pounds

32. $S = \dfrac{kwt^2}{l}$

$750 = \dfrac{k(4)(2)^2}{8} \rightarrow k = 375$

when $l = 10, w = 6$ and $t = 2$,

$S = \dfrac{(375)(6)(2)^2}{10} = 900$ pounds

33. $R = \dfrac{kl}{r^2}$

$10 = \dfrac{k(50)}{(0.006)^2} \rightarrow k = 7.2 \times 10^{-6}$

when $l = 100$ and $r = 0.007$,

$R = \dfrac{(7.2 \times 10^{-6})(100)}{(0.007)^2} = 14.69$ ohms

34. $V = \dfrac{kt}{P}$

$100 = \dfrac{k(300)}{15} \rightarrow k = 5$

when $V = 80$ and $t = 310$,

$80 = \dfrac{(5)(310)}{P} \rightarrow P = 19.375$ atmospheres

35. $v = \sqrt{g}\sqrt{r} = \sqrt{gr}$

36. $v = \sqrt{gr}$

$v = \sqrt{g(3960 + 500)} = \sqrt{(g)(4460)}$

$\approx \sqrt{(79036)(4460)} \approx 18774.998$ mph

37.
$$v = \sqrt{gr}$$
$$v = \sqrt{g(3960 + 140)} = \sqrt{(g)(4100)}$$
$$\approx \sqrt{(79036)(4100)} \approx 18001.32 \text{ mph}$$

38.
$$v = \sqrt{gr}$$
$$18630 = \sqrt{g(3960 + r)}$$
$$(18630)^2 = g(3960 + r)$$
$$\frac{(18630)^2}{g} = 3960 + r$$
$$\frac{(18630)^2}{79036} - 3960 = r$$
$$r \approx 431.38 \text{ miles}$$

39. The satellite travels the circumference of the circular orbit once in 1.5 hours. We also know that

$$\text{circumference of a circle} = 2\pi (\text{radius})$$
$$\text{distance} = (\text{rate})(\text{time})$$
$$\therefore 2\pi r = vt \rightarrow v = \frac{2\pi r}{t} = \frac{2\pi r}{1.5} = \frac{4\pi}{3} r$$

so

$$v = \sqrt{gr} = \frac{4\pi}{3} r \rightarrow gr = \frac{16\pi^2}{9} r^2$$
$$0 = \frac{16\pi^2}{9} r^2 - gr \rightarrow r\left(\frac{16\pi^2}{9} r - g\right) = 0$$
$$\rightarrow r = 0 \text{ or } \frac{16\pi^2}{9} r - g = 0 \rightarrow r = (g)\left(\frac{9}{16\pi^2}\right) \approx (79036)\left(\frac{9}{16\pi^2}\right) \approx 4504.51$$

therefore the satellite is $4504.51 - 3960 = 544.51$ miles above Earth.

40. The satellite travels the circumference of the circular orbit once in 1.5 hours. We also know that

$$\text{circumference of a circle} = 2\pi (\text{radius})$$
$$\text{distance} = (\text{rate})(\text{time})$$
$$\therefore 2\pi r = vt \rightarrow v = \frac{2\pi r}{2} = \frac{2\pi r}{2} = \pi r$$

so

$$v = \sqrt{gr} = \pi r \rightarrow gr = \pi^2 r^2$$
$$0 = \pi^2 r^2 - gr \rightarrow r(\pi^2 r - g) = 0$$
$$\rightarrow r = 0 \text{ or } \pi^2 r - g = 0 \rightarrow r = \frac{g}{\pi^2} \approx \frac{79036}{\pi^2} \approx 8008.02$$

therefore the satellite is $8008.02 - 3960 = 4048.02$ miles above Earth.

The satellite's speed is $\sqrt{gr} \approx \sqrt{(79036)(8008.02)} \approx 25157.94 \text{ mph}$.

41. $F = \dfrac{mv^2}{r}$

42. $F = \dfrac{mv^2}{r}$

$v = 120 \text{ km/hr } = \dfrac{100}{3} \text{ m/sec}$

$r = 100 \text{ m}$

$F = \dfrac{(150)\left(\dfrac{100}{3}\right)^2}{100} \approx 1666.67 \text{ newtons}$

43. $F = \dfrac{mv^2}{r}$

$v = 120 + (0.10)(120) = 132 \text{ km/hr} = \dfrac{110}{3}\text{m/sec}$

$F = \dfrac{(150)\left(\dfrac{110}{3}\right)^2}{100} \approx 2016.67 \text{ newtons}$

so the force is increased by $\dfrac{2016.67 - 1666.67}{1666.67} = \dfrac{350}{1666.67} \approx 0.21 = 21\%.$

44. $F = \dfrac{mv^2}{r}$

$21600000 = \dfrac{(150)(v)^2}{0.05} \rightarrow v = \sqrt{7200} \approx 84.85 \text{ kmph}$

45. $F = \dfrac{mv^2}{r}$

we compare $F = \dfrac{mv^2}{L}$ with $F = \dfrac{m(3v)^2}{L} = \dfrac{9mv^2}{L}$

therefore, the force needed is 9 times greater.

46. $F = \dfrac{mv^2}{r}$

we compare $F = \dfrac{mv^2}{L}$ with $F = \dfrac{mv^2}{2L} = \dfrac{1}{2}\left(\dfrac{mv^2}{L}\right)$

therefore, the force needed is half as great.

47 – 50.   Answers will vary.

Graphs

2.R Chapter Review

1. Intercepts: (0,0)
    Test for symmetry:

    x-axis: Replace y by $-y$ so $2x = 3(-y)^2$ or $2x = 3y^2$, which is
    equivalent to $2x = 3y^2$.

    y-axis: Replace x by $-x$ so $2(-x) = 3y^2$ or $-2x = 3y^2$,
    which is not equivalent to $2x = 3y^2$.

    Origin: Replace x by $-x$ and y by $-y$ so $2(-x) = 3(-y)^2$ or
    $-2x = 3y^2$, which is not equivalent to $2x = 3y^2$.

    Therefore, the graph is symmetric with respect to the x-axis.

2. Intercepts: (0, 0)
    Test for symmetry:

    x-axis: Replace y by $-y$ so $-y = 5x$ or $y = -5x$,
    which is not equivalent to $y = 5x$.

    y-axis: Replace x by $-x$ so $y = 5(-x)$ or $y = -5x$,
    which is not equivalent to $y = 5x$.

    Origin: Replace x by $-x$ and y by $-y$ so $-y = 5(-x)$ or $y = 5x$,
    which is equivalent to $y = 5x$.

    Therefore, the graph is symmetric with respect to the origin.

3. Intercepts: (0, 2), (0, -2), (4, 0), (-4, 0)
    Test for symmetry:

    x-axis: Replace y by $-y$ so $x^2 + 4(-y)^2 = 16$ or $x^2 + 4y^2 = 16$,
    which is equivalent to $x^2 + 4y^2 = 16$.

    y-axis: Replace x by $-x$ so $(-x)^2 + 4y^2 = 16$ or $x^2 + 4y^2 = 16$,
    which is equivalent to $x^2 + 4y^2 = 16$.

    Origin: Replace x by $-x$ and y by $-y$ so $(-x)^2 + 4(-y)^2 = 16$ or $x^2 + 4y^2 = 16$,
    which is equivalent to $x^2 + 4y^2 = 16$.

    Therefore, the graph is symmetric with respect to the x-axis, the y-axis and the origin.

4.   Intercepts: $(1, 0), (-1, 0)$
     Test for symmetry:

   x - axis: Replace y by $-y$ so $9x^2 - (-y)^2 = 9$ or $9x^2 - y^2 = 9$,

   which is equivalent to $9x^2 - y^2 = 9$.

   y - axis: Replace x by $-x$ so $9(-x)^2 - y^2 = 9$ or $9x^2 - y^2 = 9$,

   which is equivalent to $9x^2 - y^2 = 9$.

   Origin :   Replace x by $-x$ and y by $-y$ so $9(-x)^2 - (-y)^2 = 9$ or $9x^2 - y^2 = 9$,

   which is equivalent to $9x^2 - y^2 = 9$.

   Therefore, the graph is symmetric with respect to the x-axis, the y-axis and the origin.

5.   Intercepts: $(0, 1)$
     Test for symmetry:

   x - axis: Replace y by $-y$ so $-y = x^4 + 2x^2 + 1$,

   which is not equivalent to $y = x^4 + 2x^2 + 1$.

   y - axis: Replace x by $-x$ so $y = (-x)^4 + 2(-x)^2 + 1$ or $y = x^4 + 2x^2 + 1$,

   which is equivalent to $y = x^4 + 2x^2 + 1$.

   Origin :   Replace x by $-x$ and y by $-y$ so $-y = (-x)^4 + 2(-x)^2 + 1$ or $-y = x^4 + 2x^2 + 1$,

   which is not equivalent to $y = x^4 + 2x^2 + 1$.

   Therefore, the graph is symmetric with respect to the y-axis.

6.   Intercepts: $(0, 0), (-1, 0)$, and $(1, 0)$
     Test for symmetry:

   x - axis: Replace y by $-y$ so $-y = x^3 - x$, which is not

   equivalent to $y = x^3 - x$.

   y - axis: Replace x by $-x$ so $y = (-x)^3 - (-x)$ or $y = -x^3 + x$,

   which is not equivalent to $y = x^3 - x$.

   Origin :   Replace x by $-x$ and y by $-y$ so $-y = (-x)^3 - (-x)$ or $-y = -x^3 + x$

   or $y = x^3 - x$, which is equivalent to $y = x^3 - x$.

   Therefore, the graph is symmetric with respect to the origin.

7.   Intercepts: $(0,0), (0,-2), (-1,0)$
     Test for symmetry:

   x - axis: Replace y by $-y$ so $x^2 + x + (-y)^2 + 2(-y) = 0$ or $x^2 + x + y^2 - 2y = 0$,

   which is not equivalent to $x^2 + x + y^2 + 2y = 0$.

y-axis: Replace x by $-x$ so $(-x)^2 + (-x) + y^2 + 2y = 0$ or $x^2 - x + y^2 + 2y = 0$,

which is not equivalent to $x^2 + x + y^2 + 2y = 0$.

Origin: Replace x by $-x$ and y by $-y$ so $(-x)^2 + (-x) + (-y)^2 + 2(-y) = 0$ or

$x^2 - x + y^2 - 2y = 0$, which is not equivalent to

$x^2 + x + y^2 + 2y = 0$.

Therefore, the graph is not symmetric to the x-axis, the y-axis, or the origin.

8.   Intercepts: $(0, 0)$, $(0, 2)$, and $(-4, 0)$
Test for symmetry:

x-axis: Replace y by $-y$ so $x^2 + 4x + (-y)^2 - 2(-y) = 0$ or $x^2 + 4x + y^2 + 2y = 0$,

which is not equivalent to $x^2 + 4x + y^2 - 2y = 0$.

y-axis: Replace x by $-x$ so $(-x)^2 + 4(-x) + y^2 - 2y = 0$ or $x^2 - 4x + y^2 - 2y = 0$,

which is not equivalent to $x^2 + 4x + y^2 - 2y = 0$.

Origin: Replace x by $-x$ and y by $-y$ so $(-x)^2 + 4(-x) + (-y)^2 - 2(-y) = 0$ or

$x^2 - 4x + y^2 + 2y = 0$, which is not equivalent to

$x^2 + 4x + y^2 - 2y = 0$.

Therefore, the graph is not symmetric with respect to the x-axis, y-axis, or origin.

9.   Slope $= -2$; containing $(3, -1)$

$y - y_1 = m(x - x_1)$

$y - (-1) = -2(x - 3)$

$y + 1 = -2x + 6$

$y = -2x + 5$

$2x + y = 5$ or $y = -2x + 5$

10. Slope $= 0$; containing the point $(-5, 4)$

$y - y_1 = m(x - x_1)$

$y - 4 = 0(x - (-5))$

$y - 4 = 0$

$y = 4$

11. Slope undefined; containing $(-3, 4)$
This is a vertical line.

$x = -3$

No slope intercept form.

12. x-intercept $= 2$ or the point $(2, 0)$;
Containing the point $(4, -5)$

$m = \dfrac{-5 - 0}{4 - 2} = \dfrac{-5}{2} = -\dfrac{5}{2}$

$y - y_1 = m(x - x_1)$

$y - 0 = -\dfrac{5}{2}(x - 2)$

$y = -\dfrac{5}{2}x + 5$

$5x + 2y = 10$ or $y = -\dfrac{5}{2}x + 5$

13. y-intercept = –2; containing (5,–3)
Points are (5,–3) and (0,–2)
$$m = \frac{-2-(-3)}{0-5} = \frac{1}{-5} = -\frac{1}{5}$$
$$y = mx + b$$
$$y = \frac{-1}{5}x - 2$$
$$x + 5y = -10 \text{ or } y = \frac{-1}{5}x - 2$$

14. Containing the points (3,–4) and (2,1)
$$m = \frac{1-(-4)}{2-3} = \frac{5}{-1} = -5$$
$$y - y_1 = m(x - x_1)$$
$$y - (-4) = -5(x - 3)$$
$$y + 4 = -5x + 15$$
$$y = -5x + 11$$
$$5x + y = 11 \text{ or } y = -5x + 11$$

15. Parallel to $2x - 3y = -4$;
Slope $= \frac{2}{3}$; containing $(-5,3)$
$$y - y_1 = m(x - x_1)$$
$$y - 3 = \frac{2}{3}(x - (-5))$$
$$y - 3 = \frac{2}{3}x + \frac{10}{3}$$
$$y = \frac{2}{3}x + \frac{19}{3}$$
$$2x - 3y = -19 \text{ or } y = \frac{2}{3}x + \frac{19}{3}$$

16. Parallel to $x + y = 2$;
Slope $= -1$
Containing the point $(1, -3)$
$$y - y_1 = m(x - x_1)$$
$$y - (-3) = -1(x - 1)$$
$$y + 3 = -x + 1$$
$$y = -x - 2$$
$$x + y = -2 \text{ or } y = -x - 2$$

17. Perpendicular to $x + y = 2$;
Containing (4,–3)
Slope of perpendicular = 1
$$y - y_1 = m(x - x_1)$$
$$y - (-3) = 1(x - 4)$$
$$y + 3 = x - 4$$
$$y = x - 7$$
$$x - y = 7 \text{ or } y = x - 7$$

18. Perpendicular to $3x - y = -4$;
Slope of perpendicular $= -\frac{1}{3}$
Containing the point $(-2, 4)$
$$y - y_1 = m(x - x_1)$$
$$y - 4 = -\frac{1}{3}(x - (-2))$$
$$y - 4 = -\frac{1}{3}x - \frac{2}{3}$$
$$y = -\frac{1}{3}x + \frac{10}{3}$$
$$x + 3y = 10 \text{ or } y = -\frac{1}{3}x + \frac{10}{3}$$

19. $4x - 5y = -20$
x-intercept = –5; y-intercept = 4

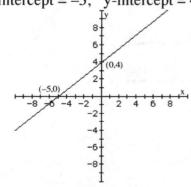

20. $3x + 4y = 12$
x-intercept = 4; y-intercept = 3

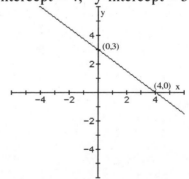

21. $\frac{1}{2}x - \frac{1}{3}y = -\frac{1}{6}$

x - intercept $= -\frac{1}{3}$;   y - intercept $= \frac{1}{2}$

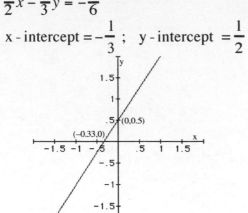

22. $-\frac{3}{4}x + \frac{1}{2}y = 0$

x-intercept $= 0$;   y-intercept $= 0$

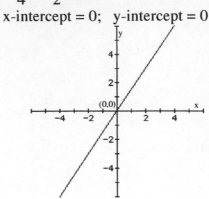

23. $\sqrt{2}x + \sqrt{3}y = \sqrt{6}$

x-intercept $= \sqrt{3}$;   y-intercept $= \sqrt{2}$

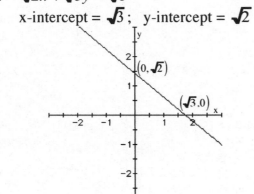

24. $\frac{x}{3} + \frac{y}{4} = 1$

x-intercept $= 3$;   y-intercept $= 4$

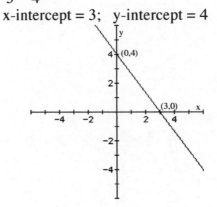

25. $x^2 + (y-1)^2 = 4$

Center: (0,1)
Radius = 2

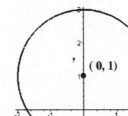

26. $(x+2)^2 + y^2 = 9$

Center: (-2,0)
Radius = 3

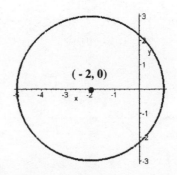

27. $x^2 + y^2 - 2x + 4y - 4 = 0$
$$x^2 - 2x + y^2 + 4y = 4$$
$$(x^2 - 2x + 1) + (y^2 + 4y + 4) = 4 + 1 + 4$$
$$(x - 1)^2 + (y + 2)^2 = 3^2$$
Center: (1,–2)   Radius = 3

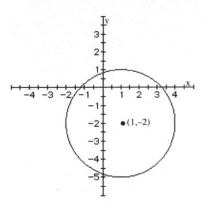

28. $x^2 + y^2 + 4x - 4y - 1 = 0$
$$x^2 + 4x + y^2 - 4y = 1$$
$$(x^2 + 4x + 4) + (y^2 - 4y + 4) = 1 + 4 + 4$$
$$(x + 2)^2 + (y - 2)^2 = 3^2$$
Center: (–2, 2)   Radius = 3

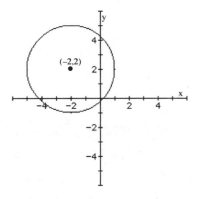

29. $3x^2 + 3y^2 - 6x + 12y = 0$
$$x^2 + y^2 - 2x + 4y = 0$$
$$x^2 - 2x + y^2 + 4y = 0$$
$$(x^2 - 2x + 1) + (y^2 + 4y + 4) = 1 + 4$$
$$(x - 1)^2 + (y + 2)^2 = \left(\sqrt{5}\right)^2$$
Center: (1,–2)   Radius = $\sqrt{5}$

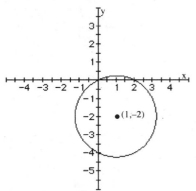

30. $2x^2 + 2y^2 - 4x = 0$
$$x^2 + y^2 - 2x = 0$$
$$x^2 - 2x + y^2 = 0$$
$$(x^2 - 2x + 1) + y^2 = 0 + 1$$
$$(x - 1)^2 + y^2 = 1^2$$
Center: (1, 0)   Radius = 1

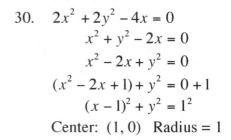

31.   Given the points $(7,4)$ and $(-3,2)$.

Slope: $m = \dfrac{2-4}{-3-7} = \dfrac{-2}{-10} = \dfrac{1}{5}$

Distance: $d = \sqrt{(-3-7)^2 + (2-4)^2} = \sqrt{100+4} = \sqrt{104} = 2\sqrt{26}$

Midpoint: $\left(\dfrac{7+(-3)}{2}, \dfrac{4+2}{2}\right) = (2,3)$

32.   Find the distance between each pair of points.

$d_{A,B} = \sqrt{(1-3)^2 + (1-4)^2} = \sqrt{4+9} = \sqrt{13}$

$d_{B,C} = \sqrt{(-2-1)^2 + (3-1)^2} = \sqrt{9+4} = \sqrt{13}$

$d_{A,C} = \sqrt{(-2-3)^2 + (3-4)^2} = \sqrt{25+1} = \sqrt{26}$

Since $AB = BC$, triangle ABC is isosceles.

33.   Given the points $A = (-2,0)$, $B = (-4,4)$, $C = (8,5)$.

(a)   Find the distance between each pair of points.

$d_{A,B} = \sqrt{(-4-(-2))^2 + (4-0)^2} = \sqrt{4+16} = \sqrt{20} = 2\sqrt{5}$

$d_{B,C} = \sqrt{(8-(-4))^2 + (5-4)^2} = \sqrt{144+1} = \sqrt{145}$

$d_{A,C} = \sqrt{(8-(-2))^2 + (5-0)^2} = \sqrt{100+25} = \sqrt{125} = 5\sqrt{5}$

$\left(\sqrt{20}\right)^2 + \left(\sqrt{125}\right)^2 = \left(\sqrt{145}\right)^2 \quad \to \quad 20+125 = 145 \quad \to \quad 145 = 145$

The Pythagorean theorem is satisfied, so this is a right triangle.

(b)   Find the slopes:

$m_{AB} = \dfrac{4-0}{-4-(-2)} = \dfrac{4}{-2} = -2$

$m_{BC} = \dfrac{5-4}{8-(-4)} = \dfrac{1}{12}$

$m_{AC} = \dfrac{5-0}{8-(-2)} = \dfrac{5}{10} = \dfrac{1}{2}$

$m_{AB} \cdot m_{AC} = -2 \cdot \dfrac{1}{2} = -1$

Since the product of the slopes is -1, the sides of the triangle are perpendicular and the triangle is a right triangle.

34.   Endpoints of the diameter are $(-3, 2)$ and $(5, -6)$.

The center is at the midpoint of the diameter:

Center: $\left(\dfrac{-3+5}{2}, \dfrac{2+(-6)}{2}\right) = (1,-2)$

Radius: $r = \sqrt{(1-(-3))^2 + (-2-2)^2} = \sqrt{16+16} = \sqrt{32} = 4\sqrt{2}$

Equation:

$$(x-1)^2 + (y+2)^2 = \left(4\sqrt{2}\right)^2$$

$$x^2 - 2x + 1 + y^2 + 4y + 4 = 32$$

$$x^2 + y^2 - 2x + 4y - 27 = 0$$

35. slope of $\overline{AB} = \dfrac{1-5}{6-2} = -1$; slope of $\overline{AC} = \dfrac{-1-5}{8-2} = -1$; slope of $\overline{BC} = \dfrac{-1-1}{8-6} = -1$

therefore the points are collinear.

36. A circle with center (-1,2) has equation $(x+1)^2 + (y-2)^2 = r^2$

point $A(1,5) \rightarrow (1+1)^2 + (5-2)^2 = r^2$

$4+9 = r^2 \rightarrow r = \sqrt{13}$

point $B(2,4) \rightarrow (2+1)^2 + (4-2)^2 = r^2$

$9+4 = r^2 \rightarrow r = \sqrt{13}$

point $C(-3,5) \rightarrow (-3+1)^2 + (5-2)^2 = r^2$

$4+9 = r^2 \rightarrow r = \sqrt{13}$

Therefore the points A, B and C lie on a circle with center point (-1, 2)
and radius $= \sqrt{13}$.

37. $Area = A = kx^2, x =$ length of a side of the triangle

$A = \dfrac{\sqrt{3}}{4}, x = 1 \rightarrow \dfrac{\sqrt{3}}{4} = (k)(1) \rightarrow k = \dfrac{\sqrt{3}}{4}$

$A = 16 \rightarrow A = \left(\dfrac{\sqrt{3}}{4}\right)(x) = 16 \rightarrow x = \dfrac{48}{\sqrt{3}} = 16\sqrt{3}$ cm.

38. $Pitch = P = k\sqrt{t}, t =$ tension of the string

$P = 300, t = 9 \rightarrow 300 = (k)\sqrt{9} \rightarrow k = 100$

$P = 400 \rightarrow P = 100\sqrt{t} = 400 \rightarrow \sqrt{t} = 4 \rightarrow t = 16$ pounds.

39. period (in days) $= T$, mean distance (in millon miles) from sun $= a$

$T^2 = ka^3$

$T = 365, a = 93 \rightarrow 365^2 = (k)(93)^3 \rightarrow k = \dfrac{365^2}{93^3} \approx 0.1656292013$

$T = 88 \rightarrow 88^2 = \left(\dfrac{365^2}{93^3}\right)(a)^3 \rightarrow a^3 = (88^2)\left(\dfrac{93^3}{365^2}\right)$

$\rightarrow a = \sqrt[3]{(88^2)\left(\dfrac{93^3}{365^2}\right)} \approx 36.025$ million miles

40. $T = \left(5\sqrt{5}\right)(365) \to \left(\left(5\sqrt{5}\right)(365)\right)^2 = \left(\dfrac{365^2}{93^3}\right)(a)^3 \to a^3 = \left(\left(5\sqrt{5}\right)(365)\right)^2 \left(\dfrac{93^3}{365^2}\right)$

$a = \sqrt[3]{125\left(93^3\right)} = 465$ million miles

41. (a)

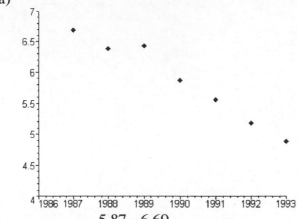

(b)   slope $= \dfrac{5.87 - 6.69}{1990 - 1987} = -0.27\overline{3}$

(c)   for each 1 year increase, the concentration decreases by $0.27\overline{3}$ ppm.

(d)   slope $= \dfrac{4.88 - 5.87}{1993 - 1990} = -0.33$

(e)   for each 1 year increase, the concentration decreases by 0.33 ppm.

(f) $y = 618.477 - 0.308x$

(g)   for each 1 year increase, the concentration decreases by 0.308 ppm.

(h)   Answers will vary.

(i)   As time passes, the average level of carbon monoxide is decreasing more rapidly.

42. (a)

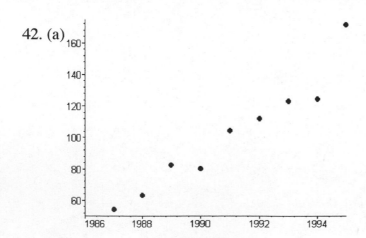

(b)   slope $= \dfrac{104.28 - 54.26}{1991 - 1987} = 12.505$

(c)   for each 1 year increase, the index value increases by 12.505 dollars

(d)   slope $= \dfrac{171.20 - 104.28}{1995 - 1991} = 16.73$

(e)   for each 1 year increase, the index value increases by 16.73 dollars.

(f) $y = -25275.241 + 12.746x$

(g)   for each 1 year increase, the index value increases by 12.746 dollars.

(h)   the slope from part (d), since it predicts the greatest yearly index increase of the three slopes

(i)   As time passes, the portfolio value is increasing at a higher rate.

43.   Answers will vary.

44. (a) $x = 0$ is a vertical line passing through the origin, that is $x = 0$ is the equation of the y-axis

(b) $y = 0$ is a horizontal line passing through the origin, that is $y = 0$ is the equation of the x-axis

(c) $x + y = 0 \rightarrow y = -x$ is line passing through the origin with slope $= -1$.

(d) $xy = 0 \rightarrow y = 0$ or $x = 0$ is a graph consisting of the coordinate axes.

(e) $x^2 + y^2 = 0 \rightarrow y = 0$ and $x = 0$ is a graph consisting of the origin.

45.   Set the axes so that the field's maximum dimension is along the x-axis.

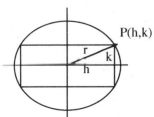

Let $2h = width$, $2k = height$, therefore the point farthest from the origin has coordinates $P(h,k)$. So the distance from the origin to point P is $r = \sqrt{h^2 + k^2}$ = the radius of the circle

Using 1 sprinkler arm:

If we place the sprinkler at the origin, we get a circle with equation $x^2 + y^2 = r^2$, where $r = \sqrt{h^2 + k^2}$. So how much water is wasted ? The area of the field = $A_F = 4hk$.

The area of the circular water pattern $A_C = \pi \cdot r^2 = \pi \cdot \left(\sqrt{h^2 + k^2}\right)^2 = \pi \cdot \left(h^2 + k^2\right)$.

Therefore the amount of water wasted = $A_C - A_F = \pi \cdot \left(h^2 + k^2\right) - 4hk$.

Using 2 sprinkler arms:

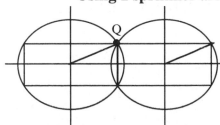

Place sprinkler 1 at $\frac{1}{4} \cdot (width)$ and sprinkler 2 at $\frac{3}{4} \cdot (width)$. Let the origin correspond to the center of the circle formed by sprinkler 1, the arm must be set so that the water will hit the point $Q\left(\frac{1}{2}h, k\right)$.

The distance from the origin to point Q is given by $r = \sqrt{\frac{1}{4}h^2 + k^2}$ = the radius of circle 1.

We need the same settings for sprinkler 2.

So the total area of the 2 circles = $2\pi \cdot r^2 = 2\pi\left(\sqrt{\frac{1}{4}h^2 + k^2}\right)^2 = 2\pi\left(\frac{1}{4}h^2 + k^2\right)$

Therefore the amount of water wasted $= A_C - A_F = 2\pi\left(\dfrac{1}{4}h^2 + k^2\right) - 4hk$.

In order to decide when to switch from Case 1 to Case 2, we want to determine when the waste in Case 2 is less than the waste in Case 1.

That is, we want to solve: $2\pi\left(\dfrac{1}{4}h^2 + k^2\right) - 4hk < \pi \cdot \left(h^2 + k^2\right) - 4hk$

$$2\pi\left(\dfrac{1}{4}h^2 + k^2\right) - 4hk < \pi \cdot \left(h^2 + k^2\right) - 4hk \rightarrow \dfrac{\pi}{2}h^2 + 2\pi k^2 - 4hk < \pi h^2 + \pi k^2 - 4hk$$

$$\dfrac{\pi}{2}h^2 + 2\pi k^2 < \pi h^2 + \pi k^2 \rightarrow \dfrac{1}{2}h^2 + 2k^2 < h^2 + k^2 \rightarrow k^2 < \dfrac{1}{2}h^2 \rightarrow k < \sqrt{\dfrac{1}{2}} \cdot h$$

So Case 2 is the better choice when the rectangle's dimensions obey the inequality $\dfrac{k}{h} < \dfrac{\sqrt{2}}{2}$.

Functions and Their Graphs

3.1 Functions

1. Function
   Domain: {Dad, Colleen, Kaleigh, Marissa}
   Range: {Jan. 8, Mar. 15, Sept. 17}

2. Function
   Domain: {Bob, Dave, John, Chuck}
   Range: {Beth, Diane, Linda, Marcia}

3. Not a function

4. Function
   Domain: {Bob, Dave, John, Chuck}
   Range: {Diane, Linda, Marcia}

5. Function
   Domain: {2, −3, 4, 1}
   Range: {6, 9, 10}

6. Function
   Domain: {−2, −1, 3, 4}
   Range: {3, 5, 7, 12}

7. Function
   Domain: {1, 2, 3, 4}
   Range: {3}

8. Function
   Domain: {0, 1, 2, 3}
   Range: {−2, 3, 7}

9. Not a function

10. Not a function

11. Function
    Domain: {−2, −1, 0, 1}
    Range: {4, 1, 0}

12. Function
    Domain: {−2, −1, 0, 1}
    Range: {3, 4, 16}

13. $f(x) = 3x^2 + 2x - 4$

(a) $f(0) = 3(0)^2 + 2(0) - 4 = -4$

(b) $f(1) = 3(1)^2 + 2(1) - 4 = 3 + 2 - 4 = 1$

(c) $f(-1) = 3(-1)^2 + 2(-1) - 4 = 3 - 2 - 4 = -3$

(d) $f(-x) = 3(-x)^2 + 2(-x) - 4 = 3x^2 - 2x - 4$

(e) $-f(x) = -(3x^2 + 2x - 4) = -3x^2 - 2x + 4$

(f) $f(x+1) = 3(x+1)^2 + 2(x+1) - 4 = 3(x^2 + 2x + 1) + 2x + 2 - 4$
$$= 3x^2 + 6x + 3 + 2x + 2 - 4 = 3x^2 + 8x + 1$$

(g) $f(2x) = 3(2x)^2 + 2(2x) - 4 = 12x^2 + 4x - 4$

(h) $f(x+h) = 3(x+h)^2 + 2(x+h) - 4 = 3(x^2 + 2xh + h^2) + 2x + 2h - 4$
$$= 3x^2 + 6xh + 3h^2 + 2x + 2h - 4$$

14. $f(x) = -2x^2 + x - 1$

(a) $f(0) = -2(0)^2 + 0 - 1 = -1$

(b) $f(1) = -2(1)^2 + 1 - 1 = -2$

(c) $f(-1) = -2(-1)^2 + (-1) - 1 = -4$

(d) $f(-x) = -2(-x)^2 + (-x) - 1 = -2x^2 - x - 1$

(e) $-f(x) = -(-2x^2 + x - 1) = 2x^2 - x + 1$

(f) $f(x+1) = -2(x+1)^2 + (x+1) - 1 = -2(x^2 + 2x + 1) + x + 1 - 1$
$$= -2x^2 - 4x - 2 + x = -2x^2 - 3x - 2$$

(g) $f(2x) = -2(2x)^2 + (2x) - 1 = -8x^2 + 2x - 1$

(h) $f(x+h) = -2(x+h)^2 + (x+h) - 1 = -2(x^2 + 2xh + h^2) + x + h - 1$
$$= -2x^2 - 4xh - 2h^2 + x + h - 1$$

15. $f(x) = \dfrac{x}{x^2 + 1}$

(a) $f(0) = \dfrac{0}{0^2 + 1} = \dfrac{0}{1} = 0$

(b) $f(1) = \dfrac{1}{1^2 + 1} = \dfrac{1}{2}$

(c) $f(-1) = \dfrac{-1}{(-1)^2 + 1} = \dfrac{-1}{1 + 1} = -\dfrac{1}{2}$

(d) $f(-x) = \dfrac{-x}{(-x)^2 + 1} = \dfrac{-x}{x^2 + 1}$

(e) $-f(x) = -\dfrac{x}{x^2 + 1} = \dfrac{-x}{x^2 + 1}$

(f) $f(x+1) = \dfrac{x+1}{(x+1)^2 + 1} = \dfrac{x+1}{x^2 + 2x + 1 + 1} = \dfrac{x+1}{x^2 + 2x + 2}$

(g) $f(2x) = \dfrac{2x}{(2x)^2 + 1} = \dfrac{2x}{4x^2 + 1}$

(h) $f(x+h) = \dfrac{x+h}{(x+h)^2 + 1} = \dfrac{x+h}{x^2 + 2xh + h^2 + 1}$

16. $f(x) = \dfrac{x^2 - 1}{x + 4}$

    (a) $f(0) = \dfrac{0^2 - 1}{0 + 4} = \dfrac{-1}{4} = -\dfrac{1}{4}$

    (b) $f(1) = \dfrac{1^2 - 1}{1 + 4} = \dfrac{0}{5} = 0$

    (c) $f(-1) = \dfrac{(-1)^2 - 1}{-1 + 4} = \dfrac{0}{3} = 0$

    (d) $f(-x) = \dfrac{(-x)^2 - 1}{-x + 4} = \dfrac{x^2 - 1}{-x + 4}$

    (e) $-f(x) = -\dfrac{x^2 - 1}{x + 4} = \dfrac{1 - x^2}{x + 4}$

    (f) $f(x + 1) = \dfrac{(x + 1)^2 - 1}{(x + 1) + 4} = \dfrac{x^2 + 2x + 1 - 1}{x + 5} = \dfrac{x^2 + 2x}{x + 5}$

    (g) $f(2x) = \dfrac{(2x)^2 - 1}{2x + 4} = \dfrac{4x^2 - 1}{2x + 4}$

    (h) $f(x + h) = \dfrac{(x + h)^2 - 1}{(x + h) + 4} = \dfrac{x^2 + 2xh + h^2 - 1}{x + h + 4}$

17. $f(x) = |x| + 4$

    (a) $f(0) = |0| + 4 = 0 + 4 = 4$

    (b) $f(1) = |1| + 4 = 1 + 4 = 5$

    (c) $f(-1) = |-1| + 4 = 1 + 4 = 5$

    (d) $f(-x) = |-x| + 4 = |x| + 4$

    (e) $-f(x) = -(|x| + 4) = -|x| - 4$

    (f) $f(x + 1) = |x + 1| + 4$

    (g) $f(2x) = |2x| + 4 = 2|x| + 4$

    (h) $f(x + h) = |x + h| + 4$

18. $f(x) = \sqrt{x^2 + x}$

    (a) $f(0) = \sqrt{0^2 + 0} = \sqrt{0} = 0$

    (b) $f(1) = \sqrt{1^2 + 1} = \sqrt{2}$

    (c) $f(-1) = \sqrt{(-1)^2 + (-1)} = \sqrt{1 - 1} = \sqrt{0} = 0$

    (d) $f(-x) = \sqrt{(-x)^2 + (-x)} = \sqrt{x^2 - x}$

    (e) $-f(x) = -\sqrt{x^2 + x}$

    (f) $f(x + 1) = \sqrt{(x + 1)^2 + (x + 1)} = \sqrt{x^2 + 2x + 1 + x + 1} = \sqrt{x^2 + 3x + 2}$

    (g) $f(2x) = \sqrt{(2x)^2 + 2x} = \sqrt{4x^2 + 2x}$

    (h) $f(x + h) = \sqrt{(x + h)^2 + (x + h)} = \sqrt{x^2 + 2xh + h^2 + x + h}$

19. $f(x) = \dfrac{2x+1}{3x-5}$

   (a) $f(0) = \dfrac{2(0)+1}{3(0)-5} = \dfrac{0+1}{0-5} = -\dfrac{1}{5}$

   (b) $f(1) = \dfrac{2(1)+1}{3(1)-5} = \dfrac{2+1}{3-5} = \dfrac{3}{-2} = -\dfrac{3}{2}$

   (c) $f(-1) = \dfrac{2(-1)+1}{3(-1)-5} = \dfrac{-2+1}{-3-5} = \dfrac{-1}{-8} = \dfrac{1}{8}$

   (d) $f(-x) = \dfrac{2(-x)+1}{3(-x)-5} = \dfrac{-2x+1}{-3x-5} = \dfrac{2x-1}{3x+5}$

   (e) $-f(x) = -\dfrac{2x+1}{3x-5} = \dfrac{-2x-1}{3x-5}$

   (f) $f(x+1) = \dfrac{2(x+1)+1}{3(x+1)-5} = \dfrac{2x+2+1}{3x+3-5} = \dfrac{2x+3}{3x-2}$

   (g) $f(2x) = \dfrac{2(2x)+1}{3(2x)-5} = \dfrac{4x+1}{6x-5}$

   (h) $f(x+h) = \dfrac{2(x+h)+1}{3(x+h)-5} = \dfrac{2x+2h+1}{3x+3h-5}$

20. $f(x) = 1 - \dfrac{1}{(x+2)^2}$

   (a) $f(0) = 1 - \dfrac{1}{(0+2)^2} = 1 - \dfrac{1}{4} = \dfrac{3}{4}$ (b) $f(1) = 1 - \dfrac{1}{(1+2)^2} = 1 - \dfrac{1}{9} = \dfrac{8}{9}$

   (c) $f(-1) = 1 - \dfrac{1}{(-1+2)^2} = 1 - \dfrac{1}{1} = 0$

   (d) $f(-x) = 1 - \dfrac{1}{(-x+2)^2} = 1 - \dfrac{1}{x^2-4x+4} = \dfrac{x^2-4x+4-1}{x^2-4x+4} = \dfrac{x^2-4x+3}{x^2-4x+4}$

   (e) $-f(x) = -\left(1 - \dfrac{1}{(x+2)^2}\right) = -1 + \dfrac{1}{x^2+4x+4} = \dfrac{-x^2-4x-4+1}{x^2+4x+4} = \dfrac{-x^2-4x-3}{x^2+4x+4}$

   (f) $f(x+1) = 1 - \dfrac{1}{(x+1+2)^2} = 1 - \dfrac{1}{(x+3)^2} = \dfrac{x^2+6x+9-1}{x^2+6x+9} = \dfrac{x^2+6x+8}{x^2+6x+9}$

   (g) $f(2x) = 1 - \dfrac{1}{(2x+2)^2} = 1 - \dfrac{1}{4x^2+8x+4} = \dfrac{4x^2+8x+4-1}{4x^2+8x+4} = \dfrac{4x^2+8x+3}{4x^2+8x+4}$

   (h) $f(x+h) = 1 - \dfrac{1}{(x+h+2)^2} = \dfrac{x^2+2xh+4x+h^2+4h+4-1}{x^2+2xh+4x+h^2+4h+4}$

   $= \dfrac{x^2+2xh+4x+h^2+4h+3}{x^2+2xh+4x+h^2+4h+4}$

21.   Graph $y = x^2$. The graph passes the vertical line test. Thus, the equation represents a function.

22.   Graph $y = x^3$. The graph passes the vertical line test. Thus, the equation represents a function.

23.   Graph $y = \dfrac{1}{x}$. The graph passes the vertical line test. Thus, the equation represents a function.

24. Graph $y = |x|$. The graph passes the vertical line test. Thus, the equation represents a function.

25. $y^2 = 4 - x^2$

Solve for y: $y = \pm\sqrt{4 - x^2}$

For $x = 0$, $y = \pm 2$. Thus, $(0,2)$ and $(0,-2)$ are on the graph. This is not a function, since a distinct x corresponds to two different y's.

26. $y = \pm\sqrt{1 - 2x}$

For $x = 0$, $y = \pm 1$. Thus, $(0,1)$ and $(0,-1)$ are on the graph. This is not a function, since a distinct x corresponds to two different y's.

27. $x = y^2$

Solve for y: $y = \pm\sqrt{x}$

For $x = 1$, $y = \pm 1$. Thus, $(1,1)$ and $(1,-1)$ are on the graph. This is not a function, since a distinct x corresponds to two different y's.

28. $x + y^2 = 1$

Solve for y: $y = \pm\sqrt{1 - x}$

For $x = 0$, $y = \pm 1$. Thus, $(0,1)$ and $(0,-1)$ are on the graph. This is not a function, since a distinct x corresponds to two different y's.

29. Graph $y = 2x^2 - 3x + 4$. The graph passes the vertical line test. Thus, the equation represents a function.

30. Graph $y = \dfrac{3x - 1}{x + 2}$. The graph passes the vertical line test. Thus, the equation represents a function.

31. $2x^2 + 3y^2 = 1$

Solve for y:

$$2x^2 + 3y^2 = 1 \rightarrow 3y^2 = 1 - 2x^2 \rightarrow y^2 = \frac{1 - 2x^2}{3}$$

$$y = \pm\sqrt{\frac{1 - 2x^2}{3}}$$

For $x = 0$, $y = \pm\sqrt{\dfrac{1}{3}}$. Thus, $\left(0, \sqrt{\dfrac{1}{3}}\right)$ and $\left(0, -\sqrt{\dfrac{1}{3}}\right)$ are on the graph. This is not a function, since a distinct x corresponds to two different y's.

32. $x^2 - 4y^2 = 1$
Solve for y:

$$x^2 - 4y^2 = 1$$

$$4y^2 = x^2 - 1$$

$$y^2 = \frac{x^2 - 1}{4}$$

$$y = \frac{\pm\sqrt{x^2 - 1}}{2}$$

For $x = \sqrt{2}$, $y = \pm\frac{1}{2}$. Thus, $\left(\sqrt{2}, \frac{1}{2}\right)$ and $\left(\sqrt{2}, -\frac{1}{2}\right)$ are on the graph. This is not a function, since a distinct x corresponds to two different y's.

33. $f(x) = -5x + 4$
Domain: {Real Numbers}

34. $f(x) = x^2 + 2$
Domain: {Real Numbers}

35. $f(x) = \dfrac{x}{x^2 + 1}$
Domain: {Real Numbers}

36. $f(x) = \dfrac{x^2}{x^2 + 1}$
Domain: {Real Numbers}

37. $g(x) = \dfrac{x}{x^2 - 16}$

$x^2 - 16 \neq 0$

$x^2 \neq 16 \rightarrow x \neq \pm 4$
Domain: $\{x \mid x \neq -4, x \neq 4\}$

38. $h(x) = \dfrac{2x}{x^2 - 4}$

$x^2 - 4 \neq 0$

$x^2 \neq 4 \rightarrow x \neq \pm 2$
Domain: $\{x \mid x \neq -2, x \neq 2\}$

39. $F(x) = \dfrac{x - 2}{x^3 + x}$

$x^3 + x \neq 0$

$x(x^2 + 1) \neq 0$

$x \neq 0, \quad x^2 \neq -1$

Domain: $\{x \mid x \neq 0\}$

40. $G(x) = \dfrac{x + 4}{x^3 - 4x}$

$x^3 - 4x \neq 0$

$x(x^2 - 4) \neq 0$

$x \neq 0, \quad x^2 \neq 4$

$x \neq 0, \quad x \neq \pm 2$

Domain: $\{x \mid x \neq 0, x \neq 2, x \neq -2\}$

41. $h(x) = \sqrt{3x - 12}$

$3x - 12 \geq 0$

$3x \geq 12$

$x \geq 4$
Domain: $\{x \mid x \geq 4\}$

42. $G(x) = \sqrt{1 - x}$

$1 - x \geq 0$

$-x \geq -1$

$x \leq 1$
Domain: $\{x \mid x \leq 1\}$

43. $f(x) = \dfrac{4}{\sqrt{x-9}}$

$x - 9 > 0$

$x > 9$

Domain: $\{x \mid x > 9\}$

44. $f(x) = \dfrac{x}{\sqrt{x-4}}$

$x - 4 > 0$

$x > 4$

Domain: $\{x \mid x > 4\}$

45. $p(x) = \sqrt{\dfrac{2}{x-1}}$

$\dfrac{2}{x-1} > 0 \quad \rightarrow \quad x - 1 > 0 \quad \rightarrow \quad x > 1$

Domain: $\{x \mid x > 1\}$

46. $q(x) = \sqrt{-x-2}$

$-x - 2 > 0 \quad \rightarrow \quad -x > 2 \quad \rightarrow \quad x < -2$

Domain: $\{x \mid x < -2\}$

47. (a) $f(0) = 3$ since $(0, 3)$ is on the graph.
$f(-6) = -3$ since $(-6, -3)$ is on the graph.

(b) $f(6) = 0$ since $(6, 0)$ is on the graph.
$f(11) = 1$ since $(11, 1)$ is on the graph.

(c) $f(3)$ is positive since $f(3) \approx 3.7$.

(d) $f(-4)$ is negative since $f(-4) = -1$.

(e) $f(x) = 0$ when $x = -3$, $x = 6$, and $x = 10$.

(f) $f(x) > 0$ when $-3 < x < 6$, and $10 < x \le 11$.

(g) The domain of f is $\{x \mid -6 \le x \le 11\}$ or $[-6, 11]$

(h) The range of f is $\{y \mid -3 \le y \le 4\}$ or $[-3, 4]$

(i) The x-intercepts are $(-3, 0)$, $(6, 0)$, and $(11, 0)$.

(j) The y-intercept is $(0, 3)$.

(k) The line $y = \dfrac{1}{2}$ intersects the graph 3 times.

(l) The line $x = 5$ intersects the graph 1 times.

(m) $f(x) = 3$ when $x = 0$ and $x = 4$.

(n) $f(x) = -2$ when $x = -5$ and $x = 8$.

48.   (a) $f(0) = 0$ since $(0,0)$ is on the graph. $f(6) = 0$ since $(6,0)$ is on the graph.

(b) $f(2) = -2$ since $(2, -2)$ is on the graph.
$f(-2) = 1$ since $(-2, 1)$ is on the graph.

(c) $f(3)$ is negative since $f(3) \approx -1$.

(d) $f(-1)$ is positive since $f(-1) \approx -0.4$.

(e) $f(x) = 0$ when $x = 0$, $x = 4$, and $x = 6$.

(f) $f(x) < 0$ when $2 < x < 4$.

(g)   The domain of f is $\{x \mid -4 \le x \le 6\}$ or $[-4, 6]$

(h)   The range of f is $\{y \mid -2 \le y \le 3\}$ or $[-2, 3]$

(i)   The x-intercepts are $(0, 0)$, $(4, 0)$, and $(6, 0)$.

(j)   The y-intercept is $(0, 0)$.

(k)   The line $y = -1$ intersects the graph 2 times.

(l)   The line $x = 1$ intersects the graph 1 times.

(m) $f(x) = 3$ when $x = 5$.

(n) $f(x) = -2$ when $x = 2$.

49.   Not a function since vertical lines will intersect the graph in more than one point.

50.   Function   (a)   Domain: $\{x \mid \text{Real Numbers}\}$;   Range: $\{y \mid y > 0\}$
(b) $(0,1)$
(c)   No symmetry to the x-axis, y-axis, or origin.

51.   Function   (a)   Domain: $\{x \mid -\pi \le x \le \pi\}$;   Range: $\{y \mid -1 \le y \le 1\}$
(b) $\left(-\dfrac{\pi}{2}, 0\right)$, $\left(\dfrac{\pi}{2}, 0\right)$, $(0,1)$ (c)   y-axis

52.   Function   (a)   Domain: $\{x \mid -\pi \le x \le \pi\}$;   Range: $\{y \mid -1 \le y \le 1\}$
(b) $(-\pi, 0)$, $(\pi, 0)$, $(0, 0)$ (c)   origin

53.   Not a function since vertical lines will intersect the graph in more than one point.

54.   Not a function since vertical lines will intersect the graph in more than one point.

55.   Function   (a)   Domain: $\{x \mid x > 0\}$;   Range: $\{y \mid y \in \text{Real Numbers}\}$

(b) $(1, 0)$

(c)   No symmetry to the x-axis, y-axis, or origin.

56.   Function   (a)   Domain: $\{x \mid 0 \le x \le 4\}$;   Range: $\{y \mid 0 \le y \le 3\}$

(b) $(0, 0)$

(c)   No symmetry to the x-axis, y-axis, or origin.

57.   Function   (a)   Domain: $\{x \mid x \in \text{Real Numbers}\}$;   Range: $\{y \mid y \le 2\}$

(b) $(-3,0), (3,0), (0,2)$

(c)   y-axis

58.   Function   (a)   Domain: $\{x \mid x \ge -3\}$;   Range: $\{y \mid y \ge 0\}$

(b) $(-3,0), (2,0), (0,2)$

(c)   No symmetry to the x-axis, y-axis, or origin.

59.   Function   (a)   Domain: $\{x \mid x \in \text{Real Numbers}\}$;   Range: $\{y \mid y \ge -3\}$

(b) $(1,0), (3,0), (0,9)$

(c)   No symmetry to the x-axis, y-axis, or origin.

60.   Function   (a)   Domain: $\{x \mid x \in \text{Real Numbers}\}$;   Range: $\{y \mid y \le 5\}$

(b) $(-1,0), (2,0), (0,4)$

(c)   No symmetry to the x-axis, y-axis, or origin.

61. $f(x) = 2x^2 - x - 1$

(a) $f(-1) = 2(-1)^2 - (-1) - 1 = 2$ $(-1,2)$ is on the graph of f.

(b) $f(-2) = 2(-2)^2 - (-2) - 1 = 9$ $(-2,9)$ is on the graph of f.

(c)   Solve for x:

$$-1 = 2x^2 - x - 1$$

$$0 = 2x^2 - x$$

$$0 = x(2x - 1)$$

$$x = 0, x = \frac{1}{2}$$

$(0, -1)$ and $\left(\frac{1}{2}, -1\right)$ are points on the graph of f.

(d)   The domain of f is: $\{x \mid x \text{ is any real number}\}$.

(e)   x-intercepts:
$$f(x) = 0$$
$$2x^2 - x - 1 = 0$$
$$(2x + 1)(x - 1) = 0$$
$$x = -\frac{1}{2}, x = 1$$
$$\left(-\frac{1}{2}, 0\right) \text{ and } (1, 0)$$

(f)   y-intercept: $f(0) = 2(0)^2 - 0 - 1 = 0 \rightarrow (0, 0)$

62. $f(x) = -3x^2 + 5x$

(a) $f(-1) = -3(-1)^2 + 5(-1) \neq -2$ (-1,2) is not on the graph of f.

(b) $f(-2) = -3(-2)^2 + 5(-2)$ (-2,-22) is on the graph of f.

(c)   Solve for x:
$$-2 = -3x^2 + 5x$$
$$3x^2 - 5x - 2 = 0$$
$$(3x + 1)(x - 2) = 0$$
$$x = -\frac{1}{3}, x = 2$$

(2, -2) and $\left(-\frac{1}{3}, -2\right)$ are points on the graph of f.

(d)   The domain of f is: $\{x | x \text{ is any real number}\}$.

(e)   x-intercepts:
$$f(x) = 0$$
$$-3x^2 + 5x = 0$$
$$x(-3x + 5) = 0$$
$$x = 0, x = \frac{5}{3}$$
$$(0, 0) \text{ and } \left(\frac{5}{3}, 0\right)$$

(f)   y-intercept: $f(0) = -3(0)^2 + 5(0) = 0 \rightarrow (0, 0)$

63. $f(x) = \dfrac{x + 2}{x - 6}$

(a) $f(3) = \dfrac{3 + 2}{3 - 6} = -\dfrac{5}{3} \neq 14$ (3,14) is not on the graph of f.

(b) $f(4) = \dfrac{4 + 2}{4 - 6} = \dfrac{6}{-2} = -3$ $(4, -3)$ is the point on the graph of f.

(c)   Solve for x:

$$2 = \frac{x+2}{x-6}$$

$$2x - 12 = x + 2 \qquad \text{(14, 2) is a point on the graph of } f.$$

$$x = 14$$

(d)   The domain of f is: $\{x \mid x \neq 6\}$.

(e)   x-intercepts:

$$f(x) = 0$$

$$\frac{x+2}{x-6} = 0$$

$$x + 2 = 0$$

$$x = -2$$

$$(-2, 0)$$

(f)   y-intercept: $f(0) = \dfrac{0+2}{0-6} = -\dfrac{1}{3} \rightarrow \left(0, -\dfrac{1}{3}\right)$

64. $f(x) = \dfrac{x^2 + 2}{x + 4}$

(a) $f(1) = \dfrac{1^2 + 2}{1 + 4} = \dfrac{3}{5} = \dfrac{3}{5} \quad \left(1, \dfrac{3}{5}\right)$ is on the graph of f.

(b) $f(0) = \dfrac{0^2 + 2}{0 + 4} = \dfrac{2}{4} = \dfrac{1}{2} \quad \left(0, \dfrac{1}{2}\right)$ is the point on the graph of f.

(c)   Solve for x:

$$\frac{1}{2} = \frac{x^2 + 2}{x + 4}$$

$$x + 4 = 2x^2 + 4$$

$$0 = 2x^2 - x \qquad \left(0, \dfrac{1}{2}\right) \text{ and } \left(\dfrac{1}{2}, \dfrac{1}{2}\right) \text{ are points on the graph of } f.$$

$$x(2x - 1) = 0$$

$$x = 0 \ \text{ or } \ x = \frac{1}{2}$$

(d)   The domain of f is: $\{x \mid x \neq -4\}$.

(e)   x-intercepts:

$$f(x) = 0$$

$$\frac{x^2 + 2}{x + 4} = 0 \rightarrow x^2 + 2 = 0 \text{ which is impossible}$$

$$\rightarrow \text{no } x - \text{intercepts}$$

(f)   y-intercept: $f(0) = \dfrac{x^2 + 2}{x + 4} = \dfrac{2}{4} = \dfrac{1}{2} \rightarrow \left(0, \dfrac{1}{2}\right)$

65. $f(x) = \dfrac{2x^2}{x^4 + 1}$

(a) $f(-1) = \dfrac{2(-1)^2}{(-1)^4 + 1} = \dfrac{2}{2} = 1 \quad (-1, 1)$ is a point on the graph of f.

(b) $f(2) = \dfrac{2(2)^2}{(2)^4+1} = \dfrac{8}{17}$ $\left(2, \dfrac{8}{17}\right)$ is a point on the graph of f.

(c) Solve for x:

$$1 = \dfrac{2x^2}{x^4+1}$$
$$x^4+1 = 2x^2$$
$$x^4 - 2x^2 + 1 = 0 \qquad \text{(1,1) and (−1,1) are points on the graph of } f.$$
$$(x^2-1)^2 = 0$$
$$x^2 - 1 = 0 \to x = \pm 1$$

(d) The domain of f is: $\{\text{Real Numbers}\}$.

(e) x-intercepts:
$$f(x) = 0$$
$$\dfrac{2x^2}{x^4+1} = 0$$
$$2x^2 = 0$$
$$x = 0$$
$$(0,0)$$

(f) y-intercept: $f(0) = \dfrac{2x^2}{x^4+1} = \dfrac{0}{0+1} = 0 \to (0,0)$

66. $f(x) = \dfrac{2x}{x-2}$

(a) $f\left(\dfrac{1}{2}\right) = \dfrac{2\left(\frac{1}{2}\right)}{\left(\frac{1}{2}-2\right)} = \dfrac{1}{\left(-\frac{3}{2}\right)} = -\dfrac{2}{3}$ $\left(\dfrac{1}{2}, -\dfrac{2}{3}\right)$ is a point on the graph of f.

(b) $f(4) = \dfrac{2(4)}{4-2} = \dfrac{8}{2} = 4$ $(4,4)$ is a point on the graph of f.

(c) Solve for x:
$$1 = \dfrac{2x}{x-2}$$
$$x - 2 = 2x$$
$$-2 = x$$
$(-2,1)$ is a point on the graph of f.

(d) The domain of f is: $\{x \mid x \neq 2\}$.

(e) x-intercepts:
$$f(x) = 0$$
$$\dfrac{2x}{x-2} = 0 \to 2x = 0$$
$$\to x = 0 \to (0,0)$$

(f) y-intercept: $f(0) = \dfrac{0}{0-2} = 0 \to (0,0)$

67.   Solving for A:

$f(x) = 2x^3 + Ax^2 + 4x - 5$ and $f(2) = 5$

$f(2) = 2(2)^3 + A(2)^2 + 4(2) - 5$

$5 = 16 + 4A + 8 - 5$

$5 = 4A + 19$

$-14 = 4A \rightarrow A = -\dfrac{7}{2}$

68.   Solve for B:

$f(x) = 3x^2 - Bx + 4$ and $f(-1) = 12$

$f(-1) = 3(-1)^2 - B(-1) + 4$

$12 = 3 + B + 4 \rightarrow B = 5$

69.   Solving for A:

$f(x) = \dfrac{3x + 8}{2x - A}$ and $f(0) = 2$

$f(0) = \dfrac{3(0) + 8}{2(0) - A}$

$2 = \dfrac{8}{-A} \rightarrow -2A = 8 \rightarrow A = -4$

70.   Solve for B:

$f(x) = \dfrac{2x - B}{3x + 4}$ and $f(2) = \dfrac{1}{2}$

$f(2) = \dfrac{2(2) - B}{3(2) + 4}$

$\dfrac{1}{2} = \dfrac{4 - B}{10} \rightarrow 5 = 4 - B \rightarrow B = -1$

71.   Solving for A:

$f(x) = \dfrac{2x - A}{x - 3}$ and $f(4) = 0$

$f(4) = \dfrac{2(4) - A}{4 - 3}$

$0 = \dfrac{8 - A}{1}$

$0 = 8 - A$

$A = 8$

f is undefined when $x = 3$.

72.   Solve for A and B:

$f(x) = \dfrac{x - B}{x - A}$ and $f(2) = 0$

$f(1)$ is undefined

$1 - A = 0 \quad \rightarrow \quad A = 1$

$f(2) = \dfrac{2 - B}{2 - 1}$

$0 = \dfrac{2 - B}{1}$

$0 = 2 - B$

$B = 2$

73.   (a)   III   (b)   IV   (c)   I   (d)   V   (e)   II

74.   (a)   II   (b)   V   (c)   IV   (d)   III   (e)   I

75.
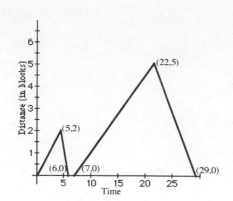

76.
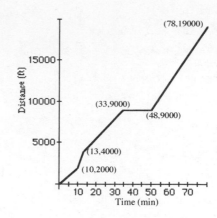

77. (a) Two times
     (b) Kevin's distance from home increased steadily at a rate of 1.5 miles per hour.
     (c) Kevin's distance from home did not change.
     (d) Kevin's distance from home decreased steadily at a rate of 10 miles per hour.
     (e) Kevin stayed at home for 0.2 hours.
     (f) Kevin's distance from home increased rapidly at the beginning and then tapered off to a very slow change in distance from home.
     (g) Kevin's distance from home did not change.
     (h) Kevin's distance from home decreased rapidly at the beginning of the interval and then tapered off as he got closer to home.
     (i) The furthest distance Kevin is from home is 3 miles.

78. (a) Michael travels fastest between 7 and 7.4 minutes.
     (b) Michael's speed is zero between 4.2 and 6 minutes.
     (c) Between 0 and 2 minutes, Michael's speed increased from 0 to 30 miles/hour.
     (d) Between 4.2 and 6 minutes, Michael was stopped.
     (e) Between 7 and 7.4 minutes, Michael was traveling at a steady rate of 50 miles/hr.
     (f) Michael's speed is constant between 2 and 4 minutes, between 4.2 and 6 minutes, between 7 and 7.4 minutes, and between 7.6 and 8 minutes.

79. (a) $H(1) = 20 - 4.9(1)^2 = 20 - 4.9 = 15.1$ meters
          $H(1.1) = 20 - 4.9(1.1)^2 = 20 - 4.9(1.21) = 20 - 5.929 = 14.071$ meters
          $H(1.2) = 20 - 4.9(1.2)^2 = 20 - 4.9(1.44) = 20 - 7.056 = 12.944$ meters
          $H(1.3) = 20 - 4.9(1.3)^2 = 20 - 4.9(1.69) = 20 - 8.281 = 11.719$ meters

     (b)
$H(x) = 15$	$H(x) = 10$	$H(x) = 5$
$15 = 20 - 4.9x^2$	$10 = 20 - 4.9x^2$	$5 = 20 - 4.9x^2$
$-5 = -4.9x^2$	$-10 = -4.9x^2$	$-15 = -4.9x^2$
$x^2 = 1.0204$	$x^2 = 2.0408$	$x^2 = 3.0612$
$x = 1.01$ seconds	$x = 1.43$ seconds	$x = 1.75$ seconds

(c) $H(x) = 0$

$$0 = 20 - 4.9x^2$$
$$-20 = -4.9x^2$$
$$x^2 = 4.0816$$
$$x = 2.02 \text{ seconds}$$

80. (a) $H(1) = 20 - 13(1)^2 = 20 - 13 = 7$ meters

$H(1.1) = 20 - 13(1.1)^2 = 20 - 13(1.21) = 20 - 15.73 = 4.27$ meters

$H(1.2) = 20 - 13(1.2)^2 = 20 - 13(1.44) = 20 - 18.72 = 1.28$ meters

(b) $H(x) = 15$ 　　　　　　 $H(x) = 10$ 　　　　　　 $H(x) = 5$

$15 = 20 - 13x^2$ 　　　　 $10 = 20 - 13x^2$ 　　　　 $5 = 20 - 13x^2$

$-5 = -13x^2$ 　　　　　 $-10 = -13x^2$ 　　　　 $-15 = -13x^2$

$x^2 = 0.3846$ 　　　　　 $x^2 = 0.7692$ 　　　　　 $x^2 = 1.1538$

$x = 0.62$ seconds 　　 $x = 0.88$ seconds 　　 $x = 1.07$ seconds

(c) $H(x) = 0$

$$0 = 20 - 13x^2$$
$$-20 = -13x^2$$
$$x^2 = 1.5385$$
$$x = 1.24 \text{ seconds}$$

81. $h(x) = \dfrac{-32x^2}{130^2} + x$

(a) $h(100) = \dfrac{-32(100)^2}{130^2} + 100 = \dfrac{-320000}{16900} + 100 = -18.93 + 100 = 81.07$ feet

(b) $h(300) = \dfrac{-32(300)^2}{130^2} + 300 = \dfrac{-2880000}{16900} + 300 = -170.41 + 300 = 129.59$ feet

(c) $h(500) = \dfrac{-32(500)^2}{130^2} + 500 = \dfrac{-8000000}{16900} + 500 = -473.37 + 500 = 26.63$ feet

(d)   Solve $h(x) = \dfrac{-32x^2}{130^2} + x = 0$

$$x\left(\dfrac{-32x}{130^2} + 1 \right) = 0$$

$x = 0$ or $\dfrac{-32x}{130^2} + 1 = 0 \rightarrow 1 = \dfrac{32x}{130^2} \rightarrow x = \dfrac{130^2}{32} = 528.125$ feet

82. $A(x) = 4x\sqrt{1 - x^2}$

(a) $A\left(\dfrac{1}{3}\right) = 4 \cdot \dfrac{1}{3}\sqrt{1 - \left(\dfrac{1}{3}\right)^2} = \dfrac{4}{3}\sqrt{\dfrac{8}{9}} = \dfrac{4}{3} \cdot \dfrac{2\sqrt{2}}{3} = \dfrac{8\sqrt{2}}{9} \approx 1.26$ ft^2

(b) $A\left(\dfrac{1}{2}\right) = 4 \cdot \dfrac{1}{2}\sqrt{1 - \left(\dfrac{1}{2}\right)^2} = 2\sqrt{\dfrac{3}{4}} = 2 \cdot \dfrac{\sqrt{3}}{2} = \sqrt{3} \approx 1.73$ ft^2

(c) $A\left(\dfrac{2}{3}\right) = 4 \cdot \dfrac{2}{3}\sqrt{1 - \left(\dfrac{2}{3}\right)^2} = \dfrac{8}{3}\sqrt{\dfrac{5}{9}} = \dfrac{8}{3} \cdot \dfrac{\sqrt{5}}{3} = \dfrac{8\sqrt{5}}{9} \approx 1.99$ ft^2

83. $C(x) = 100 + \dfrac{x}{10} + \dfrac{36000}{x}$

   (a) $C(500) = 100 + \dfrac{500}{10} + \dfrac{36000}{500} = 100 + 50 + 72 = \$222$

   (b) $C(450) = 100 + \dfrac{450}{10} + \dfrac{36000}{450} = 100 + 45 + 80 = \$225$

   (c) $C(600) = 100 + \dfrac{600}{10} + \dfrac{36000}{600} = 100 + 60 + 60 = \$220$

   (d) $C(400) = 100 + \dfrac{400}{10} + \dfrac{36000}{400} = 100 + 40 + 90 = \$230$

   (e) Graphing:

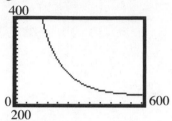

   (f) As x varies from 400 to 600 mph, the cost decreases from \$230 to \$220.

84. $W(h) = m\left(\dfrac{4000}{4000 + h}\right)^{2}$

   (a) $h = 14110$ feet ≈ 2.67 miles

$$W(2.67) = 120\left(\dfrac{4000}{4000 + 2.67}\right)^{2} \approx 119.84$$

   On Pike's Peak, Amy will weigh about 119.84 pounds.

   (b) Graphing:

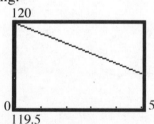

   (c) Create a TABLE:

X	Y1
0	120
.5	119.97
1	119.94
1.5	119.91
2	119.88
2.5	119.85
3	119.82

X=0

X	Y1
2	119.88
2.5	119.85
3	119.82
3.5	119.79
4	119.76
4.5	119.73
5	119.7

X=5

   (d) By refining the table, Amy will weigh 119.95 lbs at a height of about 0.8 miles.

85. Let x represent the length of the rectangle.

   Then $\dfrac{x}{2}$ represents the width of the rectangle, since the length is twice the width.

   The function for the area is: $A(x) = x \cdot \dfrac{x}{2} = \dfrac{x^{2}}{2} = \dfrac{1}{2}x^{2}$

86. Let x represent the length of one of the two equal sides.
    The function for the area is: $A(x) = \dfrac{1}{2} \cdot x \cdot x = \dfrac{1}{2}x^2$

87. Let x represent the number of hours worked.
    The function for the gross salary is: $G(x) = 10x$

88. Let x represent the number of items sold.
    The function for the gross salary is: $G(x) = 10x + 100$

89. (a) The relation is not a function because 23 is paired with both 56 and 53.

    (b)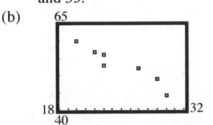

    (c) Using the points (20,60) and (30, 44) we get

    $$D = -1.6p + 92$$

    (d) As the price of the jeans increases by \$1, the demand for the jeans decreases by 1.6.

    (e) $D(p) = -1.6p + 92$

    (f) Domain: $\{p \mid p > 0\}$

    (g) $D(28) = -1.6(28) + 92$
    $$= 47.2 \approx 47$$
    Demand is about 47 pairs.

    (h) $D = -1.3355p + 86.1974$

90. (a) The relation is not a function because 24 is paired with both 343 and 341.

    (b)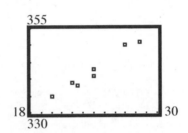

    (c) Using the points (20,335) and (28.3, 351) we get

    $$S = 1.9277A + 296.4458$$

    (d) As the advertising expenditure increases by \$1, the sales increase by \$1.9277.

    (e) $S(A) = 1.9277A + 296.4458$

    (f) Domain: $\{A \mid A \geq 0\}$

    (g) $S(25) = 1.9277(25) + 296.4458$
    $$\approx 344.638$$
    Sales are about \$344,638.

    (h) $S = 2.0667A + 292.8869$

91. (a) The relation is a function. Each time value is paired with exactly one distance value.

    (b)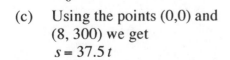

    (c) Using the points (0,0) and (8, 300) we get
    $$s = 37.5t$$

92. (a) The relation is a function. Each HS GPA value is paired with exactly one College GPA value.

    (b)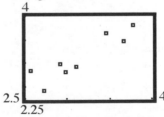

    (c) Using the points (2.73,2.43) and (3.10, 2.93) we get
    $$G = 1.3514x - 1.259$$

(d) As the time increases by 1 hour, the distance increases by 37.5 miles.

(d) As the high school GPA increases by 1, the college GPA increases by 1.3514.

(e) $s(t) = 37.5t$

(e) $G(x) = 1.3514x - 1.259$

(f) Domain: $\{t \mid t \geq 0\}$

(f) Domain: $\{x \mid x \geq 0\}$

(g) $s(11) = 37.5(11)$
$$= 412.5 \text{ miles}$$

(g) $G(3.23) = 1.3514(3.23) - 1.259$
$$= 3.1058 \approx 3.12$$
The college GPA is about 3.12.

(h) $s = 37.7833t - 19.1333$

(h) $G = 0.9639x + 0.0724$

93. (a) $h(x) = 2x$
$$h(a+b) = 2(a+b) = 2a + 2b = h(a) + h(b); \quad h(x) = 2x \text{ has the property.}$$

(b) $g(x) = x^2$
$$g(a+b) = (a+b)^2 = a^2 + 2ab + b^2 \neq a^2 + b^2 = h(a) + h(b)$$
$g(x) = x^2$ does not have the property.

(c) $F(x) = 5x - 2$
$$F(a+b) = 5(a+b) - 2 = 5a + 5b - 2 \neq 5a - 2 + 5b - 2 = h(a) + h(b)$$
$F(x) = 5x - 2$ does not have the property.

(d) $G(x) = \dfrac{1}{x}$
$$G(a+b) = \frac{1}{a+b} \neq \frac{1}{a} + \frac{1}{b} = h(a) + h(b)$$
$G(x) = \dfrac{1}{x}$ does not have the property.

94. All points of the form (5, y) and of the form (x, 0) cannot be on the graph of the function.

95. No, $x = -1$ is not in the domain of g, but it is in the domain of f.

96. Answers will vary.

97. A function may have any number of x-intercepts; it can have only one y-intercept.

98. Yes. One example is $G(x) = 2$, where the domain of G is {1}.

99. The only such function is $f(x) = 0$.

Chapter 3

Functions and Their Graphs

3.2   Properties of Functions

1.   Yes

2.   No   It is increasing.

3.   No   It only increases on (5, 10).

4.   Yes

5. f is increasing on the intervals: (–8, –2), (0, 2), (5, 10).

6. f is decreasing on the intervals: (–10, –8), (–2, 0), (2, 5).

7.   Yes. The local maximum at $x = 2$ is 10.

8.   No. There is a local minimum at $x = 5$.

9. f has local maxima at $x = -2$ and $x = 2$. The local maxima are 6 and 10, respectively.

10. f has local minima at $x = -8$, $x = 0$ and $x = 5$. The local minima are –4, 0, and 0, respectively.

11.   (a)   Intercepts: (–2,0), (2,0), and (0,3).
       (b)   Domain: $\left\{ x \mid -4 \leq x \leq 4 \right\}$; Range: $\left\{ y \mid 0 \leq y \leq 3 \right\}$.
       (c)   Interval notation: Increasing: (–2, 0) and (2, 4); Decreasing: (–4, –2) and (0, 2).
             Inequality notation: Increasing: $-2 < x < 0$ and $2 < x < 4$
             $\qquad\qquad\qquad\qquad\qquad$ Decreasing: $-4 < x < -2$ and $0 < x < 2$
       (d)   Since the graph is symmetric to the y-axis, the function is <u>even</u>.

12.   (a)   Intercepts: (–1, 0), (1, 0), and (0, 2).
       (b)   Domain: $\left\{ x \mid -3 \leq x \leq 3 \right\}$; Range: $\left\{ y \mid 0 \leq y \leq 3 \right\}$.
       (c)   Interval notation: Increasing: (–1, 0) and (1, 3); Decreasing: (–3, –1) and (0, 1).
             Inequality notation: Increasing: $-1 < x < 0$ and $1 < x < 3$
             $\qquad\qquad\qquad\qquad\qquad$ Decreasing: $-3 < x < -1$ and $0 < x < 1$
       (d)   Since the graph is symmetric to the y-axis, the function is <u>even</u>.

13. (a)   Intercepts: $(0,1)$.

    (b)   Domain: { Real Numbers }; Range: $\{y \mid y > 0\}$.

    (c)   Interval notation: Increasing: $(-\infty, +\infty)$; Decreasing: never.

        Inequality notation: Increasing: $-\infty < x < +\infty$

                        Decreasing: never

    (d)   Since the graph is not symmetric to the y-axis or the origin, the function is <u>neither</u> even nor odd.

14. (a)   Intercepts: $(1, 0)$.

    (b)   Domain: $\{x \mid x > 0\}$; Range: $\{$ Real Numbers $\}$.

    (c)   Interval notation: Increasing: $(0, +\infty)$; Decreasing: never.

        Inequality notation: Increasing: $x > 0$

                        Decreasing: never

    (d)   Since the graph is not symmetric to the y-axis or the origin, the function is <u>neither</u> even nor odd.

15. (a)   Intercepts: $(-\pi, 0), (0,0),$ and $(\pi, 0)$.

    (b)   Domain: $\{x \mid -\pi \le x \le \pi\}$; Range: $\{y \mid -1 \le y \le 1\}$.

    (c)   Interval notation: Increasing: $\left(-\frac{\pi}{2}, \frac{\pi}{2}\right)$; Decreasing: $\left(-\pi, -\frac{\pi}{2}\right)$ and $\left(\frac{\pi}{2}, \pi\right)$.

        Inequality notation: Increasing: $-\frac{\pi}{2} < x < \frac{\pi}{2}$

                      Decreasing: $-\pi < x < -\frac{\pi}{2}$ and $\frac{\pi}{2} < x < \pi$

    (d)   Since the graph is symmetric to the origin, the function is <u>odd</u>.

16. (a)   Intercepts: $\left(-\frac{\pi}{2}, 0\right), \left(\frac{\pi}{2}, 0\right),$ and $(0, 1)$.

    (b)   Domain: $\{x \mid -\pi \le x \le \pi\}$; Range: $\{y \mid -1 \le y \le 1\}$.

    (c)   Interval notation: Increasing: $(-\pi, 0)$; Decreasing: $(0, \pi)$.

        Inequality notation: Increasing: $-\pi < x < 0$

                      Decreasing: $0 < x < \pi$

    (d)   Since the graph is symmetric to the y-axis, the function is <u>even</u>.

17. (a)   Intercepts: $\left(0, \frac{1}{2}\right), \left(\frac{1}{3}, 0\right),$ and $\left(\frac{5}{2}, 0\right)$.

    (b)   Domain: $\{x \mid -3 \le x \le 3\}$; Range: $\{y \mid -1 \le y \le 2\}$.

    (c)   Interval notation: Increasing: $(2, 3)$; Decreasing: $(-1, 1)$;

                            Constant: $(-3, -1)$ and $(1, 2)$.

        Inequality notation: Increasing: $2 < x < 3$; Decreasing: $-1 < x < 1$;

                            Constant: $-3 < x < -1$ and $1 < x < 2$.

    (d)   Since the graph is not symmetric to the y-axis or the origin, the function is <u>neither</u> even nor odd.

18. (a) Intercepts: $(-2.3, 0), (3, 0)$, and $(0, 1)$.
    (b) Domain: $\{x | -3 \le x \le 3\}$; Range: $\{y | -2 \le y \le 2\}$.
    (c) Interval notation: Increasing: $(-3, -2)$ and $(0, 2)$; Decreasing: $(2, 3)$;
        Constant: $(-2, 0)$.
        Inequality notation: Increasing: $-3 < x < -2$ and $0 < x < 2$;
        Decreasing: $2 < x < 3$;   Constant: $-2 < x < 0$.
    (d) Since the graph is not symmetric to the y-axis or the origin, the function is <u>neither</u> even nor odd.

19. (a) Intercepts: $(0, 2), (-2, 0)$, and $(2, 0)$.
    (b) Domain: $\{x | -4 \le x \le 4\}$; Range: $\{y | 0 \le y \le 2\}$.
    (c) Interval notation: Increasing: $(-2, 0)$ and $(2, 4)$;
        Decreasing: $(-4, -2)$ and $(0, 2)$.
        Inequality notation: Increasing: $-2 < x < 0$ and $2 < x < 4$;
        Decreasing: $-4 < x < -2$ and $0 < x < 2$.
    (d) Since the graph is symmetric to the y-axis, the function is <u>even</u>.

20. (a) Intercepts: $(0, 0), (-4, 0)$, and $(4, 0)$.
    (b) Domain: $\{x | -4 \le x \le 4\}$; Range: $\{y | -2 \le y \le 2\}$.
    (c) Interval notation: Increasing: $(-2, 2)$;
        Decreasing: $(-4, -2)$ and $(2, 4)$.
        Inequality notation: Increasing: $-2 < x < 2$;
        Decreasing: $-4 < x < -2$ and $2 < x < 4$.
    (d) Since the graph is symmetric to the origin, the function is <u>odd</u>.

21. (a) f has a local maximum of 3 at $x = 0$.
    (b) f has a local minimum of 0 at both $x = -2$ and $x = 2$.

22. (a) f has a local maximum of 2 at $x = 0$.
    (b) f has a local minimum of 0 at both $x = -1$ and $x = 1$.

23. (a) f has a local maximum of 1 at $x = \dfrac{\pi}{2}$.
    (b) f has a local minimum of -1 at $x = -\dfrac{\pi}{2}$.

24. (a) f has a local maximum of 1 at $x = 0$.
    (b) f has a local minimum of -1 at $x = \pi$ and at $x = -\pi$.

25. $f(x) = 5x$

(a) $\dfrac{f(x) - f(1)}{x - 1} = \dfrac{5x - 5}{x - 1}$

(b) $= \dfrac{5(x-1)}{x-1} = 5$

$\dfrac{f(2) - f(1)}{2 - 1} = \dfrac{10 - 5}{2 - 1} = \dfrac{5}{1} = 5$

(c) Slope = 5; Containing (1, 5):

$y - 5 = 5(x - 1)$

$y - 5 = 5x - 5$

$y = 5x$

26. $f(x) = -4x$

(a) $\dfrac{f(x) - f(1)}{x - 1} = \dfrac{-4x + 4}{x - 1}$

(b) $= \dfrac{-4(x-1)}{x-1} = -4$

$\dfrac{f(2) - f(1)}{2 - 1} = \dfrac{-8 + 4}{2 - 1} = \dfrac{-4}{1} = -4$

(c) Slope = –4; Containing (1, –4):

$y - (-4) = -4(x - 1)$

$y + 4 = -4x + 4$

$y = -4x$

27. $f(x) = 1 - 3x$

(a) $\dfrac{f(x) - f(1)}{x - 1} = \dfrac{1 - 3x - (-2)}{x - 1}$

$= \dfrac{-3x + 3}{x - 1} = \dfrac{-3(x-1)}{x-1} = -3$

(b) $\dfrac{f(2) - f(1)}{2 - 1} = \dfrac{1 - 3(2) - (-2)}{2 - 1}$

$= \dfrac{-3}{1} = -3$

(c) Slope = –3; Containing (1, –2):

$y - (-2) = -3(x - 1)$

$y + 2 = -3x + 3$

$y = -3x + 1$

28. $f(x) = x^2 + 1$

(a) $\dfrac{f(x) - f(1)}{x - 1} = \dfrac{x^2 + 1 - 2}{x - 1}$

$= \dfrac{x^2 - 1}{x - 1} = \dfrac{(x+1)(x-1)}{x-1} = x + 1$

(b) $\dfrac{f(2) - f(1)}{2 - 1} = \dfrac{2^2 + 1 - 2}{2 - 1} = \dfrac{3}{1} = 3$

(c) Slope = 3; Containing (1, 2):

$y - 2 = 3(x - 1)$

$y - 2 = 3x - 3$

$y = 3x - 1$

29. $f(x) = x^2 - 2x$

(a) $\dfrac{f(x) - f(1)}{x - 1} = \dfrac{x^2 - 2x - (-1)}{x - 1}$

$= \dfrac{x^2 - 2x + 1}{x - 1} = \dfrac{(x-1)^2}{x-1} = x - 1$

(b) $\dfrac{f(2) - f(1)}{2 - 1} = \dfrac{2^2 - 2(2) - (-1)}{2 - 1} = \dfrac{1}{1} = 1$

Slope = 1; Containing (1, –1):

(c) $y - (-1) = 1(x - 1)$

$y + 1 = 1x - 1$

$y = x - 2$

30 $f(x) = x - 2x^2$

(a) $\dfrac{f(x) - f(1)}{x - 1} = \dfrac{x - 2x^2 - (-1)}{x - 1}$

$= \dfrac{-2x^2 + x + 1}{x - 1} = \dfrac{(-2x - 1)(x - 1)}{x - 1}$

$= -2x - 1$

(b) $\dfrac{f(2) - f(1)}{2 - 1} = \dfrac{2 - 2 \cdot 2^2 - (-1)}{2 - 1}$

$= \dfrac{-5}{1} = -5$

(c) Slope = –5; Containing (1, –1):

$y - (-1) = -5(x - 1)$

$y + 1 = -5x + 5$

$y = -5x + 4$

31. $f(x) = x^3 - x$

(a) $\dfrac{f(x) - f(1)}{x - 1} = \dfrac{x^3 - x - 0}{x - 1} = \dfrac{x^3 - x}{x - 1}$

$= \dfrac{x(x-1)(x+1)}{x-1} = x^2 + x$

(b) $\dfrac{f(2) - f(1)}{2 - 1} = \dfrac{2^3 - 2 - 0}{2 - 1} = \dfrac{6}{1} = 6$

(c) Slope = 6; Containing $(1, 0)$:
$y - 0 = 6(x - 1)$
$y = 6x - 6$

32. $f(x) = x^3 + x$

(a) $\dfrac{f(x) - f(1)}{x - 1} = \dfrac{x^3 + x - 2}{x - 1}$

$= \dfrac{(x-1)(x^2 + x + 2)}{x-1} = x^2 + x + 2$

(b) $\dfrac{f(2) - f(1)}{2 - 1} = \dfrac{2^3 + 2 - 2}{2 - 1} = \dfrac{8}{1} = 8$

(c) Slope = 8; Containing $(1, 2)$:
$y - 2 = 8(x - 1)$
$y - 2 = 8x - 8$
$y = 8x - 6$

33. $f(x) = \dfrac{2}{x + 1}$

(a) $\dfrac{f(x) - f(1)}{x - 1} = \dfrac{\left(\dfrac{2}{x+1} - 1\right)}{x - 1} = \dfrac{\left(\dfrac{2 - x - 1}{x+1}\right)}{x - 1}$

$= \dfrac{1 - x}{(x-1)(x+1)} = \dfrac{-1}{x+1}$

(b) $\dfrac{f(2) - f(1)}{2 - 1} = \dfrac{\left(\dfrac{2}{2+1} - 1\right)}{2 - 1}$

(c) $= \dfrac{\left(-\dfrac{1}{3}\right)}{1} = -\dfrac{1}{3}$

Slope = $-\dfrac{1}{3}$; Containing $(1, 1)$:

$y - 1 = -\dfrac{1}{3}(x - 1)$

$y - 1 = -\dfrac{1}{3}x + \dfrac{1}{3} \rightarrow y = -\dfrac{1}{3}x + \dfrac{4}{3}$

34. $f(x) = \dfrac{1}{x^2}$

(a) $\dfrac{f(x) - f(1)}{x - 1} = \dfrac{\left(\dfrac{1}{x^2} - 1\right)}{x - 1} = \dfrac{\left(\dfrac{1 - x^2}{x^2}\right)}{x - 1}$

$= \dfrac{(1-x)(1+x)}{x^2(x-1)} = \dfrac{-x-1}{x^2}$

(b)

(c) $\dfrac{f(2) - f(1)}{2 - 1} = \dfrac{\left(\dfrac{1}{2^2} - 1\right)}{2 - 1} = \dfrac{\left(-\dfrac{3}{4}\right)}{1} = -\dfrac{3}{4}$

Slope = $-\dfrac{3}{4}$; Containing $(1, 1)$:
$y - 1 = -\dfrac{3}{4}(x - 1)$
$y - 1 = -\dfrac{3}{4}x + \dfrac{3}{4}$
$y = -\dfrac{3}{4}x + \dfrac{7}{4}$

35. $f(x) = \sqrt{x}$

(a) $\dfrac{f(x) - f(1)}{x - 1} = \dfrac{\sqrt{x} - 1}{x - 1}$

(b) $\dfrac{f(2) - f(1)}{2 - 1} = \dfrac{\sqrt{2} - 1}{1} = \sqrt{2} - 1$

Slope = $\sqrt{2} - 1$; Containing $(1, 1)$:

(c) $y - 1 = \left(\sqrt{2} - 1\right)(x - 1)$

$y - 1 = \left(\sqrt{2} - 1\right)x - \left(\sqrt{2} - 1\right)$

$y = \left(\sqrt{2} - 1\right)x - \sqrt{2} + 2$

36. $f(x) = \sqrt{x + 3}$

(a) $\dfrac{f(x) - f(1)}{x - 1} = \dfrac{\sqrt{x+3} - 2}{x - 1}$

(b) $\dfrac{f(2) - f(1)}{2 - 1} = \dfrac{\sqrt{5} - 2}{1} = \sqrt{5} - 2$

Slope = $\sqrt{5} - 2$; Containing $(1, 2)$:

(c) $y - 2 = \left(\sqrt{5} - 2\right)(x - 1)$

$y - 2 = \left(\sqrt{5} - 2\right)x - \left(\sqrt{5} - 2\right)$

$y = \left(\sqrt{5} - 2\right)x - \sqrt{5} + 4$

37. $f(x) = 4x^3$

   $f(-x) = 4(-x)^3 = -4x^3$

   f is odd.

38. $f(x) = 2x^4 - x^2$

   $f(-x) = 2(-x)^4 - (-x)^2 = 2x^4 - x^2$

   f is even.

39. $g(x) = -3x^2 - 5$

   $g(-x) = -3(-x)^2 - 5 = -3x^2 - 5$

   g is even.

40. $h(x) = 3x^3 + 5$

   $h(-x) = 3(-x)^3 + 5 = -3x^3 + 5$

   h is neither even nor odd.

41. $F(x) = \sqrt[3]{x}$

   $F(-x) = \sqrt[3]{-x} = -\sqrt[3]{x}$

   F is odd.

42. $G(x) = \sqrt{x}$

   $G(-x) = \sqrt{-x}$

   G is neither even nor odd.

43. $f(x) = x + |x|$

   $f(-x) = -x + |-x| = -x + |x|$

   f is neither even nor odd.

44. $f(x) = \sqrt[3]{2x^2 + 1}$

   $f(-x) = \sqrt[3]{2(-x)^2 + 1} = \sqrt[3]{2x^2 + 1}$

   f is even.

45. $g(x) = \dfrac{1}{x^2}$

   $g(-x) = \dfrac{1}{(-x)^2} = \dfrac{1}{x^2}$

   g is even.

46. $h(x) = \dfrac{x}{x^2 - 1}$

   $h(-x) = \dfrac{-x}{(-x)^2 - 1} = \dfrac{-x}{x^2 - 1}$

   h is odd.

47. $h(x) = \dfrac{-x^3}{3x^2 - 9}$

   $h(-x) = \dfrac{-(-x)^3}{3(-x)^2 - 9} = \dfrac{x^3}{3x^2 - 9}$

   h is odd.

48. $F(x) = \dfrac{2x}{|x|}$

   $F(-x) = \dfrac{2(-x)}{|-x|} = \dfrac{-2x}{|x|}$

   F is odd.

49. $f(x) = 2x + 5$

   $m_{sec} = \dfrac{f(x+h) - f(x)}{h} = \dfrac{2(x+h) + 5 - 2x - 5}{h} = \dfrac{2h}{h} = 2$

50. $f(x) = -3x + 2$

   $m_{sec} = \dfrac{f(x+h) - f(x)}{h} = \dfrac{-3(x+h) + 2 - (-3x + 2)}{h} = \dfrac{-3h}{h} = -3$

51. $f(x) = x^2 + 2x$

   $m_{sec} = \dfrac{f(x+h) - f(x)}{h} = \dfrac{(x+h)^2 + 2(x+h) - (x^2 + 2x)}{h}$

   $= \dfrac{x^2 + 2xh + h^2 + 2x + 2h - x^2 - 2x}{h} = \dfrac{2xh + h^2 + 2h}{h} = 2x + h + 2$

52. $f(x) = 2x^2 + x$

$$m_{\text{sec}} = \frac{f(x+h)-f(x)}{h} = \frac{2(x+h)^2+(x+h)-(2x^2+x)}{h}$$

$$= \frac{2(x^2+2xh+h^2)+x+h-2x^2-x}{h} = \frac{2x^2+4xh+2h^2+x+h-2x^2-x}{h}$$

$$= \frac{4xh+2h^2+h}{h} = 4x+2h+1$$

53. $f(x) = 2x^2 - 3x + 1$

$$m_{\text{sec}} = \frac{f(x+h)-f(x)}{h} = \frac{2(x+h)^2-3(x+h)+1-(2x^2-3x+1)}{h}$$

$$= \frac{2(x^2+2xh+h^2)-3x-3h+1-2x^2+3x-1}{h}$$

$$= \frac{2x^2+4xh+2h^2-3x-3h+1-2x^2+3x-1}{h}$$

$$= \frac{4xh+2h^2-3h}{h} = 4x+2h-3$$

54. $f(x) = -x^2 + 3x - 2$

$$m_{\text{sec}} = \frac{f(x+h)-f(x)}{h} = \frac{-(x+h)^2+3(x+h)-2-(-x^2+3x-2)}{h}$$

$$= \frac{-(x^2+2xh+h^2)+3x+3h-2+x^2-3x+2}{h}$$

$$= \frac{-x^2-2xh-h^2+3x+3h-2+x^2-3x+2}{h}$$

$$= \frac{-2xh-h^2+3h}{h} = -2x-h+3$$

55. $f(x) = \dfrac{1}{x}$

$$m_{\text{sec}} = \frac{f(x+h)-f(x)}{h} = \frac{\left(\dfrac{1}{x+h}-\dfrac{1}{x}\right)}{h}$$

$$= \frac{\left(\dfrac{x-(x+h)}{(x+h)x}\right)}{h} = \left(\frac{x-x-h}{(x+h)x}\right)\left(\frac{1}{h}\right) = \left(\frac{-h}{(x+h)x}\right)\left(\frac{1}{h}\right)$$

$$= -\frac{1}{(x+h)x}$$

56.
$$f(x) = \frac{1}{x^2}$$

$$m_{\text{sec}} = \frac{f(x+h)-f(x)}{h} = \frac{\left(\dfrac{1}{(x+h)^2} - \dfrac{1}{x^2}\right)}{h}$$

$$= \frac{\left(\dfrac{x^2-(x+h)^2}{(x+h)^2 x^2}\right)}{h} = \left(\frac{x^2-(x^2+2xh+h^2)}{(x+h)^2 x^2}\right)\left(\frac{1}{h}\right) = \left(\frac{-2xh-h^2}{(x+h)^2 x^2}\right)\left(\frac{1}{h}\right) = \frac{-2x-h}{(x+h)^2 x^2}$$

57.   (a), (b), (e)

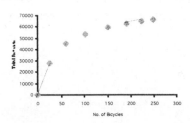

(c)   Average rate of change $= \dfrac{28000-0}{25-0} = \dfrac{28000}{25} = 1120$

(d)   For each additional bicycle sold between 0 and 25, the total revenue increases by $1120.

(f)   Average rate of change $= \dfrac{64835-62360}{223-190} = \dfrac{2475}{33} = 75$

(g)   For each additional bicycle sold between 190 and 223, the total revenue increases by $75.

58.   (a), (b), (e)

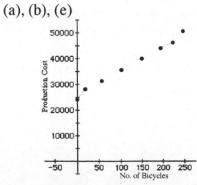

(c)   Average rate of change $= \dfrac{27750-24000}{25-0} = \dfrac{3750}{25} = 150$

(d)   For each additional bicycle made between 0 and 25, the total production cost increases by $150.

(f)   Average rate of change $= \dfrac{46500-42750}{223-190} = \dfrac{3750}{33} = 113.64$

(g)   For each additional bicycle made between 190 and 223, the total production cost increases by $113.64.

59.   (a), (b), (e)

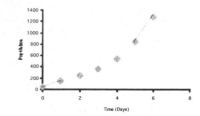

(c)   Average rate of change $= \dfrac{153-50}{1-0} = \dfrac{103}{1} = 103$

(d)   The population is increasing at a rate of 103 per day between day 0 and day 1.

(f)   Average rate of change $= \dfrac{1280-839}{6-5} = \dfrac{441}{1} = 441$

(g)   The population is increasing at a rate of 441 per day between day 5 and day 6.

(h)   As time passes, the average rate of change of the population is increasing.

60.   (a), (b), (e)

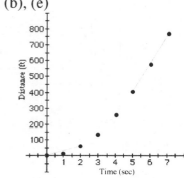

(c)   Average rate of change $= \dfrac{64-0}{2-0} = \dfrac{64}{2} = 32$ ft per sec

(d)   The distance is increasing at a rate of 32 feet per second between 1 and 2 seconds.

(f)   Average rate of change $= \dfrac{784-400}{7-5} = \dfrac{384}{2} = 192$ ft per sec

(g)   The distance is increasing at a rate of 192 feet per second between 5 and 7 seconds.

(h)   As time passes, the average rate of change of the distance is increasing.

61.   One at most because if f is increasing it could only cross the x-axis at most one time. It could not "turn" and cross it again or it would start to decrease.

62.   The only such function is $f(x) = 0$.

Functions and Their Graphs

3.3   Library of Functions; Piecewise-Defined Functions

1.   C   2.   A   3.   E   4.   G

5.   B   6.   D   7.   F   8.   H

9.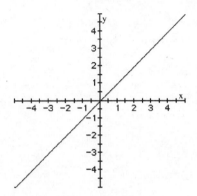

10.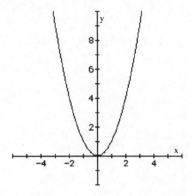

11.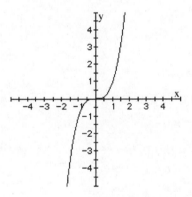

12.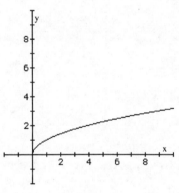

13.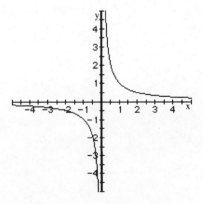

14.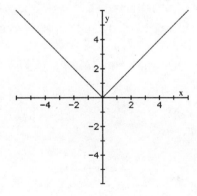

15. (a) $f(-2) = (-2)^2 = 4$
    (b) $f(0) = 2$
    (c) $f(2) = 2(2) + 1 = 5$

16. (a) $f(-1) = (-1)^3 = -1$
    (b) $f(0) = 3(0) + 2 = 2$
    (c) $f(1) = 3(1) + 2 = 5$

17. (a) $f(1.2) = \text{int}(2(1.2)) = \text{int}(2.4) = 2$
    (b) $f(1.6) = \text{int}(2(1.6)) = \text{int}(3.2) = 3$
    (c) $f(-1.8) = \text{int}(2(-1.8)) = \text{int}(-3.6) = -4$

18. (a) $f(1.2) = \text{int}\left(\dfrac{1.2}{2}\right) = \text{int}(0.6) = 0$
    (b) $f(1.6) = \text{int}\left(\dfrac{1.6}{2}\right) = \text{int}(0.8) = 0$
    (c) $f(-1.8) = \text{int}\left(\dfrac{-1.8}{2}\right) = \text{int}(-0.9) = -1$

19. $f(x) = \begin{cases} 2x & \text{if } x \neq 0 \\ 1 & \text{if } x = 0 \end{cases}$
    (a) Domain: {Real Numbers}
    (b) x-intercept: none
        y-intercept: (0,1)
    (c)

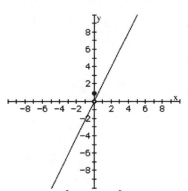

    (d) Range: $\{y \mid y \neq 0\}$

20. $f(x) = \begin{cases} 3x & \text{if } x \neq 0 \\ 4 & \text{if } x = 0 \end{cases}$
    (a) Domain: {Real Numbers}
    (b) x-intercept: none
        y-intercept: (0, 4)
    (c)

    (d) Range: $\{y \mid y \neq 0\}$

21. $f(x) = \begin{cases} -2x+3 & \text{if } x < 1 \\ 3x-2 & \text{if } x \geq 1 \end{cases}$

    (a) Domain: {Real Numbers}

    (b) x-intercept: none

          y-intercept: (0,3)

    (c)

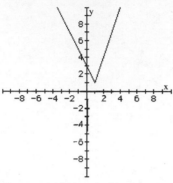

    (d) Range: $\{y \mid y \geq 1\}$

22. $f(x) = \begin{cases} x+3 & \text{if } x < -2 \\ -2x-3 & \text{if } x \geq -2 \end{cases}$

    (a) Domain: {Real Numbers}

    (b) x-intercept: (–3, 0), (–1.5, 0)

          y-intercept: (0, –3)

    (c)

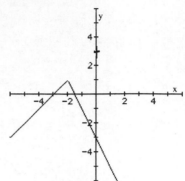

    (d) Range: $\{y \mid y \leq 1\}$

23. $f(x) = \begin{cases} x+3 & \text{if } -2 \leq x < 1 \\ 5 & \text{if } x = 1 \\ -x+2 & \text{if } x > 1 \end{cases}$

    (a) Domain: $\{x \mid x \geq -2\}$

    (b) x-intercept: (2, 0)

          y-intercept: (0, 3)

    (c)

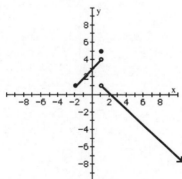

    (d) Range: $\{y \mid y < 4\} \cup \{5\}$

24. $f(x) = \begin{cases} 2x+5 & \text{if } -3 \leq x < 0 \\ -3 & \text{if } x = 0 \\ -5x & \text{if } x > 0 \end{cases}$

    (a) Domain: $\{x \mid x \geq -3\}$

    (b) x-intercept: (–2.5, 0)

          y-intercept: (0, –3)

    (c)

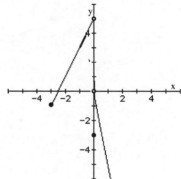

    (d) Range: $\{y \mid y < 5\}$

25. $f(x) = \begin{cases} 1 + x & \text{if } x < 0 \\ x^2 & \text{if } x \geq 0 \end{cases}$

   (a)   Domain: {Real Numbers}

   (b)   x-intercept: (−1,0), (0,0)

       y-intercept: (0,0)

   (c)

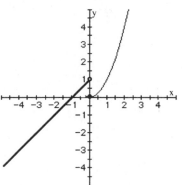

   (d)   Range: {Real Numbers}

26. $f(x) = \begin{cases} \dfrac{1}{x} & \text{if } x < 0 \\ \sqrt{x} & \text{if } x \geq 0 \end{cases}$

   (a)   Domain: {Real Numbers}

   (b)   x-intercept: (0,0)

       y-intercept: (0,0)

   (c)

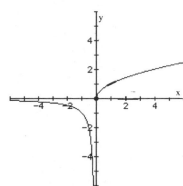

   (d)   Range: {Real Numbers}

27. $f(x) = \begin{cases} |x| & \text{if } -2 \leq x < 0 \\ 1 & \text{if } x = 0 \\ x^3 & \text{if } x > 0 \end{cases}$

   (a)   Domain: $\{x \mid x \geq -2\}$

   (b)   x-intercept: none

       y-intercept: (0, 1)

   (c)

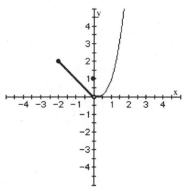

   (d)   Range: $\{y \mid y > 0\}$

28. $f(x) = \begin{cases} 3 + x & \text{if } -3 \leq x < 0 \\ 3 & \text{if } x = 0 \\ \sqrt{x} & \text{if } x > 0 \end{cases}$

   (a)   Domain: $\{x \mid x \geq -3\}$

   (b)   x-intercept: (−3, 0)

       y-intercept: (0, 3)

   (c)

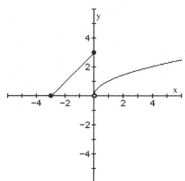

   (d)   Range: $\{y \mid y \geq 0\}$

29. $h(x) = 2\text{int}(x)$
     (a) Domain: {Real Numbers}
     (b) x-intercept: all ordered pairs
          $(x,0)$ when $0 \le x < 1$.
          y-intercept: (0,0)
     (c)

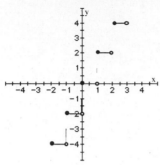

     (d) Range: {Even Integers}

30. $f(x) = \text{int}(2x)$
     (a) Domain: {Real Numbers}
     (b) x-intercept: all ordered pairs
          $(x,0)$ when $0 \le x < \dfrac{1}{2}$.
          y-intercept: (0,0)
     (c)

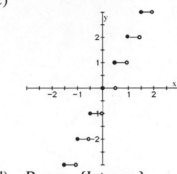

     (d) Range: {Integers}

31. $f(x) = \begin{cases} -x & \text{if } -1 \le x \le 0 \\ \dfrac{1}{2}x & \text{if } 0 < x \le 2 \end{cases}$

32. $f(x) = \begin{cases} x & \text{if } -1 \le x \le 0 \\ 1 & \text{if } 0 < x \le 2 \end{cases}$

33. $f(x) = \begin{cases} -x & \text{if } x \le 0 \\ -x+2 & \text{if } 0 < x \le 2 \end{cases}$

34. $f(x) = \begin{cases} 2x + 2 & \text{if } -1 \le x \le 0 \\ x & \text{if } x > 0 \end{cases}$

35. (a) Charge for 50 therms: $C = 9.45 + 0.36375(50) + 0.3128(50) = \$43.28$
     (b) Charge for 500 therms:
          $C = 9.45 + 0.36375(50) + 0.11445(450) + 0.3128(500) = \$235.54$
     (c) The monthly charge function:
          $$C = \begin{cases} 9.45 + 0.36375x + 0.3128x & \text{for } 0 \le x \le 50 \\ 9.45 + 0.36375(50) + 0.11445(x-50) + 0.3128x & \text{for } x > 50 \end{cases}$$
          $$= \begin{cases} 9.45 + 0.67655x & \text{for } 0 \le x \le 50 \\ 9.45 + 18.1875 + 0.11445x - 5.7225 + 0.3128x & \text{for } x > 50 \end{cases}$$
          $$= \begin{cases} 9.45 + 0.67655x & \text{for } 0 \le x \le 50 \\ 21.915 + 0.42725x & \text{for } x > 50 \end{cases}$$
     (d)

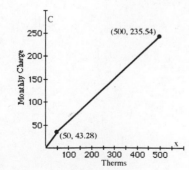

288

36. (a) Charge for 40 therms:
$$C = 6.45 + 0.2012(20) + 0.1117(20) + 0.3209(40) = \$25.54$$

(b) Charge for 202 therms:
$$C = 6.45 + 0.2012(20) + 0.1117(30) + 0.0374(152) + 0.3209(202) = \$84.33$$

(c) The monthly charge function:
$$C = \begin{cases} 6.45 + 0.2012x + 0.3209x & \text{for } 0 \le x \le 20 \\ 6.45 + 0.2012(20) + 0.1117(x-20) + 0.3209x & \text{for } 20 < x \le 50 \\ 6.45 + 0.2012(20) + 0.1117(30) + 0.0374(x-50) + 0.3209x & \text{for } x > 50 \end{cases}$$

$$= \begin{cases} 6.45 + 0.5221x & \text{for } 0 \le x \le 20 \\ 6.45 + 4.024 + 0.1117x - 2.234 + 0.3209x & \text{for } 20 < x \le 50 \\ 6.45 + 4.024 + 3.351 + 0.0374x - 1.87 + 0.3209x & \text{for } x > 50 \end{cases}$$

$$= \begin{cases} 6.45 + 0.5221x & \text{for } 0 \le x \le 20 \\ 8.24 + 0.4326x & \text{for } 20 < x \le 50 \\ 11.955 + 0.3583x & \text{for } x > 50 \end{cases}$$

(d)

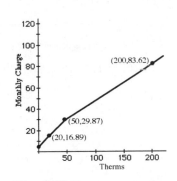

37. (a) $W = 10°C$

(b) $W = 33 - \dfrac{(10.45 + 10\sqrt{5} - 5)(33 - 10)}{22.04} = 3.98°C$

(c) $W = 33 - \dfrac{(10.45 + 10\sqrt{15} - 15)(33 - 10)}{22.04} = -2.67°C$

(d) $W = 33 - 1.5958(33 - 10) = -3.7°C$

(e) When $0 \le v < 1.79$, the wind speed is so small that there is no effect on the temperature.

(f) For each drop of $1°$ in temperature, the wind chill factor drops approximately $1.6°C$. When the wind speed exceeds 20, there is a constant drop in temperature.

38. (a) $W = -10°C$

(b) $W = 33 - \dfrac{(10.45 + 10\sqrt{5} - 5)(33 - (-10))}{22.04} = -21.26°C$

(c) $W = 33 - \dfrac{(10.45 + 10\sqrt{15} - 15)(33 - (-10))}{22.04} = -33.68°C$

(d) $W = 33 - 1.5958(33 - (-10)) = -35.62°C$

39.   Each graph is that of $y = x^2$, but shifted vertically. If $y = x^2 + k$, $k > 0$, the shift is up k units; if $y = x^2 + k$, $k < 0$, the shift is down $|k|$ units. The graph of $y = x^2 - 4$ is the same as the graph of $y = x^2$, but shifted down 4 units. The graph of $y = x^2 + 5$ is the graph of $y = x^2$, but shifted up 5 units.

40.   Each graph is that of $y = x^2$, but shifted horizontally. If $y = (x - k)^2$, $k > 0$, the shift is to the right k units; if $y = (x - k)^2$, $k < 0$, the shift is to the left $|k|$ units. The graph of $y = (x + 4)^2$ is the same as the graph of $y = x^2$, but shifted to the left 4 units. The graph of $y = (x - 5)^2$ is the graph of $y = x^2$, but shifted to the right 5 units.

41.   Each graph is that of $y = |x|$, but either compressed or stretched. If $y = k|x|$ and $k > 1$, the graph is stretched; if $y = k|x|$ and $0 < k < 1$, the graph is compressed. The graph of $y = \frac{1}{4}|x|$ is the same as the graph of $y = |x|$, but compressed. The graph of $y = 5|x|$ is the same as the graph of $y = |x|$, but stretched.

42.   The graph of $y = -x^2$ is the reflection of the graph of $y = x^2$ on the x-axis. The graph of $y = -|x|$ is the reflection of the graph of $y = |x|$ on the x-axis. Multiplying a function by -1 causes the graph to be a reflection on the x-axis of the original function's graph.

43.   The graph of $y = \sqrt{-x}$ is the reflection about the y-axis of the graph of $y = \sqrt{x}$. The same type of reflection occurs when graphing $y = 2x + 1$ and $y = 2(-x) + 1$. The conclusion is that the graph of $y = f(-x)$ is the reflection about the y-axis of the graph of $y = f(x)$.

44.   The graph of $y = (x - 1)^3 + 2$ is a shifting of the graph of $y = x^3$ one unit to the right and two units up.

45.   For the graph of $y = x^n$, n a positive even integer, as n increases, the graph of the function is narrower for $|x| > 1$ and flatter for $|x| < 1$.

46.   For the graph of $y = x^n$, n a positive odd integer, as n increases, the graph of the function increases at a greater rate for $|x| > 1$ and is closer to zero for $|x| < 1$. They have the same basic shape.

47. $f(x) = \begin{cases} 1 & \text{if } x \text{ is rational} \\ 0 & \text{if } x \text{ is irrational} \end{cases}$ Domain = { all real numbers}   Range = {0,1}

y-intercept: $x = 0 \to x$ is rational $\to y = 1$, so the y-intercept is (0, 1).

x-intercept: $y = 0 \to x$ is irrational, so the graph has infinitely many x-intercepts, namely, there is an x-intercept at each irrational value for x.

$f(-x) = 1 = f(x)$ when x is rational; $f(-x) = 0 = f(x)$ when x is irrational

$\therefore f$ is even.

The graph of f consists of 2 infinite clusters of distinct points, extending horizontally in both directions.

One cluster is located 1 unit above the x-axis, and the other is located along the x-axis.

48.   For $0 < x < 1$, the graph of $y = x^n$ flattens down toward the x-axis as n gets bigger.

For $1 < x$, the graph of $y = x^n$ grows more steeply as n gets bigger.

Functions and Their Graphs

3.4   Graphing Techniques: Transformations

1.   B   2.   E   3.   H   4.   D

5.   I   6.   A   7.   L   8.   C

9.   F   10. J   11. G   12. K

13. $y = (x-4)^3$ 14. $y = (x+4)^3$ 15. $y = x^3 + 4$ 16. $y = x^3 - 4$

17. $y = -x^3$ 18. $y = -x^3$ 19. $y = 4x^3$ 20. $y = \left(\frac{1}{4}x\right)^3 = \frac{x^3}{64}$

21. (1) $y = \sqrt{x} + 2$ 22. (1) $y = -\sqrt{x}$
     (2) $y = -\left(\sqrt{x} + 2\right)$ (2) $y = -\sqrt{x-3}$
     (3) $y = -\left(\sqrt{-x} + 2\right)$ (3) $y = -\sqrt{x-3} - 2$

23. (1) $y = -\sqrt{x}$ 24. (1) $y = \sqrt{x} + 2$
     (2) $y = -\sqrt{x} + 2$ (2) $y = \sqrt{-x} + 2$
     (3) $y = -\sqrt{x+3} + 2$ (3) $y = \sqrt{-(x+3)} + 2 = \sqrt{-x-3} + 2$

25. C   26. D   27. C   28.   A

29. $f(x) = x^2 - 1$ 30. $f(x) = x^2 + 4$
     Using the graph of $y = x^2$, vertically   Using the graph of $y = x^2$, vertically
     shift downward 1 unit.   shift upward 4 units.

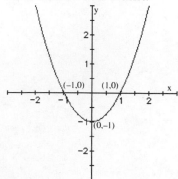

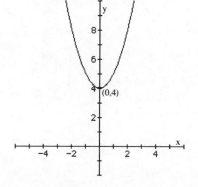

31. $g(x) = x^3 + 1$

Using the graph of $y = x^3$, vertically shift upward 1 unit.

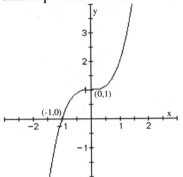

32. $g(x) = x^3 - 1$

Using the graph of $y = x^3$, vertically shift downward 1 unit.

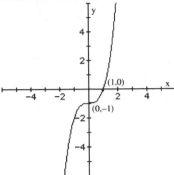

33. $h(x) = \sqrt{x - 2}$

Using the graph of $y = \sqrt{x}$, horizontally shift to the right 2 units.

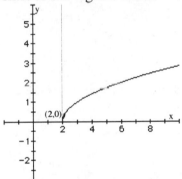

34. $h(x) = \sqrt{x + 1}$

Using the graph of $y = \sqrt{x}$, horizontally shift to the left 1 unit.

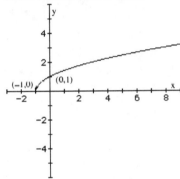

35. $f(x) = (x - 1)^3 + 2$

Using the graph of $y = x^3$, horizontally shift to the right 1 unit, then vertically shift up 2 units.

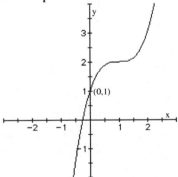

36. $f(x) = (x + 2)^3 - 3$

Using the graph of $y = x^3$, horizontally shift to the left 2 units, then vertically shift down 3 units.

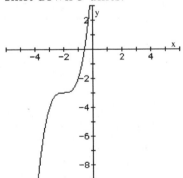

37. $g(x) = 4\sqrt{x}$

Using the graph of $y = \sqrt{x}$, vertically stretch by a factor of 4.

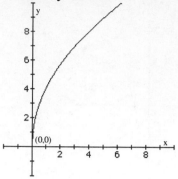

38. $g(x) = \dfrac{1}{2}\sqrt{x}$

Using the graph of $y = \sqrt{x}$, vertically compress by a factor of $\dfrac{1}{2}$.

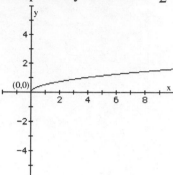

39. $h(x) = \dfrac{1}{2x}$

Using the graph of $y = \dfrac{1}{x}$, vertically compress by a factor of $\dfrac{1}{2}$.

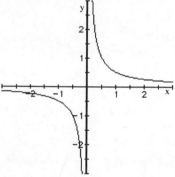

40. $h(x) = \dfrac{4}{x}$

Using the graph of $y = \dfrac{1}{x}$, vertically stretch by a factor of 4.

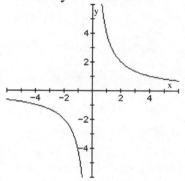

41. $f(x) = -|x|$

Reflect the graph of $y = |x|$, about the x-axis.

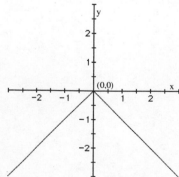

42. $f(x) = -\sqrt{x}$

Reflect the graph of $y = \sqrt{x}$, about the x-axis.

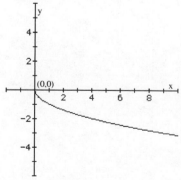

43.　$g(x) = |-x|$
Reflect the graph of $y = |x|$, about the y-axis.

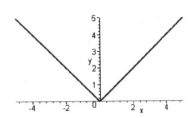

44.　$g(x) = -x^3$
Reflect the graph of $y = x^3$, about the x-axis.

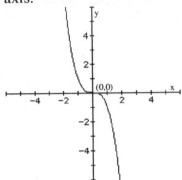

45.　$h(x) = -x^3 + 2$
Reflect the graph of $y = x^3$ on the x-axis, vertically shift upward 2 units.

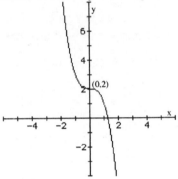

46.　$h(x) = \dfrac{1}{-x}$

Reflect the graph of $y = \dfrac{1}{x}$, about the y-axis.

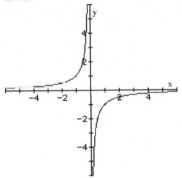

47.　$f(x) = 2(x + 1)^2 - 3$
Using the graph of $y = x^2$, horizontally shift to the left 1 unit, vertically stretch by a factor of 2, and vertically shift downward 3 units.

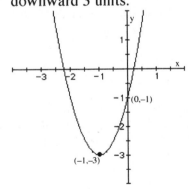

48.　$f(x) = 3(x - 2)^2 + 1$
Using the graph of $y = x^2$, horizontally shift to the right 2 units, vertically stretch by a factor of 3, and vertically shift upward 1 units.

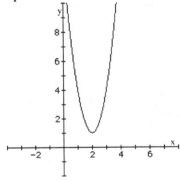

49. $g(x) = \sqrt{x-2} + 1$

Using the graph of $y = \sqrt{x}$, horizontally shift to the right 2 units and vertically shift upward 1 unit.

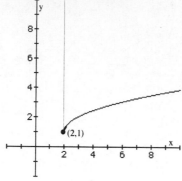

50. $g(x) = |x+1| - 3$

Using the graph of $y = |x|$, horizontally shift to the left 1 unit and vertically shift downward 3 units.

51. $h(x) = \sqrt{-x} - 2$

Reflect the graph of $y = \sqrt{x}$, about the y-axis and vertically shift downward 2 units.

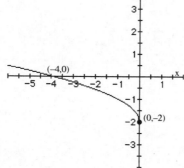

52. $h(x) = \dfrac{4}{x} + 2$

Stretch the graph of $y = \dfrac{1}{x}$ by a factor of 4, and vertically shift upward 2 units.

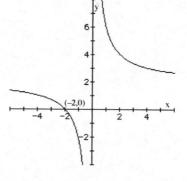

53. $f(x) = -(x+1)^3 - 1$

Using the graph of $y = x^3$, horizontally shift to the left 1 units, reflect the graph on the x-axis, and vertically shift downward 1 unit.

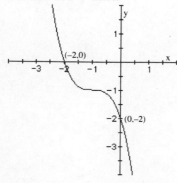

54. $f(x) = -4\sqrt{x-1}$

Using the graph of $y = \sqrt{x}$, horizontally shift to the right 1 unit, reflect the graph on the x-axis, and stretch vertically by a factor of 4.

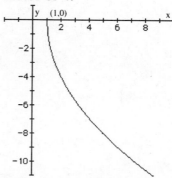

55. $g(x) = 2|1 - x| = 2|x - 1|$
Using the graph of $y = |x|$, horizontally shift to the right 1 unit, and vertically stretch by a factor or 2.

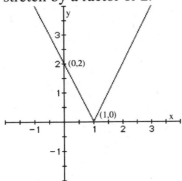

56. $g(x) = 4\sqrt{2 - x} = 4\sqrt{-(x - 2)}$
Reflect the graph of $y = \sqrt{x}$ on the y-axis, horizontally shift to the right 2 units, and vertically stretch by a factor of 4.

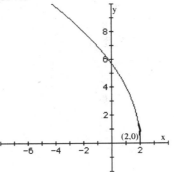

57. $h(x) = 2\text{int}(x - 1)$
Using the graph of $y = \text{int}(x)$, horizontally shift to the right 1 unit, and vertically stretch by a factor of 2.

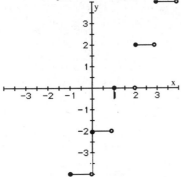

58. $h(x) = \text{int}(-x)$
Reflect the graph of $y = \text{int}(x)$, about the y-axis.

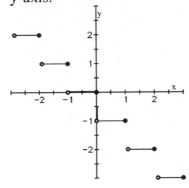

59. (a) $F(x) = f(x) + 3$
Shift up 3 units.

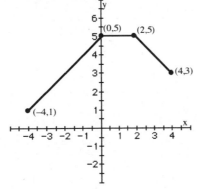

(b) $G(x) = f(x + 2)$
Shift left 2 units.

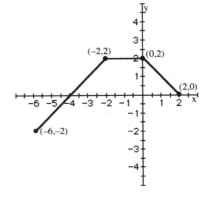

(c) $P(x) = -f(x)$
Reflect about the x-axis.

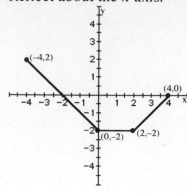

(d) $H(x) = f(x+1) - 2$
Shift left 1 unit and shift down 2 units.

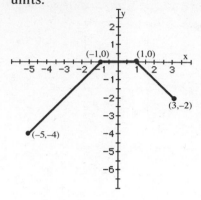

(e) $Q(x) = \dfrac{1}{2} f(x)$

Compress vertically by a factor of $\dfrac{1}{2}$.

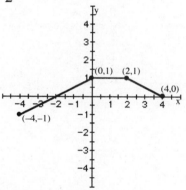

(f) $g(x) = f(-x)$
Reflect about y-axis.

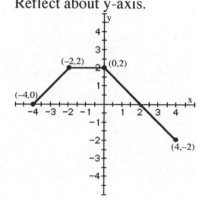

(g) $h(x) = f(2x)$
Compress horizontally by a factor of $\dfrac{1}{2}$.

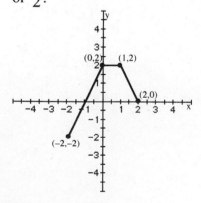

60. (a) $F(x) = f(x) + 3$
Shift up 3 units.

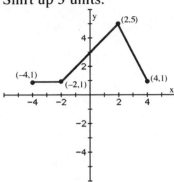

(b) $G(x) = f(x + 2)$
Shift left 2 units.

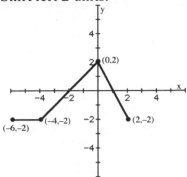

(c) $P(x) = -f(x)$
Reflect about the x-axis.

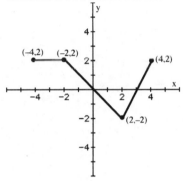

(d) $H(x) = f(x + 1) - 2$
Shift left 1 unit and shift down 2 units.

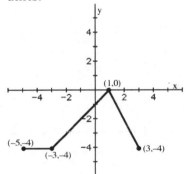

(e) $Q(x) = \dfrac{1}{2} f(x)$
Compress vertically by a factor of $\dfrac{1}{2}$.

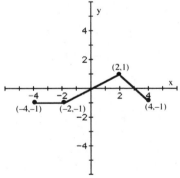

(f) $g(x) = f(-x)$
Reflect about y-axis.

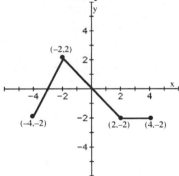

(g) $h(x) = f(2x)$
Compress horizontally by a factor
of $\dfrac{1}{2}$.

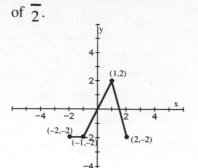

61.   (a) $F(x) = f(x) + 3$
Shift up 3 units.

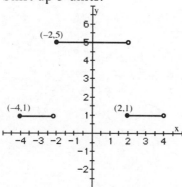

(b) $G(x) = f(x + 2)$
Shift left 2 units.

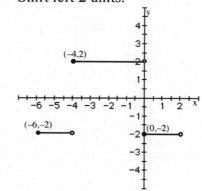

(c) $P(x) = -f(x)$
Reflect about the x-axis.

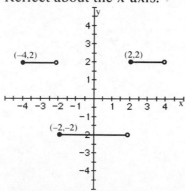

(d) $H(x) = f(x + 1) - 2$
Shift left 1 unit and shift down 2 units.

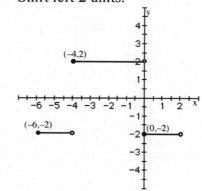

(e) $Q(x) = \dfrac{1}{2} f(x)$

Compress vertically by a factor of $\dfrac{1}{2}$.

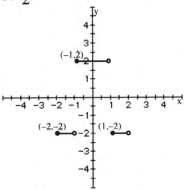

(f) $g(x) = f(-x)$
Reflect about y-axis.

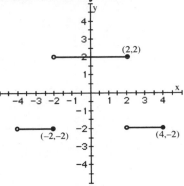

(g) $h(x) = f(2x)$

Compress horizontally by a factor of $\dfrac{1}{2}$.

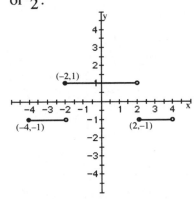

62.   (a) $F(x) = f(x) + 3$
Shift up 3 units.

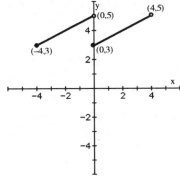

(b) $G(x) = f(x + 2)$
Shift left 2 units.

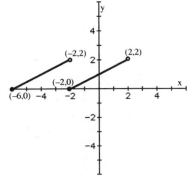

(c) $P(x) = -f(x)$
Reflect about the x-axis.

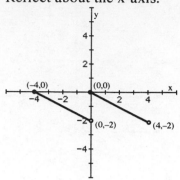

(d) $H(x) = f(x+1) - 2$
Shift left 1 unit and shift down 2 units.

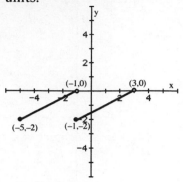

(e) $Q(x) = \frac{1}{2} f(x)$
Compress vertically by a factor of $\frac{1}{2}$.

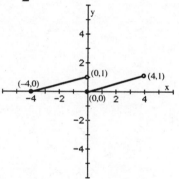

(f) $g(x) = f(-x)$
Reflect about y-axis.

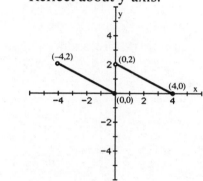

(g) $h(x) = f(2x)$
Compress horizontally by a factor of $\frac{1}{2}$.

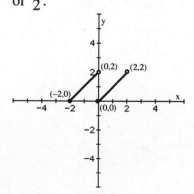

63. (a) $F(x) = f(x) + 3$
     Shift up 3 units.

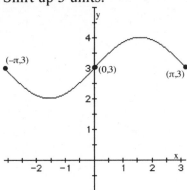

(b) $G(x) = f(x+2)$
     Shift left 2 units.

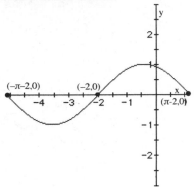

(c) $P(x) = -f(x)$
     Reflect about the x-axis.

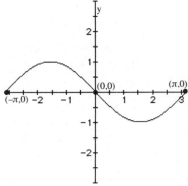

(d) $H(x) = f(x+1) - 2$
     Shift left 1 unit and shift down 2 units.

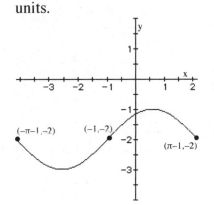

(e) $Q(x) = \dfrac{1}{2} f(x)$
     Compress vertically by a factor of $\dfrac{1}{2}$.

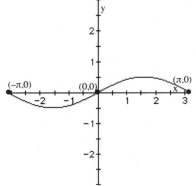

(f) $g(x) = f(-x)$
     Reflect about y-axis.

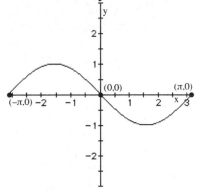

(g) $h(x) = f(2x)$
Compress horizontally by a factor of $\dfrac{1}{2}$.

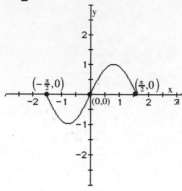

64. (a) $F(x) = f(x) + 3$
Shift up 3 units.

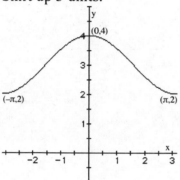

(b) $G(x) = f(x + 2)$
Shift left 2 units.

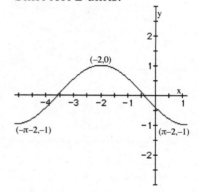

(c) $P(x) = -f(x)$
Reflect about the x-axis.

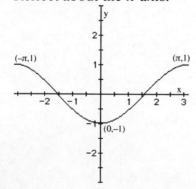

(d) $H(x) = f(x + 1) - 2$
Shift left 1 unit and shift down 2 units.

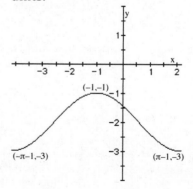

(e) $Q(x) = \dfrac{1}{2} f(x)$

Compress vertically by a factor

of $\dfrac{1}{2}$.

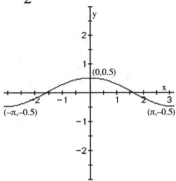

(f) $g(x) = f(-x)$

Reflect about y-axis.

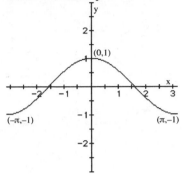

(g) $h(x) = f(2x)$

Compress horizontally by a factor

of $\dfrac{1}{2}$.

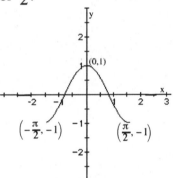

65. (a) $y = |x + 1|$

$y = x + 1$

(b) $y = |4 - x^2|$

$y = 4 - x^2$

(c) $y = |x^3 + x|$

$y = x^3 + x$

(d) Any part of the graph of $y = f(x)$ that lies below the x-axis is reflected about the x-axis to obtain the graph of $y = |f(x)|$.

66. (a) $y = |x| + 1$

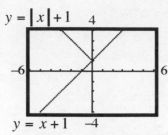

$y = x + 1$

(b)

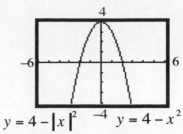

$y = 4 - |x|^2$ $y = 4 - x^2$

(c) $y = |x|^3 + |x|$

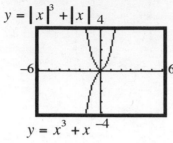

$y = x^3 + x$

(d) Any part of the graph of $y = f(x)$ that lies to the right of the y-axis is reflected about the y-axis to obtain the graph of $y = f(|x|)$.

67. (a) $y = |f(x)|$

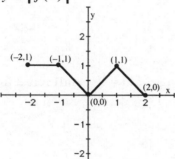

(b) $y = f(|x|)$

68. (a) $y = |f(x)|$

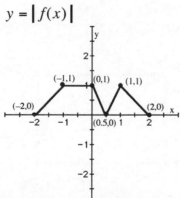

(b) $y = f(|x|)$

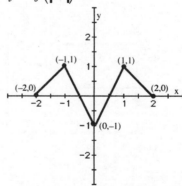

306

69. $f(x) = x^2 + 2x$
    $f(x) = (x^2 + 2x + 1) - 1$
    $f(x) = (x + 1)^2 - 1$
    Using $f(x) = x^2$, shift left 1 unit and shift down 1 unit.

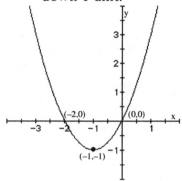

70. $f(x) = x^2 - 6x$
    $f(x) = (x^2 - 6x + 9) - 9$
    $f(x) = (x - 3)^2 - 9$
    Using $f(x) = x^2$, shift right 3 units and shift down 9 units.

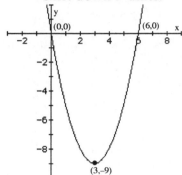

71. $f(x) = x^2 - 8x + 1$
    $f(x) = (x^2 - 8x + 16) + 1 - 16$
    $f(x) = (x - 4)^2 - 15$
    Using $f(x) = x^2$, shift right 4 units and shift down 15 units.

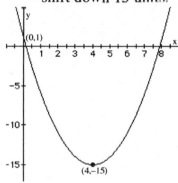

72. $f(x) = x^2 + 4x + 2$
    $f(x) = (x^2 + 4x + 4) + 2 - 4$
    $f(x) = (x + 2)^2 - 2$
    Using $f(x) = x^2$, shift left 2 units and shift down 2 units.

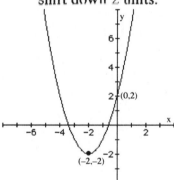

73. $f(x) = x^2 + x + 1$

$f(x) = \left(x^2 + x + \dfrac{1}{4}\right) + 1 - \dfrac{1}{4}$

$f(x) = \left(x + \dfrac{1}{2}\right)^2 + \dfrac{3}{4}$

Using $f(x) = x^2$, shift left $\dfrac{1}{2}$ unit and shift up $\dfrac{3}{4}$ unit.

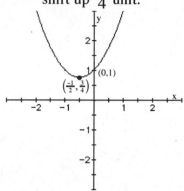

74. $f(x) = x^2 - x + 1$

$f(x) = \left(x^2 - x + \dfrac{1}{4}\right) + 1 - \dfrac{1}{4}$

$f(x) = \left(x - \dfrac{1}{2}\right)^2 + \dfrac{3}{4}$

Using $f(x) = x^2$, shift right $\dfrac{1}{2}$ unit and shift up $\dfrac{3}{4}$ unit.

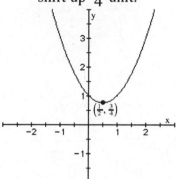

75. $y = (x - c)^2$

If $c = 0$, $y = x^2$.

If $c = 3$, $y = (x - 3)^2$; shift right 3 units.

If $c = -2$, $y = (x + 2)^2$; shift left 2 units.

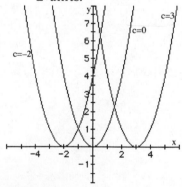

76. $y = x^2 + c$

If $c = 0$, $y = x^2$.

If $c = 3$, $y = x^2 + 3$; shift up 3 units.

If $c = -2$, $y = x^2 - 2$; shift down 2 units.

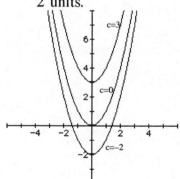

77. $F = \dfrac{9}{5}C + 32$ $F = \dfrac{9}{5}(K - 273) + 32$

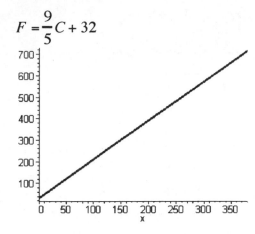

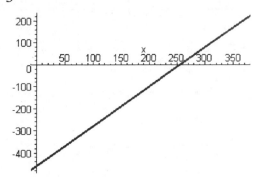

Shift the graph 273 units to the right.

78. (a)   Graph: (b)   Graph:

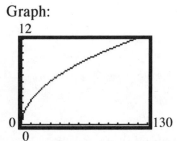

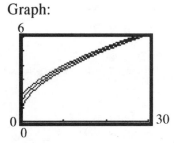

(c)   As the length of the pendulum increases, the period increases.

(d)   Graph:

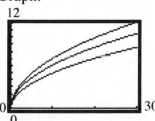

(e)   If the length of the pendulum is multiplied by k, the period is multiplied by $\sqrt{k}$.

79. (a)

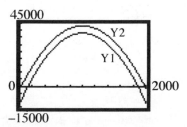

(b)   Select the 10% tax since the profits are higher.

(c)   The graph of Y1 is obtained by shifting the graph of $p(x)$ vertically down 10,000. The graph of Y2 is obtained by multiplying the y-coordinate of the graph of $p(x)$ by 0.9. Thus, Y2 is the graph of $p(x)$ vertically compressed by a factor of 0.9.

(d)   Select the 10% tax since the graph of $Y1 = 0.9 p(x) \geq Y2 = -0.05x^2 + 100x - 6800$ for all x in the domain.

Chapter 3

Functions and Their Graphs

3.5 Operations on Functions; Composite Functions

1. $f(x) = 3x + 4$ $g(x) = 2x - 3$
   (a) $(f + g)(x) = 3x + 4 + 2x - 3 = 5x + 1$ The domain is all real numbers.
   (b) $(f - g)(x) = (3x + 4) - (2x - 3) = 3x + 4 - 2x + 3 = x + 7$
        The domain is all real numbers.
   (c) $(f \cdot g)(x) = (3x + 4)(2x - 3) = 6x^2 - 9x + 8x - 12 = 6x^2 - x - 12$
        The domain is all real numbers.
   (d) $\left(\dfrac{f}{g}\right)(x) = \dfrac{3x + 4}{2x - 3}$ The domain is all real numbers except $\dfrac{3}{2}$.

2. $f(x) = 2x + 1$ $g(x) = 3x - 2$
   (a) $(f + g)(x) = 2x + 1 + 3x - 2 = 5x - 1$ The domain is all real numbers.
   (b) $(f - g)(x) = (2x + 1) - (3x - 2) = 2x + 1 - 3x + 2 = -x + 3$
        The domain is all real numbers.
   (c) $(f \cdot g)(x) = (2x + 1)(3x - 2) = 6x^2 - 4x + 3x - 2 = 6x^2 - x - 2$
        The domain is all real numbers.
   (d) $\left(\dfrac{f}{g}\right)(x) = \dfrac{2x + 1}{3x - 2}$ The domain is all real numbers except $\dfrac{2}{3}$.

3. $f(x) = x - 1$ $g(x) = 2x^2$
   (a) $(f + g)(x) = x - 1 + 2x^2 = 2x^2 + x - 1$ The domain is all real numbers.
   (b) $(f - g)(x) = (x - 1) - (2x^2) = x - 1 - 2x^2 = -2x^2 + x - 1$
        The domain is all real numbers.
   (c) $(f \cdot g)(x) = (x - 1)(2x^2) = 2x^3 - 2x^2$ The domain is all real numbers.
   (d) $\left(\dfrac{f}{g}\right)(x) = \dfrac{x - 1}{2x^2}$ The domain is all real numbers except 0.

4. $f(x) = 2x^2 + 3$ $g(x) = 4x^3 + 1$
   (a) $(f + g)(x) = 2x^2 + 3 + 4x^3 + 1 = 4x^3 + 2x^2 + 4$ The domain is all real numbers.
   (b) $(f - g)(x) = \left(2x^2 + 3\right) - \left(4x^3 + 1\right) = 2x^2 + 3 - 4x^3 - 1 = -4x^3 + 2x^2 + 2$
        The domain is all real numbers.
   (c) $(f \cdot g)(x) = \left(2x^2 + 3\right)\left(4x^3 + 1\right) = 8x^5 + 12x^3 + 2x^2 + 3$
        The domain is all real numbers.
   (d) $\left(\dfrac{f}{g}\right)(x) = \dfrac{2x^2 + 3}{4x^3 + 1}$ The domain is all real numbers except $x = \sqrt[3]{-\dfrac{1}{4}}$.

5. $f(x) = \sqrt{x}$ $g(x) = 3x - 5$
    (a) $(f + g)(x) = \sqrt{x} + 3x - 5$ The domain is $\left\{x \mid x \geq 0\right\}$.
    (b) $(f - g)(x) = \sqrt{x} - (3x - 5) = \sqrt{x} - 3x + 5$ The domain is $\left\{x \mid x \geq 0\right\}$.
    (c) $(f \cdot g)(x) = \sqrt{x}(3x - 5) = 3x\sqrt{x} - 5\sqrt{x}$ The domain is $\left\{x \mid x \geq 0\right\}$.
    (d) $\left(\dfrac{f}{g}\right)(x) = \dfrac{\sqrt{x}}{3x - 5}$ The domain is $\left\{x \mid x \geq 0 \text{ and } x \neq \dfrac{5}{3}\right\}$.

6. $f(x) = |x|$ $g(x) = x$
    (a) $(f + g)(x) = |x| + x$ The domain is all real numbers.
    (b) $(f - g)(x) = |x| - x$ The domain is all real numbers.
    (c) $(f \cdot g)(x) = |x| \cdot x$ The domain is all real numbers.
    (d) $\left(\dfrac{f}{g}\right)(x) = \dfrac{|x|}{x}$ The domain is all real numbers except 0.

7. $f(x) = 1 + \dfrac{1}{x}$ $g(x) = \dfrac{1}{x}$
    (a) $(f + g)(x) = 1 + \dfrac{1}{x} + \dfrac{1}{x} = 1 + \dfrac{2}{x}$ The domain is $\left\{x \mid x \neq 0\right\}$.
    (b) $(f - g)(x) = 1 + \dfrac{1}{x} - \dfrac{1}{x} = 1$ The domain is $\left\{x \mid x \neq 0\right\}$.
    (c) $(f \cdot g)(x) = \left(1 + \dfrac{1}{x}\right)\dfrac{1}{x} = \dfrac{1}{x} + \dfrac{1}{x^2}$ The domain is $\left\{x \mid x \neq 0\right\}$.
    (d) $\left(\dfrac{f}{g}\right)(x) = \dfrac{\left(1 + \dfrac{1}{x}\right)}{\left(\dfrac{1}{x}\right)} = \dfrac{\left(\dfrac{x + 1}{x}\right)}{\left(\dfrac{1}{x}\right)} = \dfrac{x + 1}{x} \cdot \dfrac{x}{1} = x + 1$ The domain is $\left\{x \mid x \neq 0\right\}$.

8. $f(x) = \sqrt{x - 2}$ $g(x) = \sqrt{4 - x}$
    (a) $(f + g)(x) = \sqrt{x - 2} + \sqrt{4 - x}$
        The domain is all $\left\{x \mid 2 \leq x \leq 4\right\}$.
    (b) $(f - g)(x) = \sqrt{x - 2} - \sqrt{4 - x}$
        The domain is all $\left\{x \mid 2 \leq x \leq 4\right\}$.
    (c) $(f \cdot g)(x) = \left(\sqrt{x - 2}\right)\left(\sqrt{4 - x}\right)$
        The domain is all $\left\{x \mid 2 \leq x \leq 4\right\}$.
    (d) $\left(\dfrac{f}{g}\right)(x) = \dfrac{\sqrt{x - 2}}{\sqrt{4 - x}}$ The domain is $\left\{x \mid 2 \leq x < 4\right\}$.

9. $f(x) = \dfrac{2x + 3}{3x - 2}$ $g(x) = \dfrac{4x}{3x - 2}$
    (a) $(f + g)(x) = \dfrac{2x + 3}{3x - 2} + \dfrac{4x}{3x - 2} = \dfrac{2x + 3 + 4x}{3x - 2} = \dfrac{6x + 3}{3x - 2}$
        The domain is $\left\{x \mid x \neq \dfrac{2}{3}\right\}$.

(b) $(f-g)(x) = \dfrac{2x+3}{3x-2} - \dfrac{4x}{3x-2} = \dfrac{2x+3-4x}{3x-2} = \dfrac{-2x+3}{3x-2}$

The domain is $\left\{ x \middle| x \neq \dfrac{2}{3} \right\}$.

(c) $(f \cdot g)(x) = \left(\dfrac{2x+3}{3x-2}\right)\left(\dfrac{4x}{3x-2}\right) = \dfrac{8x^2+12x}{(3x-2)^2}$

The domain is $\left\{ x \middle| x \neq \dfrac{2}{3} \right\}$.

(d) $\left(\dfrac{f}{g}\right)(x) = \dfrac{\left(\dfrac{2x+3}{3x-2}\right)}{\left(\dfrac{4x}{3x-2}\right)} = \dfrac{2x+3}{3x-2} \cdot \dfrac{3x-2}{4x} = \dfrac{2x+3}{4x}$

The domain is $\left\{ x \middle| x \neq \dfrac{2}{3} \text{ and } x \neq 0 \right\}$.

10. $f(x) = \sqrt{x+1}$ $g(x) = \dfrac{2}{x}$

(a) $(f+g)(x) = \sqrt{x+1} + \dfrac{2}{x}$ The domain is $\{ x | x \geq -1,\ x \neq 0 \}$.

(b) $(f-g)(x) = \sqrt{x+1} - \dfrac{2}{x}$ The domain is $\{ x | x \geq -1,\ x \neq 0 \}$.

(c) $(f \cdot g)(x) = \sqrt{x+1} \cdot \dfrac{2}{x} = \dfrac{2\sqrt{x+1}}{x}$ The domain is $\{ x | x \geq -1,\ x \neq 0 \}$.

(d) $\left(\dfrac{f}{g}\right)(x) = \dfrac{\sqrt{x+1}}{\dfrac{2}{x}} = \dfrac{x\sqrt{x+1}}{2}$ The domain is $\{ x | x \geq -1,\ x \neq 0 \}$.

11. $f(x) = 3x+1$ $(f+g)(x) = 6 - \dfrac{1}{2}x$

$6 - \dfrac{1}{2}x = 3x + 1 + g(x)$

$5 - \dfrac{7}{2}x = g(x) \rightarrow g(x) = 5 - \dfrac{7}{2}x$

12. $f(x) = \dfrac{1}{x}$ $\left(\dfrac{f}{g}\right)(x) = \dfrac{x+1}{x^2-x}$

$\dfrac{x+1}{x^2-x} = \dfrac{\left(\dfrac{1}{x}\right)}{g(x)} \rightarrow g(x) = \dfrac{\left(\dfrac{1}{x}\right)}{\left(\dfrac{x+1}{x^2-x}\right)} = \dfrac{1}{x} \cdot \dfrac{x^2-x}{x+1} = \dfrac{1}{x} \cdot \dfrac{x(x-1)}{x+1} = \dfrac{x-1}{x+1}$

13. $f(x) = 2x$ $g(x) = 3x^2+1$

(a) $(f \circ g)(4) = f(g(4)) = f(3(4)^2+1) = f(49) = 2(49) = 98$

(b) $(g \circ f)(2) = g(f(2)) = g(2 \cdot 2) = g(4) = 3(4)^2+1 = 48+1 = 49$

(c) $(f \circ f)(1) = f(f(1)) = f(2(1)) = f(2) = 2(2) = 4$

(d) $(g \circ g)(0) = g(g(0)) = g(3(0)^2+1) = g(1) = 3(1)^2+1 = 4$

14. $f(x) = 3x + 2$ $g(x) = 2x^2 - 1$

(a) $(f \circ g)(4) = f(g(4)) = f(2(4)^2 - 1) = f(31) = 3(31) + 2 = 95$

(b) $(g \circ f)(2) = g(f(2)) = g(3(2) + 2) = g(8) = 2(8)^2 - 1 = 128 - 1 = 127$

(c) $(f \circ f)(1) = f(f(1)) = f(3(1) + 2) = f(5) = 3(5) + 2 = 17$

(d) $(g \circ g)(0) = g(g(0)) = g(2(0)^2 - 1) = g(-1) = 2(-1)^2 - 1 = 1$

15. $f(x) = 4x^2 - 3$ $g(x) = 3 - \dfrac{1}{2}x^2$

(a) $(f \circ g)(4) = f(g(4)) = f\left(3 - \dfrac{1}{2}(4)^2\right) = f(-5) = 4(-5)^2 - 3 = 97$

(b) $(g \circ f)(2) = g(f(2)) = g(4(2)^2 - 3) = g(13) = 3 - \dfrac{1}{2}(13)^2 = 3 - \dfrac{169}{2} = -\dfrac{163}{2}$

(c) $(f \circ f)(1) = f(f(1)) = f(4(1)^2 - 3) = f(1) = 4(1)^2 - 3 = 1$

(d) $(g \circ g)(0) = g(g(0)) = g\left(3 - \dfrac{1}{2}(0)^2\right) = g(3) = 3 - \dfrac{1}{2}(3)^2 = 3 - \dfrac{9}{2} = -\dfrac{3}{2}$

16. $f(x) = 2x^2$ $g(x) = 1 - 3x^2$

(a) $(f \circ g)(4) = f(g(4)) = f(1 - 3(4)^2) = f(-47) = 2(-47)^2 = 4418$

(b) $(g \circ f)(2) = g(f(2)) = g(2(2)^2) = g(8) = 1 - 3(8)^2 = 1 - 192 = -191$

(c) $(f \circ f)(1) = f(f(1)) = f(2(1)^2) = f(2) = 2(2)^2 = 8$

(d) $(g \circ g)(0) = g(g(0)) = g(1 - 3(0)^2) = g(1) = 1 - 3(1)^2 = 1 - 3 = -2$

17. $f(x) = \sqrt{x}$ $g(x) = 2x$

(a) $(f \circ g)(4) = f(g(4)) = f(2(4)) = f(8) = \sqrt{8} = 2\sqrt{2}$

(b) $(g \circ f)(2) = g(f(2)) = g(\sqrt{2}) = 2\sqrt{2}$

(c) $(f \circ f)(1) = f(f(1)) = f(\sqrt{1}) = f(1) = \sqrt{1} = 1$

(d) $(g \circ g)(0) = g(g(0)) = g(2(0)) = g(0) = 2(0) = 0$

18. $f(x) = \sqrt{x + 1}$ $g(x) = 3x$

(a) $(f \circ g)(4) = f(g(4)) = f(3(4)) = f(12) = \sqrt{12 + 1} = \sqrt{13}$

(b) $(g \circ f)(2) = g(f(2)) = g(\sqrt{2 + 1}) = g(\sqrt{3}) = 3\sqrt{3}$

(c) $(f \circ f)(1) = f(f(1)) = f(\sqrt{1 + 1}) = f(\sqrt{2}) = \sqrt{\sqrt{2} + 1}$

(d) $(g \circ g)(0) = g(g(0)) = g(3(0)) = g(0) = 3(0) = 0$

19. $f(x) = |x|$ $g(x) = \dfrac{1}{x^2 + 1}$

(a) $(f \circ g)(4) = f(g(4)) = f\left(\dfrac{1}{4^2 + 1}\right) = f\left(\dfrac{1}{17}\right) = \left|\dfrac{1}{17}\right| = \dfrac{1}{17}$

(b) $(g \circ f)(2) = g(f(2)) = g(|2|) = g(2) = \dfrac{1}{2^2 + 1} = \dfrac{1}{5}$

(c) $(f \circ f)(1) = f(f(1)) = f(|1|) = f(1) = |1| = 1$

(d) $(g \circ g)(0) = g(g(0)) = g\left(\dfrac{1}{0^2 + 1}\right) = g(1) = \dfrac{1}{1^2 + 1} = \dfrac{1}{2}$

20. $f(x) = |x - 2| \qquad g(x) = \dfrac{3}{x^2 + 2}$

(a) $(f \circ g)(4) = f(g(4)) = f\left(\dfrac{3}{4^2 + 2}\right) = f\left(\dfrac{3}{18}\right) = f\left(\dfrac{1}{6}\right) = \left|\dfrac{1}{6} - 2\right| = \left|-\dfrac{11}{6}\right| = \dfrac{11}{6}$

(b) $(g \circ f)(2) = g(f(2)) = g(|2 - 2|) = g(0) = \dfrac{3}{0^2 + 2} = \dfrac{3}{2}$

(c) $(f \circ f)(1) = f(f(1)) = f(|1 - 2|) = f(1) = |1 - 2| = 1$

(d) $(g \circ g)(0) = g(g(0)) = g\left(\dfrac{3}{0^2 + 2}\right) = g\left(\dfrac{3}{2}\right) = \dfrac{3}{\left(\dfrac{3}{2}\right)^2 + 2} = \dfrac{3}{\left(\dfrac{17}{4}\right)} = \dfrac{12}{17}$

21. $f(x) = \dfrac{3}{x + 1} \qquad g(x) = \sqrt{x}$

(a) $(f \circ g)(4) = f(g(4)) = f\left(\sqrt{4}\right) = f(2) = \dfrac{3}{2 + 1} = \dfrac{3}{3} = 1$

(b) $(g \circ f)(2) = g(f(2)) = g\left(\dfrac{3}{2 + 1}\right) = g\left(\dfrac{3}{3}\right) = \sqrt{1} = 1$

(c) $(f \circ f)(1) = f(f(1)) = f\left(\dfrac{3}{1 + 1}\right) = f\left(\dfrac{3}{2}\right) = \dfrac{3}{\left(\dfrac{3}{2}\right) + 1} = \dfrac{3}{\left(\dfrac{5}{2}\right)} = \dfrac{6}{5}$

(d) $(g \circ g)(0) = g(g(0)) = g\left(\sqrt{0}\right) = g(0) = \sqrt{0} = 0$

22. $f(x) = x^{3/2} \qquad g(x) = \dfrac{2}{x + 1}$

(a) $(f \circ g)(4) = f(g(4)) = f\left(\dfrac{2}{4 + 1}\right) = f\left(\dfrac{2}{5}\right) = \left(\dfrac{2}{5}\right)^{3/2} = \left(\sqrt{\dfrac{2}{5}}\right)^3$

(b) $(g \circ f)(2) = g(f(2)) = g\left(2^{3/2}\right) = g\left(2\sqrt{2}\right) = \dfrac{2}{2\sqrt{2} + 1}$

(c) $(f \circ f)(1) = f(f(1)) = f\left(1^{3/2}\right) = f(1) = 1^{3/2} = 1$

(d) $(g \circ g)(0) = g(g(0)) = g\left(\dfrac{2}{0 + 1}\right) = g(2) = \dfrac{2}{2 + 1} = \dfrac{2}{3}$

23.   The domain of g is $\{x \mid x \neq 0\}$. The domain of f is $\{x \mid x \neq 1\}$.
      Thus, $g(x) \neq 1$, so we solve:
$$g(x) = 1$$
$$\dfrac{2}{x} = 1$$
$$x = 2$$
      Thus, $x \neq 2$; so the domain of $f \circ g$ is $\{x \mid x \neq 0, \ x \neq 2\}$.

24.   The domain of g is $\{x \mid x \neq 0\}$. The domain of f is $\{x \mid x \neq -3\}$.

     Thus, $g(x) \neq -3$, so we solve:

$$g(x) = -3$$

$$-\frac{2}{x} = -3$$

$$x = \frac{2}{3}$$

     Thus, $x \neq \frac{2}{3}$; so the domain of $f \circ g$ is $\left\{x \mid x \neq 0,\ x \neq \frac{2}{3}\right\}$.

25.   The domain of g is $\{x \mid x \neq 0\}$. The domain of f is $\{x \mid x \neq 1\}$.

     Thus, $g(x) \neq 1$, so we solve:

$$g(x) = 1$$

$$-\frac{4}{x} = 1$$

$$x = -4$$

     Thus, $x \neq -4$; so the domain of $f \circ g$ is $\{x \mid x \neq -4,\ x \neq 0\}$.

26.   The domain of g is $\{x \mid x \neq 0\}$. The domain of f is $\{x \mid x \neq -3\}$.

     Thus, $g(x) \neq -3$, so we solve:

$$g(x) = -3$$

$$\frac{2}{x} = -3$$

$$x = -\frac{2}{3}$$

     Thus, $x \neq -\frac{2}{3}$; so the domain of $f \circ g$ is $\left\{x \mid x \neq 0,\ x \neq -\frac{2}{3}\right\}$.

27.   The domain of g is $\{\text{Real Numbers}\}$. The domain of f is $\{x \mid x \geq 0\}$.

     Thus, $g(x) \geq 0$, so we solve:

$$g(x) \geq 0$$

$$2x + 3 \geq 0$$

$$x \geq -\frac{3}{2}$$

     Thus, the domain of $f \circ g$ is $\left\{x \mid x \geq -\frac{3}{2}\right\}$.

28.   The domain of f is $\{\text{Real Numbers}\}$. The domain of g is $\{x \mid x \leq 1\}$.

     Thus, the domain of $f \circ g$ is $\{x \mid x \leq 1\}$.

29. The domain of g is $\{x \mid x \geq 1\}$. The domain of f is {Real Numbers}.

Thus, the domain of $f \circ g$ is $\{x \mid x \geq 1\}$.

30. The domain of g is $\{x \mid x \geq 2\}$. The domain of f is {Real Numbers}.

Thus, the domain of $f \circ g$ is $\{x \mid x \geq 2\}$.

31. $f(x) = 2x + 3 \qquad g(x) = 3x$
The domain of f is all real numbers. The domain of g is all real numbers.
(a) $(f \circ g)(x) = f(g(x)) = f(3x) = 2(3x) + 3 = 6x + 3$ Domain: All real numbers.
(b) $(g \circ f)(x) = g(f(x)) = g(2x + 3) = 3(2x + 3) = 6x + 9$
        Domain: All real numbers.
(c) $(f \circ f)(x) = f(f(x)) = f(2x + 3) = 2(2x + 3) + 3 = 4x + 6 + 3 = 4x + 9$
        Domain: All real numbers.
(d) $(g \circ g)(x) = g(g(x)) = g(3x) = 3(3x) = 9x$ Domain: All real numbers.

32. $f(x) = -x \qquad g(x) = 2x - 4$
The domain of f is all real numbers. The domain of g is all real numbers.
(a) $(f \circ g)(x) = f(g(x)) = f(2x - 4) = -(2x - 4) = -2x + 4$
        Domain: All real numbers.
(b) $(g \circ f)(x) = g(f(x)) = g(-x) = 2(-x) - 4 = -2x - 4$
        Domain: All real numbers.
(c) $(f \circ f)(x) = f(f(x)) = f(-x) = -(-x) = x$ Domain: All real numbers.
(d) $(g \circ g)(x) = g(g(x)) = g(2x - 4) = 2(2x - 4) - 4 = 4x - 8 - 4 = 4x - 12$
        Domain: All real numbers.

33. $f(x) = 3x + 1 \qquad g(x) = x^2$
The domain of f is all real numbers. The domain of g is all real numbers.
(a) $(f \circ g)(x) = f(g(x)) = f\left(x^2\right) = 3x^2 + 1$ Domain: All real numbers.
(b) $(g \circ f)(x) = g(f(x)) = g(3x + 1) = (3x + 1)^2 = 9x^2 + 6x + 1$
        Domain: All real numbers.
(c) $(f \circ f)(x) = f(f(x)) = f(3x + 1) = 3(3x + 1) + 1 = 9x + 3 + 1 = 9x + 4$
        Domain: All real numbers.
(d) $(g \circ g)(x) = g(g(x)) = g\left(x^2\right) = \left(x^2\right)^2 = x^4$ Domain: All real numbers.

34. $f(x) = x + 1 \qquad g(x) = x^2 + 4$
The domain of f is all real numbers. The domain of g is all real numbers.
(a) $(f \circ g)(x) = f(g(x)) = f\left(x^2 + 4\right) = x^2 + 4 + 1 = x^2 + 5$
        Domain: All real numbers.
(b) $(g \circ f)(x) = g(f(x)) = g(x + 1) = (x + 1)^2 + 4 = x^2 + 2x + 1 + 4 = x^2 + 2x + 5$
        Domain: All real numbers.
(c) $(f \circ f)(x) = f(f(x)) = f(x + 1) = (x + 1) + 1 = x + 2$
        Domain: All real numbers.

(d) $(g \circ g)(x) = g(g(x)) = g(x^2 + 4) = (x^2 + 4)^2 + 4 = x^4 + 8x^2 + 16 + 4$
$$= x^4 + 8x^2 + 20 \qquad \text{Domain: All real numbers.}$$

35. $f(x) = x^2 \qquad g(x) = x^2 + 4$
The domain of f is all real numbers. The domain of g is all real numbers.

(a) $(f \circ g)(x) = f(g(x)) = f(x^2 + 4) = (x^2 + 4)^2 = x^4 + 8x^2 + 16$
Domain: All real numbers.

(b) $(g \circ f)(x) = g(f(x)) = g(x^2) = (x^2)^2 + 4 = x^4 + 4$ Domain: All real numbers.

(c) $(f \circ f)(x) = f(f(x)) = f(x^2) = (x^2)^2 = x^4$ Domain: All real numbers.

(d) $(g \circ g)(x) = g(g(x)) = g(x^2 + 4) = (x^2 + 4)^2 + 4 = x^4 + 8x^2 + 16 + 4$
$$= x^4 + 8x^2 + 20 \text{ Domain: All real numbers.}$$

36. $f(x) = x^2 + 1 \qquad g(x) = 2x^2 + 3$
The domain of f is all real numbers. The domain of g is all real numbers.

(a) $(f \circ g)(x) = f(g(x)) = f(2x^2 + 3) = (2x^2 + 3)^2 + 1 = 4x^4 + 12x^2 + 9 + 1$
$$= 4x^4 + 12x^2 + 10 \qquad \text{Domain: All real numbers.}$$

(b) $(g \circ f)(x) = g(f(x)) = g(x^2 + 1) = 2(x^2 + 1)^2 + 3 = 2(x^4 + 2x^2 + 1) + 3$
$$= 2x^4 + 4x^2 + 2 + 3 = 2x^4 + 4x^2 + 5$$
Domain: All real numbers.

(c) $(f \circ f)(x) = f(f(x)) = f(x^2 + 1) = (x^2 + 1)^2 + 1 = x^4 + 2x^2 + 1 + 1 = x^4 + 2x^2 + 2$
Domain: All real numbers.

(d) $(g \circ g)(x) = g(g(x)) = g(2x^2 + 3) = 2(2x^2 + 3)^2 + 3 = 2(4x^4 + 12x^2 + 9) + 3$
$$= 8x^4 + 24x^2 + 18 + 3 = 8x^4 + 24x^2 + 21$$
Domain: All real numbers.

37. $f(x) = \dfrac{3}{x-1} \qquad g(x) = \dfrac{2}{x}$ The domain of f is $\{x \mid x \neq 1\}$.
The domain of g is $\{x \mid x \neq 0\}$.

(a) $(f \circ g)(x) = f(g(x)) = f\left(\dfrac{2}{x}\right) = \dfrac{3}{\left(\dfrac{2}{x} - 1\right)} = \dfrac{3}{\left(\dfrac{2-x}{x}\right)} = \dfrac{3x}{2-x}$

Domain of $f \circ g$ is $\{x \mid x \neq 0,\ x \neq 2\}$.

(b) $(g \circ f)(x) = g(f(x)) = g\left(\dfrac{3}{x-1}\right) = \dfrac{2}{\left(\dfrac{3}{x-1}\right)} = \dfrac{2(x-1)}{3}$

Domain of $g \circ f$ is $\{x \mid x \neq 1\}$

(c) $(f \circ f)(x) = f(f(x)) = f\left(\dfrac{3}{x-1}\right) = \dfrac{3}{\left(\dfrac{3}{x-1} - 1\right)} = \dfrac{3}{\left(\dfrac{3-(x-1)}{x-1}\right)} = \dfrac{3(x-1)}{4-x}$

Domain of $f \circ f$ is $\{x \mid x \neq 1,\ x \neq 4\}$.

(d) $(g \circ g)(x) = g(g(x)) = g\left(\dfrac{2}{x}\right) = \dfrac{2}{\left(\dfrac{2}{x}\right)} = \dfrac{2x}{2} = x$

Domain of $g \circ g$ is $\{x \mid x \neq 0\}$.

38. $f(x) = \dfrac{1}{x+3}$ $g(x) = -\dfrac{2}{x}$

The domain of f is $\{x \mid x \neq -3\}$. The domain of g is $\{x \mid x \neq 0\}$.

(a) $(f \circ g)(x) = f(g(x)) = f\left(-\dfrac{2}{x}\right) = \dfrac{1}{\left(-\dfrac{2}{x}+3\right)} = \dfrac{1}{\left(\dfrac{-2+3x}{x}\right)} = \dfrac{x}{3x-2}$

Domain of $f \circ g$ is $\left\{x \mid x \neq 0, \ x \neq \dfrac{2}{3}\right\}$.

(b) $(g \circ f)(x) = g(f(x)) = g\left(\dfrac{1}{x+3}\right) = -\dfrac{2}{\left(\dfrac{1}{x+3}\right)} = \dfrac{-2(x+3)}{1} = -2x-6$

Domain of $g \circ f$ is $\{x \mid x \neq -3\}$.

(c) $(f \circ f)(x) = f(f(x)) = f\left(\dfrac{1}{x+3}\right) = \dfrac{1}{\left(\dfrac{1}{x+3}+3\right)} = \dfrac{1}{\left(\dfrac{1+3x+9}{x+3}\right)} = \dfrac{x+3}{3x+10}$

Domain of $f \circ f$ is $\left\{x \mid x \neq -3, \ x \neq -\dfrac{10}{3}\right\}$.

(d) $(g \circ g)(x) = g(g(x)) = g\left(-\dfrac{2}{x}\right) = -\dfrac{2}{\left(-\dfrac{2}{x}\right)} = \dfrac{-2x}{-2} = x$

Domain of $g \circ g$ is $\{x \mid x \neq 0\}$.

39. $f(x) = \dfrac{x}{x-1}$ $g(x) = -\dfrac{4}{x}$

The domain of f is $\{x \mid x \neq 1\}$. The domain of g is $\{x \mid x \neq 0\}$.

(a) $(f \circ g)(x) = f(g(x)) = f\left(-\dfrac{4}{x}\right) = \dfrac{\left(-\dfrac{4}{x}\right)}{\left(-\dfrac{4}{x}-1\right)} = \dfrac{\left(-\dfrac{4}{x}\right)}{\left(\dfrac{-4-x}{x}\right)} = \dfrac{-4}{-4-x} = \dfrac{4}{4+x}$

Domain of $f \circ g$ is $\{x \mid x \neq -4, \ x \neq 0\}$.

(b) $(g \circ f)(x) = g(f(x)) = g\left(\dfrac{x}{x-1}\right) = -\dfrac{4}{\left(\dfrac{x}{x-1}\right)} = \dfrac{-4(x-1)}{x}$

Domain of $g \circ f$ is $\{x \mid x \neq 0, \ x \neq 1\}$.

(c) $\quad (f \circ f)(x) = f(f(x)) = f\left(\dfrac{x}{x-1}\right) = \dfrac{\left(\dfrac{x}{x-1}\right)}{\left(\dfrac{x}{x-1}-1\right)} = \dfrac{\left(\dfrac{x}{x-1}\right)}{\left(\dfrac{x-(x-1)}{x-1}\right)} = \dfrac{x}{1} = x$

Domain of $f \circ f$ is $\{x \,|\, x \ne 1\}$.

(d) $\quad (g \circ g)(x) = g(g(x)) = g\left(-\dfrac{4}{x}\right) = -\dfrac{4}{\left(-\dfrac{4}{x}\right)} = \dfrac{-4x}{-4} = x$

Domain of $g \circ g$ is $\{x \,|\, x \ne 0\}$.

40. $\quad f(x) = \dfrac{x}{x+3} \qquad g(x) = \dfrac{2}{x}$

The domain of f is $\{x \,|\, x \ne -3\}$. The domain of g is $\{x \,|\, x \ne 0\}$.

(a) $\quad (f \circ g)(x) = f(g(x)) = f\left(\dfrac{2}{x}\right) = \dfrac{\left(\dfrac{2}{x}\right)}{\left(\dfrac{2}{x}+3\right)} = \dfrac{\left(\dfrac{2}{x}\right)}{\left(\dfrac{2+3x}{x}\right)} = \dfrac{2}{2+3x}$

Domain of $f \circ g$ is $\left\{x \,\middle|\, x \ne 0, x \ne -\dfrac{2}{3}\right\}$.

(b) $\quad (g \circ f)(x) = g(f(x)) = g\left(\dfrac{x}{x+3}\right) = \dfrac{2}{\left(\dfrac{x}{x+3}\right)} = \dfrac{2(x+3)}{x} = \dfrac{2x+6}{x}$

Domain of $g \circ f$ is $\{x \,|\, x \ne 0, x \ne -3\}$.

(c) $\quad (f \circ f)(x) = f(f(x)) = f\left(\dfrac{x}{x+3}\right) = \dfrac{\left(\dfrac{x}{x+3}\right)}{\left(\dfrac{x}{x+3}+3\right)} = \dfrac{\left(\dfrac{x}{x+3}\right)}{\left(\dfrac{x+3x+9}{x+3}\right)} = \dfrac{x}{4x+9}$

Domain of $f \circ f$ is $\left\{x \,\middle|\, x \ne -3, x \ne -\dfrac{9}{4}\right\}$.

(d) $\quad (g \circ g)(x) = g(g(x)) = g\left(\dfrac{2}{x}\right) = \dfrac{2}{\left(\dfrac{2}{x}\right)} = \dfrac{2x}{2} = x$

Domain of $g \circ g$ is $\{x \,|\, x \ne 0\}$.

41. $\quad f(x) = \sqrt{x} \qquad g(x) = 2x+3$

The domain of f is $\{x \,|\, x \ge 0\}$. The domain of g is $\{\text{Real Numbers}\}$.

(a) $\quad (f \circ g)(x) = f(g(x)) = f(2x+3) = \sqrt{2x+3}$ Domain of $f \circ g$ is $\left\{x \,\middle|\, x \ge -\dfrac{3}{2}\right\}$.

(b) $\quad (g \circ f)(x) = g(f(x)) = g(\sqrt{x}) = 2\sqrt{x}+3$ Domain of $g \circ f$ is $\{x \,|\, x \ge 0\}$.

(c) $\quad (f \circ f)(x) = f(f(x)) = f(\sqrt{x}) = \sqrt{\sqrt{x}} = x^{1/4} = \sqrt[4]{x}$

Domain of $f \circ f$ is $\{x \,|\, x \ge 0\}$.

(d) $(g \circ g)(x) = g(g(x)) = g(2x+3) = 2(2x+3)+3 = 4x+6+3 = 4x+9$
      Domain of $g \circ g$ is {Real Numbers}.

42. $f(x) = \sqrt{x-2}$ $g(x) = 1-2x$
      The domain of f is $\{x \mid x \geq 2\}$. The domain of g is {Real Numbers}.

(a) $(f \circ g)(x) = f(g(x)) = f(1-2x) = \sqrt{1-2x-2} = \sqrt{-2x-1}$
      Domain of $f \circ g$ is $\{x \mid x \leq -\frac{1}{2}\}$.

(b) $(g \circ f)(x) = g(f(x)) = g(\sqrt{x-2}) = 1-2\sqrt{x-2}$ Domain of $g \circ f$ is $\{x \mid x \geq 2\}$.

(c) $(f \circ f)(x) = f(f(x)) = f(\sqrt{x-2}) = \sqrt{\sqrt{x-2}-2}$ Domain of $f \circ f$ is $\{x \mid x \geq 6\}$.

(d) $(g \circ g)(x) = g(g(x)) = g(1-2x) = 1-2(1-2x) = 1-2+4x = 4x-1$
      Domain of $g \circ g$ is {Real Numbers}.

43.
      $f(x) = x^2+1$ $g(x) = \sqrt{x-1}$
      The domain of f is {Real Numbers}. The domain of g is $\{x \mid x \geq 1\}$.

(a) $(f \circ g)(x) = f(g(x)) = f(\sqrt{x-1}) = (\sqrt{x-1})^2 + 1 = x-1+1 = x$
      Domain of $f \circ g$ is $\{x \mid x \geq 1\}$.

(b) $(g \circ f)(x) = g(f(x)) = g(x^2+1) = \sqrt{x^2+1-1} = \sqrt{x^2} = |x|$
      Domain of $g \circ f$ {Real Numbers}.

(c) $(f \circ f)(x) = f(f(x)) = f(x^2+1) = (x^2+1)^2 + 1 = x^4+2x^2+1+1 = x^4+2x^2+2$
      Domain of $f \circ f$ is {Real Numbers}.

(d)   Domain of $g \circ g$ is $\{x \mid x \geq 2\}$.
      $(g \circ g)(x) = g(g(x)) = g(\sqrt{x-1}) = \sqrt{\sqrt{x-1}-1}$

44. $f(x) = x^2+4$ $g(x) = \sqrt{x-2}$
      The domain of f is {Real Numbers}. The domain of g is $\{x \mid x \geq 2\}$.

(a) $(f \circ g)(x) = f(g(x)) = f(\sqrt{x-2}) = (\sqrt{x-2})^2 + 4 = x-2+4 = x+2$
      Domain of $f \circ g$ is $\{x \mid x \geq 2\}$.

(b) $(g \circ f)(x) = g(f(x)) = g(x^2+4) = \sqrt{x^2+4-2} = \sqrt{x^2+2}$
      Domain of $g \circ f$ {Real Numbers}.

(c) $(f \circ f)(x) = f(f(x)) = f(x^2+4) = (x^2+1)^2 + 4 = x^4+2x^2+1+4$
      $= x^4+2x^2+5$
      Domain of $f \circ f$ is {Real Numbers}.

(d)
      $(g \circ g)(x) = g(g(x)) = g(\sqrt{x-1}) = \sqrt{\sqrt{x-1}-1}$
      Domain of $g \circ g$ is $\{x \mid x \geq 1\}$.

45. $f(x) = ax + b$ $g(x) = cx + d$ The domain of f is {Real Numbers}.

The domain of g is {Real Numbers}.

(a) $(f \circ g)(x) = f(g(x)) = f(cx + d) = a(cx + d) + b = acx + ad + b$

Domain of $f \circ g$ is {Real Numbers}.

(b) $(g \circ f)(x) = g(f(x)) = g(ax + b) = c(ax + b) + d = acx + bc + d$

Domain of $g \circ f$ is {Real Numbers}.

(c) $(f \circ f)(x) = f(f(x)) = f(ax + b) = a(ax + b) + b = a^2 x + ab + b$

Domain of $f \circ f$ is {Real Numbers}.

(d) $(g \circ g)(x) = g(g(x)) = g(cx + d) = c(cx + d) + d = c^2 x + cd + d$

Domain of $g \circ g$ is {Real Numbers}.

46. $f(x) = \dfrac{ax + b}{cx + d}$ $g(x) = mx$ The domain of f is $\left\{ x \middle| x \neq -\dfrac{d}{c} \right\}$.

The domain of g is {Real Numbers}.

(a) $(f \circ g)(x) = f(g(x)) = f(mx) = \dfrac{a(mx) + b}{c(mx) + d} = \dfrac{amx + b}{cmx + d}$

Domain of $f \circ g$ is $\left\{ x \middle| x \neq -\dfrac{d}{cm} \right\}$.

(b) $(g \circ f)(x) = g(f(x)) = g\left(\dfrac{ax + b}{cx + d}\right) = m\left(\dfrac{ax + b}{cx + d}\right) = \dfrac{amx + bm}{cx + d}$

Domain of $g \circ f$ is $\left\{ x \middle| x \neq -\dfrac{d}{c} \right\}$.

(c) $(f \circ f)(x) = f(f(x)) = f\left(\dfrac{ax + b}{cx + d}\right) = \dfrac{a\left(\dfrac{ax + b}{cx + d}\right) + b}{c\left(\dfrac{ax + b}{cx + d}\right) + d} = \dfrac{\left(\dfrac{a^2 x + ab + bcx + bd}{cx + d}\right)}{\left(\dfrac{acx + bc + cdx + d^2}{cx + d}\right)}$

$= \dfrac{a^2 x + ab + bcx + bd}{acx + bc + cdx + d^2}$

$acx + bc + cdx + d^2 \neq 0$

$(ac + cd)x \neq -bc - d^2$

$x \neq \dfrac{-bc - d^2}{ac + cd}$

Domain of $f \circ f$ is $\left\{ x \middle| x \neq \dfrac{-bc - d^2}{ac + cd}, x \neq -\dfrac{d}{c} \right\}$.

(d) $(g \circ g)(x) = g(g(x)) = g(mx) = m(mx) = m^2 x$

Domain of $g \circ g$ is {Real Numbers}.

47. $(f \circ g)(x) = f(g(x)) = f\left(\dfrac{1}{2}x\right) = 2\left(\dfrac{1}{2}x\right) = x$

$(g \circ f)(x) = g(f(x)) = g(2x) = \dfrac{1}{2}(2x) = x$

48. $(f \circ g)(x) = f(g(x)) = f\left(\frac{1}{4}x\right) = 4\left(\frac{1}{4}x\right) = x$

$(g \circ f)(x) = g(f(x)) = g(4x) = \frac{1}{4}(4x) = x$

49. $(f \circ g)(x) = f(g(x)) = f\left(\sqrt[3]{x}\right) = \left(\sqrt[3]{x}\right)^3 = x$

$(g \circ f)(x) = g(f(x)) = g\left(x^3\right) = \sqrt[3]{x^3} = x$

50. $(f \circ g)(x) = f(g(x)) = f(x - 5) = x - 5 + 5 = x$

$(g \circ f)(x) = g(f(x)) = g(x + 5) = x + 5 - 5 = x$

51. $(f \circ g)(x) = f(g(x)) = f\left(\frac{1}{2}(x + 6)\right) = 2\left(\frac{1}{2}(x + 6)\right) - 6 = x + 6 - 6 = x$

$(g \circ f)(x) = g(f(x)) = g(2x - 6) = \frac{1}{2}((2x - 6) + 6) = \frac{1}{2}(2x) = x$

52. $(f \circ g)(x) = f(g(x)) = f\left(\frac{1}{3}(4 - x)\right) = 4 - 3\left(\frac{1}{3}(4 - x)\right) = 4 - 4 + x = x$

$(g \circ f)(x) = g(f(x)) = g(4 - 3x) = \frac{1}{3}(4 - (4 - 3x)) = \frac{1}{3}(3x) = x$

53. $(f \circ g)(x) = f(g(x)) = f\left(\frac{1}{a}(x - b)\right) = a\left(\frac{1}{a}(x - b)\right) + b = x - b + b = x$

$(g \circ f)(x) = g(f(x)) = g(ax + b) = \frac{1}{a}((ax + b) - b) = \frac{1}{a}(ax) = x$

54. $(f \circ g)(x) = f(g(x)) = f\left(\frac{1}{x}\right) = \frac{1}{\left(\frac{1}{x}\right)} = 1 \cdot \frac{x}{1} = x$

$(g \circ f)(x) = g(f(x)) = g\left(\frac{1}{x}\right) = \frac{1}{\left(\frac{1}{x}\right)} = 1 \cdot \frac{x}{1} = x$

55. $H(x) = (2x + 3)^4$ $f(x) = x^4, \quad g(x) = 2x + 3$

56. $H(x) = \left(1 + x^2\right)^3$ $f(x) = x^3, \quad g(x) = 1 + x^2$

57. $H(x) = \sqrt{x^2 + 1}$ $f(x) = \sqrt{x}, \quad g(x) = x^2 + 1$

58. $H(x) = \sqrt{1 - x^2}$ $f(x) = \sqrt{x}, \quad g(x) = 1 - x^2$

59. $H(x) = |2x + 1|$ $f(x) = |x|, \quad g(x) = 2x + 1$

60. $H(x) = \left|2x^2 + 3\right|$ $\qquad$ $f(x) = |x|, \quad g(x) = 2x^2 + 3$

61. $f(x) = 2x^3 - 3x^2 + 4x - 1 \qquad g(x) = 2$
$(f \circ g)(x) = f(g(x)) = f(2) = 2(2)^3 - 3(2)^2 + 4(2) - 1 = 16 - 12 + 8 - 1 = 11$
$(g \circ f)(x) = g(f(x)) = g\left(2x^3 - 3x^2 + 4x - 1\right) = 2$

62. $f(x) = \dfrac{x}{x-1}$

$(f \circ f)(x) = f(f(x)) = f\left(\dfrac{x}{x-1}\right) = \dfrac{\left(\dfrac{x}{x-1}\right)}{\left(\dfrac{x}{x-1} - 1\right)} = \dfrac{\left(\dfrac{x}{x-1}\right)}{\left(\dfrac{x - x + 1}{x-1}\right)} = \dfrac{x}{1} = x$

63. $f(x) = 2x^2 + 5 \qquad g(x) = 3x + a$
$(f \circ g)(x) = f(g(x)) = f(3x + a) = 2(3x + a)^2 + 5$
When $x = 0$, $(f \circ g)(0) = 23$
Solving:
$$2(3 \cdot 0 + a)^2 + 5 = 23$$
$$2a^2 + 5 = 23$$
$$2a^2 = 18$$
$$a^2 = 9 \rightarrow a = -3 \text{ or } 3$$

64. $f(x) = 3x^2 - 7 \qquad g(x) = 2x + a$
$(f \circ g)(x) = f(g(x)) = f(2x + a) = 3(2x + a)^2 - 7$
When $x = 0$, $(f \circ g)(0) = 68$
Solving:
$$3(2 \cdot 0 + a)^2 - 7 = 68$$
$$3a^2 - 7 = 68$$
$$3a^2 = 75$$
$$a^2 = 25 \rightarrow a = -5 \text{ or } 5$$

65. $S(r) = 4\pi r^2 \qquad r(t) = \dfrac{2}{3}t^3, \ t \geq 0$

$S(r(t)) = S\left(\dfrac{2}{3}t^3\right) = 4\pi\left(\dfrac{2}{3}t^3\right)^2 = 4\pi\left(\dfrac{4}{9}t^6\right) = \dfrac{16}{9}\pi t^6$

66. $V(r) = \dfrac{4}{3}\pi r^3 \qquad r(t) = \dfrac{2}{3}t^3, \ t \geq 0$

$V(r(t)) = V\left(\dfrac{2}{3}t^3\right) = \dfrac{4}{3}\pi\left(\dfrac{2}{3}t^3\right)^3 = \dfrac{4}{3}\pi\left(\dfrac{8}{27}t^9\right) = \dfrac{32}{81}\pi t^9$

67. $N(t) = 100t - 5t^2, \ 0 \le t \le 10 \qquad C(N) = 15000 + 8000N$

$C(N(t)) = C(100t - 5t^2) = 15000 + 8000(100t - 5t^2)$

$\qquad\qquad = 15,000 + 800,000t - 40,000t^2$

68. $A(r) = \pi r^2 \qquad r(t) = 200\sqrt{t}$

$A(r(t)) = A(200\sqrt{t}) = \pi(200\sqrt{t})^2 = 40000\pi t$

69. $p = -\dfrac{1}{4}x + 100 \qquad 0 \le x \le 400$

$\dfrac{1}{4}x = 100 - p \rightarrow x = 4(100 - p)$

$C = \dfrac{\sqrt{x}}{25} + 600 = \dfrac{\sqrt{4(100 - p)}}{25} + 600 = \dfrac{2\sqrt{100 - p}}{25} + 600$

70. $p = -\dfrac{1}{5}x + 200 \qquad 0 \le x \le 1000$

$\dfrac{1}{5}x = 200 - p \rightarrow x = 5(200 - p)$

$C = \dfrac{\sqrt{x}}{10} + 400 = \dfrac{\sqrt{5(200 - p)}}{10} + 400 = \dfrac{\sqrt{1000 - 5p}}{10} + 400$

71. $V = \pi r^2 h \qquad h = 2r$

$V(r) = \pi r^2 (2r) = 2\pi r^3$

72. $V = \dfrac{1}{3}\pi r^2 h \qquad h = 2r$

$V(r) = \dfrac{1}{3}\pi r^2 (2r) = \dfrac{2}{3}\pi r^3$

73. Given that f and g are odd functions, we know that
$f(-x) = -f(x)$ and $g(-x) = -g(x)$ for all x in the domain of f and g respectively.

The composite function $f \circ g = f(g(x))$ has the following property:
$f(g(-x)) = f(-g(x))$ since g is odd
$\quad = -f(g(x))$ since f is odd, $\therefore \ f \circ g$ is odd

74. Given that f is odd and g is even, we know that
$f(-x) = -f(x)$ and $g(-x) = g(x)$ for all x in the domain of f and g respectively.

The composite function $f \circ g = f(g(x))$ has the following property:
$f(g(-x)) = f(g(x))$ since g is even, $\therefore \ f \circ g$ is even

The composite function $g \circ f = g(f(x))$ has the following property:

$g(f(-x)) = g(-f(x))$ since f is odd

$= g(f(x))$ since g is even, $\therefore g \circ f$ is even

Chapter 3

Functions and Their Graphs

3.6 Mathematical Models; Constructing Functions

1. If $V = \pi r^2 h$ and $h = 2r$, then $V(r) = \pi r^2 (2r) = 2\pi r^3$.

2. If $V = \frac{1}{3}\pi r^2 h$ and $h = 2r$, then $V(r) = \frac{1}{3}\pi r^2 (2r) = \frac{2}{3}\pi r^3$.

3. (a) If $p = -\frac{1}{6}x + 100$ and $R = x\,p$, then $R(x) = x\left(-\frac{1}{6}x + 100\right) = -\frac{1}{6}x^2 + 100x$.

   (b) $R(200) = -\frac{1}{6}(200)^2 + 100(200) = \$13,333$

   (c) Graphing:

   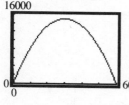

   (d) 300; \$15,000   (e) $p = -\frac{1}{6}(300) + 100 = -50 + 100 = \$50$

4. (a) If $p = -\frac{1}{3}x + 100$ and $R = x\,p$, then $R(x) = x\left(-\frac{1}{3}x + 100\right) = -\frac{1}{3}x^2 + 100x$

   (b) $R(100) = -\frac{1}{3}(100)^2 + 100(100) = \$6,666.67$

   (c) Graphing:

   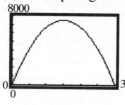

   (d) 150; \$7,500   (e) $p = -\frac{1}{3}(150) + 100 = -50 + 100 = \$50$

5.   (a)   If $x = -5p + 100$ and $R = xp$, then $p = \dfrac{100-x}{5}$ and

$$R(x) = x\left(\frac{100-x}{5}\right) = -\frac{1}{5}x^2 + 20x.$$

(b) $R(15) = -\dfrac{1}{5}(15)^2 + 20(15) = \$255$

(c)   Graphing:

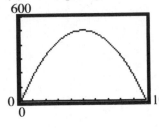

(d)50; $500   (e) $p = \dfrac{100-50}{5} = \dfrac{50}{5} = \$10$

6.   (a)   If $x = -20p + 500$ and $R = xp$, then $p = \dfrac{500-x}{20}$ and

$$R(x) = x\left(\frac{500-x}{20}\right) = -\frac{1}{20}x^2 + 25x.$$

(b) $R(20) = -\dfrac{1}{20}(20)^2 + 25(20) = -20 + 500 = \$480$

(c)   Graphing:

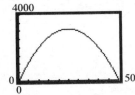

(d)   250; $3,125

(e) $p = \dfrac{500-250}{20} = \dfrac{250}{20} = \$12.50$

7.   (a)   Let x be the width of the rectangle and let y be the length of the rectangle.
Then, the perimeter is: $P = 2y + 2x = 400$.

Solving for y: $y = \dfrac{400-2x}{2} = 200 - x$.

The area function is: $A(x) = y(x) = (200 - x)x = -x^2 + 200x$.

(b)   The domain is: $\{x \mid 0 < x < 200\}$

(c)   Graphing:

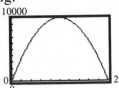

The area is largest when $x = 100$ yards.

8.   (a)   Let x be the length of the side parallel to the river and let y be the width of the field. Then, the amount of fencing used is: $P = x + 2y = 3000$.

Solving for y: $y = \dfrac{3000 - x}{2} = 1500 - \dfrac{1}{2}x$.

The area function is: $A(x) = y(x) = \left(1500 - \dfrac{1}{2}x\right)x = -\dfrac{1}{2}x^2 + 1500x$.

     (b)   Graphing:

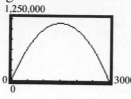

The area is largest when $x = 1500$ feet.

9.   (a)   The distance d from P to the origin is $d = \sqrt{x^2 + y^2}$. Since P is a point on the graph of $y = x^2 - 8$, we have:
$$d(x) = \sqrt{x^2 + (x^2 - 8)^2} = \sqrt{x^4 - 15x^2 + 64}$$

     (b) $d(0) = \sqrt{0^4 - 15(0)^2 + 64} = \sqrt{64} = 8$

     (c) $d(1) = \sqrt{(1)^4 - 15(1)^2 + 64} = \sqrt{1 - 15 + 64} = \sqrt{50} = 5\sqrt{2} \approx 7.07$

     (d)   Graphing:

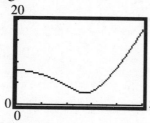

     (e) d is smallest when x is 2.74.

10. (a)   The distance d from P to $(0, -1)$ is $d = \sqrt{x^2 + (y+1)^2}$. Since P is a point on the graph of $y = x^2 - 8$, we have:
$$d(x) = \sqrt{x^2 + (x^2 - 8 + 1)^2} = \sqrt{x^2 + \left(x^2 - 7\right)^2} = \sqrt{x^4 - 13x^2 + 49}$$

     (b) $d(0) = \sqrt{0^4 - 13(0)^2 + 49} = \sqrt{49} = 7$

     (c) $d(-1) = \sqrt{(-1)^4 - 13(-1)^2 + 49} = \sqrt{1 - 13 + 49} = \sqrt{37} \approx 6.08$

     (d)   Graphing:

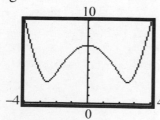

     (e) d is smallest when x is 2.55 or −2.55.

11. (a) The distance d from P to the point $(1, 0)$ is $d = \sqrt{(x-1)^2 + y^2}$. Since P is a point on the graph of $y = \sqrt{x}$, we have:
$$d(x) = \sqrt{(x-1)^2 + \left(\sqrt{x}\right)^2} = \sqrt{x^2 - x + 1}$$

   (b) Graphing: (c) d is smallest when x is 0.50.

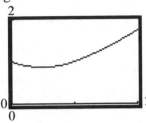

12. (a) The distance d from P to the origin is $d = \sqrt{x^2 + y^2}$. Since P is a point on the graph of $y = \dfrac{1}{x}$, we have:
$$d(x) = \sqrt{x^2 + \left(\frac{1}{x}\right)^2} = \sqrt{x^2 + \frac{1}{x^2}} = \sqrt{\frac{x^4 + 1}{x^2}}$$

   (b) Graphing: (c) d is smallest when x is 1 or −1.

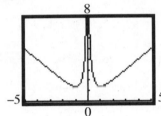

13. By definition, a triangle has area $A = \dfrac{1}{2}bh$, $b = $ base, $h = $ height. Because a vertex of the triangle is at the origin, we know that $b = x$ and $h = y$. Expressing the area of the triangle as a function of x, we have: $A(x) = \dfrac{1}{2}xy = \dfrac{1}{2}x\left(x^3\right) = \dfrac{1}{2}x^4$.

14. By definition, a triangle has area $A = \dfrac{1}{2}bh$, $b = $ base, $h = $ height. Because a vertex of the triangle is at the origin, we know that $b = x$ and $h = y$. Expressing the area of the triangle as a function of x, we have: $A(x) = \dfrac{1}{2}xy = \dfrac{1}{2}x\left(9 - x^2\right) = \dfrac{9}{2}x - \dfrac{1}{2}x^3$.

15. (a) $A(x) = xy = x\left(16 - x^2\right) = -x^3 + 16x$
   (b) Domain: $\left\{x \mid 0 < x < 4\right\}$
   (c) Graphing: The area is largest when x is approximately 2.31.

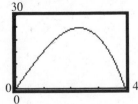

16. (a) $A(x) = 2xy = 2x\sqrt{4 - x^2}$ (b) $p(x) = 2(2x) + 2(y) = 4x + 2\sqrt{4 - x^2}$

(c) Graphing the area equation: (d) Graphing the perimeter equation:

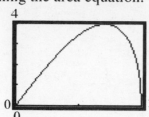   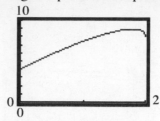

The area is largest when x is approximately 1.41.   The perimeter is largest when x is approximately 1.79.

17. (a) $A(x) = (2x)(2y) = 4x(4 - x^2)^{1/2}$

(b) $p(x) = 2(2x) + 2(2y) = 4x + 4(4 - x^2)^{1/2}$

(c) Graphing: (d) Graphing:

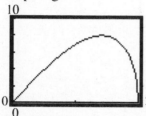   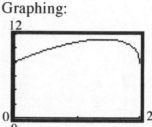

The area is largest when x is approximately 1.41.   The perimeter is largest when x is approximately 1.41.

18. (a) $A(r) = (2r)(2r) = 4r^2$ (b) $p(r) = 4(2r) = 8r$

19. (a) C = circumference, A = area, r = radius, x = side of square

$$C = 2\pi r = 10 - 4x \quad \rightarrow \quad r = \frac{5 - 2x}{\pi}$$

$$A(x) = x^2 + \pi r^2 = x^2 + \pi\left(\frac{5 - 2x}{\pi}\right)^2 = x^2 + \frac{25 - 20x + 4x^2}{\pi}$$

(b) Since the lengths must be positive, we have:

$$10 - 4x > 0 \quad \text{and} \quad x > 0$$

$$-4x > -10 \rightarrow x < 2.5 \text{ and } x > 0$$

Domain: $\{x \mid 0 < x < 2.5\}$

(c) Graphing: The area is smallest when x is approximately 1.40 meters.

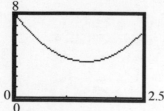

20. (a) C = circumference, A = area, r = radius, x = side of equilateral triangle

$$C = 2\pi r = 10 - 3x \quad \rightarrow \quad r = \frac{10 - 3x}{2\pi}$$

height of the equilateral triangle is $\frac{\sqrt{3}}{2}x$

$$A(x) = \frac{1}{2}x\left(\frac{\sqrt{3}}{2}x\right) + \pi r^2 = \frac{\sqrt{3}}{4}x^2 + \pi\left(\frac{10 - 3x}{2\pi}\right)^2 = \frac{\sqrt{3}}{4}x^2 + \frac{100 - 60x + 9x^2}{4\pi}$$

(b)   Since the lengths must be positive, we have:
$$10 - 3x > 0 \quad \text{and } x > 0$$

$$-3x > -10 \rightarrow x < \frac{10}{3} \text{ and } x > 0$$

Domain: $\left\{x \middle| 0 < x < \frac{10}{3}\right\}$

(c)   Graphing:

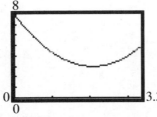

The area is smallest when x is approximately 2.08 meters.

21. (a)   Since the wire of length x is bent into a circle, the circumference is x.
Therefore, $C(x) = x$.

(b)   Since $C = x = 2\pi r$, $r = \frac{x}{2\pi}$.

$$A(x) = \pi r^2 = \pi\left(\frac{x}{2\pi}\right)^2 = \frac{x^2}{4\pi}.$$

22. (a)   Since the wire of length x is bent into a square, the perimeter is x.
Therefore, $P(x) = x$.

(b)   Since $P = x = 4s$, $s = \frac{x}{4}$. $\qquad A(x) = s^2 = \left(\frac{x}{4}\right)^2 = \frac{x^2}{16}.$

23. (a) A = area, r = radius; diameter = $2r$ $\qquad$ (b) p = perimeter
$$A(r) = (2r)(r) = 2r^2 \qquad\qquad\qquad p(r) = 2(2r) + 2r = 6r$$

24. A = area, r = radius; x = length of a side of the triangle

$$r^2 = \left(\frac{r}{2}\right)^2 + \left(\frac{x}{2}\right)^2$$

$$r^2 - \frac{r^2}{4} = \frac{x^2}{4}$$

$$3r^2 = x^2$$

$$r^2 = \frac{x^2}{3}$$

$$C(x) = 2\pi r = 2\pi\left(\frac{x}{\sqrt{3}}\right) = \frac{2\pi\sqrt{3}}{3}x$$

25.   Area of the equilateral triangle $= \dfrac{1}{2}x \cdot \dfrac{\sqrt{3}}{2}x = \dfrac{\sqrt{3}}{4}x^2$

Area of $\frac{1}{3}$ of the equilateral triangle $= \dfrac{1}{2}x\sqrt{r^2 - \left(\dfrac{x}{2}\right)^2} = \dfrac{1}{2}x\sqrt{r^2 - \dfrac{x^2}{4}} = \dfrac{1}{3} \cdot \dfrac{\sqrt{3}}{4}x^2$

Solving for r^2:

$$\dfrac{1}{2}x\sqrt{r^2 - \dfrac{x^2}{4}} = \dfrac{1}{3} \cdot \dfrac{\sqrt{3}}{4}x^2$$

$$\sqrt{r^2 - \dfrac{x^2}{4}} = \dfrac{2}{x} \cdot \dfrac{\sqrt{3}}{12}x^2$$

$$\sqrt{r^2 - \dfrac{x^2}{4}} = \dfrac{\sqrt{3}}{6}x \rightarrow r^2 - \dfrac{x^2}{4} = \dfrac{3}{36}x^2 \rightarrow r^2 = \dfrac{x^2}{3}$$

Area inside the circle, but outside the triangle:

$$A(x) = \pi r^2 - \dfrac{\sqrt{3}}{4}x^2 = \pi\dfrac{x^2}{3} - \dfrac{\sqrt{3}}{4}x^2 = \left(\dfrac{\pi}{3} - \dfrac{\sqrt{3}}{4}\right)x^2$$

26.   (a)   Let x represent the number of miles and C be the cost of transportation.

$$C(x) = \begin{cases} 0.50x & \text{if } 0 \le x \le 100 \\ 0.50(100) + 0.40(x - 100) & \text{if } 100 < x \le 400 \\ 0.50(100) + 0.40(300) + 0.25(x - 400) & \text{if } 400 < x \le 800 \\ 0.50(100) + 0.40(300) + 0.25(400) + 0(x - 800) & \text{if } 800 < x \le 960 \end{cases}$$

$$C(x) = \begin{cases} 0.50x & \text{if } 0 \le x \le 100 \\ 10 + 0.40x & \text{if } 100 < x \le 400 \\ 70 + 0.25x & \text{if } 400 < x \le 800 \\ 270 & \text{if } 800 < x \le 960 \end{cases}$$

Graphing:

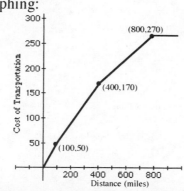

(b)   For hauls between 100 and 400 miles the cost is: $C(x) = 10 + 0.40x$.

(c)   For hauls between 400 and 800 miles the cost is: $C(x) = 70 + 0.25x$.

27.

$$C = \begin{cases} 95 & \text{if } x = 7 \\ 119 & \text{if } 7 < x \le 8 \\ 143 & \text{if } 8 < x \le 9 \\ 167 & \text{if } 9 < x \le 10 \\ 190 & \text{if } 10 < x \le 14 \end{cases}$$

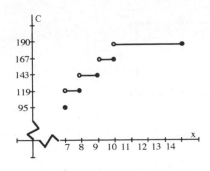

28.

$$C = \begin{cases} 219 & \text{if } x = 7 \\ 264 & \text{if } 7 < x \le 8 \\ 309 & \text{if } 8 < x \le 9 \\ 354 & \text{if } 9 < x \le 10 \\ 399 & \text{if } 10 < x \le 11 \\ 438 & \text{if } 11 < x \le 14 \end{cases}$$

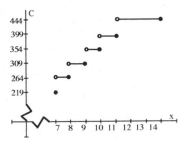

29.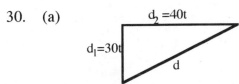

$$d^2 = d_1^{\,2} + d_2^{\,2}$$
$$d^2 = (30t)^2 + (40t)^2$$
$$d(t) = \sqrt{900t^2 + 1600t^2}$$
$$d(t) = \sqrt{2500t^2} = 50t$$

30. (a)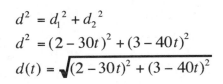

$$d^2 = d_1^{\,2} + d_2^{\,2}$$
$$d^2 = (2 - 30t)^2 + (3 - 40t)^2$$
$$d(t) = \sqrt{(2 - 30t)^2 + (3 - 40t)^2}$$

(b) Graphing:

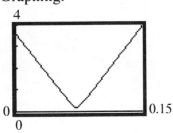

The distance is smallest at $t = 0.072$ hours.

31. (a) length $= 24 - 2x$
width $= 24 - 2x$
height $= x$
$$V(x) = x(24 - 2x)(24 - 2x) = x(24 - 2x)^2$$

(b) $V(3) = 3(24 - 2(3))^2 = 3(18)^2 = 3(324) = 972$ cu. in.

(c) $V(10) = 3(24 - 2(10))^2 = 3(4)^2 = 3(16) = 48$ cu. in.

(d)

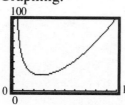

The volume is largest when $x = 4$ inches.

32. (a)   Let A = amount of material, x = side of base, h = height, V = volume

$$V = x^2h = 10 \quad \rightarrow \quad h = \frac{10}{x^2}$$

$$A = x^2 + 4xh = x^2 + 4x\left(\frac{10}{x^2}\right) = x^2 + \frac{40}{x}$$

(b) $A = 1^2 + \dfrac{40}{1} = 1 + 40 = 41$ ft^2 (c) $A = 2^2 + \dfrac{40}{2} = 4 + 20 = 24$ ft^2

(d)   Graphing:

The amount of material is least when $x = 2.71$ ft.

33. r = radius of cylinder, h = height of cylinder, V = volume of cylinder

$$r^2 + \left(\frac{h}{2}\right)^2 = R^2 \rightarrow r^2 + \frac{h^2}{4} = R^2$$

$$r^2 = R^2 - \frac{h^2}{4} \rightarrow r^2 = \frac{4R^2 - h^2}{4}$$

$$V = \pi r^2 h \longrightarrow V(h) = \pi\left(\frac{4R^2 - h^2}{4}\right)h = \frac{\pi}{4}\left(4R^2h - h^3\right)$$

34. r = radius of cylinder, h = height of cylinder, V = volume of cylinder

By similar triangles: $\dfrac{H}{R} = \dfrac{H - h}{r}$

$$Hr = R(H - h)$$
$$Hr = RH - Rh$$
$$Rh = RH - Hr$$
$$h = \frac{RH - Hr}{R} = H - \frac{Hr}{R}$$

$$V = \pi r^2 h = \pi r^2\left(H - \frac{Hr}{R}\right) = H\pi r^2\left(1 - \frac{r}{R}\right)$$

334

35. (a) The total cost of installing the cable along the road is $10x$. If cable is installed x miles along the road, there are $5 - x$ miles left from the road to the house and where the cable ends.

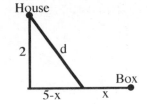

$$d = \sqrt{(5 - x)^2 + 2^2} = \sqrt{25 - 10x + x^2 + 4}$$
$$= \sqrt{x^2 - 10x + 29}$$

The total cost of installing the cable is:
$$C(x) = 10x + 14\sqrt{x^2 - 10x + 29}$$

Domain: $\{x \mid 0 < x < 5\}$

(b) $C(1) = 10(1) + 14\sqrt{1^2 - 10(1) + 29} = 10 + 14\sqrt{20} \approx 10 + 62.61 = \$72.61$

(c) $C(3) = 10(3) + 14\sqrt{3^2 - 10(3) + 29} = 30 + 14\sqrt{8} \approx 30 + 39.60 = \$69.60$

(d)

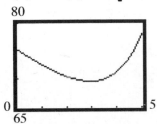

X	Y1
1.5	71.436
2	70.478
2.5	69.822
3	69.598
3.5	70
4	71.305
4.5	73.862

X=4.5

The table indicates that $x = 3$ results in the least cost.

(e) Using MINIMUM, the graph indicates that $x = 2.96$ results in the least cost.

36. (a) The time on the boat is given by $\dfrac{d}{3}$. The time on land is given by $\dfrac{12 - x}{5}$.

$$d = \sqrt{x^2 + 2^2} = \sqrt{x^2 + 4}$$

The total time for the trip is:
$$T(x) = \frac{12 - x}{5} + \frac{d}{3} = \frac{12 - x}{5} + \frac{\sqrt{x^2 + 4}}{3}$$

(b) Domain: $\{x \mid 0 \le x \le 12\}$

(c) $T(4) = \dfrac{12 - 4}{5} + \dfrac{\sqrt{4^2 + 4}}{3} = \dfrac{8}{5} + \dfrac{\sqrt{20}}{3} \approx 3.09$ hours

(d) $T(8) = \dfrac{12 - 8}{5} + \dfrac{\sqrt{8^2 + 4}}{3} = \dfrac{4}{5} + \dfrac{\sqrt{68}}{3} \approx 3.55$ hours

37. Consider the diagram shown below.

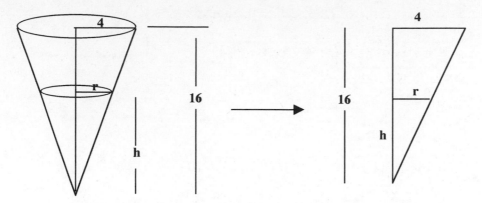

We can extract a pair of similar triangles from the diagram.
Since the smaller triangle is similar to the larger triangle, we have the proportion

$$\frac{r}{h} = \frac{4}{16} \rightarrow \frac{r}{h} = \frac{1}{4} \rightarrow r = \frac{1}{4}h$$

Substituting into the volume formula for the conical portion of water,

$$V = \frac{1}{3}\pi r^2 h = \frac{1}{3}\pi\left(\frac{1}{4}h\right)^2 h = \frac{1}{48}\pi h^3, \text{ so we have the volume function } V(h) = \frac{1}{48}\pi h^3.$$

38. For schedule X:

$$f(x) = \begin{cases} 0.15x & \text{if } 0 < x \le 25{,}750 \\ 3{,}862.50 + 0.28(x - 25{,}750) & \text{if } 25{,}750 < x \le 62{,}450 \\ 14{,}138.50 + 0.31(x - 62{,}450) & \text{if } 62{,}450 < x \le 130{,}250 \\ 35{,}156.50 + 0.36(x - 130{,}250) & \text{if } 130{,}250 < x \le 283{,}150 \\ 90{,}200.50 + 0.396(x - 283{,}150) & \text{if } x > 283{,}150 \end{cases}$$

For Schedule Y-1:

$$f(x) = \begin{cases} 0.15x & \text{if } 0 < x \le 43{,}050 \\ 6{,}457.50 + 0.28(x - 43{,}050) & \text{if } 43{,}050 < x \le 104{,}050 \\ 23{,}537.50 + 0.31(x - 104{,}050) & \text{if } 104{,}050 < x \le 158{,}550 \\ 40{,}432.50 + 0.36(x - 158{,}550) & \text{if } 158{,}550 < x \le 283{,}150 \\ 85{,}288.50 + 0.396(x - 283{,}150) & \text{if } x > 283{,}150 \end{cases}$$

Chapter 3

Functions and Their Graphs

3.R Chapter Review

1. $f(4) = -5$ gives the ordered pair $(4, -5)$. $f(0) = 3$ gives $(0, 3)$.

   Finding the slope: $m = \dfrac{3-(-5)}{0-4} = \dfrac{8}{-4} = -2$

   Using slope-intercept form: $f(x) = -2x + 3$

2. $m = -4$, $g(-2) = 2$ gives the ordered pair $(-2, 2)$.

   Using point-slope form:
   $$y - 2 = -4(x - (-2))$$
   $$y - 2 = -4x - 8$$
   $$y = -4x - 6$$
   $$g(x) = -4x - 6$$

3. $f(x) = \dfrac{Ax + 5}{6x - 2}$ and $f(1) = 4$

   Solving:
   $$\frac{A(1) + 5}{6(1) - 2} = 4$$
   $$\frac{A + 5}{4} = 4$$
   $$A + 5 = 16$$
   $$A = 11$$

4. $g(x) = \dfrac{A}{x} + \dfrac{8}{x^2}$ and $g(-1) = 0$

   Solving:
   $$\frac{A}{-1} + \frac{8}{(-1)^2} = 0 \quad \rightarrow \quad -A + 8 = 0 \quad \rightarrow \quad A = 8$$

5. (b), (c), and (d) pass the vertical line test and therefore are functions.

6. (a) Domain: $\left\{x \mid -5 \le x \le 4\right\}$ Range: $\left\{y \mid -3 \le y \le 1\right\}$
   (b) $f(-1) = 1$
   (c) Intercepts: $(0, 0)$, $(4, 0)$
   (d) Increasing: $(3, 4)$; Decreasing: $(-1, 3)$; Constant: $(-5, -1)$
   (e) The function is neither even nor odd.

7. $f(x) = \dfrac{3x}{x^2 - 4}$

(a) $f(-x) = \dfrac{3(-x)}{(-x)^2 - 4} = \dfrac{-3x}{x^2 - 4}$

(b) $-f(x) = -\left(\dfrac{3x}{x^2 - 4}\right) = \dfrac{-3x}{x^2 - 4}$

(c) $f(x+2) = \dfrac{3(x+2)}{(x+2)^2 - 4} = \dfrac{3x+6}{x^2 + 4x + 4 - 4} = \dfrac{3x+6}{x^2 + 4x}$

(d) $f(x-2) = \dfrac{3(x-2)}{(x-2)^2 - 4} = \dfrac{3x-6}{x^2 - 4x + 4 - 4} = \dfrac{3x-6}{x^2 - 4x}$

(e) $f(2x) = \dfrac{3(2x)}{(2x)^2 - 4} = \dfrac{6x}{4x^2 - 4} = \dfrac{3x}{2x^2 - 2}$

8. $f(x) = \dfrac{x^2}{x+2}$

(a) $f(-x) = \dfrac{(-x)^2}{-x+2} = \dfrac{x^2}{-x+2}$

(b) $-f(x) = -\dfrac{x^2}{x+2} = \dfrac{-x^2}{x+2}$

(c) $f(x+2) = \dfrac{(x+2)^2}{(x+2)+2} = \dfrac{x^2 + 4x + 4}{x+4}$

(d) $f(x-2) = \dfrac{(x-2)^2}{(x-2)+2} = \dfrac{x^2 - 4x + 4}{x}$

(e) $f(2x) = \dfrac{(2x)^2}{(2x)+2} = \dfrac{4x^2}{2x+2} = \dfrac{2(2x^2)}{2(x+2)} = \dfrac{2x^2}{x+2}$

9. $f(x) = \sqrt{x^2 - 4}$

(a) $f(-x) = \sqrt{(-x)^2 - 4} = \sqrt{x^2 - 4}$

(b) $-f(x) = -\sqrt{x^2 - 4}$

(c) $f(x+2) = \sqrt{(x+2)^2 - 4} = \sqrt{x^2 + 4x + 4 - 4} = \sqrt{x^2 + 4x}$

(d) $f(x-2) = \sqrt{(x-2)^2 - 4} = \sqrt{x^2 - 4x + 4 - 4} = \sqrt{x^2 - 4x}$

(e) $f(2x) = \sqrt{(2x)^2 - 4} = \sqrt{4x^2 - 4} = 2\sqrt{x^2 - 1}$

10. $f(x) = \left| x^2 - 4 \right|$

(a) $f(-x) = \left| (-x)^2 - 4 \right| = \left| x^2 - 4 \right|$

(b) $-f(x) = -\left| x^2 - 4 \right|$

(c) $f(x+2) = \left| (x+2)^2 - 4 \right| = \left| x^2 + 4x + 4 - 4 \right| = \left| x^2 + 4x \right|$

(d) $f(x-2) = \left| (x-2)^2 - 4 \right| = \left| x^2 - 4x + 4 - 4 \right| = \left| x^2 - 4x \right|$

(e) $f(2x) = \left| (2x)^2 - 4 \right| = \left| 4x^2 - 4 \right| = 4\left| x^2 - 1 \right|$

11. $f(x) = \dfrac{x^2 - 4}{x^2}$

   (a) $f(-x) = \dfrac{(-x)^2 - 4}{(-x)^2} = \dfrac{x^2 - 4}{x^2}$

   (b) $-f(x) = -\left(\dfrac{x^2 - 4}{x^2}\right) = \dfrac{4 - x^2}{x^2}$

   (c) $f(x + 2) = \dfrac{(x + 2)^2 - 4}{(x + 2)^2} = \dfrac{x^2 + 4x + 4 - 4}{x^2 + 4x + 4} = \dfrac{x^2 + 4x}{x^2 + 4x + 4}$

   (d) $f(x - 2) = \dfrac{(x - 2)^2 - 4}{(x - 2)^2} = \dfrac{x^2 - 4x + 4 - 4}{x^2 - 4x + 4} = \dfrac{x^2 - 4x}{x^2 - 4x + 4}$

   (e) $f(2x) = \dfrac{(2x)^2 - 4}{(2x)^2} = \dfrac{4x^2 - 4}{4x^2} = \dfrac{x^2 - 1}{x^2}$

12. $f(x) = \dfrac{x^3}{x^2 - 4}$

   (a) $f(-x) = \dfrac{(-x)^3}{(-x)^2 - 4} = \dfrac{-x^3}{x^2 - 4}$

   (b) $-f(x) = -\dfrac{x^3}{x^2 - 4} = \dfrac{-x^3}{x^2 - 4}$

   (c) $f(x + 2) = \dfrac{(x + 2)^3}{(x + 2)^2 - 4} = \dfrac{x^3 + 6x^2 + 12x + 8}{x^2 + 4x + 4 - 4} = \dfrac{x^3 + 6x^2 + 12x + 8}{x^2 + 4x}$

   (d) $f(x - 2) = \dfrac{(x - 2)^3}{(x - 2)^2 - 4} = \dfrac{x^3 - 6x^2 + 12x - 8}{x^2 - 4x + 4 - 4} = \dfrac{x^3 - 6x^2 + 12x - 8}{x^2 - 4x}$

   (e) $f(2x) = \dfrac{(2x)^3}{(2x)^2 - 4} = \dfrac{8x^3}{4x^2 - 4} = \dfrac{4(2x^3)}{4(x^2 - 1)} = \dfrac{2x^3}{x^2 - 1}$

13. $f(x) = \dfrac{x}{x^2 - 9}$

   The denominator cannot be zero:
   $$x^2 - 9 \neq 0$$
   $$(x + 3)(x - 3) \neq 0$$
   $$x \neq -3 \text{ or } 3$$
   Domain: $\{x \mid x \neq -3, x \neq 3\}$

14. $f(x) = \dfrac{3x^2}{x - 2}$

   The denominator cannot be zero:
   $$x - 2 \neq 0$$
   $$x \neq 2$$
   Domain: $\{x \mid x \neq 2\}$

15. $f(x) = \sqrt{2 - x}$

   The radicand must be positive:
   $$2 - x \geq 0$$
   $$x \leq 2$$
   Domain: $\{x \mid x \leq 2\}$ or $(-\infty, 2]$

16. $f(x) = \sqrt{x + 2}$

   The radicand must be positive:
   $$x + 2 \geq 0$$
   $$x \geq -2$$
   Domain: $\{x \mid x \geq -2\}$ or $[-2, +\infty)$

17. $f(x) = \dfrac{\sqrt{x}}{|x|}$

   The radicand must be positive and the
   denominator cannot be zero: $x > 0$
   Domain: $\{x \mid x > 0\}$ or $(0, +\infty)$

18. $g(x) = \dfrac{|x|}{x}$

   The denominator cannot be zero:
   $$x \neq 0$$
   Domain: $\{x \mid x \neq 0\}$

19. $f(x) = \dfrac{x}{x^2 + 2x - 3}$

The denominator cannot be zero:
$$x^2 + 2x - 3 \neq 0$$
$$(x + 3)(x - 1) \neq 0$$
$$x \neq -3 \text{ or } 1$$
Domain: $\{x \mid x \neq -3, x \neq 1\}$

20. $F(x) = \dfrac{1}{x^2 - 3x - 4}$

The denominator cannot be zero:
$$x^2 - 3x - 4 \neq 0$$
$$(x + 1)(x - 4) \neq 0$$
$$x \neq -1 \text{ or } 4$$
Domain: $\{x \mid x \neq -1, x \neq 4\}$

21. $f(x) = \begin{cases} 3x - 2 & \text{if } x \leq 1 \\ x + 1 & \text{if } x > 1 \end{cases}$

  (a) Domain: {Real Numbers}

  (b) x-intercept: $\left(\dfrac{2}{3}, 0\right)$

       y-intercept: $(0, -2)$

  (c)

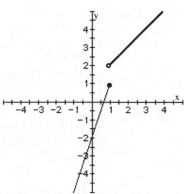

  (d) Range: $\{y > 2\} \cup \{y \leq 1\}$

22. $f(x) = \begin{cases} x - 1 & \text{if } -3 < x < 0 \\ 3x - 1 & \text{if } x \geq 0 \end{cases}$

  (a) Domain: $\{x \mid x > -3\}$

  (b) x-intercept: $\left(\dfrac{1}{3}, 0\right)$

       y-intercept: $(0, -1)$

  (c)

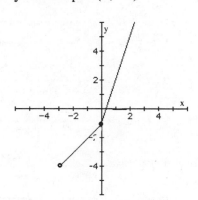

  (d) Range: $\{y > -4\}$

23. $f(x) = \begin{cases} x & \text{if } -4 \leq x < 0 \\ 1 & \text{if } x = 0 \\ 3x & \text{if } x > 0 \end{cases}$

  (a) Domain: $\{x \mid x \geq -4\}$

  (b) x-intercept: none

       y-intercept: $(0, 1)$

  (c)

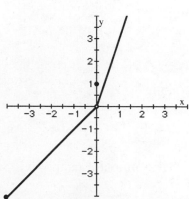

  (d) Range: $\{y \mid y \geq -4, y \neq 0\}$

24. $f(x) = \begin{cases} x^2 & \text{if } -2 \leq x \leq 2 \\ 2x - 1 & \text{if } x > 2 \end{cases}$

  (a) Domain: $\{x \mid x \geq -2\}$

  (b) x-intercept: $(0, 0)$

       y-intercept: $(0, 0)$

  (c)

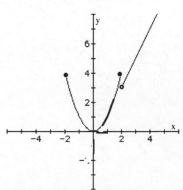

  (d) Range: $\{y \mid y \geq 0\}$

25. $f(x) = 2 - 5x$

$$\frac{f(x) - f(2)}{x - 2} = \frac{2 - 5x - (-8)}{x - 2} = \frac{-5x + 10}{x - 2} = \frac{-5(x - 2)}{x - 2} = -5$$

26. $f(x) = 2x^2 + 7$

$$\frac{f(x) - f(2)}{x - 2} = \frac{2x^2 + 7 - 15}{x - 2} = \frac{2x^2 - 8}{x - 2} = \frac{2(x - 2)(x + 2)}{x - 2} = 2x + 4$$

27. $f(x) = 3x - 4x^2$

$$\frac{f(x) - f(2)}{x - 2} = \frac{3x - 4x^2 - (-10)}{x - 2} = \frac{-4x^2 + 3x + 10}{x - 2}$$

$$= \frac{-(4x^2 - 3x - 10)}{x - 2} = \frac{-(4x + 5)(x - 2)}{x - 2} = -4x - 5$$

28. $f(x) = x^2 - 3x + 2$

$$\frac{f(x) - f(2)}{x - 2} = \frac{x^2 - 3x + 2 - 0}{x - 2} = \frac{x^2 - 3x + 2}{x - 2} = \frac{(x - 2)(x - 1)}{x - 2} = x - 1$$

29. $f(x) = x^3 - 4x$

$$f(-x) = (-x)^3 - 4(-x) = -x^3 + 4x = -\left(x^3 - 4x\right) = -f(x)$$

f is odd.

30. $g(x) = \dfrac{4 + x^2}{1 + x^4}$

$$g(-x) = \frac{4 + (-x)^2}{1 + (-x)^4} = \frac{4 + x^2}{1 + x^4} = g(x) \qquad\qquad g \text{ is even.}$$

31. $h(x) = \dfrac{1}{x^4} + \dfrac{1}{x^2} + 1$

$$h(-x) = \frac{1}{(-x)^4} + \frac{1}{(-x)^2} + 1 = \frac{1}{x^4} + \frac{1}{x^2} + 1 = h(x) \qquad h \text{ is even.}$$

32. $F(x) = \sqrt{1 - x^3}$

$$F(-x) = \sqrt{1 - (-x)^3} = \sqrt{1 + x^3} \neq F(x) \text{ or } -F(x) \qquad F \text{ is neither even nor odd.}$$

33. $G(x) = 1 - x + x^3$

$$G(-x) = 1 - (-x) + (-x)^3 = 1 + x - x^3 \neq -G(x) \neq G(x)$$

G is neither even nor odd.

34. $H(x) = 1 + x + x^2$

$$H(-x) = 1 + (-x) + (-x)^2 = 1 - x + x^2 \neq -H(x) \text{ or } H(x)$$

H is neither even nor odd.

35. $f(x) = \dfrac{x}{1 + x^2}$

$f(-x) = \dfrac{-x}{1 + (-x)^2} = \dfrac{-x}{1 + x^2} = -f(x)$ f is odd.

36. $g(x) = \dfrac{1 + x^2}{x^3}$

$g(-x) = \dfrac{1 + (-x)^2}{(-x)^3} = \dfrac{1 + x^2}{-x^3} = -\dfrac{1 + x^2}{x^3} = -g(x)$ g is odd.

37. $F(x) = |x| - 4$

Using the graph of $y = |x|$, vertically shift the graph downward 4 units.

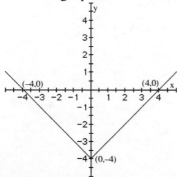

Intercepts: (–4,0), (4,0), (0,–4)
Domain: {Real Numbers}
Range: $\{y \mid y \geq -4\}$

38. $f(x) = |x| + 4$

Using the graph of $y = |x|$, vertically shift the graph upward 4 units.

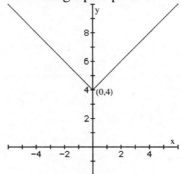

Intercepts: (0, 4)
Domain: {Real Numbers}
Range: $\{y \mid y \geq 4\}$

39. $g(x) = -2|x|$

Reflect the graph of $y = |x|$ about the x-axis and vertically stretch the graph by a factor of 2.

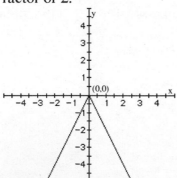

Intercepts: (0,0)
Domain: {Real Numbers}
Range: $\{y \mid y \leq 0\}$

40. $g(x) = \dfrac{1}{2}|x|$

Using the graph of $y = |x|$, vertically shrink the graph by a factor of $\dfrac{1}{2}$.

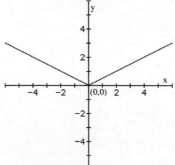

Intercepts: (0,0)
Domain: {Real Numbers}
Range: $\{y \mid y \geq 0\}$

41. $h(x) = \sqrt{x-1}$

Using the graph of $y = \sqrt{x}$, horizontally
shift the graph to the right 1 unit.
Intercepts: (1,0)
Domain: $\left\{x \mid x \geq 1\right\}$
Range: $\left\{y \mid y \geq 0\right\}$

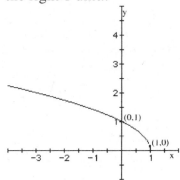

42. $h(x) = \sqrt{x} - 1$

Using the graph of $y = \sqrt{x}$, vertically
shift the graph downward 1 unit.

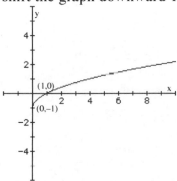

Intercepts: (1,0), (0, −1)
Domain: $\left\{x \mid x \geq 0\right\}$
Range: $\left\{y \mid y \geq -1\right\}$

43. $f(x) = \sqrt{1-x} = \sqrt{-1(x-1)}$

Reflect the graph of $y = \sqrt{x}$ about the y-
axis and horizontally shift the graph to
the right 1 unit..

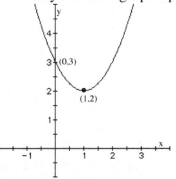

Intercepts: (1,0), (0,1)
Domain: $\left\{x \mid x \leq 1\right\}$
Range: $\left\{y \mid y \geq 0\right\}$

44. $f(x) = -\sqrt{x+3}$

Using the graph of $y = \sqrt{x}$, horizontally
shift the graph to the left 3 units, and
reflect on the x-axis.

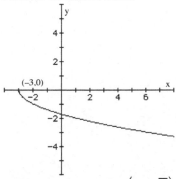

Intercepts: (−3,0), $\left(0, \sqrt{3}\right)$
Domain: $\left\{x \mid x \geq -3\right\}$
Range: $\left\{y \mid y \leq 0\right\}$

45. $h(x) = (x-1)^2 + 2$

Using the graph of $y = x^2$, horizontally
shift the graph to the right 1 unit and
vertically shift the graph up 2 units.

Intercepts: (0,3)
Domain: {Real Numbers}
Range: $\left\{y \mid y \geq 2\right\}$

46. $h(x) = (x+2)^2 - 3$

Using the graph of $y = x^2$, horizontally shift the graph to the left 2 units and vertically shift the graph down 3 units.

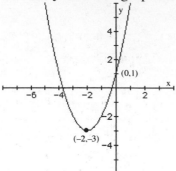

Intercepts: $(0,1)$,
$$\left(-2+\sqrt{3}, 0\right), \left(-2-\sqrt{3}, 0\right)$$
Domain: {Real Numbers}
Range: $\left\{y \mid y \geq -3\right\}$

47. $g(x) = 3(x-1)^3 + 1$

Using the graph of $y = x^3$, horizontally shift the graph to the right 1 unit, vertically stretch the graph by a factor of 3, and vertically shift the graph up 1 unit.

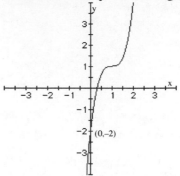

Intercepts: $(0,-2)$, $\left(1 - \dfrac{\sqrt[3]{3}}{3}, 0\right)$

Domain: {Real Numbers}
Range: {Real Numbers}

48. $g(x) = -2(x+2)^3 - 8$

Using the graph of $y = x^3$, horizontally shift the graph to the left 2 units, vertically stretch the graph by a factor of 2, reflect about the x-axis, and vertically shift the graph down 8 units.

Intercepts: $(0,-24)$, $\left(-2 - \sqrt[3]{4}, 0\right)$

Domain: {Real Numbers}
Range: {Real Numbers}

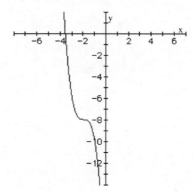

49. $f(x) = 3x - 5$ $g(x) = 1 - 2x^2$

(a) $(f \circ g)(2) = f(g(2)) = f\left(1 - 2(2)^2\right) = f(-7) = 3(-7) - 5 = -26$

(b) $(g \circ f)(-2) = g(f(-2)) = g(3(-2) - 5) = g(-11) = 1 - 2(-11)^2 = -241$

(c) $(f \circ f)(4) = f(f(4)) = f(3(4) - 5) = f(7) = 3(7) - 5 = 16$

(d) $(g \circ g)(-1) = g(g(-1)) = g\left(1 - 2(-1)^2\right) = g(-1) = 1 - 2(-1)^2 = -1$

50. $f(x) = 4 - x$ $g(x) = 1 + x^2$

(a) $(f \circ g)(2) = f(g(2)) = f\left(1 + 2^2\right) = f(5) = 4 - 5 = -1$

(b) $(g \circ f)(-2) = g(f(-2)) = g(4 - (-2)) = g(6) = 1 + 6^2 = 37$

(c) $(f \circ f)(4) = f(f(4)) = f(4 - 4) = f(0) = 4 - 0 = 4$

(d) $(g \circ g)(-1) = g(g(-1)) = g\left(1 + (-1)^2\right) = g(2) = 1 + 2^2 = 5$

51. $f(x) = \sqrt{x+2}$ $g(x) = 2x^2 + 1$

(a) $(f \circ g)(2) = f(g(2)) = f\left(2(2)^2 + 1\right) = f(9) = \sqrt{9+2} = \sqrt{11}$

(b) $(g \circ f)(-2) = g(f(-2)) = g\left(\sqrt{-2+2}\right) = g(0) = 2(0)^2 + 1 = 1$

(c) $(f \circ f)(4) = f(f(4)) = f\left(\sqrt{4+2}\right) = f\left(\sqrt{6}\right) = \sqrt{\sqrt{6}+2}$

(d) $(g \circ g)(-1) = g(g(-1)) = g\left(2(-1)^2 + 1\right) = g(3) = 2(3)^2 + 1 = 19$

52. $f(x) = 1 - 3x^2$ $g(x) = \sqrt{4 - x}$

(a) $(f \circ g)(2) = f(g(2)) = f\left(\sqrt{4-2}\right) = f\left(\sqrt{2}\right) = 1 - 3\left(\sqrt{2}\right)^2 = 1 - 3 \cdot 2 = -5$

(b) $(g \circ f)(-2) = g(f(-2)) = g\left(1 - 3(-2)^2\right) = g(-11) = \sqrt{4 - (-11)} = \sqrt{15}$

(c) $(f \circ f)(4) = f(f(4)) = f\left(1 - 3(4)^2\right) = f(-47) = 1 - 3(-47)^2 = -6626$

(d) $(g \circ g)(-1) = g(g(-1)) = g\left(\sqrt{4 - (-1)}\right) = g\left(\sqrt{5}\right) = \sqrt{4 - \sqrt{5}}$

53. $f(x) = \dfrac{1}{x^2 + 4}$ $g(x) = 3x - 2$

(a) $(f \circ g)(2) = f(g(2)) = f(3(2) - 2) = f(4) = \dfrac{1}{4^2 + 4} = \dfrac{1}{20}$

(b) $(g \circ f)(-2) = g(f(-2)) = g\left(\dfrac{1}{(-2)^2 + 4}\right) = g\left(\dfrac{1}{8}\right) = 3\left(\dfrac{1}{8}\right) - 2 = \dfrac{-13}{8}$

(c) $(f \circ f)(4) = f(f(4)) = f\left(\dfrac{1}{4^2 + 4}\right) = f\left(\dfrac{1}{20}\right) = \dfrac{1}{\left(\dfrac{1}{20}\right)^2 + 4} = \dfrac{1}{\left(\dfrac{1601}{400}\right)} = \dfrac{400}{1601}$

(d) $(g \circ g)(-1) = g(g(-1)) = g(3(-1) - 2) = g(-5) = 3(-5) - 2 = -17$

54. $f(x) = \dfrac{2}{1 + 2x^2}$ $g(x) = 3x$

(a) $(f \circ g)(2) = f(g(2)) = f(3(2)) = f(6) = \dfrac{2}{1 + 2(6)^2} = \dfrac{2}{73}$

(b) $(g \circ f)(-2) = g(f(-2)) = g\left(\dfrac{2}{1 + 2(-2)^2}\right) = g\left(\dfrac{2}{9}\right) = 3\left(\dfrac{2}{9}\right) = \dfrac{2}{3}$

(c) $(f \circ f)(4) = f(f(4)) = f\left(\dfrac{2}{1 + 2 \cdot 4^2}\right) = f\left(\dfrac{2}{33}\right) = \dfrac{2}{1 + 2\left(\dfrac{2}{33}\right)^2} = \dfrac{2}{\left(\dfrac{1097}{1089}\right)} = \dfrac{2178}{1097}$

(d) $(g \circ g)(-1) = g(g(-1)) = g(3(-1)) = g(-3) = 3(-3) = -9$

55. $f(x) = 2 - x$ $g(x) = 3x + 1$

The domain of f is all real numbers. The domain of g is all real numbers.

(a) $(f \circ g)(x) = f(g(x)) = f(3x + 1) = 2 - (3x + 1) = 2 - 3x - 1 = 1 - 3x$
   Domain: All real numbers.

(b) $(g \circ f)(x) = g(f(x)) = g(2 - x) = 3(2 - x) + 1 = 6 - 3x + 1 = 7 - 3x$
   Domain: All real numbers.

(c) $(f \circ f)(x) = f(f(x)) = f(2 - x) = 2 - (2 - x) = 2 - 2 + x = x$
   Domain: All real numbers.

(d) $(g \circ g)(x) = g(g(x)) = g(3x + 1) = 3(3x + 1) + 1 = 9x + 3 + 1 = 9x + 4$
        Domain: All real numbers.

56. $f(x) = 2x - 1$ $g(x) = 2x + 1$
        The domain of f is all real numbers. The domain of g is all real numbers.
        (a) $(f \circ g)(x) = f(g(x)) = f(2x + 1) = 2(2x + 1) - 1 = 4x + 2 - 1 = 4x + 1$
                Domain: All real numbers.
        (b) $(g \circ f)(x) = g(f(x)) = g(2x - 1) = 2(2x - 1) + 1 = 4x - 2 + 1 = 4x - 1$
                Domain: All real numbers.
        (c) $(f \circ f)(x) = f(f(x)) = f(2x - 1) = 2(2x - 1) - 1 = 4x - 2 - 1 = 4x - 3$
                Domain: All real numbers.
        (d) $(g \circ g)(x) = g(g(x)) = g(2x + 1) = 2(2x + 1) + 1 = 4x + 2 + 1 = 4x + 3$
                Domain: All real numbers.

57. $f(x) = 3x^2 + x + 1$ $g(x) = |3x|$
        The domain of f is all real numbers. The domain of g is all real numbers.
        (a) $(f \circ g)(x) = f(g(x)) = f(|3x|) = 3(|3x|)^2 + (|3x|) + 1 = 27x^2 + 3|x| + 1$
                Domain: All real numbers.
        (b) $(g \circ f)(x) = g(f(x)) = g(3x^2 + x + 1) = |3(3x^2 + x + 1)| = |9x^2 + 3x + 3|$
                Domain: All real numbers.
        (c) $(f \circ f)(x) = f(f(x)) = f(3x^2 + x + 1) = 3(3x^2 + x + 1)^2 + (3x^2 + x + 1) + 1$
                $= 3(9x^4 + 6x^3 + 7x^2 + 2x + 1) + 3x^2 + x + 1 + 1$
                $= 27x^4 + 18x^3 + 24x^2 + 7x + 5$
                Domain: All real numbers.
        (d) $(g \circ g)(x) = g(g(x)) = g(|3x|) = |3\,|3x|\,| = 9|x|$
                Domain: All real numbers.

58. $f(x) = \sqrt{3x}$ $g(x) = 1 + x$
        The domain of f is $\{x \mid x \geq 0\}$. The domain of g is all real numbers.
        (a) $(f \circ g)(x) = f(g(x)) = f(1 + x) = \sqrt{3(1 + x)} = \sqrt{3 + 3x}$
                $3 + 3x \geq 0$
                $x \geq -1$ Domain: $\{x \mid x \geq -1\}$.
        (b) $(g \circ f)(x) = g(f(x)) = g(\sqrt{3x}) = 1 + \sqrt{3x}$
                Domain: $\{x \mid x \geq 0\}$.
        (c) $(f \circ f)(x) = f(f(x)) = f(\sqrt{3x}) = \sqrt{3\sqrt{3x}}$ Domain: $\{x \mid x \geq 0\}$.
        (d) $(g \circ g)(x) = g(g(x)) = g(1 + x) = 1 + (1 + x) = 2 + x$ Domain: All real numbers.

59. $f(x) = \dfrac{x+1}{x-1}$ $g(x) = \dfrac{1}{x}$

The domain of f is $\{x \mid x \neq 1\}$. The domain of g is $\{x \mid x \neq 0\}$.

(a) $(f \circ g)(x) = f(g(x)) = f\left(\dfrac{1}{x}\right) = \dfrac{\left(\dfrac{1}{x}+1\right)}{\left(\dfrac{1}{x}-1\right)} = \dfrac{\left(\dfrac{1+x}{x}\right)}{\left(\dfrac{1-x}{x}\right)} = \dfrac{1+x}{1-x}$

Domain of $f \circ g$ is $\{x \mid x \neq 0,\ x \neq 1\}$.

(b) $(g \circ f)(x) = g(f(x)) = g\left(\dfrac{x+1}{x-1}\right) = \dfrac{1}{\left(\dfrac{x+1}{x-1}\right)} = \dfrac{x-1}{x+1}$

Domain of $g \circ f$ is $\{x \mid x \neq -1,\ x \neq 1\}$.

(c) $(f \circ f)(x) = f(f(x)) = f\left(\dfrac{x+1}{x-1}\right) = \dfrac{\left(\dfrac{x+1}{x-1}+1\right)}{\left(\dfrac{x+1}{x-1}-1\right)} = \dfrac{\left(\dfrac{x+1+x-1}{x-1}\right)}{\left(\dfrac{x+1-(x-1)}{x-1}\right)} = \dfrac{2x}{2} = x$

Domain of $f \circ f$ is $\{x \mid x \neq 1\}$.

(d) $(g \circ g)(x) = g(g(x)) = g\left(\dfrac{1}{x}\right) = \dfrac{1}{\left(\dfrac{1}{x}\right)} = x$ Domain of $g \circ g$ is $\{x \mid x \neq 0\}$.

60. $f(x) = \sqrt{x-3}$ $g(x) = 3x$

The domain of f is $\{x \mid x \geq 3\}$. The domain of g is {Real numbers}.

(a) $(f \circ g)(x) = f(g(x)) = f(3x) = \sqrt{3x-3}$

$3x - 3 \geq 0$

$\rightarrow x \geq 1$ Domain of $f \circ g$ is $\{x \mid x \geq 1\}$.

(b) $(g \circ f)(x) = g(f(x)) = g\left(\sqrt{x-3}\right) = 3\sqrt{x-3}$

Domain of $g \circ f$ is $\{x \mid x \geq 3\}$.

(c) $(f \circ f)(x) = f(f(x)) = f\left(\sqrt{x-3}\right) = \sqrt{\sqrt{x-3}-3}$

$\sqrt{x-3} - 3 \geq 0 \rightarrow \sqrt{x-3} \geq 3 \rightarrow x - 3 \geq 9 \rightarrow x \geq 12$

Domain of $f \circ f$ is $\{x \mid x \geq 12\}$.

(d) $(g \circ g)(x) = g(g(x)) = g(3x) = 3(3x) = 9x$

Domain of $g \circ g$ is {Real Numbers}.

61. (a) $y = f(-x)$
Reflect about the y-axis.

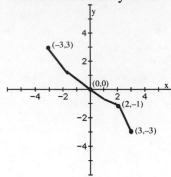

(b) $y = -f(x)$
Reflect about the x-axis.

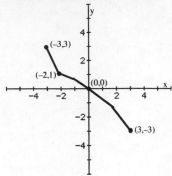

(c) $y = f(x + 2)$
Horizontally shift left 2 units.

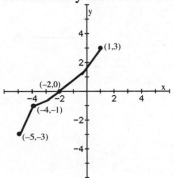

(d) $y = f(x) + 2$
Vertically shift up 2 units.

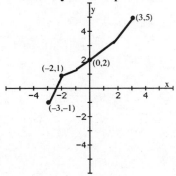

(e) $y = 2f(x)$
Vertical stretch by a factor of 2.

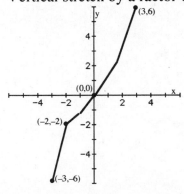

(f) $y = f(3x)$

Horizontal compression by $\dfrac{1}{3}$.

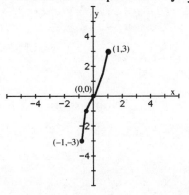

62. (a) $y = f(-x)$
    Reflect about the y-axis.

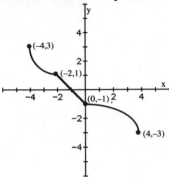

(b) $y = -f(x)$
    Reflect about the x-axis.

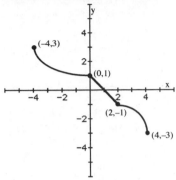

(c) $y = f(x + 2)$
    Horizontally shift left 2 units.

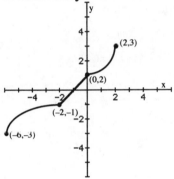

(d) $y = f(x) + 2$
    Vertically shift up 2 units.

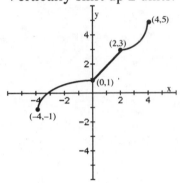

(e) $y = 2f(x)$
    Vertical stretch by a factor of 2.

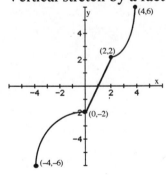

(f) $y = f(3x)$

    Horizontal compression by $\dfrac{1}{3}$.

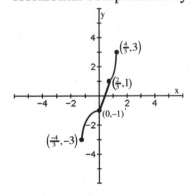

63. we have the points $(h_1, T_1) = (0, 30)$ and $(h_2, T_2) = (10000, 5)$

$$slope = \frac{\Delta T}{\Delta h} = \frac{5 - 30}{10000 - 0} = \frac{-25}{10000} = -0.0025$$

using the point-slope formula yields

$$T - T_1 = m(h - h_1) \rightarrow T - 30 = -0.0025(h - 0)$$

$$T - 30 = -0.0025h \rightarrow T = -0.0025h + 30$$

$$\therefore T(h) = -0.0025h + 30$$

64. we have the point $(t_1, v_1) = (20, 80)$ and $slope = m = 5$
using the point-slope formula yields

$$v - v_1 = m(t - t_1) \rightarrow v - 80 = 5(t - 20)$$

$$v - 80 = 5t - 100 \rightarrow v = 5t - 20$$

$$\therefore v(t) = 5t - 20$$

after 30 seconds, $v(30) = 5(30) - 20 = 150 - 20 = 130$ feet per second.

65. $S = kxd^3$, $x = $ width; $d = $ depth

in the diagram, depth = diameter of the log = 6

$$S(x) = kx(6)^3 = 216kx \qquad\qquad \text{domain is } \{x \mid 0 \le x \le 6\}$$

66. (a)

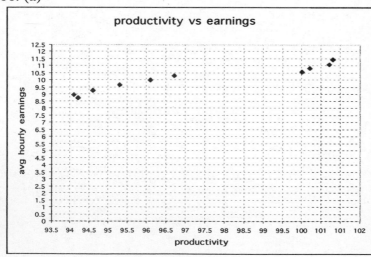

(b)

(c)   average rate of change $= \dfrac{10.32 - 8.76}{96.7 - 94.2} = \dfrac{1.56}{2.5} = 0.624$ dollars per unit of productivity

(d)   for each 1 unit increase in productivity, the avg. hourly earning increases by 0.624 dollars.

(e)

(f)   average rate of change $= \dfrac{11.44 - 10.32}{100.8 - 96.7} = \dfrac{1.12}{4.1} = 0.273$ dollars per unit of productivity

(g) for each 1 unit increase in productivity, the avg. hourly earning increases by 0.273 dollars

(h) the average rate of change of hourly earnings is decreasing as the productivity increases

67. (a)

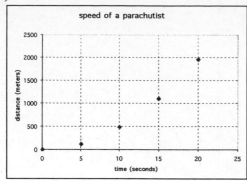

(b)

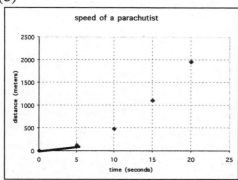

(c)   average rate of change $=\dfrac{112.5-0}{5-0}=\dfrac{112.5}{5}=22.5$ feet per second

(d)   for each 1 second increase in time, the distance fallen increases by 22.5 feet

(e)

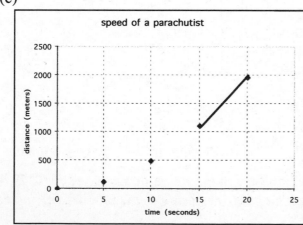

(f)   average rate of change $=\dfrac{1960-1102.5}{20-15}=\dfrac{857.5}{5}=171.5$ feet per second

(g)   for each 1 second increase in time, the distance fallen increases by 171.5 feet

(h)   the average rate of change of distance is increasing as time passes

68. (a) We are given that the volume = 100 cubic feet, so we have

$$V = \pi r^2 h = 100 \rightarrow h = \frac{100}{\pi r^2}$$

The amount of material needed to construct the barrel = the surface area of the barrel
The cylindrical body of the barrel can be viewed as a rectangle whose dimensions are given by

$2\pi r$

h

A = area of top + area of bottom + area of body

$$= \pi r^2 + \pi r^2 + 2\pi rh = 2\pi r^2 + 2\pi rh, \quad \therefore A(r) = 2\pi r^2 + 2\pi r\left(\frac{100}{\pi r^2}\right) = 2\pi r^2 + \frac{200}{r}$$

(b) $A(3) = 2\pi(3)^2 + \dfrac{200}{3} = 18\pi + \dfrac{200}{3} \approx 123.22$ square feet

(c) $A(4) = 2\pi(4)^2 + \dfrac{200}{4} = 32\pi + 50 \approx 150.53$ square feet

(d) $A(5) = 2\pi(5)^2 + \dfrac{200}{5} = 50\pi + 40 \approx 197.08$ square feet

(e)

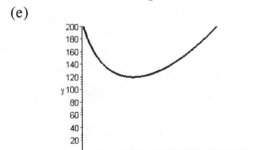

The minimum value occurs at $x \approx 2.51 \rightarrow A(2.51) \approx 119.27$ square feet

69. (a) We are given that the volume = 500 cubic feet, so we have

$$V = \pi r^2 h = 100 \rightarrow h = \frac{500}{\pi r^2}$$

Total Cost = cost of top + cost of bottom + cost of body

= 2(cost of top) + cost of body

= 2(area of top)(cost per area of top) + (area of body)(cost per area of body)

$$= 2(\pi r^2)(.06) + (2\pi rh)(.04) = 0.12\pi r^2 + .08\pi rh = .12\pi r^2 + .08\pi r\left(\frac{500}{\pi r^2}\right)$$

$$= .12\pi r^2 + \frac{40}{r}, \quad \therefore C(r) = .12\pi r^2 + \frac{40}{r}$$

(b) $C(4) = .12\pi(4)^2 + \dfrac{40}{4} = 1.92\pi + 10 \approx 16.03$ dollars

(c) $C(8) = .12\pi(8)^2 + \dfrac{40}{8} = 7.68\pi + 5 \approx 29.13$ dollars

(d)

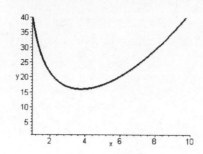

The minimum value occurs at $r \approx 3.79 \rightarrow C(3.79) \approx \$15.97$

70. we can consider the following diagram

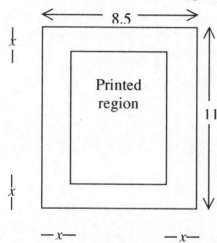   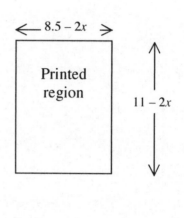

(a) The printed region is a rectangle, so its area is given by

$A = (length)(width) = (11 - 2x)(8.5 - 2x)$

$\therefore A(x) = (11 - 2x)(8.5 - 2x)$

(b) To find the domain of $A(x) = (11 - 2x)(8.5 - 2x)$ we need to remember that the dimensions of a rectangle must be non-negative.

That is, we need

$$x \geq 0 \quad and \quad 11 - 2x \geq 0 \quad and \quad 8.5 - 2x \geq 0$$

$$\rightarrow x \geq 0 \quad and \quad x \leq 5.5 \quad and \quad x \leq 4.25$$

$$\therefore \text{domain is } \{x \mid 0 \leq x \leq 4.25\}$$

The range of $A(x) = (11 - 2x)(8.5 - 2x)$ is given by

$$A(4.25) \leq A \leq A(0) \rightarrow 0 \leq A \leq 93.5$$

(c) $A(1) = (11 - 2(1))(8.5 - 2(1)) = 9 \cdot 6.5 = 58.5$ square inches

   $A(1.2) = (11 - 2(1.2))(8.5 - 2(1.2)) = 8.6 \cdot 5.6 = 48.16$ square inches

   $A(1.5) = (11 - 2(1.5))(8.5 - 2(1.5)) = 8 \cdot 5.5 = 44$ square inches

(d)

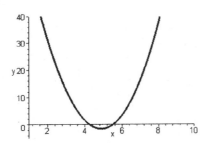

(e)

   $A = 70$ when $x \approx 0.643$ inches $A = 50$ when $x \approx 1.29$ inches

71. $S = 4\pi r^2 \rightarrow r = \sqrt{\dfrac{S}{4\pi}}$ $V(S) = \dfrac{4}{3}\pi r^3 = \dfrac{4\pi}{3}\left(\sqrt{\dfrac{S}{4\pi}}\right)^3 = \dfrac{4\pi}{3} \cdot \dfrac{S}{4\pi}\sqrt{\dfrac{S}{4\pi}} = \dfrac{S}{6}\sqrt{\dfrac{S}{\pi}}$

   $V(2S) = \dfrac{2S}{6}\sqrt{\dfrac{2S}{\pi}} = 2\sqrt{2}\left(\dfrac{S}{6}\sqrt{\dfrac{S}{\pi}}\right)$ The volume is $2\sqrt{2}$ times as large.

72.   (a) $x^2 h = 10 \rightarrow h = \dfrac{10}{x^2}$ $A(x) = 2x^2 + 4xh = 2x^2 + 4x\left(\dfrac{10}{x^2}\right) = 2x^2 + \dfrac{40}{x}$

      (b) $A(1) = 2 \cdot 1^2 + \dfrac{40}{1} = 2 + 40 = 42$ ft^2

      (c) $A(2) = 2 \cdot 2^2 + \dfrac{40}{2} = 8 + 20 = 28$ ft^2

      (d)   Graphing:

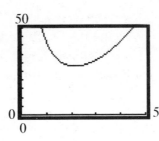

            The area is smallest when $x = 2.15$.

Chapter 4

Polynomial and Rational Functions

4.1   Quadratic Functions and Models

1. D   2. F   3. A   4. H   5. B   6. C

7. E   8. G

9. $f(x) = \dfrac{1}{4}x^2$

Using the function $y = x^2$, compress

vertically by a factor of $\dfrac{1}{4}$.

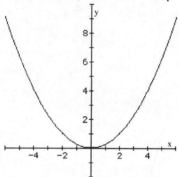

10. $f(x) = 2x^2$

Using the function $y = x^2$, stretch
vertically by a factor of 2.

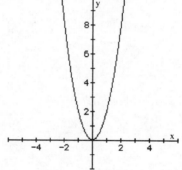

11. $f(x) = \dfrac{1}{4}x^2 - 2$

Using the function $y = x^2$, compress

vertically by a factor of $\dfrac{1}{4}$, and shift

downward 2 units.

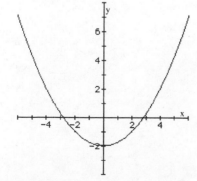

12. $f(x) = 2x^2 - 3$

Using the function $y = x^2$, stretch
vertically by a factor of 2, and shift
downward 3 units.

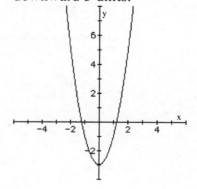

13. $f(x) = \dfrac{1}{4}x^2 + 2$

Using the function $y = x^2$, compress vertically by a factor of $\dfrac{1}{4}$, and shift upward 2 units.

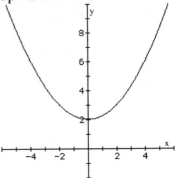

14. $f(x) = 2x^2 + 4$

Using the function $y = x^2$, stretch vertically by a factor of 2, and shift upward 4 units.

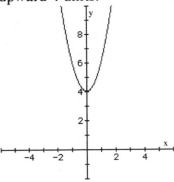

15. $f(x) = \dfrac{1}{4}x^2 + 1$

Using the function $y = x^2$, compress vertically by a factor of $\dfrac{1}{4}$, and shift upward 1 unit.

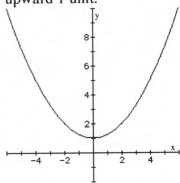

16. $f(x) = -2x^2 - 2$

Using the function $y = x^2$, stretch vertically by a factor of 2, reflect about the x-axis, and shift downward 2 units.

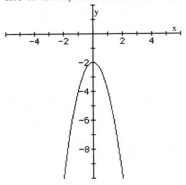

17. $f(x) = x^2 + 4x + 2$
Completing the square:
$f(x) = (x^2 + 4x + 4) + 2 - 4$
$\quad = (x + 2)^2 - 2$

Using the function $y = x^2$, shift the graph to the left 2 units, and shift downward 2 units.

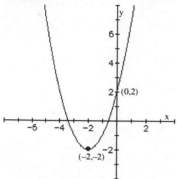

18. $f(x) = x^2 - 6x - 1$
Completing the square:
$f(x) = (x^2 - 6x + 9) - 1 - 9$
$\quad = (x - 3)^2 - 10$

Using the function $y = x^2$, shift the graph to the right 3 units, and shift downward 10 units.

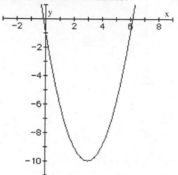

19. $f(x) = 2x^2 - 4x + 1$
Completing the square:
$f(x) = 2(x^2 - 2x + 1) + 1 - 2$
$\quad = 2(x - 1)^2 - 1$

Using the function $y = x^2$, shift the graph to the right 1 unit, stretch the graph vertically by a factor of 2, and shift downward 1 unit.

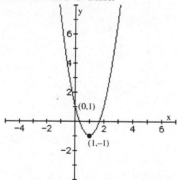

20. $f(x) = 3x^2 + 6x$
Completing the square:
$f(x) = 3(x^2 + 2x + 1) - 3$
$\quad = 3(x + 1)^2 - 3$

Using the function $y = x^2$, shift the graph to the left 1 unit, stretch the graph vertically by a factor of 3, and shift downward 3 units.

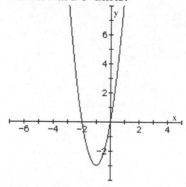

21. $f(x) = -x^2 - 2x$
Completing the square:
$f(x) = -(x^2 + 2x + 1) + 1$
$= -(x + 1)^2 + 1$
Using the function $y = x^2$, shift the graph to the left 1 unit, reflect the graph on the x-axis, and shift upward 1 unit.

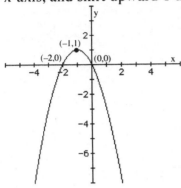

22. $f(x) = -2x^2 + 6x + 2$
Completing the square:
$f(x) = -2\left(x^2 - 3x + \dfrac{9}{4}\right) + 2 + \dfrac{9}{2}$
$= -2\left(x - \dfrac{3}{2}\right)^2 + \dfrac{13}{2}$
Using the function $y = x^2$, shift the graph to the right $\dfrac{3}{2}$ units, stretch vertically by a factor of 2, reflect the graph on the x-axis, and shift upward $\dfrac{13}{2}$ units.

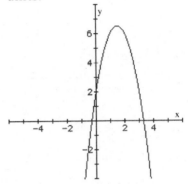

23. $f(x) = \dfrac{1}{2}x^2 + x - 1$
Completing the square:
$f(x) = \dfrac{1}{2}(x^2 + 2x + 1) - 1 - \dfrac{1}{2}$
$= \dfrac{1}{2}(x + 1)^2 - \dfrac{3}{2}$
Using the function $y = x^2$, shift the graph to the left 1 unit, compress the graph vertically by a factor of $\dfrac{1}{2}$, and shift downward $\dfrac{3}{2}$ units.

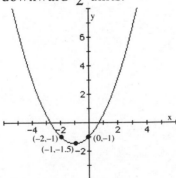

24. $f(x) = \dfrac{2}{3}x^2 + \dfrac{4}{3}x - 1$
Completing the square:
$f(x) = \dfrac{2}{3}(x^2 + 2x + 1) - 1 - \dfrac{2}{3}$
$= \dfrac{2}{3}(x + 1)^2 - \dfrac{5}{3}$
Using the function $y = x^2$, shift the graph to the left 1 unit, compress the graph vertically by a factor of $\dfrac{2}{3}$, and shift downward $\dfrac{5}{3}$ units.

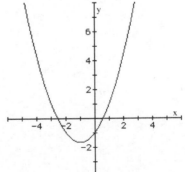

25. $f(x) = -x^2 - 6x$

$a = -1, b = -6, c = 0$. Since $a = -1 < 0$, the graph opens down.

The x-coordinate of the vertex is $x = \dfrac{-b}{2a} = \dfrac{-(-6)}{2(-1)} = \dfrac{6}{-2} = -3$.

The y-coordinate of the vertex is $f\left(\dfrac{-b}{2a}\right) = f(-3) = -(-3)^2 - 6(-3) = -9 + 18 = 9$.

Thus, the vertex is (–3, 9).
The axis of symmetry is the line $x = -3$.
The discriminant is:

$b^2 - 4ac = (-6)^2 - 4(-1)(0) = 36 > 0$,

so the graph has two x-intercepts.
The x-intercepts are found by solving:

$-x^2 - 6x = 0$

$-x(x + 6) = 0$

$x = 0$ or $x = -6$

The x-intercepts are –6 and 0.
The y-intercept is $f(0) = 0$.

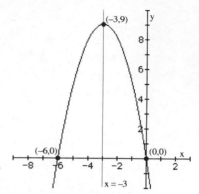

26. $f(x) = -x^2 + 4x$

$a = -1, b = 4, c = 0$. Since $a = -1 < 0$, the graph opens down.

The x-coordinate of the vertex is $x = \dfrac{-b}{2a} = \dfrac{-4}{2(-1)} = \dfrac{-4}{-2} = 2$.

The y-coordinate of the vertex is $f\left(\dfrac{-b}{2a}\right) = f(2) = -(2)^2 + 4(2) = -4 + 8 = 4$.

Thus, the vertex is (2, 4).
The axis of symmetry is the line $x = 2$.
The discriminant is:

$b^2 - 4ac = 4^2 - 4(-1)(0) = 16 > 0$,

so the graph has two x-intercepts.
The x-intercepts are found by solving:

$-x^2 + 4x = 0$

$-x(x - 4) = 0$

$x = 0$ or $x = 4$

The x-intercepts are 0 and 4.
The y-intercept is $f(0) = 0$.

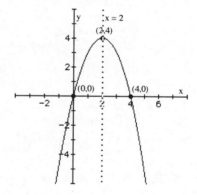

27. $f(x) = 2x^2 - 8x$

$a = 2, b = -8, c = 0$. Since $a = 2 > 0$, the graph opens up.

The x-coordinate of the vertex is $x = \dfrac{-b}{2a} = \dfrac{-(-8)}{2(2)} = \dfrac{8}{4} = 2$.

The y-coordinate of the vertex is $f\left(\dfrac{-b}{2a}\right) = f(2) = 2(2)^2 - 8(2) = 8 - 16 = -8$.

Thus, the vertex is (2, –8).
The axis of symmetry is the line $x = 2$.
The discriminant is:
$$b^2 - 4ac = (-8)^2 - 4(2)(0) = 64 > 0,$$
so the graph has two x-intercepts.
The x-intercepts are found by solving:
$$2x^2 - 8x = 0$$
$$2x(x - 4) = 0$$
$$x = 0 \text{ or } x = 4$$
The x-intercepts are 0 and 4.
The y-intercept is $f(0) = 0$.

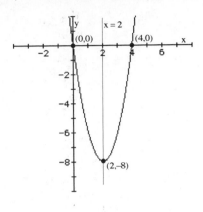

28. $f(x) = 3x^2 + 18x$
$a = 3, b = 18, c = 0$. Since $a = 3 > 0$, the graph opens up.

The x-coordinate of the vertex is $x = \dfrac{-b}{2a} = \dfrac{-18}{2(3)} = \dfrac{-18}{6} = -3$.

The y-coordinate of the vertex is $f\left(\dfrac{-b}{2a}\right) = f(-3) = 3(-3)^2 + 18(-3) = 27 - 54 = -27$.

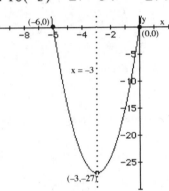

Thus, the vertex is (–3, –27).
The axis of symmetry is the line $x = -3$.
The discriminant is:
$$b^2 - 4ac = (18)^2 - 4(3)(0) = 324 > 0,$$
so the graph has two x-intercepts.
The x-intercepts are found by solving:
$$3x^2 + 18x = 0$$
$$3x(x + 6) = 0$$
$$x = 0 \text{ or } x = -6$$
The x-intercepts are 0 and –6.
The y-intercept is $f(0) = 0$.

29. $f(x) = x^2 + 2x - 8$

$a = 1, b = 2, c = -8.$ Since $a = 1 > 0,$ the graph opens up.

The x-coordinate of the vertex is $x = \dfrac{-b}{2a} = \dfrac{-2}{2(1)} = \dfrac{-2}{2} = -1.$

The y-coordinate of the vertex is $f\left(\dfrac{-b}{2a}\right) = f(-1) = (-1)^2 + 2(-1) - 8 = 1 - 2 - 8 = -9.$

Thus, the vertex is $(-1, -9).$
The axis of symmetry is the line $x = -1.$
The discriminant is:

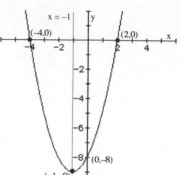

$$b^2 - 4ac = 2^2 - 4(1)(-8) = 4 + 32 = 36 > 0,$$

so the graph has two x-intercepts.
The x-intercepts are found by solving:

$$x^2 + 2x - 8 = 0$$
$$(x + 4)(x - 2) = 0$$
$$x = -4 \text{ or } x = 2$$

The x-intercepts are –4 and 2.
The y-intercept is $f(0) = -8.$

30. $f(x) = x^2 - 2x - 3$

$a = 1, b = -2, c = -3.$ Since $a = 1 > 0,$ the graph opens up.

The x-coordinate of the vertex is $x = \dfrac{-b}{2a} = \dfrac{-(-2))}{2(1)} = \dfrac{2}{2} = 1.$

The y-coordinate of the vertex is $f\left(\dfrac{-b}{2a}\right) = f(1) = 1^2 - 2(1) - 3 = 1 - 2 - 3 = -4.$

Thus, the vertex is $(1, -4).$
The axis of symmetry is the line $x = 1.$
The discriminant is:

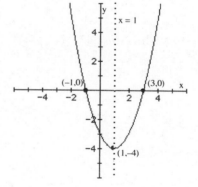

$$b^2 - 4ac = (-2)^2 - 4(1)(-3) = 4 + 12 = 16 > 0,$$

so the graph has two x-intercepts.
The x-intercepts are found by solving:

$$x^2 - 2x - 3 = 0$$
$$(x + 1)(x - 3) = 0$$
$$x = -1 \text{ or } x = 3$$

The x-intercepts are –1 and 3.
The y-intercept is $f(0) = -3.$

31. $f(x) = x^2 + 2x + 1$

$a = 1, b = 2, c = 1.$ Since $a = 1 > 0,$ the graph opens up.

The x-coordinate of the vertex is $x = \dfrac{-b}{2a} = \dfrac{-2}{2(1)} = \dfrac{-2}{2} = -1.$

The y-coordinate of the vertex is $f\left(\dfrac{-b}{2a}\right) = f(-1) = (-1)^2 + 2(-1) + 1 = 1 - 2 + 1 = 0.$

Thus, the vertex is (–1, 0).
The axis of symmetry is the line $x = -1$.
The discriminant is:
$$b^2 - 4ac = 2^2 - 4(1)(1) = 4 - 4 = 0,$$
so the graph has one x-intercept.
The x-intercept is found by solving:
$$x^2 + 2x + 1 = 0$$
$$(x + 1)^2 = 0$$
$$x = -1$$
The x-intercept is –1.
The y-intercept is $f(0) = 1$.

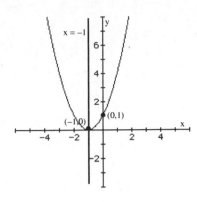

32. $f(x) = x^2 + 6x + 9$

$a = 1, b = 6, c = 9$. Since $a = 1 > 0$, the graph opens up.

The x-coordinate of the vertex is $x = \dfrac{-b}{2a} = \dfrac{-6}{2(1)} = \dfrac{-6}{2} = -3$. The y-coordinate of the

vertex is $f\left(\dfrac{-b}{2a}\right) = f(-3) = (-3)^2 + 6(-3) + 9 = 9 - 18 + 9 = 0$.

Thus, the vertex is (–3, 0).
The axis of symmetry is the line $x = -3$.
The discriminant is:
$$b^2 - 4ac = 6^2 - 4(1)(9) = 36 - 36 = 0,$$
so the graph has one x-intercept.
The x-intercept is found by solving:
$$x^2 + 6x + 9 = 0$$
$$(x + 3)^2 = 0$$
$$x = -3$$
The x-intercept is –3.
The y-intercept is $f(0) = 9$.

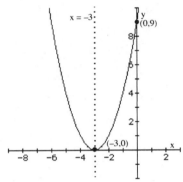

33. $f(x) = 2x^2 - x + 2$

$a = 2, b = -1, c = 2$. Since $a = 2 > 0$, the graph opens up.

The x-coordinate of the vertex is $x = \dfrac{-b}{2a} = \dfrac{-(-1)}{2(2)} = \dfrac{1}{4}$.

The y-coordinate of the vertex is $f\left(\dfrac{-b}{2a}\right) = f\left(\dfrac{1}{4}\right) = 2\left(\dfrac{1}{4}\right)^2 - \dfrac{1}{4} + 2 = \dfrac{1}{8} - \dfrac{1}{4} + 2 = \dfrac{15}{8}$.

Thus, the vertex is $\left(\dfrac{1}{4}, \dfrac{15}{8}\right)$.

The axis of symmetry is the line $x = \dfrac{1}{4}$.

The discriminant is:

$\qquad b^2 - 4ac = (-1)^2 - 4(2)(2) = 1 - 16 = -15$,

so the graph has no x-intercepts.

The y-intercept is $f(0) = 2$.

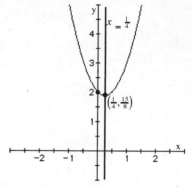

34. $f(x) = 4x^2 - 2x + 1$

$a = 4, b = -2, c = 1$. Since $a = 4 > 0$, the graph opens up.

The x-coordinate of the vertex is $x = \dfrac{-b}{2a} = \dfrac{-(-2)}{2(4)} = \dfrac{2}{8} = \dfrac{1}{4}$. The y-coordinate of the

vertex is $f\left(\dfrac{-b}{2a}\right) = f\left(\dfrac{1}{4}\right) = 4\left(\dfrac{1}{4}\right)^2 - 2\left(\dfrac{1}{4}\right) + 1 = \dfrac{1}{4} - \dfrac{1}{2} + 1 = \dfrac{3}{4}$.

Thus, the vertex is $\left(\dfrac{1}{4}, \dfrac{3}{4}\right)$.

The axis of symmetry is the line $x = \dfrac{1}{4}$.

The discriminant is:

$\qquad b^2 - 4ac = (-2)^2 - 4(4)(1) = 4 - 16 = -12$,

so the graph has no x-intercepts.

The y-intercept is $f(0) = 1$.

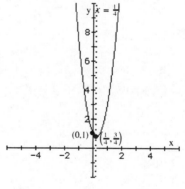

35. $f(x) = -2x^2 + 2x - 3$

$a = -2, b = 2, c = -3$. Since $a = -2 < 0$, the graph opens down.

The x-coordinate of the vertex is $x = \dfrac{-b}{2a} = \dfrac{-(2)}{2(-2)} = \dfrac{-2}{-4} = \dfrac{1}{2}$. The y-coordinate of the

vertex is $f\left(\dfrac{-b}{2a}\right) = f\left(\dfrac{1}{2}\right) = -2\left(\dfrac{1}{2}\right)^2 + 2\left(\dfrac{1}{2}\right) - 3 = -\dfrac{1}{2} + 1 - 3 = -\dfrac{5}{2}$.

Thus, the vertex is $\left(\dfrac{1}{2}, -\dfrac{5}{2}\right)$.

The axis of symmetry is the line $x = \dfrac{1}{2}$.

The discriminant is:
$$b^2 - 4ac = 2^2 - 4(-2)(-3) = 4 - 24 = -20,$$
so the graph has no x-intercepts.
The y-intercept is $f(0) = -3$.

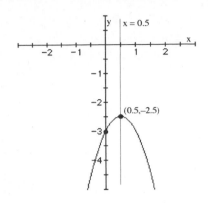

36. $f(x) = -3x^2 + 3x - 2$

$a = -3, b = 3, c = -2$. Since $a = -3 < 0$, the graph opens down.

The x-coordinate of the vertex is $x = \dfrac{-b}{2a} = \dfrac{-3}{2(-3)} = \dfrac{-3}{-6} = \dfrac{1}{2}$. The y-coordinate of the

vertex is $f\left(\dfrac{-b}{2a}\right) = f\left(\dfrac{1}{2}\right) = -3\left(\dfrac{1}{2}\right)^2 + 3\left(\dfrac{1}{2}\right) - 2 = -\dfrac{3}{4} + \dfrac{3}{2} - 2 = -\dfrac{5}{4}$.

Thus, the vertex is $\left(\dfrac{1}{2}, -\dfrac{5}{4}\right)$.

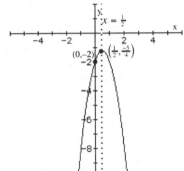

The axis of symmetry is the line $x = \dfrac{1}{2}$.

The discriminant is:
$$b^2 - 4ac = 3^2 - 4(-3)(-2) = 9 - 24 = -15,$$
so the graph has no x-intercepts.
The y-intercept is $f(0) = -2$.

37. $f(x) = 3x^2 + 6x + 2$

$a = 3, b = 6, c = 2$. Since $a = 3 > 0$, the graph opens up.

The x-coordinate of the vertex is $x = \dfrac{-b}{2a} = \dfrac{-6}{2(3)} = \dfrac{-6}{6} = -1$. The y-coordinate of the

vertex is $f\left(\dfrac{-b}{2a}\right) = f(-1) = 3(-1)^2 + 6(-1) + 2 = 3 - 6 + 2 = -1$.

Thus, the vertex is $(-1, -1)$.
The axis of symmetry is the line $x = -1$.
The discriminant is:
$$b^2 - 4ac = 6^2 - 4(3)(2) = 36 - 24 = 12,$$
so the graph has two x-intercepts.
The x-intercepts are found by solving:

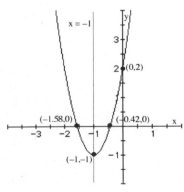

$$x = \dfrac{-b \pm \sqrt{b^2 - 4ac}}{2a} = \dfrac{-6 \pm \sqrt{12}}{2(3)}$$

$$= \dfrac{-6 \pm 2\sqrt{3}}{6} = \dfrac{-3 \pm \sqrt{3}}{3} \approx \dfrac{-3 \pm 1.732}{3}$$

The x-intercepts are approximately –0.42 and –1.58.
The y-intercept is $f(0) = 2$.

38. $f(x) = 2x^2 + 5x + 3$

   $a = 2, b = 5, c = 3$. Since $a = 2 > 0$, the graph opens up.

   The x-coordinate of the vertex is $x = \dfrac{-b}{2a} = \dfrac{-5}{2(2)} = -\dfrac{5}{4}$. The y-coordinate of the vertex is

   $$f\left(\dfrac{-b}{2a}\right) = f\left(-\dfrac{5}{4}\right) = 2\left(-\dfrac{5}{4}\right)^2 + 5\left(-\dfrac{5}{4}\right) + 3 = \dfrac{25}{8} - \dfrac{25}{4} + 3 = -\dfrac{1}{8}.$$

   Thus, the vertex is $\left(-\dfrac{5}{4}, -\dfrac{1}{8}\right)$.

   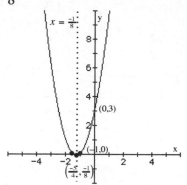

   The axis of symmetry is the line $x = -\dfrac{5}{4}$.

   The discriminant is:
   $$b^2 - 4ac = 5^2 - 4(2)(3) = 25 - 24 = 1,$$
   so the graph has two x-intercepts.
   The x-intercepts are found by solving:
   $$(2x + 3)(x + 1) = 0$$
   $$x = -\dfrac{3}{2} \text{ or } x = -1$$

   The x-intercepts are $-\dfrac{3}{2}$ and -1.
   The y-intercept is $f(0) = 3$.

39. $f(x) = -4x^2 - 6x + 2$

   $a = -4, b = -6, c = 2$. Since $a = -4 < 0$, the graph opens down.

   The x-coordinate of the vertex is $x = \dfrac{-b}{2a} = \dfrac{-(-6)}{2(-4)} = \dfrac{6}{-8} = -\dfrac{3}{4}$. The y-coordinate of the

   vertex is $f\left(\dfrac{-b}{2a}\right) = f\left(-\dfrac{3}{4}\right) = -4\left(-\dfrac{3}{4}\right)^2 - 6\left(-\dfrac{3}{4}\right) + 2 = -\dfrac{9}{4} + \dfrac{9}{2} + 2 = \dfrac{17}{4}.$

   Thus, the vertex is $\left(-\dfrac{3}{4}, \dfrac{17}{4}\right)$.

   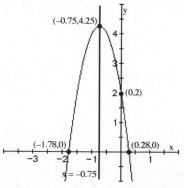

   The axis of symmetry is the line $x = -\dfrac{3}{4}$.

   The discriminant is:
   $$b^2 - 4ac = (-6)^2 - 4(-4)(2) = 36 + 32 = 68,$$
   so the graph has two x-intercepts.
   The x-intercepts are found by solving:
   $$x = \dfrac{-b \pm \sqrt{b^2 - 4ac}}{2a} = \dfrac{-(-6) \pm \sqrt{68}}{2(-4)}$$

   $$= \dfrac{6 \pm 2\sqrt{17}}{-8} = \dfrac{-3 \pm \sqrt{17}}{4} \approx \dfrac{-3 \pm 4.123}{4}$$

   The x-intercepts are approximately -1.78 and 0.28.
   The y-intercept is $f(0) = 2$.

40. $f(x) = 3x^2 - 8x + 2$

$a = 3, b = -8, c = 2$. Since $a = 3 > 0$, the graph opens up.

The x-coordinate of the vertex is $x = \dfrac{-b}{2a} = \dfrac{-(-8)}{2(3)} = \dfrac{8}{6} = \dfrac{4}{3}$. The y-coordinate of the vertex

is $f\left(\dfrac{-b}{2a}\right) = f\left(\dfrac{4}{3}\right) = 3\left(\dfrac{4}{3}\right)^2 - 8\left(\dfrac{4}{3}\right) + 2 = \dfrac{16}{3} - \dfrac{32}{3} + 2 = -\dfrac{10}{3}$.

Thus, the vertex is $\left(\dfrac{4}{3}, -\dfrac{10}{3}\right)$.

The axis of symmetry is the line $x = \dfrac{4}{3}$.

The discriminant is:

$b^2 - 4ac = (-8)^2 - 4(3)(2) = 64 - 24 = 40$,

so the graph has two x-intercepts.

The x-intercepts are found by solving:

$x = \dfrac{-b \pm \sqrt{b^2 - 4ac}}{2a} = \dfrac{-(-8) \pm \sqrt{40}}{2(3)}$

$= \dfrac{8 \pm 2\sqrt{10}}{6} = \dfrac{4 \pm \sqrt{10}}{3} \approx \dfrac{4 \pm 3.162}{3}$

The x-intercepts are approximately 0.28 and 2.39.
The y-intercept is $f(0) = 2$.

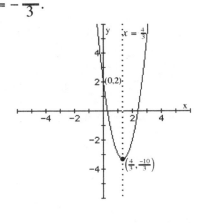

41. $f(x) = 2x^2 + 12x$, $a = 2, b = 12, c = 0$. Since $a = 2 > 0$, the graph opens up, so
the vertex is a minimum point. The minimum occurs at

$x = \dfrac{-b}{2a} = \dfrac{-12}{2(2)} = \dfrac{-12}{4} = -3$. The minimum value is

$f\left(\dfrac{-b}{2a}\right) = f(-3) = 2(-3)^2 + 12(-3) = 18 - 36 = -18$.

42. $f(x) = -2x^2 + 12x$, $a = -2, b = 12, c = 0$. Since $a = -2 < 0$, the graph opens
down, so the vertex is a maximum point. The maximum occurs at

$x = \dfrac{-b}{2a} = \dfrac{-12}{2(-2)} = \dfrac{-12}{-4} = 3$. The maximum value is

$f\left(\dfrac{-b}{2a}\right) = f(3) = -2(3)^2 + 12(3) = -18 + 36 = 18$.

43. $f(x) = 2x^2 + 12x - 3$, $a = 2, b = 12, c = -3$. Since $a = 2 > 0$, the graph opens up,
so the vertex is a minimum point. The minimum occurs at

$x = \dfrac{-b}{2a} = \dfrac{-12}{2(2)} = \dfrac{-12}{4} = -3$. The minimum value is

$f\left(\dfrac{-b}{2a}\right) = f(-3) = 2(-3)^2 + 12(-3) - 3 = 18 - 36 - 3 = -21$.

44. $f(x) = 4x^2 - 8x + 3$, $a = 4, b = -8, c = 3$. Since $a = 4 > 0$, the graph opens up, so

the vertex is a minimum point. The minimum occurs at $x = \dfrac{-b}{2a} = \dfrac{-(-8)}{2(4)} = \dfrac{8}{8} = 1$.

The minimum value is $f\left(\dfrac{-b}{2a}\right) = f(1) = 4 \cdot 1^2 - 8(1) + 3 = 4 - 8 + 3 = -1$.

45. $f(x) = -x^2 + 10x - 4$

$a = -1, b = 10, c = -4$. Since $a = -1 < 0$, the graph opens down, so the vertex is a maximum point. The maximum occurs at $x = \dfrac{-b}{2a} = \dfrac{-10}{2(-1)} = \dfrac{-10}{-2} = 5$. The maximum value is $f\left(\dfrac{-b}{2a}\right) = f(5) = -(5)^2 + 10(5) - 4 = -25 + 50 - 4 = 21$.

46. $f(x) = -2x^2 + 8x + 3$

$a = -2, b = 8, c = 3$. Since $a = -2 < 0$, the graph opens down, so the vertex is a maximum point. The maximum occurs at $x = \dfrac{-b}{2a} = \dfrac{-8}{2(-2)} = \dfrac{-8}{-4} = 2$. The maximum value is $f\left(\dfrac{-b}{2a}\right) = f(2) = -2(2)^2 + 8(2) + 3 = -8 + 16 + 3 = 11$.

47. $f(x) = -3x^2 + 12x + 1$

$a = -3, b = 12, c = 1$. Since $a = -3 < 0$, the graph opens down, so the vertex is a maximum point. The maximum occurs at $x = \dfrac{-b}{2a} = \dfrac{-12}{2(-3)} = \dfrac{-12}{-6} = 2$. The maximum value is $f\left(\dfrac{-b}{2a}\right) = f(2) = -3(2)^2 + 12(2) + 1 = -12 + 24 + 1 = 13$.

48. $f(x) = 4x^2 - 4x$

$a = 4, b = -4, c = 0$. Since $a = 4 > 0$, the graph opens up, so the vertex is a minimum point. The minimum occurs at $x = \dfrac{-b}{2a} = \dfrac{-(-4)}{2(4)} = \dfrac{4}{8} = \dfrac{1}{2}$. The minimum value is

$$f\left(\dfrac{-b}{2a}\right) = f\left(\dfrac{1}{2}\right) = 4\left(\dfrac{1}{2}\right)^2 - 4\left(\dfrac{1}{2}\right) = 1 - 2 = -1.$$

49. (a) $f(x) = 1(x - (-3))(x - 1) = 1(x + 3)(x - 1) = 1\left(x^2 + 2x - 3\right) = x^2 + 2x - 3$

$f(x) = 2(x - (-3))(x - 1) = 2(x + 3)(x - 1) = 2\left(x^2 + 2x - 3\right) = 2x^2 + 4x - 6$

$f(x) = -2(x - (-3))(x - 1) = -2(x + 3)(x - 1)$

$$= -2\left(x^2 + 2x - 3\right) = -2x^2 - 4x + 6$$

$f(x) = 5(x - (-3))(x - 1) = 5(x + 3)(x - 1) = 5\left(x^2 + 2x - 3\right) = 5x^2 + 10x - 15$

(b) The value of a multiplies the value of the y-intercept by the value of a. The values of the x-intercepts are not changed.

(c) The axis of symmetry is unaffected by the value of a.

(d) The y-coordinate of the vertex is multiplied by the value of a.

(e) The x-coordinate of the vertex is the midpoint of the x-intercepts.

50. (a) $f(x) = 1(x-(-5))(x-3) = 1(x+5)(x-3) = 1(x^2+2x-15) = x^2+2x-15$

$f(x) = 2(x-(-5))(x-3) = 2(x+5)(x-3) = 2(x^2+2x-15) = 2x^2+4x-30$

$f(x) = -2(x-(-5))(x-3) = -2(x+5)(x-3) = -2(x^2+2x-15) = -2x^2-4x+30$

$f(x) = 5(x-(-5))(x-3) = 5(x+5)(x-3) = 5(x^2+2x-15) = 5x^2+10x-75$

(b)   The value of a multiplies the value of the y-intercept by the value of a. The values of the x-intercepts are not changed.

(c)   The axis of symmetry is unaffected by the value of a.

(d)   The y-coordinate of the vertex is multiplied by the value of a.

(e)   The x-coordinate of the vertex is the midpoint of the x-intercepts.

51. $R(p) = -4p^2 + 4000p$

$a = -4$, $b = 4000$, $c = 0$. Since $a = -4 < 0$, the graph is a parabola that opens down, so the vertex is a maximum point. The maximum occurs at

$$p = \frac{-b}{2a} = \frac{-4000}{2(-4)} = \frac{-4000}{-8} = 500.$$

$R(500) = -4(500)^2 + 4000(500) = -1000000 + 2000000 = 1,000,000$.

Thus, the unit price should be $500 for maximum revenue. The maximum revenue is $1,000,000.

52. $R(p) = -\frac{1}{2}p^2 + 1900p$

$a = -\frac{1}{2}$, $b = 1900$, $c = 0$. Since $a = -\frac{1}{2} < 0$, the graph is a parabola that opens down, so the vertex is a maximum point. The maximum occurs at

$$p = \frac{-b}{2a} = \frac{-1900}{2\left(-\frac{1}{2}\right)} = \frac{-1900}{-1} = 1900$$

$R(1900) = -\frac{1}{2}(1900)^2 + 1900(1900) = -1805000 + 3610000 = 1,805,000$.

Thus, the unit price should be $1900 for maximum revenue. The maximum revenue is $1,805,000

53. (a) $R(x) = x\left(-\frac{1}{6}x + 100\right) = -\frac{1}{6}x^2 + 100x$

(b) $R(200) = \frac{-1}{6}(200)^2 + 100(200) = \frac{-20000}{3} + 20000 = \frac{40000}{3} \approx \$13,333$

(c) $x = \frac{-b}{2a} = \frac{-100}{2\left(-\frac{1}{6}\right)} = \frac{-100}{\left(-\frac{1}{3}\right)} = \frac{300}{1} = 300$

$R(300) = -\frac{1}{6}(300)^2 + 100(300) = -15000 + 30000 = \$15,000$

(d) $p = -\frac{1}{6}(300) + 100 = -50 + 100 = \$50$

54. (a) $R(x) = x\left(-\dfrac{1}{3}x + 100\right) = -\dfrac{1}{3}x^2 + 100x$

(b) $R(100) = -\dfrac{1}{3}(100)^2 + 100(100) = \dfrac{-10000}{3} + 10000 = \dfrac{20000}{3} \approx \$6,666.67$

(c) $x = \dfrac{-b}{2a} = \dfrac{-100}{2\left(-\dfrac{1}{3}\right)} = \dfrac{-100}{\left(-\dfrac{2}{3}\right)} = \dfrac{300}{2} = 150$

$R(150) = -\dfrac{1}{3}(150)^2 + 100(150) = -7500 + 15000 = \$7,500$

(d) $p = -\dfrac{1}{3}(150) + 100 = -50 + 100 = \$50$

55. (a) If $x = -5p + 100$, then $p = \dfrac{100 - x}{5}$. $R(x) = x\left(\dfrac{100 - x}{5}\right) = -\dfrac{1}{5}x^2 + 20x$

(b) $R(15) = -\dfrac{1}{5}(15)^2 + 20(15) = -45 + 300 = \$255$

(c) $x = \dfrac{-b}{2a} = \dfrac{-20}{2\left(-\dfrac{1}{5}\right)} = \dfrac{-20}{\left(-\dfrac{2}{5}\right)} = \dfrac{100}{2} = 50$

$R(50) = -\dfrac{1}{5}(50)^2 + 20(50) = -500 + 1000 = \$500$

(d) $p = \dfrac{100 - 50}{5} = \dfrac{50}{5} = \$10$

56. (a) If $x = -20p + 500$, then $p = \dfrac{500 - x}{20}$. $R(x) = x\left(\dfrac{500 - x}{20}\right) = -\dfrac{1}{20}x^2 + 25x$

(b) $R(20) = -\dfrac{1}{20}(20)^2 + 25(20) = -20 + 500 = \$480$

(c) $x = \dfrac{-b}{2a} = \dfrac{-25}{2\left(-\dfrac{1}{20}\right)} = \dfrac{-25}{\left(-\dfrac{1}{10}\right)} = \dfrac{250}{1} = 250$

$R(250) = -\dfrac{1}{20}(250)^2 + 25(250) = -3125 + 6250 = \$3125$

(d) $p = \dfrac{500 - 250}{20} = \dfrac{250}{20} = \$12.50$

57. (a) Let x = width and y = length of the rectangular area.
$P = 2x + 2y = 400$

$y = \dfrac{400 - 2x}{2} = 200 - x$

Then $A(x) = (200 - x)x = 200x - x^2 = -x^2 + 200x$

(b) $x = \dfrac{-b}{2a} = \dfrac{-200}{2(-1)} = \dfrac{-200}{-2} = 100$ yards

(c) $A(100) = -100^2 + 200(100) = -10000 + 20000 = 10,000$ sq yds.

58. (a)   Let x = length and y = width of the rectangular field.
$$P = 2x + 2y = 3000$$
$$y = \frac{3000 - 2x}{2} = 1500 - x$$
Then $A(x) = (1500 - x)x = 1500x - x^2 = -x^2 + 1500x$

(b) $x = \dfrac{-b}{2a} = \dfrac{-1500}{2(-1)} = \dfrac{-1500}{-2} = 750$ feet

(c) $A(750) = -750^2 + 1500(750) = -562500 + 1125000 = 562{,}500$ sq ft.

59. Let x = width and y = length of the rectangular area.
$$2x + y = 4000 \quad \rightarrow \quad y = 4000 - 2x$$
Then $A(x) = (4000 - 2x)x = 4000x - 2x^2 = -2x^2 + 4000x$
$$x = \frac{-b}{2a} = \frac{-4000}{2(-2)} = \frac{-4000}{-4} = 1000$$
$$A(1000) = -2(1000)^2 + 4000(1000) = -2000000 + 4000000 = 2{,}000{,}000$$
The largest area that can be enclosed is 2,000,000 square meters.

60. Let x = width and y = length of the rectangular area.
$$2x + y = 2000 \quad \rightarrow \quad y = 2000 - 2x$$
Then $A(x) = (2000 - 2x)x = 2000x - 2x^2 = -2x^2 + 2000x$
$$x = \frac{-b}{2a} = \frac{-2000}{2(-2)} = \frac{-2000}{-4} = 500$$
$$A(500) = -2(500)^2 + 2000(500) = -500000 + 1000000 = 500{,}000$$
The largest area that can be enclosed is 500,000 square meters.

61. (a) $a = -\dfrac{32}{2500}, b = 1, c = 200.$ The maximum height occurs when
$$x = \frac{-b}{2a} = \frac{-1}{2\left(-\dfrac{32}{2500}\right)} = \frac{2500}{64} = 39.0625 \text{ feet from base of the cliff.}$$

(b)   The maximum height is
$$h(39.0625) = \frac{-32(39.0625)^2}{2500} + 39.0625 + 200 = 219.53 \text{ feet.}$$

(c)   Solving when $h(x) = 0$:
$$-\frac{32}{2500}x^2 + x + 200 = 0$$
$$x = \frac{-1 \pm \sqrt{1^2 - 4\left(-\dfrac{32}{2500}\right)(200)}}{2\left(-\dfrac{32}{2500}\right)} = \frac{-1 \pm \sqrt{11.24}}{-0.0256}$$

$$x \approx -91.90 \text{ or } x \approx 170.02$$
Since the distance cannot be negative, the projectile strikes the water 170.02 feet from the base of the cliff.

(d)   Graphing:

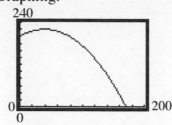

(e)   Solving when $h(x) = 100$:

$$-\frac{32}{2500}x^2 + x + 200 = 100$$

$$-\frac{32}{2500}x^2 + x + 100 = 0$$

$$x = \frac{-1 \pm \sqrt{1^2 - 4\left(-\frac{32}{2500}\right)(100)}}{2\left(-\frac{32}{2500}\right)} = \frac{-1 \pm \sqrt{6.12}}{-0.0256}; \quad x \approx -57.57 \text{ or } x \approx 135.70$$

Since the distance cannot be negative, the projectile is 100 feet above the water 135.70 feet from the base of the cliff.

62. (a) $a = -\frac{32}{10000}, b = 1, c = 0.$ The maximum height occurs when

$$x = \frac{-b}{2a} = \frac{-1}{2\left(-\frac{32}{10000}\right)} = \frac{10000}{64} = 156.25 \text{ feet.}$$

(b)   The maximum height is

$$h(156.25) = \frac{-32(156.25)^2}{10000} + 156.25 = 78.125 \text{ feet.}$$

(c)   Solving when $h(x) = 0$:

$$-\frac{32}{2500}x^2 + x = 0$$

$$x\left(-\frac{32}{10000}x + 1\right) = 0 \rightarrow x = 0 \text{ or } x = 312.5$$

Since the distance cannot be zero, the projectile lands 312.5 feet from where it was fired.

(d) Graphing:

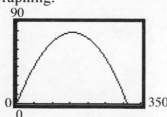

(e)   Solving when $h(x) = 50$:

$$-\frac{32}{10000}x^2 + x = 50$$

$$-\frac{32}{10000}x^2 + x - 50 = 0$$

$$x = \frac{-1 \pm \sqrt{1^2 - 4\left(-\frac{32}{10000}\right)(-50)}}{2\left(-\frac{32}{10000}\right)} = \frac{-1 \pm \sqrt{0.36}}{-0.0064} = \frac{-1 \pm 0.6}{-0.0064}$$

$$x = 62.5 \text{ or } x = 250$$

The projectile is 50 feet above the ground 62.5 feet and 250 feet from where it was fired.

63.   Locate the origin at the point where the cable touches the road. Then the equation of the parabola is of the form: $y = ax^2$, where $a > 0$. Since the point $(200, 75)$ is on the parabola, we can find the constant a:

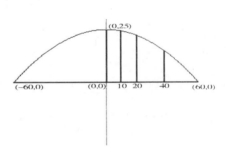

$$75 = a(200)^2 \quad \rightarrow \quad a = \frac{75}{200^2} = 0.001875$$

When $x = 100$, we have:
$$y = 0.001875(100)^2 = 18.75 \text{ meters}.$$

64.   Locate the origin at the point directly under the highest point of the arch. Then the equation of the parabola is of the form:
$y = -ax^2 + k$, where $a > 0$. Since the maximum height is 25 feet, when $x = 0$, $y = k = 25$. Since the point $(60, 0)$ is on the parabola, we can find the constant a:

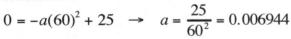

$$0 = -a(60)^2 + 25 \quad \rightarrow \quad a = \frac{25}{60^2} = 0.006944$$

The equation of the parabola is:
$$y = -\frac{25}{60^2}x^2 + 25.$$

At $x = 10$: $y = -\frac{25}{60^2}(10)^2 + 25 = -\frac{25}{36} + 25 = 24.31 \text{ feet}$

At $x = 20$: $y = -\frac{25}{60^2}(20)^2 + 25 = -\frac{25}{9} + 25 = 22.22 \text{ feet}$

At $x = 40$: $y = -\frac{25}{60^2}(40)^2 + 25 = -\frac{100}{9} + 25 = 13.89 \text{ feet}$

65. Let x = the depth of the gutter and y = the width of the gutter.
Then $A = xy$ is the cross-sectional area of the gutter.
Since the aluminum sheets for the gutter are 12 inches wide, we have
$$2x + y = 12 \text{ or } y = 12 - 2x.$$
The area is to be maximized, so: $A = xy = x(12 - 2x) = -2x^2 + 12x.$
This equation is a parabola opening down; thus, it has a maximum when
$$x = \frac{-b}{2a} = \frac{-12}{2(-2)} = \frac{-12}{-4} = 3.$$
Thus, a depth of 3 inches produces a maximum cross-sectional area.

66. Let x = width of the window and y = height of the rectangular part of the window.
The perimeter of the window is: $x + 2y + \frac{\pi x}{2} = 20 \rightarrow y = \frac{40 - 2x - \pi x}{4}$
The area of the window is:
$$A(x) = x\left(\frac{40 - 2x - \pi x}{4}\right) + \frac{1}{2}\pi\left(\frac{x}{2}\right)^2 = 10x - \frac{x^2}{2} - \frac{\pi x^2}{4} + \frac{\pi x^2}{8} = \left(-\frac{1}{2} - \frac{\pi}{8}\right)x^2 + 10x$$
This equation is a parabola opening down; thus, it has a maximum when
$$x = \frac{-b}{2a} = \frac{-10}{2\left(-\frac{1}{2} - \frac{\pi}{8}\right)} = \frac{10}{\left(1 + \frac{\pi}{4}\right)} \approx 5.60 \text{ feet}$$
$$y = \frac{40 - 2(5.60) - \pi(5.60)}{4} \approx 2.80 \text{ feet}$$
The width of the window is about 5.60 feet and the height of the rectangular part is about 2.80 feet.

67. Let x = the width of the rectangle or the diameter of the semicircle.
Let y = the length of the rectangle.
The perimeter of each semicircle is $\frac{\pi x}{2}$.
The perimeter of the track is given by: $\frac{\pi x}{2} + \frac{\pi x}{2} + y + y = 1500$.
Solving for x:
$$\frac{\pi x}{2} + \frac{\pi x}{2} + y + y = 1500$$
$$\pi x + 2y = 1500 \rightarrow \pi x = 1500 - 2y \rightarrow x = \frac{1500 - 2y}{\pi}$$
The area of the rectangle is: $A = xy = \left(\frac{1500 - 2y}{\pi}\right)y = \frac{-2}{\pi}y^2 + \frac{1500}{\pi}y$
This equation is a parabola opening down; thus, it has a maximum when
$$y = \frac{-b}{2a} = \frac{\frac{-1500}{\pi}}{2\left(\frac{-2}{\pi}\right)} = \frac{-1500}{-4} = 375. \text{ Thus, } x = \frac{1500 - 2(375)}{\pi} = \frac{750}{\pi} \approx 238.73.$$
The dimensions for the rectangle with maximum area are $\frac{750}{\pi} \approx 238.73$ meters by 375 meters.

68. Let x = width of the window and y = height of the rectangular part of the window.

The perimeter of the window is: $3x + 2y = 16 \quad \rightarrow \quad y = \dfrac{16 - 3x}{2}$.

The area of the window is:

$$A(x) = x\left(\frac{16 - 3x}{2}\right) + \frac{\sqrt{3}}{4}x^2 = 8x - \frac{3}{2}x^2 + \frac{\sqrt{3}}{4}x^2 = \left(-\frac{3}{2} + \frac{\sqrt{3}}{4}\right)x^2 + 8x.$$

This equation is a parabola opening down; thus, it has a maximum when

$$x = \frac{-b}{2a} = \frac{-8}{2\left(-\frac{3}{2} + \frac{\sqrt{3}}{4}\right)} = \frac{-8}{-3 + \frac{\sqrt{3}}{2}} \approx 3.75 \text{ feet.} \qquad y = \frac{16 - 3(3.75)}{2} \approx 2.38.$$

The window is about 3.75 feet wide and 2.38 feet high (rectangular part).

Problems 69 – 73. The equations for the curves that are graphed on the screens use many more decimal places in order to get the desired accuracy.

69. (a)   Graphing: The data appear to be quadratic with $a < 0$.

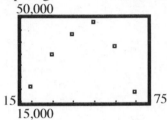

(b) $I(x) = -42.6x^2 + 3806x - 38526$

$$x = \frac{-b}{2a} = \frac{-3806}{2(-42.6)} = 44.695$$

An individual will earn the most income at an age of 44.7 years.

(c)   The maximum income will be:

$$I(44.7) = -42.6(44.7)^2 + 3805(44.7) - 38526 = \$46{,}438.87$$

(d) and (e)   Graphing the quadratic function of best fit:

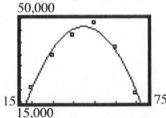

70. (a)   Graphing: The data appear to be quadratic with $a < 0$.

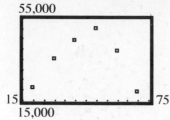

(b) $I(x) = -44.8x^2 + 4009x - 41392$

$$x = \frac{-b}{2a} = \frac{-4009}{2(-44.8)} \approx 44.74$$

An individual will earn the most income at an age of 44.8 years.

(c)   The maximum income will be:

$$I(44.7) = -44.8(44.7)^2 + 4009(44.7) - 41392 = \$48,295.87$$

(d) and (e)   Graphing the quadratic function of best fit:

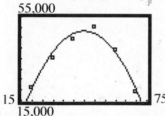

71. (a)   Graphing: The data appears to be quadratic with $a > 0$.

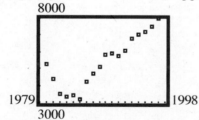

(b)   Note: The coefficients given in the text are incorrect. The correct function is:

$$I(x) = 17.199x^2 - 68147.78x + 67507955$$

$$x = \frac{-b}{2a} = \frac{-(-68147.78)}{2(17.199)} \approx 1981.16 \qquad \text{Imports were lowest in 1981.}$$

(c)   The predicted number of barrels imported in 1998 (using the equation to many more decimal places) is: $I(1998) \approx 3165$ thousand barrels

(d) and (e)   Graphing the quadratic function of best fit:

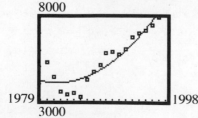

72. (a)   Graphing: The data appears to be quadratic with $a < 0$.

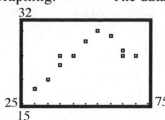

(b) $M(s) = -0.018s^2 + 1.93s - 25.34$

$s = \dfrac{-b}{2a} = \dfrac{-1.93}{2(-0.018)} = 53.61$ The speed that maximizes miles per gallon is about 54 miles per hour.

(c)   The predicted miles per gallon when the speed is 63 miles per hour is:
$M(63) = 24.81$ miles per gallon.

(d) and (e)   Graphing the quadratic function of best fit:

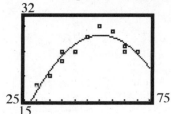

73. (a)   Graphing: The data appears to be quadratic with $a < 0$.

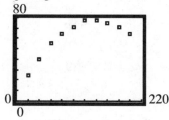

(b) $h(x) = -0.0037x^2 + 1.03x + 5.7$

$x = \dfrac{-b}{2a} = \dfrac{-1.03}{2(-0.0037)} \approx 139.19$ feet

The ball travels about 139 feet before reaching its maximum height.

(c)   The maximum height will be: (using the equation to many more decimal places)

$h(139) = -0.0037(139)^2 + 1.03(139) + 5.7 \approx 77.38$ feet

(d) and (e)   Graphing the quadratic function of best fit:

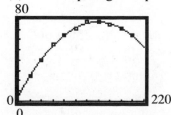

377

74. We are given: $V(x) = kx(a - x) = -kx^2 + akx$

The reaction rate is a maximum when: $x = \dfrac{-b}{2a} = \dfrac{-ak}{2(-k)} = \dfrac{ak}{2k} = \dfrac{a}{2}$

75. We have:

$$a(-h)^2 + b(-h) + c = ah^2 - bh + c = y_0$$
$$a(0)^2 + b(0) + c = c = y_1$$
$$a(h)^2 + b(h) + c = ah^2 + bh + c = y_2$$

Equating the two equations for the area, we have:

$$y_0 + 4y_1 + y_2 = ah^2 - bh + c + 4c + ah^2 + bh + c = 2ah^2 + 6c$$

Therefore, Area $= \dfrac{h}{3}\left(2ah^2 + 6c\right) = \dfrac{h}{3}\left(y_0 + 4y_1 + y_2\right)$.

76. $f(x) = -5x^2 + 8 \quad h = 1$:

Area $= \dfrac{h}{3}\left(2ah^2 + 6c\right) = \dfrac{1}{3}\left(2(-5)(1)^2 + 6(8)\right) = \dfrac{1}{3}(-10 + 48) = \dfrac{38}{3} \approx 12.67$

77. $f(x) = 2x^2 + 8, \quad h = 2$

Area $= \dfrac{2}{3}\left(2(2)(2)^2 + 6(8)\right) = \dfrac{2}{3}(16 + 48) = \dfrac{2}{3}(64) = \dfrac{128}{3}$

78. $f(x) = x^2 + 3x + 5, \quad h = 4$

Area $= \dfrac{h}{3}\left(2ah^2 + 6c\right) = \dfrac{4}{3}\left(2(1)(4)^2 + 6(5)\right) = \dfrac{4}{3}(32 + 30) = \dfrac{248}{3} \approx 82.67$

79. $f(x) = -x^2 + x + 4, \quad h = 1$

Area $= \dfrac{1}{3}\left(2(-1)(1)^2 + 6(4)\right) = \dfrac{1}{3}(-2 + 24) = \dfrac{1}{3}(22) = \dfrac{22}{3}$

80. $A(x) = x(10 - x) = -x^2 + 10x$

The area is a maximum when: $x = \dfrac{-b}{2a} = \dfrac{-10}{2(-1)} = \dfrac{10}{2} = 5$

$A(5) = -(5)^2 + 10(5) = -25 + 50 = 25$

The largest area that can be enclosed is 25 square units.

81. If x is even, then ax^2 and bx are even. When two even numbers are added to an odd number the result is odd. Thus, $f(x)$ is odd.

If x is odd, then ax^2 and bx are odd. The sum of three odd numbers results in an odd number. Thus, $f(x)$ is odd.

82. $f(x) = -(x + 2)^2 = -x^2 - 4x - 4$ opens down and has only one x-intercept (- 2, 0).

In general, a quadratic function that has only one x-intercept must have the form $f(x) = ax^2 + bx + c$ such that $b^2 - 4ac = 0$, since discriminant = 0 means the associated quadratic equation has exactly one real solution.

Also, we must have $a < 0$ in order for the parabola to open downwards.

83. $f(x) = x^2 + 2x - 3$; $f(x) = x^2 + 2x + 1$; $f(x) = x^2 + 2x$

each member of this family will be a parabola with the following characteristics:

- opens upwards since a > 0
- vertex occurs at $x = \dfrac{-b}{2a} = \dfrac{-2}{2(1)} = -1$
- there is at least one x-intercept since $b^2 - 4ac \geq 0$

84. $f(x) = x^2 - 4x + 1$; $f(x) = x^2 + 1$; $f(x) = x^2 + 4x + 1$

each member of this family will be a parabola with the following characteristics:

- opens upwards since a > 0
- y-intercept occurs at (0, 1)

Polynomial and Rational Functions

4.2 Polynomial Functions

1. $f(x) = 4x + x^3$ is a polynomial function of degree 3.

2. $f(x) = 5x^2 + 4x^4$ is a polynomial function of degree 4.

3. $g(x) = \dfrac{1-x^2}{2} = \dfrac{1}{2} - \dfrac{1}{2}x^2$ is a polynomial function of degree 2.

4. $h(x) = 3 - \dfrac{1}{2}x$ is a polynomial function of degree 1.

5. $f(x) = 1 - \dfrac{1}{x} = 1 - x^{-1}$ is not a polynomial function because it contains a negative exponent.

6. $f(x) = x(x-1) = x^2 - x$ is a polynomial function of degree 2.

7. $g(x) = x^{3/2} - x^2 + 2$ is not a polynomial function because it contains a fractional exponent.

8. $h(x) = \sqrt{x}\left(\sqrt{x} - 1\right) = x - \sqrt{x}$ is not a polynomial function because it contains a square root.

9. $F(x) = 5x^4 - \pi x^3 + \dfrac{1}{2}$ is a polynomial function of degree 4.

10. $F(x) = \dfrac{x^2 - 5}{x^3} = \dfrac{1}{x} - \dfrac{5}{x^3}$ is not a polynomial function because it contains a variable with a positive exponent in the denominator.

11. $G(x) = 2(x-1)^2(x^2 + 1)$ is a polynomial function of degree 4.

12. $G(x) = -3x^2(x+2)^3$ is a polynomial function of degree 5.

13. $f(x) = (x+1)^4$

Using the graph of $y = x^4$, shift the graph horizontally, 1 unit to the left.

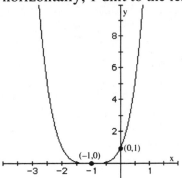

14. $f(x) = (x-2)^5$

Using the graph of $y = x^5$, shift the graph horizontally to the right 2 units.

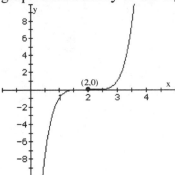

15. $f(x) = x^5 - 3$

Using the graph of $y = x^5$, shift the graph vertically, 3 units down.

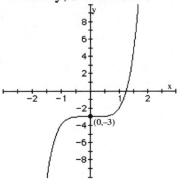

16. $f(x) = x^4 + 2$

Using the graph of $y = x^4$, shift the graph vertically up 2 units.

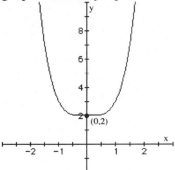

17. $f(x) = \dfrac{1}{2}x^4$

Using the graph of $y = x^4$, compress the graph vertically by a factor of $\dfrac{1}{2}$.

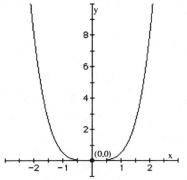

18. $f(x) = 3x^5$

Using the graph of $y = x^5$, stretch the graph vertically by a factor of 3.

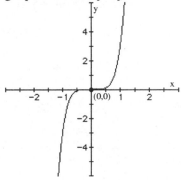

19. $f(x) = -x^5$

Using the graph of $y = x^5$, reflect the graph about the x-axis.

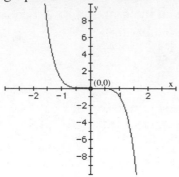

20. $f(x) = -x^4$

Using the graph of $y = x^4$, reflect the graph about the x-axis.

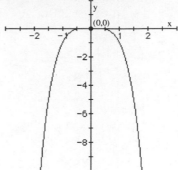

21. $f(x) = (x-1)^5 + 2$

Using the graph of $y = x^5$, shift the graph horizontally, 1 unit to the right, and shift vertically 2 units up.

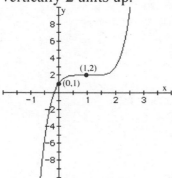

22. $f(x) = (x+2)^4 - 3$

Using the graph of $y = x^4$, shift the graph horizontally left 2 units, and shift vertically down 3 units.

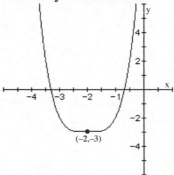

23. $f(x) = 2(x+1)^4 + 1$

Using the graph of $y = x^4$, shift the graph horizontally, 1 unit to the left, stretch vertically by a factor of 2, and shift vertically 1 unit up.

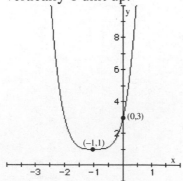

24. $f(x) = \frac{1}{2}(x-1)^5 - 2$

Using the graph of $y = x^5$, shift the graph horizontally 1 unit to the right, shrink vertically by a factor of $\frac{1}{2}$, and shift vertically down 2 units.

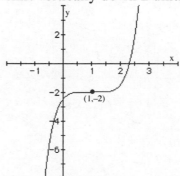

25. $f(x) = 4 - (x-2)^5 = -(x-2)^5 + 4$
Using the graph of $y = x^5$, shift the graph horizontally, 2 units to the right, reflect about the x-axis, and shift vertically 4 units up.

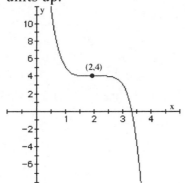

26. $f(x) = 3 - (x+2)^4 = -(x+2)^4 + 3$
Using the graph of $y = x^4$, shift the graph horizontally, 2 units to the left, reflect about the x-axis, and shift vertically 3 units up.

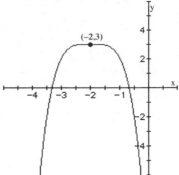

27. $f(x) = a(x-(-1))(x-1)(x-3)$
For $a = 1$: $f(x) = (x+1)(x-1)(x-3)$
$$f(x) = \left(x^2 - 1\right)(x-3) = x^3 - 3x^2 - x + 3$$

28. $f(x) = a(x-(-2))(x-2)(x-3)$
For $a = 1$: $f(x) = (x+2)(x-2)(x-3)$
$$f(x) = \left(x^2 - 4\right)(x-3) = x^3 - 3x^2 - 4x + 12$$

29. $f(x) = a(x-(-3))(x-0)(x-4)$
For $a = 1$: $f(x) = (x+3)(x)(x-4)$
$$f(x) = \left(x^2 + 3x\right)(x-4) = x^3 - 4x^2 + 3x^2 - 12x = x^3 - x^2 - 12x$$

30. $f(x) = a(x-(-4))(x-0)(x-2)$
For $a = 1$: $f(x) = (x+4)(x)(x-2)$
$$f(x) = \left(x^2 + 4x\right)(x-2) = x^3 - 2x^2 + 4x^2 - 8x = x^3 + 2x^2 - 8x$$

31. $f(x) = a(x-(-4))(x-(-1))(x-2)(x-3)$
For $a = 1$: $f(x) = (x+4)(x+1)(x-2)(x-3)$
$$f(x) = \left(x^2 + 5x + 4\right)\left(x^2 - 5x + 6\right)$$
$$f(x) = x^4 - 5x^3 + 6x^2 + 5x^3 - 25x^2 + 30x + 4x^2 - 20x + 24$$
$$f(x) = x^4 - 15x^2 + 10x + 24$$

32. $f(x) = a(x-(-3))(x-(-1))(x-2)(x-5)$
For $a = 1$: $f(x) = (x+3)(x+1)(x-2)(x-5)$
$$f(x) = \left(x^2 + 4x + 3\right)\left(x^2 - 7x + 10\right)$$
$$f(x) = x^4 - 7x^3 + 10x^2 + 4x^3 - 28x^2 + 40x + 3x^2 - 21x + 30$$
$$f(x) = x^4 - 3x^3 - 15x^2 + 19x + 30$$

33. The real zeros of $f(x) = 3(x - 7)(x + 3)^2$ are: 7, with multiplicity one; and –3, with multiplicity two. The graph crosses the x-axis at 7 and touches it at –3. The function resembles $y = 3x^3$ for large values of $|x|$.

34. The real zeros of $f(x) = 4(x + 4)(x + 3)^3$ are: –4, with multiplicity one; and –3, with multiplicity three. The graph crosses the x-axis at –4 and at –3. The function resembles $y = 4x^3$ for large values of $|x|$.

35. The real zeros of $f(x) = 4(x^2 + 1)(x - 2)^3$ are: 2, with multiplicity three. $x^2 + 1 = 0$ has no real solution. The graph crosses the x-axis at 2. The function resembles $y = 4x^5$ for large values of $|x|$.

36. The real zeros of $f(x) = 2(x - 3)(x + 4)^3$ are: 3, with multiplicity one; and –4, with multiplicity three. The graph crosses the x-axis at 3 and at –4. The function resembles $y = 2x^4$ for large values of $|x|$.

37. The real zeros of $f(x) = -2\left(x + \frac{1}{2}\right)^2 (x^2 + 4)^2$ are: $-\frac{1}{2}$, with multiplicity two. $x^2 + 4 = 0$ has no real solution. The graph touches the x-axis at $\frac{-1}{2}$. The function resembles $y = 2x^6$ for large values of $|x|$.

38. The real zeros of $f(x) = \left(x - \frac{1}{3}\right)^2 (x - 1)^3$ are: $\frac{1}{3}$, with multiplicity two; and 1, with multiplicity 3. The graph touches the x-axis at $\frac{1}{3}$, and crosses the x-axis at 1. The function resembles $y = x^5$ for large values of $|x|$.

39. The real zeros of $f(x) = (x - 5)^3 (x + 4)^2$ are: 5, with multiplicity three; and –4, with multiplicity two. The graph crosses the x-axis at 5 and touches it at –4. The function resembles $y = x^5$ for large values of $|x|$.

40. The real zeros of $f(x) = (x + \sqrt{3})^2 (x - 2)^4$ are: $-\sqrt{3}$, with multiplicity two; and 2, with multiplicity four. The graph touches the x-axis at $-\sqrt{3}$ and at 2. The function resembles $y = x^6$ for large values of $|x|$.

41. $f(x) = 3(x^2 + 8)(x^2 + 9)^2$ has no real zeros. $x^2 + 8 = 0$ and $x^2 + 9 = 0$ have no real solutions. The graph neither touches nor crosses the x-axis. The function resembles $y = 3x^6$ for large values of $|x|$.

42. $f(x) = -2(x^2 + 3)^3$ has no real zeros. $x^2 + 3 = 0$ has no real solutions.

The graph neither touches nor crosses the x-axis. The function resembles $y = -2x^6$ for large values of $|x|$.

43.   The real zeros of $f(x) = -2x^2(x^2 - 2)$ are: $-\sqrt{2}$ and $\sqrt{2}$ with multiplicity one; and 0, with multiplicity two. The graph touches the x-axis at $-\sqrt{2}$ and $\sqrt{2}$ and crosses the x-axis at 2.The function resembles $y = -2x^4$ for large values of $|x|$.

44.   The real zeros of $f(x) = 4x(x^2 - 3)$ are: $-\sqrt{3}, \sqrt{3}$ and 0, with multiplicity one. The graph crosses the x-axis at $-\sqrt{3}, \sqrt{3}$ and 0.The function resembles $y = 4x^3$ for large values of $|x|$.

45. $f(x) = (x - 1)^2$
    (a)   x-intercept: 1; y-intercept: 1
    (b)   touches x-axis at x = 1
    (c) $y = x^2$
    (d)   1
    (e)

interval	$x < 1$	$x > 1$
test number	-1	2
Value of f	$f(-1) = 4$	$f(2) = 1$
Above or below x-axis	above	above
Point on graph	(-1,4)	(2,1)

   f is above the x-axis for
$$(-\infty, 1) \cup (1, \infty)$$
    (f)

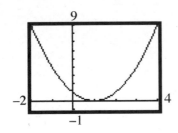

46. $f(x) = (x - 2)^3$

    (a)   x-intercept: 2; y-intercept: –8
    (b)   crosses x-axis at x = 2
    (d) $y = x^3$
    (c)   2
    (e)

interval	$x < 2$	$x > 2$
test number	1	3
Value of f	$f(1) = -1$	$f(3) = 1$
Above or below x-axis	below	above
Point on graph	(1,-1)	(3,1)

   f is below the x-axis for $(-\infty, 2)$
    f is above the x-axis for $(2, \infty)$
    (f)

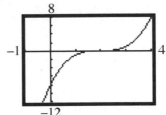

47. $f(x) = x^2(x - 3)$
   (a)   x-intercepts: 0, 3; y-intercept: 0
   (b)   touches x-axis at $x = 0$; crosses x-axis at $x = 3$
   (c) $y = x^3$ (d)   2
   (e)

interval	$x < 0$	$0 < x < 3$	$x > 3$
Test number	-1	2	4
Value of f	$f(-1) = -4$	$f(2) = -4$	$f(4) = 16$
Above or below x-axis	below	below	above
Point on graph	(-1,-4)	(2,-4)	(4,16)

f is below the x-axis for $(-\infty, 0) \cup (0,3)$; f is above the x-axis for $(3, \infty)$
   (f)

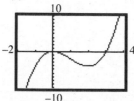

48. $f(x) = x(x + 2)^2$

   (a)   x-intercepts: –2, 0; y-intercept: 0
   (b)   touches x-axis at $x = -2$; crosses x-axis at $x = 0$
   (c) $y = x^3$ (d)   2
   (e)

interval	$x < -2$	$-2 < x < 0$	$x > 0$
Test number	-3	-1	1
Value of f	$f(-3) = -3$	$f(-1) = -1$	$f(1) = 9$
Above or below x-axis	below	below	above
Point on graph	(-3,-3)	(-1,-1)	(1,9)

f is below the x-axis for $(-\infty, -2) \cup (-2,0)$; f is above the x-axis for $(0, \infty)$
   (f)

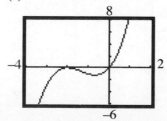

49. $f(x) = 6x^3(x + 4)$
   (a)   x-intercepts: –4, 0; y-intercept: 0
   (b)   crosses x-axis at $x = -4$ and $x = 0$
   (c) $y = 6x^4$ (d)   3

(e)

interval	$x < -4$	$-4 < x < 0$	$x > 0$
Test number	-5	-2	1
Value of f	$f(-5) = 750$	$f(-2) = -96$	$f(1) = 30$
Above or below x-axis	above	below	above
Point on graph	(-5,750)	(-2,-96)	(1,30)

f is above the x-axis for $(-\infty,-4) \cup (0,\infty)$; f is below the x-axis for $(-4,0)$

(f)

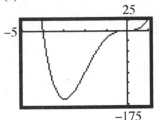

50. $f(x) = 5x(x-1)^3$

   (a)   x-intercepts: 0, 1; y-intercept: 0;   (b)   crosses x-axis at x = 0 and x = 1

   (c) $y = 5x^4$ (d)   3

   (e)

interval	$x < 0$	$0 < x < 1$	$x > 1$
Test number	-1	0.5	2
Value of f	$f(-1) = 40$	$f(0.5) = 0.3125$	$f(2) = 10$
Above or below x-axis	above	below	above
Point on graph	(-1,40)	(0.5,0.3125)	(2,10)

f is above the x-axis for $(-\infty,0) \cup (1,\infty)$; f is below the x-axis for $(0,1)$

   (f)

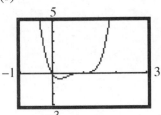

51. $f(x) = -4x^2(x+2)$

   (a)   x-intercepts: 0, - 2; y-intercept: 0

   (b)   crosses x-axis at x = - 2 ; touches x-axis at x = 0

   (c) $y = -4x^3$ (d)   2

   (e)

interval	$x < -2$	$-2 < x < 0$	$x > 0$
Test number	-3	-1	1
Value of f	$f(-3) = 36$	$f(-1) = -4$	$f(1) = -12$
Above or below x-axis	above	below	below
Point on graph	(-3,36)	(-1,-4)	(1,-12)

f is above the x-axis for $(-\infty,-2)$

f is below the x-axis for $(-2,0) \cup (0,\infty)$

(f)

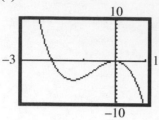

52. $f(x) = -\dfrac{1}{2}x^3(x+4)$

(a)   x-intercepts: 0, - 4; y-intercept: 0

(b)   crosses x-axis at x = - 4 and x = 0

(c) $y = -\dfrac{1}{2}x^4$ (d)   3

(e)

interval	x < - 4	- 4 < x < 0	x > 0
Test number	-5	-2	1
Value of f	$f(-5) = 62.5$	$f(-2) = 8$	$f(1) = -2.5$
Above or below x-axis	below	above	below
Point on graph	(-5,62.5)	(-2,8)	(1,-2.5)

f is above the x-axis for $(-4,0)$

f is below the x-axis for $(-\infty,-4) \cup (0,\infty)$

(f)

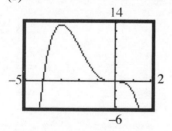

53. $f(x) = x(x-2)(x+4)$

(a)   x-intercepts: 0, - 4, 2; y-intercept: 0

(b)   crosses x-axis at x = 0, x = - 4 and x = 2

(c) $y = x^3$ (d)   2

(e)

interval	x < - 4	- 4 < x < 0	0 < x < 2	x > 2
Test number	-5	-2	1	3
Value of f	$f(-5) = -35$	$f(-2) = 16$	$f(1) = -5$	$f(3) = 21$
Above or below x-axis	below	above	below	above
Point on graph	(-5,-35)	(-2,16)	(1,-5)	(3,21)

f is above the x-axis for $(-4,0) \cup (2,\infty)$; f is below the x-axis for $(-\infty,-4) \cup (0,2)$

(f)

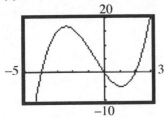

54. $f(x) = x(x+4)(x-3)$

(a)   x-intercepts: 0, - 4, 3; y-intercept: 0   (b)   crosses x-axis at x = 0, x = - 4 and x = 3

(c) $y = x^3$ (d)   2

(e)

interval	$x < -4$	$-4 < x < 0$	$0 < x < 3$	$x > 3$
Test number	-5	-2	1	4
Value of f	$f(-5) = -40$	$f(-2) = 20$	$f(1) = -10$	$f(4) = 32$
Above or below x-axis	below	above	below	above
Point on graph	(-5,-40)	(-2,20)	(1,-10)	(4,32)

f is above the x-axis for $(-4,0) \cup (3,\infty)$; f is below the x-axis for $(-\infty,-4) \cup (0,3)$

(f)

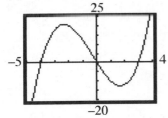

55. $f(x) = 4x - x^3 = x(4 - x^2) = x(2 + x)(2 - x)$

(a)   x-intercepts: 0, - 2, 2; y-intercept: 0

(b)   crosses x-axis at x = 0, x = - 2 and x = 2

(c) $y = -x^3$ (d)   2

(e)

interval	$x < -2$	$-2 < x < 0$	$0 < x < 2$	$x > 2$
Test number	-3	-1	1	3
Value of f	$f(-3) = 15$	$f(-1) = -3$	$f(1) = 3$	$f(3) = -15$
Above or below x-axis	above	below	above	below
Point on graph	(-3,15)	(-1,-3)	(1,3)	(3,-15)

f is above the x-axis for $(-\infty,-2) \cup (0,2)$; f is below the x-axis for $(-2,0) \cup (2,\infty)$

(f)

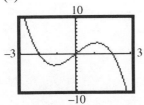

56. $f(x) = x - x^3 = x(1 - x^2) = x(1 + x)(1 - x)$

(a)   x-intercepts: 0, - 1, 1; y-intercept: 0

(b)   crosses x-axis at x = 0, x = - 2 and x = 2

(c) $y = -x^3$ (d)   2

(e)

interval	$x < -1$	$-1 < x < 0$	$0 < x < 1$	$x > 1$
Test number	-2	-0.5	0.5	2
Value of f	$f(-2) = 6$	$f(-0.5) = -0.375$	$f(0.5) = 0.375$	$f(2) = -6$
Above or below x-axis	above	below	above	below
Point on graph	(-2,6)	(-0.5,-0.375)	(0.5,0.375)	(2,-6)

f is above the x-axis for $(-\infty,-1) \cup (0,1)$; f is below the x-axis for $(-1,0) \cup (1,\infty)$

(f)

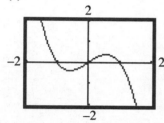

57. $f(x) = x^2(x - 2)(x + 2)$

(a)   x-intercepts: 0, - 2, 2; y-intercept: 0

(b)   crosses x-axis at x = - 2 and x = 2; touches x-axis at x = 0

(c) $y = x^4$ (d)   3

(e)

interval	$x < -2$	$-2 < x < 0$	$0 < x < 2$	$x > 2$
Test number	-3	-1	1	3
Value of f	$f(-3) = 45$	$f(-1) = -3$	$f(1) = -3$	$f(3) = 45$
Above or below x-axis	above	below	below	above
Point on graph	(-3,45)	(-1,-3)	(1,-3)	(3,45)

f is above the x-axis for $(-\infty,-2) \cup (2,\infty)$; f is below the x-axis for $(-2,0) \cup (0,2)$

(f)

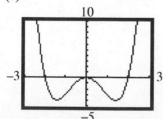

58. $f(x) = x^2(x-3)(x+4)$
   (a)   x-intercepts: 0, - 4, 3; y-intercept: 0
   (b)   crosses x-axis at x = - 4 and x = 3; touches x-axis at x = 0
   (c) $y = x^4$ (d)   3
   (e)

interval	$x < -4$	$-4 < x < 0$	$0 < x < 3$	$x > 3$
Test number	-5	-2	1	4
Value of f	$f(-5) = 200$	$f(-2) = -40$	$f(1) = -10$	$f(4) = 128$
Above or below x-axis	above	below	below	above
Point on graph	(-5,200)	(-2,-40)	(1,-10)	(4,128)

   f is above the x-axis for $(-\infty,-4) \cup (3,\infty)$; f is below the x-axis for $(-4,0) \cup (0,3)$
   (f)

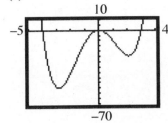

59. $f(x) = x^2(x-2)^2$
   (a)   x-intercepts: 0, 2; y-intercept: 0
   (b)   touches x-axis at x = 0 and x = 2
   (c) $y = x^4$ (d)   3
   (e)

interval	$x < 0$	$0 < x < 2$	$x > 2$
Test number	-1	1	3
Value of f	$f(-1) = 9$	$f(1) = 1$	$f(1) = 9$
Above or below x-axis	above	above	above
Point on graph	(-1,9)	(1,1)	(1,9)

   f is above the x-axis for $(-\infty,0) \cup (0,2) \cup (2,\infty)$
   (f)

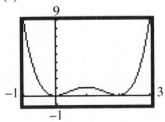

60. $f(x) = x^3(x-3)$
   (a)   x-intercepts: 0,3; y-intercept: 0
   (b)   crosses x-axis at x = 0 and x = 3
   (c) $y = x^4$ (d)   3
   (e)

interval	$x < 0$	$0 < x < 3$	$x > 3$
Test number	-1	1	4
Value of f	$f(-1) = 4$	$f(1) = -2$	$f(4) = 64$
Above or below x-axis	above	below	above
Point on graph	(-1,4)	(1,-2)	(4,64)

f is above the x-axis for $(-\infty,0)\cup(3,\infty)$; f is below the x-axis for $(0,3)$

(f)

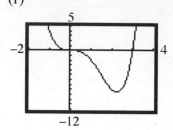

61. $f(x) = x^2(x-3)(x+1)$
   (a)   x-intercepts: 0, - 1, 3; y-intercept: 0
   (b)   crosses x-axis at x = - 1 and x = 3; touches x-axis at x = 0
   (c) $y = x^4$ (d)   3
   (e)

interval	$x < -1$	$-1 < x < 0$	$0 < x < 3$	$x > 3$
Test number	-2	-0.5	2	4
Value of f	$f(-2) = 20$	$f(-0.5) = -0.4375$	$f(2) = -12$	$f(4) = 80$
Above or below x-axis	above	below	below	above
Point on graph	(-2,20)	(-0.5,-0.4375)	(2,-12)	(4,80)

f is above the x-axis for $(-\infty,-1)\cup(3,\infty)$; f is below the x-axis for $(-1,0)\cup(0,3)$

(f)

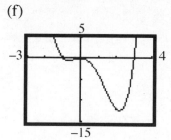

62. $f(x) = x^2(x-3)(x-1)$

(a)   x-intercepts: 0, 1, 3; y-intercept: 0

(b)   crosses x-axis at x = 1 and x = 3; touches x-axis at x = 0

(c) $y = x^4$ (d)   3

(e)

interval	$x < 0$	$0 < x < 1$	$1 < x < 3$	$x > 3$
Test number	-1	0.5	2	4
Value of f	$f(-1) = 8$	$f(0.5) = 0.3125$	$f(2) = -4$	$f(4) = 48$
Above or below x-axis	above	above	below	above
Point on graph	(-1,8)	(0.5,0.3125)	(2,-4)	(4,48)

f is above the x-axis for $(-\infty,0) \cup (0,1) \cup (3,\infty)$

f is below the x-axis for $(1,3)$

(f)

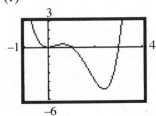

63. $f(x) = (x+2)^2(x-4)^2$

(a)   x-intercepts: - 2, 4; y-intercept: 64

(b)   touches x-axis at x = - 2 and x = 4

(c) $y = x^4$ (d)   3

(e)

interval	$x < -2$	$-2 < x < 4$	$x > 4$
Test number	-3	0	5
Value of f	$f(-3) = 49$	$f(0) = 64$	$f(5) = 49$
Above or below x-axis	above	above	above
Point on graph	(-3,49)	(0,64)	(5,49)

f is above the x-axis for $(-\infty,-2) \cup (-2,4) \cup (4,\infty)$

(f)

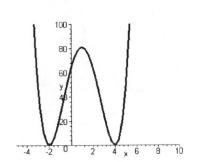

64. $f(x) = x(x-2)^2(x+2)(x+4)$

   (a) x-intercepts: 0, - 4, - 2,2; y-intercept: 32

   (b) crosses x-axis at x = - 4, x = - 2 and x = 0; touches x-axis at x = 2

   (c) $y = x^5$ (d) 4

   (e)

interval	$x < -4$	$-4 < x < -2$	$-2 < x < 0$	$0 < x < 2$
Test number	-5	-3	0	3
Value of f	$f(-5) = 147$	$f(-3) = -25$	$f(0) = 32$	$f(3) = 35$
Above or below x-axis	below	above	below	above
Point on graph	(-5,147)	(-3,-25)	(0,32)	(3,35)

  f is above the x-axis for $(-4,-2) \cup (0,2) \cup (2,\infty)$

  f is below the x-axis for $(-\infty,-4) \cup (-2,0)$

   (f)

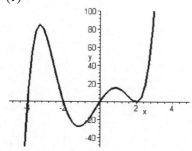

65. $f(x) = x^2(x-2)(x^2+3)$

   (a) x-intercepts: 0, 2; y-intercept: 0

   (b) crosses x-axis at x = 2 ; touches x-axis at x = 0

   (c) $y = x^5$ (d) 4

   (e)

interval	$x < 0$	$0 < x < 2$	$x > 2$
Test number	-1	1	3
Value of f	$f(-1) = -12$	$f(1) = -4$	$f(3) = 108$
Above or below x-axis	below	below	above
Point on graph	(-1,-12)	(1,-4)	(3,108)

  f is above the x-axis for $(2,\infty)$; f is below the x-axis for $(-\infty,0) \cup (0,2)$

   (f)

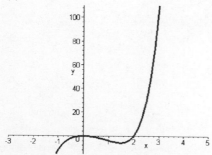

66. $f(x) = x^2(x^2 + 1)(x + 4)$

(a)   x-intercepts: 0, - 4; y-intercept: 0

(b)   crosses x-axis at x = - 4; touches x-axis at x = 0

(c) $y = x^5$ (d)   4

(e)

interval	$x < -4$	$-4 < x < 0$	$x > 0$
Test number	-5	-2	1
Value of f	$f(-5) = -650$	$f(-2) = 40$	$f(1) = 10$
Above or below x-axis	below	above	above
Point on graph	(-5,-650)	(-2,40)	(1,10)

f is above the x-axis for $(-4,0) \cup (0,\infty)$

f is below the x-axis for $(-\infty,-4)$

(f)

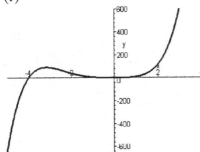

67. $f(x) = -x^2(x^2 - 1)(x + 1) = -x^2(x - 1)(x + 1)(x + 1) = -x^2(x - 1)(x + 1)^2$

(a)   x-intercepts: 0, - 1, 1; y-intercept: 0

(b)   crosses x-axis at x = 1; touches x-axis at x = 0 and x = - 1

(c) $y = -x^5$ (d)   4

(e)

interval	$x < -1$	$-1 < x < 0$	$0 < x < 1$	$x > 1$
Test number	-2	-0.5	0.5	2
Value of f	$f(-2) = 12$	$f(-0.5) = 0.09375$	$f(0.5) = 0.28125$	$f(2) = -36$
Above or below x-axis	above	above	above	below
Point on graph	(-3,360)	(-0.5,0.09375)	(0.5,0.28125)	(2,-36)

f is above the x-axis for $(-\infty,-1) \cup (-1,0) \cup (0,1)$

f is below the x-axis for $(1,\infty)$

(f)

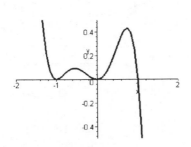

68. $f(x) = -x^2(x^2 - 4)(x - 5)$
(a)   x-intercepts: 0, - 2, 2,5; y-intercept: 0
(b)   crosses x-axis at x = - 2, x = 2 and x = 5; touches x-axis at x = 0
(c) $y = -x^5$ (d)   4
(e)

interval	$x < -2$	$-2 < x < 0$	$0 < x < 2$	$2 < x < 5$	$5 < x$
Test number	-3	-1	1	3	6
Value of f	$f(-3) = 360$	$f(-1) = -18$	$f(1) = -12$	$f(3) = 90$	$f(6) = -1152$
Above or below x-axis	above	below	below	above	below
Point on graph	(-3,360)	(-1,-18)	(1,-12)	(3,90)	(6,-1152)

f is above the x-axis for $(-\infty, -2) \cup (2,5)$
f is below the x-axis for $(-2,0) \cup (0,2) \cup (5,\infty)$
(f)

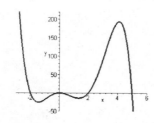

69.   c, e and f   70. c, e and f   71. c and e   72.   d and f

73.

$f(x) = x^3 + 0.2x^2 - 1.5876x - 0.31752$ x-intercepts: −1.26, −0.2, 1.26

turning points: (−0.80, 0.57);
(0.66, −0.99)

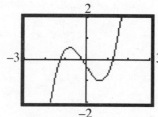

74.

$f(x) = x^3 - 0.8x^2 - 4.6656x + 3.73248$

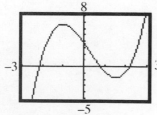

x-intercepts: −2.16, 0.8, 2.16

turning points: (−1.01, 6.60);
(1.54, −1.70)

75.

$f(x) = x^3 + 2.56x^2 - 3.31x + 0.89$

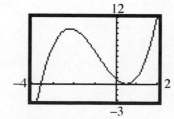

x-intercepts: −3.56, 0.50

turning points: (−2.21, 9.91);
(0.50, 0)

76.

$$f(x) = x^3 - 2.91x^2 - 7.668x - 3.8151$$

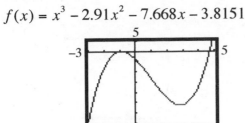

x-intercepts: –0.90, 4.71

turning points: (–0.90, 0);
(2.84, –26.16)

77. $f(x) = x^4 - 2.5x^2 + 0.5625$

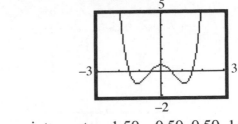

x-intercepts: –1.50, –0.50, 0.50, 1.50

turning points: (0, 0.5625);
(–1.12, –1);
(1.12, –1)

78. $f(x) = x^4 - 18.5x^2 + 50.2619$

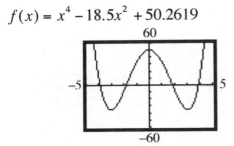

x-intercepts: –3.90, –1.82, 1.82, 3.90
turning points: (0, 50.26);
(–3.04, –35.30);
(3.04, –35.30)

79. $f(x) = x^4 + 0.65x^3 - 16.6319x^2$
$$+ 14.209335x - 3.1264785$$

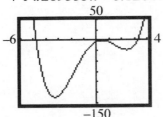

x-intercepts: –4.78, 0.45, 3.23

turning points: (0.45, 0)
(–3.32, –135.92);
(2.38, –22.67)

80. $f(x) = x^4 + 3.45x^3 - 11.6639x^2$
$$- 5.864241x - 0.69257738$$

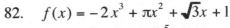

x-intercepts: –5.41, –0.23, 2.42

turning points: (–0.23, 0);
(–3.97, –128.71);
(1.61, –19.25)

81. $f(x) = \pi x^3 + \sqrt{2}x^2 - x - 2$

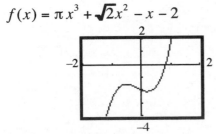

x-intercept: 0.84
turning points: (–0.51, –1.54);
(0.21, –2.12)

82. $f(x) = -2x^3 + \pi x^2 + \sqrt{3}x + 1$

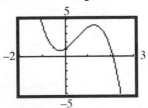

x-intercept: 2.10
turning points: (1.27, 4.17);
(–0.23, 0.79)

83. $f(x) = 2x^4 - \pi x^3 + \sqrt{5}\,x - 4$

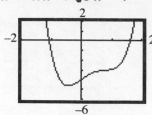

x-intercepts: $-1.07, 1.62$
turning point: $(-0.42, -4.64)$

84. $f(x) = -1.2x^4 + 0.5x^2 - \sqrt{3}\,x + 2$

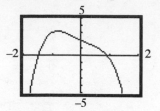

x-intercepts: $-1.47, 0.91$
turning point: $(-0.81, 3.21)$

85. $f(x) = -2x^5 - \sqrt{2}x^2 - x - \sqrt{2}$

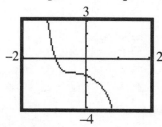

x-intercept: -0.98
no turning points

86. $f(x) = \pi x^5 + \pi x^4 + \sqrt{3}x + 1$

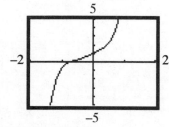

x-intercept: -0.71
no turning points

87.   (a)   Graphing: The graph may be a cubic relation.

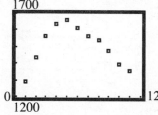

(b) $M(x) = 1.52x^3 - 39.81x^2 + 282.29x + 1035.5$
    $M(8) = 1.52(8)^3 - 39.81(8)^2 + 282.29(8) + 1035.5 = 1580.22$
    According to the function there would be approximately 1,580,220 motor vehicle thefts in 1994.

(c) and (d)   Graphing the cubic function of best fit:

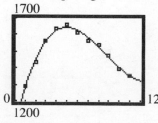

(e) answers will vary

88. (a)   Graphing: The graph may be a cubic relation.

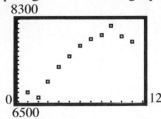

  (b) $L(x) = -4.372x^3 + 59.29x^2 - 14.02x + 6578$

  $L(12) = -4.37(12)^3 + 59.29(12)^2 - 14.02(12) + 6578 \approx 7396.13$

  The predicted number of larceny thefts in 1994 is 7,396,130.

  (c) and (d)   Graphing the cubic function of best fit:

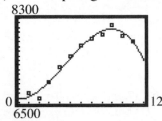

  (e) answers will vary

89. (a)   Graphing: The graph may be a cubic relation.

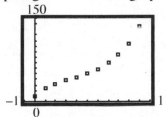

  (b)   Average rate of change $= \dfrac{50 - 43}{5 - 4} = \dfrac{7}{1} = 7$

  (c)   Average rate of change $= \dfrac{105 - 85}{9 - 8} = \dfrac{20}{1} = 20$

  (d) $C(x) = 0.2x^3 - 2.3x^2 + 14.3x + 10.2$

  $C(11) = 0.2(11)^3 - 2.3(11)^2 + 14.3(11) + 10.2 \approx 155.4$

  The cost of manufacturing 11 Cavaliers in 1 hour would be approximately $155,400.

  (e) and (f)   Graphing the cubic function of best fit:

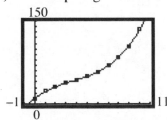

  (g)   The y-intercept would indicate the fixed costs before any cars are made.

90.   (a)   Graphing: The graph may be a cubic relation.

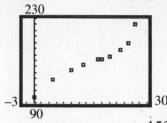

(b)   Average rate of change = $\dfrac{153.5 - 144}{13 - 10} = \dfrac{9.5}{3} \approx 3.167$

(c)   Average rate of change = $\dfrac{166.3 - 162.6}{20 - 18} = \dfrac{3.7}{2} \approx 1.85$

(d) $C(x) = 0.015x^3 - 0.595x^2 + 9.15x + 98.43$

$C(22) = 0.015(22)^3 - 0.595(22)^2 + 9.15(22) + 98.43 \approx 176.3$

The cost of producing 22,000 texts per week would be about $176,300.

(e) and (f)   Graphing the cubic function of best fit:

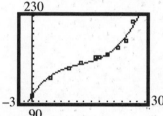

(g)   The y-intercept represents the fixed costs.

91.   The graph of a polynomial function will always have a y-intercept since the domain of every polynomial function is the set of real numbers. Therefore $f(0)$ will always produce a y-coordinate on the graph.

A polynomial function might have no x-intercepts. For example $f(x) = x^2 + 1$ has no x-intercepts since the equation $x^2 + 1 = 0$ has no real solutions.

92.   Answers will vary

93.   Answers will vary, one such polynomial is $f(x) = x^2(x+1)(4-x)(x-2)^2$

94.   Answers will vary , $f(x) = (x+2)(x-1)^2$ and $g(x) = (x+2)^3(x-1)^2$ are two such polynomials

95. $f(x) = \dfrac{1}{x}$ is piecewise smooth and not continuous; $g(x) = |x|$ is continuous but not smooth.

96. $f(x) = x^3 + bx^2 + cx + d$

(a)   true since every polynomial function has exactly one y-intercept, in this case (0,d)

(b)   true, a third degree polynomial will have at most 3 x-intercepts since the equation $x^3 + bx^2 + cx + d = 0$ will have at most 3 real solutions

(c)   true, a third degree polynomial will have at least 1 x-intercept since the equation $x^3 + bx^2 + cx + d = 0$ will have at least 1 real solution

(d)   true, since f has degree $= 3$ and the leading coefficient $= 1$.

(e)   false, since $f(-x) = (-x)^3 + b(-x)^2 + c(-x) + d = -x^3 + bx^2 - cx + d \neq -f(x)$

(f)   true only if $d = 0$, otherwise the statement is false.

Chapter 4

Polynomial and Rational Functions

4.3   Rational Functions I

1. In $R(x) = \dfrac{4x}{x-3}$, the denominator, $q(x) = x - 3$, has a zero at 3. Thus, the domain of $R(x)$ is all real numbers except 3.

2. In $R(x) = \dfrac{5x^2}{3+x}$, the denominator, $q(x) = 3 + x$, has a zero at -3. Thus, the domain of $R(x)$ is all real numbers except -3.

3. In $H(x) = \dfrac{-4x^2}{(x-2)(x+4)}$, the denominator, $q(x) = (x-2)(x+4)$, has zeros at 2 and -4. Thus, the domain of $H(x)$ is all real numbers except 2 and -4.

4. In $G(x) = \dfrac{6}{(x+3)(4-x)}$, the denominator, $q(x) = (x+3)(4-x)$, has zeros at -3 and 4. Thus, the domain of $G(x)$ is all real numbers except -3 and 4.

5. In $F(x) = \dfrac{3x(x-1)}{2x^2 - 5x - 3}$, the denominator, $q(x) = 2x^2 - 5x - 3 = (2x+1)(x-3)$, has zeros at $-\dfrac{1}{2}$ and 3. Thus, the domain of $F(x)$ is all real numbers except $-\dfrac{1}{2}$ and 3.

6. In $Q(x) = \dfrac{-x(1-x)}{3x^2 + 5x - 2}$, the denominator, $q(x) = 3x^2 + 5x - 2 = (3x-1)(x+2)$, has zeros at $\dfrac{1}{3}$ and -2. Thus, the domain of $Q(x)$ is all real numbers except $\dfrac{1}{3}$ and -2.

7. In $R(x) = \dfrac{x}{x^3 - 8}$, the denominator, $q(x) = x^3 - 8 = (x-2)(x^2 + 2x + 4)$, has a zero at 2. ($x^2 + 2x + 4$ has no real zeros.) Thus, the domain of $R(x)$ is all real numbers except 2.

8. In $R(x) = \dfrac{x}{x^4 - 1}$, the denominator, $q(x) = x^4 - 1 = (x-1)(x+1)(x^2 + 1)$, has zeros at -1 and 1. ($x^2 + 1$ has no real zeros.) Thus, the domain of $R(x)$ is all real numbers except -1 and 1.

9. In $H(x) = \dfrac{3x^2 + x}{x^2 + 4}$, the denominator, $q(x) = x^2 + 4$, has no real zeros. Thus, the domain of $H(x)$ is all real numbers

10.   In $G(x) = \dfrac{x-3}{x^4+1}$, the denominator, $q(x) = x^4+1$, has no real zeros. Thus, the domain of $G(x)$ is all real numbers.

11.   In $R(x) = \dfrac{3(x^2-x-6)}{4(x^2-9)}$, the denominator, $q(x) = 4(x^2-9) = 4(x-3)(x+3)$, has zeros at 3 and –3. Thus, the domain of $R(x)$ is all real numbers except 3 and –3.

12.   In $F(x) = \dfrac{-2(x^2-4)}{3(x^2+4x+4)}$, the denominator, $q(x) = 3(x^2+4x+4) = 3(x+2)^2$, has a zero at –2. Thus, the domain of $F(x)$ is all real numbers except –2.

13.   (a)   Domain: $\left\{x \mid x \neq 2\right\}$; Range: $\left\{y \mid y \neq 1\right\}$
      (b)   Intercept: $(0,0)$ (c)   Horizontal Asymptote: $y = 1$
      (d)   Vertical Asymptote: $x = 2$ (e)   Oblique Asymptote: none

14.   (a)   Domain: $\left\{x \mid x \neq -1\right\}$; Range: $\left\{y \mid y > 0\right\}$
      (b)   Intercept: $(0,2)$ (c)   Horizontal Asymptote: $y = 0$
      (d)   Vertical Asymptote: $x = -1$ (e)   Oblique Asymptote: none

15.   (a)   Domain: $\left\{x \mid x \neq 0\right\}$; Range: all real numbers
      (b)   Intercepts: $(-1,0), (1,0)$ (c)   Horizontal Asymptote: none
      (d)   Vertical Asymptote: $x = 0$ (e)   Oblique Asymptote: $y = 2x$

16.   (a)   Domain: $\left\{x \mid x \neq 0\right\}$; Range: $\left\{y \mid y > 2 \text{ or } y < -2\right\}$
      (b)   Intercepts: none   (c)   Horizontal Asymptote: none
      (d)   Vertical Asymptote: $x = 0$ (e)   Oblique Asymptote: $y = -x$

17.   (a)   Domain: $\left\{x \mid x \neq -2, x \neq 2\right\}$; Range: $\left\{y \mid y \leq 0 \text{ or } y > 1\right\}$
      (b)   Intercept: $(0,0)$ (c)   Horizontal Asymptote: $y = 1$
      (d)   Vertical Asymptotes: $x = -2, x = 2$ (e)   Oblique Asymptote: none

18.   (a)   Domain: $\left\{x \mid x \neq -1, x \neq 1\right\}$; Range: all real numbers
      (b)   Intercept: $(0,0)$ (c)   Horizontal Asymptote: $y = 0$
      (d)   Vertical Asymptotes: $x = -1, x = 1$ (e)   Oblique Asymptote: none

19. $F(x) = 2 + \dfrac{1}{x}$

Using the function, $y = \dfrac{1}{x}$, shift the graph vertically 2 units to up.

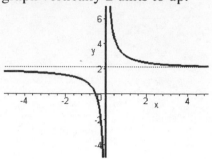

20. $R(x) = 3 + \dfrac{1}{x^2}$

Using the function $y = \dfrac{1}{x^2}$, shift the graph vertically 3 units to up.

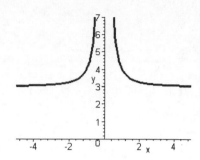

21. $R(x) = \dfrac{1}{(x-1)^2}$

Using the function, $y = \dfrac{1}{x^2}$, shift the graph horizontally 1 unit to the right.

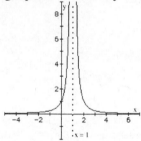

22. $R(x) = \dfrac{3}{x}$

Using the function $y = \dfrac{1}{x}$, stretch the graph vertically by a factor of 3.

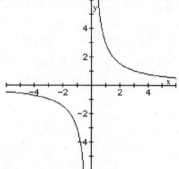

23. $H(x) = \dfrac{-2}{x+1}$

Using the function $y = \dfrac{1}{x}$, shift the graph horizontally 1 unit to the left, reflect about the x-axis, and stretch vertically by a factor of 2.

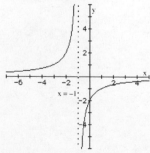

24. $G(x) = \dfrac{2}{(x+2)^2}$

Using the function $y = \dfrac{1}{x^2}$, shift the graph horizontally 2 units to the left, and stretch vertically by a factor of 2.

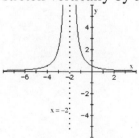

25. $R(x) = \dfrac{-1}{x^2 + 4x + 4} = \dfrac{-1}{(x+2)^2}$

Using the function $y = \dfrac{1}{x^2}$, shift the graph horizontally 2 units to the left, then reflect across the x-axis

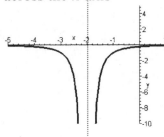

26. $R(x) = \dfrac{1}{x-1} + 1$

Using the function $y = \dfrac{1}{x}$, shift the graph horizontally 1 unit to the right, and shift vertically 1 unit up.

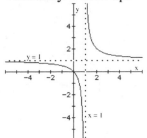

27. $G(x) = 1 + \dfrac{2}{(x-3)^2} = \dfrac{2}{(x-3)^2} + 1$

Using the function $y = \dfrac{1}{x^2}$, shift the graph 3 units right, stretch vertically by a factor of 2, and shift vertically 1 unit up.

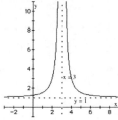

28. $F(x) = 2 - \dfrac{1}{x+1} = \dfrac{-1}{x+1} + 2$

Using the function $y = \dfrac{1}{x}$, shift the graph 1 unit left, reflect about the x-axis, and shift vertically 2 units up.

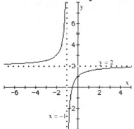

29. $R(x) = \dfrac{x^2 - 4}{x^2} = 1 - \dfrac{4}{x^2}$

Using the function $y = \dfrac{1}{x^2}$, reflect about the x-axis, stretch vertically by a factor of 4 and shift vertically 1 unit up.

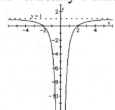

30. $R(x) = \dfrac{x-4}{x} = 1 - \dfrac{4}{x}$

Using the function $y = \dfrac{1}{x}$, reflect about the x-axis, stretch vertically by a factor of 4 and shift vertically 1 unit up.

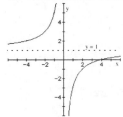

31. $R(x) = \dfrac{3x}{x+4}$

The degree of the numerator, $p(x) = 3x$, is $n = 1$. The degree of the denominator, $q(x) = x+4$, is $m = 1$. Since $n = m$, the line $y = \dfrac{3}{1} = 3$ is a horizontal asymptote. The denominator is zero at $x = -4$, so $x = -4$ is a vertical asymptote.

32. $R(x) = \dfrac{3x+5}{x-6}$

The degree of the numerator, $p(x) = 3x+5$, is $n = 1$. The degree of the denominator, $q(x) = x-6$, is $m = 1$. Since $n = m$, the line $y = \dfrac{3}{1} = 3$ is a horizontal asymptote. The denominator is zero at $x = 6$, so $x = 6$ is a vertical asymptote.

33. $H(x) = \dfrac{x^4 + 2x^2 + 1}{x^2 - x + 1}$

The degree of the numerator, $p(x) = x^4 + 2x^2 + 1$, is $n = 4$. The degree of the denominator, $q(x) = x^2 - x + 1$, is $m = 2$. Since $n > m+1$, there is no horizontal asymptote or oblique asymptote. The denominator has no real zeros, so there is no vertical asymptote.

34. $G(x) = \dfrac{-x^2 + 1}{x+5}$

The degree of the numerator, $p(x) = -x^2 + 1$, is $n = 2$. The degree of the denominator, $q(x) = x+5$, is $m = 1$. Since $n = m+1$, there is an oblique asymptote.
Dividing:

$$
\begin{array}{r}
-x + 5 \\
x+5 \overline{\smash{)}-x^2 + 0x + 1} \\
\underline{-x^2 - 5x} \\
5x + 1 \\
\underline{5x + 25} \\
-24
\end{array}
\qquad
G(x) = -x + 5 + \dfrac{-24}{x+5}
$$

Thus, the oblique asymptote is $y = -x + 5$.
The denominator is zero at $x = -5$, so $x = -5$ is a vertical asymptote.

35. $T(x) = \dfrac{x^3}{x^4 - 1}$

The degree of the numerator, $p(x) = x^3$, is $n = 3$. The degree of the denominator, $q(x) = x^4 - 1$ is $m = 4$. Since $n < m$, the line $y = 0$ is a horizontal asymptote. The denominator is zero at $x = -1$ and $x = 1$, so $x = -1$ and $x = 1$ are vertical asymptotes.

36. $P(x) = \dfrac{4x^5}{x^3 - 1}$

The degree of the numerator, $p(x) = 4x^5$, is $n = 5$. The degree of the denominator, $q(x) = x^3 - 1$ is $m = 3$. Since $n > m+1$, there is no horizontal asymptote and there is no oblique asymptote. The denominator is zero at $x = 1$, so $x = 1$ is a vertical asymptote.

37. $Q(x) = \dfrac{5 - x^2}{3x^4}$

The degree of the numerator, $p(x) = 5 - x^2$, is $n = 2$. The degree of the denominator, $q(x) = 3x^4$ is $m = 4$. Since $n < m$, the line $y = 0$ is a horizontal asymptote. The denominator is zero at $x = 0$, so $x = 0$ is a vertical asymptote.

38. $F(x) = \dfrac{-2x^2 + 1}{2x^3 + 4x^2} = \dfrac{-2x^2 + 1}{2x^2(x + 2)}$

The degree of the numerator, $p(x) = -2x^2 + 1$, is $n = 2$. The degree of the denominator, $q(x) = 2x^3 + 4x^2$ is $m = 3$. Since $n < m$, the line $y = 0$ is a horizontal asymptote. The denominator is zero at $x = 0$ and $x = -2$, so $x = 0$ and $x = -2$ are vertical asymptotes.

39. $R(x) = \dfrac{3x^4 + 4}{x^3 + 3x}$

The degree of the numerator, $p(x) = 3x^4 + 4$, is $n = 4$. The degree of the denominator, $q(x) = x^3 + 3x$ is $m = 3$. Since $n = m + 1$, there is an oblique asymptote.
Dividing:

$$
\begin{array}{r}
3x \\
x^3 + 3x \overline{\smash{\big)}\, 3x^4 + 0x^3 + 0x^2 + 0x + 4} \\
\underline{3x^4 + 9x^2 } \\
-9x^2 + 0x + 4
\end{array}
\qquad
R(x) = 3x + \dfrac{-9x^2 + 4}{x^3 + 3x}
$$

Thus, the oblique asymptote is $y = 3x$.
The denominator is zero at $x = 0$, so $x = 0$ is a vertical asymptote.

40. $R(x) = \dfrac{6x^2 + x + 12}{3x^2 - 5x - 2} = \dfrac{6x^2 + x + 12}{(3x + 1)(x - 2)}$

The degree of the numerator, $p(x) = 6x^2 + x + 12$, is $n = 2$. The degree of the denominator, $q(x) = 3x^2 - 5x - 2$ is $m = 2$. Since $n = m$, the line $y = \dfrac{6}{3} = 2$ is a horizontal asymptote.
The denominator is zero at $x = -\dfrac{1}{3}$ and $x = 2$, so $x = -\dfrac{1}{3}$ and $x = 2$ are vertical asymptotes.

41. $G(x) = \dfrac{x^3 - 1}{x - x^2}, \; x \ne 1$

The degree of the numerator, $p(x) = x^3 - 1$, is $n = 3$. The degree of the denominator, $q(x) = x - x^2$ is $m = 2$. Since $n = m + 1$, there is an oblique asymptote.
Dividing:

$$
\begin{array}{r}
-x - 1 \\
-x^2 + x \overline{\smash{\big)}\, x^3 + 0x^2 + 0x - 1} \\
\underline{x^3 - x^2 } \\
x^2 + 0x \\
\underline{x^2 - x } \\
x - 1
\end{array}
\qquad
G(x) = -x - 1 + \dfrac{x - 1}{x - x^2} = -x - 1 - \dfrac{1}{x}, \; x \ne 1
$$

Thus, the oblique asymptote is $y = -x - 1$.

$G(x)$ must be in lowest terms to find the vertical asymptote:

$$G(x) = \frac{x^3 - 1}{x - x^2} = \frac{(x-1)(x^2 + x + 1)}{-x(x-1)} = \frac{x^2 + x + 1}{-x}$$

The denominator is zero at $x = 0$, so $x = 0$ is a vertical asymptotes.

42. $$F(x) = \frac{x-1}{x-x^3} = \frac{x-1}{-x(x^2 - 1)} = \frac{x-1}{-x(x-1)(x+1)} = \frac{1}{-x(x+1)}$$

The degree of the numerator, $p(x) = x - 1$, is $n = 1$. The degree of the denominator, $q(x) = x - x^3$ is $m = 3$. Since $n < m$, the line $y = 0$ is a horizontal asymptote. The denominator is zero at $x = 0$, and $x = -1$, so $x = 0$, and $x = -1$ are vertical asymptotes.

43. $$g(h) = \frac{3.99 \times 10^{14}}{\left(6.374 \times 10^6 + h\right)^2}$$

(a) $$g(0) = \frac{3.99 \times 10^{14}}{\left(6.374 \times 10^6 + 0\right)^2} \approx 9.821 \ m/s^2$$

(b) $$g(443) = \frac{3.99 \times 10^{14}}{\left(6.374 \times 10^6 + 443\right)^2} \approx 9.8195 \ m/s^2$$

(c) $$g(8448) = \frac{3.99 \times 10^{14}}{\left(6.374 \times 10^6 + 8448\right)^2} \approx 9.795 \ m/s^2$$

(d) $$g(h) = \frac{3.99 \times 10^{14}}{\left(6.374 \times 10^6 + h\right)^2} \approx \frac{3.99 \times 10^{14}}{h^2} \to 0 \ as \ h \to \infty$$

$\therefore y = 0$ is the horizontal asymptote.

(e)

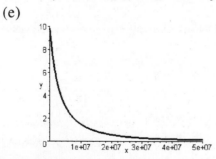

(f) $$g(h) = \frac{3.99 \times 10^{14}}{\left(6.374 \times 10^6 + h\right)^2} = 0, \text{to solve this equation would require that}$$

$3.99 \times 10^{14} = 0$, which is impossible. Therefore, there is no height above sea level at which $g = 0$. In other words, there is no point in the entire universe that is unaffected by the Earth's gravity!

44. $P(t) = \dfrac{50(1+0.5t)}{(2+0.01t)}$

(a) $P(0) = \dfrac{50(1+0)}{(2+0)} = \dfrac{50}{2} = 25$ insects

(b) $P(5) = \dfrac{50(1+0.5(5))}{(2+0.01(5))} = \dfrac{175}{2.05} \approx 85$ insects

(c) $P(t) = \dfrac{50(1+0.5t)}{(2+0.01t)} \approx \dfrac{50(0.5t)}{0.01t} = 2500$ as $t \to \infty$

$\therefore y = 2500$ is the horizontal asymptote.

The area can sustain a maximum population of 2500 insects.

(d)

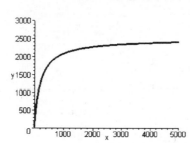

(e) $P(10000000000) = \dfrac{50(1+0.5(10000000000))}{(2+0.01(10000000000))} \approx 2499.9999505$

45.   A rational function $R(x) = \dfrac{p(x)}{q(x)}$ has a vertical asymptote at x = c in each of these cases:

Case 1: $R(c) = \dfrac{nonzero}{zero}$

That is, whenever x = c yields a zero in the denominator of the function formula. And the denominator will equal zero only if it contains the factor $(x-c)^n$, for some $n > 0$.

Case 2: $R(c) = \dfrac{(x-c)^m}{(x-c)^n}$, where $n > 0$, $m > 0$ and $n > m$.

That is, whenever x = c yields a zero in the numerator and denominator of the function formula such that the multiplicity is greater in the denominator.

46. If $R(x) = \dfrac{p(x)}{q(x)}$ has horizontal asymptote $y = 2$, then, as $x \to \pm\infty, \dfrac{p(x)}{q(x)} \to 2$.

    In other words, eventually, $\dfrac{p(x)}{q(x)} \approx 2$. Therefore, as $x \to \pm\infty, p(x) \approx 2q(x)$. But this is only

    possible when the degree of $p(x)$ = the degree of $q(x)$.

47. No, $R(x) = \dfrac{p(x)}{q(x)}$ has an oblique asymptote only when the degree of $p(x)$ is exceeds the

    degree of $q(x)$ by exactly 1.

    Moreover, $R(x) = \dfrac{p(x)}{q(x)}$ has a horizontal asymptote only when the degree of $p(x)$ is less than

    or equal to the degree of $q(x)$.

    These conditions are mutually exclusive.

48. We need $R(x) = \dfrac{p(x)}{q(x)} = 2x + 1 + \dfrac{h(x)}{q(x)}$, with $h(x) \neq 0$ for some x.

    Letting $q(x) = x + 1$, we have

    $$2x + 1 + \frac{h(x)}{q(x)} = 2x + 1 + \frac{h(x)}{x+1} = \frac{(2x+1)(x+1) + h(x)}{x+1} = \frac{2x^2 + 3x + 1 + h(x)}{x+1}.$$

    So choosing $h(x) = 1$, we get $R(x) = \dfrac{2x^2 + 3x + 1 + 1}{x+1} = \dfrac{2x^2 + 3x + 2}{x+1}$.

Chapter 4

Polynomial and Rational Functions

4.4 Rational Functions II: Analyzing Graphs

In problems 1-38, we will use the terminology: $R(x) = \dfrac{p(x)}{q(x)}$, *where the degree of* $p(x) = n$ *and the degree of* $q(x) = m$. *The graphs in Step 6 are in dot mode.*

1. $R(x) = \dfrac{x+1}{x(x+4)}$ $p(x) = x+1$; $q(x) = x(x+4) = x^2 + 4x$; $n = 1$; $m = 2$

    Step 1:   Domain: $\{x \mid x \neq -4, x \neq 0\}$

    Step 2:   (a)   The x-intercept is the zero of $p(x)$: -1

    　　　　　(b)   There is no y-intercept; $R(0)$ is not defined, since $q(0) = 0$.

    Step 3: $R(-x) = \dfrac{-x+1}{-x(-x+4)} = \dfrac{-x+1}{x^2 - 4x}$; this is neither $R(x)$ nor $-R(x)$, so there is no symmetry.

    Step 4:   The vertical asymptotes are the zeros of $q(x)$: $x = -4$ and $x = 0$

    Step 5:   Since $n < m$, the line $y = 0$ is the horizontal asymptote.

    　　　　　$R(x)$ intersects $y = 0$ at $(-1, 0)$.

    Step 6:   Graphing:　　　　　　　　　Step 7:   Graphing by hand:

    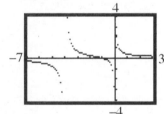　　　　　　　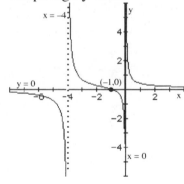

2. $R(x) = \dfrac{x}{(x-1)(x+2)}$ $p(x) = x$; $q(x) = (x-1)(x+2) = x^2 + x - 2$; $n = 1$; $m = 2$

    Step 1:   Domain: $\{x \mid x \neq -2, x \neq 1\}$

    Step 2:   (a)   The x-intercept is the zero of $p(x)$: 0

    　　　　　(b)   The y-intercept; $R(0) = 0$

    Step 3: $R(-x) = \dfrac{-x}{(-x-1)(-x+2)} = \dfrac{-x}{x^2 - x - 2}$; this is neither $R(x)$ nor $-R(x)$, so there is no symmetry.

    Step 4:   The vertical asymptotes are the zeros of $q(x)$: $x = -2$ and $x = 1$

    Step 5:   Since $n < m$, the line $y = 0$ is the horizontal asymptote.

    　　　　　$R(x)$ intersects $y = 0$ at $(0, 0)$.

411

Step 6:   Graphing: Step 7:   Graphing by hand:

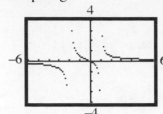

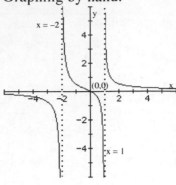

3. $R(x) = \dfrac{3x+3}{2x+4}$ $p(x) = 3x+3;\ q(x) = 2x+4;\ n=1;\ m=1$

Step 1:   Domain: $\{x \mid x \neq -2\}$

Step 2:   (a)   The x-intercept is the zero of $p(x)$: -1

          (b)   The y-intercept is $R(0) = \dfrac{3(0)+3}{2(0)+4} = \dfrac{3}{4}$.

Step 3: $R(-x) = \dfrac{3(-x)+3}{2(-x)+4} = \dfrac{-3x+3}{-2x+4} = \dfrac{3x-3}{2x-4}$; this is neither $R(x)$ nor $-R(x)$, so there
          is no symmetry.

Step 4:   The vertical asymptote is the zero of $q(x)$: $x=-2$

Step 5:   Since $n=m$, the line $y=\dfrac{3}{2}$ is the horizontal asymptote.

          $R(x)$ does not intersect $y=\dfrac{3}{2}$.

Step 6:   Graphing: Step 7:   Graphing by hand:

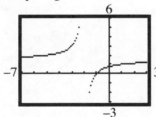

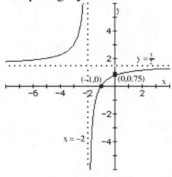

4. $R(x) = \dfrac{2x+4}{x-1}$ $p(x) = 2x+4;\ q(x) = x-1;\ n=1;\ m=1$

Step 1:   Domain: $\{x \mid x \neq 1\}$

Step 2:   (a)   The x-intercept is the zero of $p(x)$: -2

          (b)   The y-intercept is $R(0) = \dfrac{2(0)+4}{0-1} = \dfrac{4}{-1} = -4$.

Step 3: $R(-x) = \dfrac{2(-x)+4}{(-x)-1} = \dfrac{-2x+4}{-x-1} = \dfrac{2x-4}{x+1}$; this is neither $R(x)$ nor $-R(x)$, so there
          is no symmetry.

Step 4:   The vertical asymptote is the zero of $q(x)$: $x=1$

Step 5:   Since $n = m$, the line $y = 2$ is the horizontal asymptote.

$R(x)$ does not intersect $y = 2$.

Step 6:   Graphing:

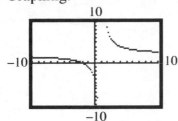

Step 7:   Graphing by hand:

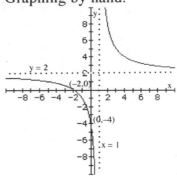

5. $R(x) = \dfrac{3}{x^2 - 4}$ $p(x) = 3;$ $q(x) = x^2 - 4;$ $n = 0;$ $m = 2$

Step 1:   Domain: $\left\{ x \mid x \neq -2, x \neq 2 \right\}$

Step 2:   (a)   There is no x-intercept.

(b)   The y-intercept is $R(0) = \dfrac{3}{0^2 - 4} = \dfrac{3}{-4} = -\dfrac{3}{4}.$

Step 3: $R(-x) = \dfrac{3}{(-x)^2 - 4} = \dfrac{3}{x^2 - 4} = R(x);$ $R(x)$ is symmetric to the y-axis.

Step 4:   The vertical asymptotes are the zeros of $q(x)$: $x = -2$ and $x = 2$

Step 5:   Since $n < m$, the line $y = 0$ is the horizontal asymptote.

$R(x)$ does not intersect $y = 0$.

Step 6:   Graphing:

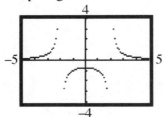

Step 7:   Graphing by hand:

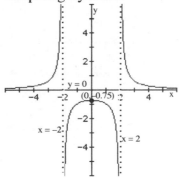

6. $R(x) = \dfrac{6}{x^2 - x - 6} = \dfrac{6}{(x - 3)(x + 2)}$ $p(x) = 6;$ $q(x) = x^2 - x - 6;$ $n = 0;$ $m = 2$

Step 1:   Domain: $\left\{ x \mid x \neq -2, x \neq 3 \right\}$

Step 2:   (a)   There is no x-intercept.

(b)   The y-intercept is $R(0) = \dfrac{6}{0^2 - 0 - 6} = \dfrac{6}{-6} = -1.$

Step 3: $R(-x) = \dfrac{6}{(-x)^2 - (-x) - 6} = \dfrac{6}{x^2 + x - 6};$ this is neither $R(x)$ nor $-R(x)$, so there is no symmetry.

Step 4:   The vertical asymptotes are the zeros of $q(x)$: $x = -2$ and $x = 3$

Step 5:   Since $n < m$, the line $y = 0$ is the horizontal asymptote.

$R(x)$ does not intersect $y = 0$.

Step 6:   Graphing:

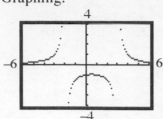

Step 7:   Graphing by hand:

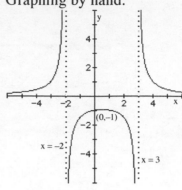

7. $P(x) = \dfrac{x^4 + x^2 + 1}{x^2 - 1}$ $p(x) = x^4 + x^2 + 1;\ \ q(x) = x^2 - 1;\ \ n = 4;\ \ m = 2$

Step 1:   Domain: $\left\{x \mid x \neq -1,\ x \neq 1\right\}$

Step 2:   (a)   There is no x-intercept.

(b)   The y-intercept is $P(0) = \dfrac{0^4 + 0^2 + 1}{0^2 - 1} = \dfrac{1}{-1} = -1$.

Step 3: $P(-x) = \dfrac{(-x)^4 + (-x)^2 + 1}{(-x)^2 - 1} = \dfrac{x^4 + x^2 + 1}{x^2 - 1} = P(x);\ P(x)$ is symmetric to the y-axis.

Step 4:   The vertical asymptotes are the zeros of $q(x)$: $x = -1$ and $x = 1$

Step 5:   Since $n > m + 1$, there is no horizontal asymptote and no oblique asymptote.

Step 6:   Graphing:

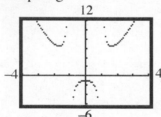

Step 7:   Graphing by hand:

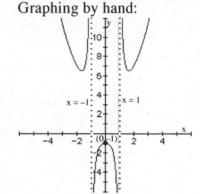

8. $Q(x) = \dfrac{x^4 - 1}{x^2 - 4} = \dfrac{(x^2 + 1)(x + 1)(x - 1)}{(x + 2)(x - 2)}$ $p(x) = x^4 - 1;\ \ q(x) = x^2 - 4;\ \ n = 4;\ \ m = 2$

Step 1:   Domain: $\left\{x \mid x \neq -2,\ x \neq 2\right\}$

Step 2:   (a)   The x-intercepts are the zeros of $p(x)$:   −1 and 1.

(b)   The y-intercept is $Q(0) = \dfrac{0^4 - 1}{0^2 - 4} = \dfrac{-1}{-4} = \dfrac{1}{4}$.

Step 3: $Q(-x) = \dfrac{(-x)^4 - 1}{(-x)^2 - 4} = \dfrac{x^4 - 11}{x^2 - 4} = Q(x);\ Q(x)$ is symmetric to the y-axis.

Step 4:   The vertical asymptotes are the zeros of $q(x)$: $x = -2$ and $x = 2$

Step 5:   Since $n > m + 1$, there is no horizontal asymptote and no oblique asymptote.

Step 6: Graphing:

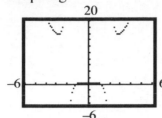

Step 7:   Graphing by hand:

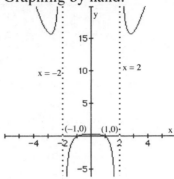

9. $H(x) = \dfrac{x^3 - 1}{x^2 - 9}$ $p(x) = x^3 - 1;\ \ q(x) = x^2 - 9;\ \ n = 3;\ \ m = 2$

Step 1: Domain: $\left\{ x \mid x \neq -3, x \neq 3 \right\}$

Step 2: (a)   The x-intercept is the zero of $p(x)$: 1.

(b)   The y-intercept is $H(0) = \dfrac{0^3 - 1}{0^2 - 9} = \dfrac{-1}{-9} = \dfrac{1}{9}$.

Step 3: $H(-x) = \dfrac{(-x)^3 - 1}{(-x)^2 - 9} = \dfrac{-x^3 - 1}{x^2 - 9}$; this is neither $H(x)$ nor $-H(x)$, so there is no symmetry.

Step 4: The vertical asymptotes are the zeros of $q(x)$: $x = -3$ and $x = 3$

Step 5: Since $n = m + 1$, there is an oblique asymptote. Dividing:

$$\begin{array}{r} x \\ x^2 - 9 \overline{)\, x^3 + 0x^2 + 0x - 1 } \\ \underline{x^3 - 9x } \\ 9x - 1 \end{array} \qquad H(x) = x + \dfrac{9x - 1}{x^2 - 9}$$

The oblique asymptote is $y = x$.

Solve to find intersection points:

$$\dfrac{x^3 - 1}{x^2 - 9} = x \;\rightarrow\; x^3 - 1 = x^3 - 9x$$

$$-1 = -9x \rightarrow x = \dfrac{1}{9}$$

The oblique asymptote intersects $H(x)$ at $\left(\dfrac{1}{9}, \dfrac{1}{9} \right)$.

Step 6: Graphing:

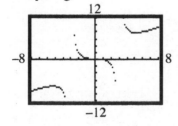

Step 7:   Graphing by hand:

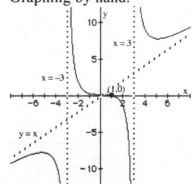

10. $G(x) = \dfrac{x^3 + 1}{x^2 + 2x} = \dfrac{(x+1)(x^2 - x + 1)}{x(x+2)}$ $p(x) = x^3 + 1;$ $q(x) = x^2 + 2x;$ $n = 3;$ $m = 2$

Step 1: Domain: $\{x \mid x \neq -2, x \neq 0\}$

Step 2: (a)   The x-intercept is the zero of $p(x)$: -1.

(b)   The y-intercept is $G(0) = \dfrac{0^3 + 1}{0^2 + 2(0)} = \dfrac{1}{0}$. No y-intercept.

Step 3: $G(-x) = \dfrac{(-x)^3 + 1}{(-x)^2 + 2(-x)} = \dfrac{-x^3 + 1}{x^2 - 2x}$; this is neither $G(x)$ nor $-G(x)$, so there is no symmetry.

Step 4: The vertical asymptotes are the zeros of $q(x)$: $x = -2$ and $x = 0$

Step 5: Since $n = m + 1$, there is an oblique asymptote. Dividing:

$$x^2 + 2x \overline{\smash{\big)}\ x^3 + 0x^2 + 0x + 1} \quad \begin{array}{l} x - 2 \end{array}$$

$$\begin{array}{r} x^3 + 2x^2 \\ \hline -2x^2 \quad\quad + 1 \\ -2x^2 - 4x \\ \hline 4x + 1 \end{array}$$

$G(x) = x - 2 + \dfrac{4x + 1}{x^2 + 2x}$

The oblique asymptote is $y = x - 2$.

Solve to find intersection points:

$$\frac{x^3 + 1}{x^2 + 2x} = x - 2 \to x^3 + 1 = x^3 - 4x \to 1 = -4x \to x = -\frac{1}{4}$$

The oblique asymptote intersects $G(x)$ at $\left(-\dfrac{1}{4}, -\dfrac{9}{4}\right)$.

Step 6: Graphing:

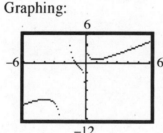

Step 7:   Graphing by hand:

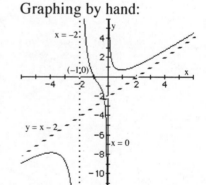

11. $R(x) = \dfrac{x^2}{x^2 + x - 6} = \dfrac{x^2}{(x+3)(x-2)}$ $p(x) = x^2;$ $q(x) = x^2 + x - 6;$ $n = 2;$ $m = 2$

Step 1: Domain: $\{x \mid x \neq -3, x \neq 2\}$

Step 2: (a)   The x-intercept is the zero of $p(x)$: 0

(b)   The y-intercept is $R(0) = \dfrac{0^2}{0^2 + 0 - 6} = \dfrac{0}{-6} = 0$.

Step 3: $R(-x) = \dfrac{(-x)^2}{(-x)^2 + (-x) - 6} = \dfrac{x^2}{x^2 - x - 6}$; this is neither $R(x)$ nor $-R(x)$, so there is no symmetry.

416

Step 4:   The vertical asymptotes are the zeros of $q(x)$: $x = -3$ and $x = 2$

Step 5:   Since $n = m$, the line $y = 1$ is the horizontal asymptote.

$R(x)$ intersects $y = 1$ at $(6, 1)$, since:

$$\frac{x^2}{x^2 + x - 6} = 1 \rightarrow x^2 = x^2 + x - 6 \rightarrow 0 = x - 6 \rightarrow x = 6$$

Step 6:   Graphing: Step 7:   Graphing by hand:

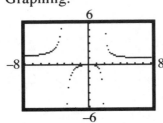
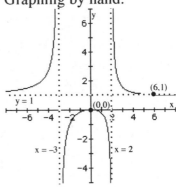

12. $R(x) = \dfrac{x^2 + x - 12}{x^2 - 4} = \dfrac{(x+4)(x-3)}{(x+2)(x-2)}$ $p(x) = x^2 + x - 12$; $q(x) = x^2 - 4$; $n = 2$; $m = 2$

Step 1:   Domain: $\{x \mid x \neq -2, x \neq 2\}$

Step 2:   (a)   The x-intercept is the zero of $p(x)$: -4 and 3

   (b)   The y-intercept is $R(0) = \dfrac{0^2 + 0 - 12}{0^2 - 4} = \dfrac{-12}{-4} = 3$.

Step 3: $R(-x) = \dfrac{(-x)^2 + (-x) - 12}{(-x)^2 - 4} = \dfrac{x^2 - x - 12}{x^2 - 4}$; this is neither $R(x)$ nor $-R(x)$, so there is no symmetry.

Step 4:   The vertical asymptotes are the zeros of $q(x)$: $x = -2$ and $x = 2$

Step 5:   Since $n = m$, the line $y = 1$ is the horizontal asymptote.

$R(x)$ intersects $y = 1$ at $(8, 1)$, since:

$$\frac{x^2 + x - 12}{x^2 - 4} = 1 \rightarrow x^2 + x - 12 = x^2 - 4 \rightarrow x = 8$$

Step 6:   Graphing: Step 7:   Graphing by hand:

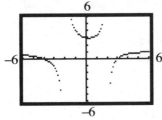
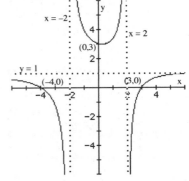

417

13. $G(x) = \dfrac{x}{x^2 - 4} = \dfrac{x}{(x+2)(x-2)}$ $p(x) = x;\ q(x) = x^2 - 4;\ n = 1;\ m = 2$

Step 1: Domain: $\left\{x \mid x \neq -2,\ x \neq 2\right\}$

Step 2: (a) The x-intercept is the zero of $p(x)$: 0

(b) The y-intercept is $G(0) = \dfrac{0}{0^2 - 4} = \dfrac{0}{-4} = 0$.

Step 3: $G(-x) = \dfrac{-x}{(-x)^2 - 4} = \dfrac{-x}{x^2 - 4} = -G(x)$; $G(x)$ is symmetric to the origin.

Step 4: The vertical asymptotes are the zeros of $q(x)$: $x = -2$ and $x = 2$

Step 5: Since $n < m$, the line $y = 0$ is the horizontal asymptote.

$G(x)$ intersects $y = 0$ at $(0, 0)$.

Step 6: Graphing:

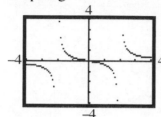

Step 7: Graphing by hand:

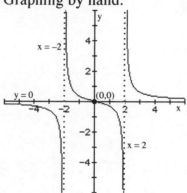

14. $G(x) = \dfrac{3x}{x^2 - 1} = \dfrac{3x}{(x+1)(x-1)}$ $p(x) = 3x;\ q(x) = x^2 - 1;\ n = 1;\ m = 2$

Step 1: Domain: $\left\{x \mid x \neq -1,\ x \neq 1\right\}$

Step 2: (a) The x-intercept is the zero of $p(x)$: 0

(b) The y-intercept is $G(0) = \dfrac{3(0)}{0^2 - 1} = \dfrac{0}{-1} = 0$.

Step 3: $G(-x) = \dfrac{-3x}{(-x)^2 - 1} = \dfrac{-3x}{x^2 - 1} = -G(x)$; $G(x)$ is symmetric to the origin.

Step 4: The vertical asymptotes are the zeros of $q(x)$: $x = -1$ and $x = 1$

Step 5: Since $n < m$, the line $y = 0$ is the horizontal asymptote.

$G(x)$ intersects $y = 0$ at $(0, 0)$.

Step 6: Graphing:

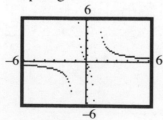

Step 7: Graphing by hand:

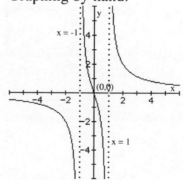

15. $R(x) = \dfrac{3}{(x-1)(x^2-4)} = \dfrac{3}{(x-1)(x+2)(x-2)}$ $p(x) = 3;\ q(x) = (x-1)(x^2-4);$
$n = 0;\ m = 3$

Step 1: Domain: $\{x \mid x \ne -2,\ x \ne 1,\ x \ne 2\}$

Step 2: (a) There is no x-intercept.

   (b) The y-intercept is $R(0) = \dfrac{3}{(0-1)(0^2-4)} = \dfrac{3}{4}.$

Step 3: $R(-x) = \dfrac{3}{(-x-1)\big((-x)^2-4\big)} = \dfrac{3}{(-x-1)(x^2-4)}$; this is neither $R(x)$ nor $-R(x)$,

   so there is no symmetry.

Step 4: The vertical asymptotes are the zeros of $q(x)$: $x = -2, x = 1,$ and $x = 2$

Step 5: Since $n < m$, the line $y = 0$ is the horizontal asymptote.
   $R(x)$ does not intersect $y = 0$.

Step 6: Graphing: Step 7:   Graphing by hand:

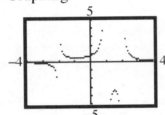

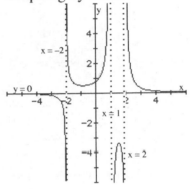

16. $R(x) = \dfrac{-4}{(x+1)(x^2-9)} = \dfrac{-4}{(x+1)(x+3)(x-3)}$ $p(x) = -4;\ q(x) = (x+1)(x^2-9);$
$n = 0;\ m = 3$

Step 1: Domain: $\{x \mid x \ne -3,\ x \ne -1,\ x \ne 3\}$

Step 2: (a) There is no x-intercept.

   (b) The y-intercept is $R(0) = \dfrac{-4}{(0+1)(0^2-9)} = \dfrac{-4}{-9} = \dfrac{4}{9}.$

Step 3: $R(-x) = \dfrac{-4}{(-x+1)\big((-x)^2-9\big)} = \dfrac{-4}{(-x+1)(x^2-9)}$; this is neither $R(x)$ nor $-R(x)$,

   so there is no symmetry.

Step 4: The vertical asymptotes are the zeros of $q(x)$: $x = -3, x = -1,$ and $x = 3$

Step 5: Since $n < m$, the line $y = 0$ is the horizontal asymptote.
   $R(x)$ does not intersect $y = 0$.

Step 6:   Graphing:

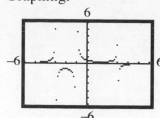

Step 7:   Graphing by hand:

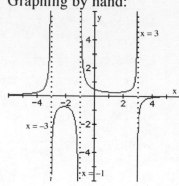

17. $H(x) = \dfrac{4(x^2 - 1)}{x^4 - 16} = \dfrac{4(x - 1)(x + 1)}{(x^2 + 4)(x + 2)(x - 2)}$ $p(x) = 4(x^2 - 1);\ q(x) = x^4 - 16;$
$n = 2;\ m = 4$

Step 1:   Domain: $\{x \mid x \neq -2,\ x \neq 2\}$

Step 2:   (a)   The x-intercepts are the zeros of $p(x)$: -1 and 1

(b)   The y-intercept is $H(0) = \dfrac{4(0^2 - 1)}{0^4 - 16} = \dfrac{-4}{-16} = \dfrac{1}{4}$.

Step 3: $H(-x) = \dfrac{4\left((-x)^2 - 1\right)}{(-x)^4 - 16} = \dfrac{4\left(x^2 - 1\right)}{x^4 - 16} = H(x);\ H(x)$ is symmetric to the y-axis.

Step 4:   The vertical asymptotes are the zeros of $q(x)$: $x = -2$, and $x = 2$

Step 5:   Since $n < m$, the line $y = 0$ is the horizontal asymptote.
$H(x)$ intersects $y = 0$ at $(-1, 0)$ and $(1, 0)$.

Step 6:   Graphing:

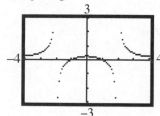

Step 7:   Graphing by hand:

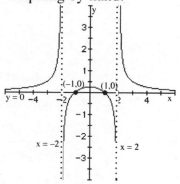

18. $H(x) = \dfrac{x^2 + 4}{x^4 - 1} = \dfrac{x^2 + 4}{(x^2 + 1)(x + 1)(x - 1)}$ $p(x) = x^2 + 4;\ q(x) = x^4 - 1;$
$n = 2;\ m = 4$

Step 1:   Domain: $\{x \mid x \neq -1,\ x \neq 1\}$

Step 2:   (a)   There are no x-intercepts.

(b)   The y-intercept is $H(0) = \dfrac{0^2 + 4}{0^4 - 1} = \dfrac{4}{-1} = -4$.

Step 3: $H(-x) = \dfrac{(-x)^2 + 4}{(-x)^4 - 1} = \dfrac{x^2 + 4}{x^4 - 1} = H(x);\ H(x)$ is symmetric to the y-axis.

Step 4:   The vertical asymptotes are the zeros of $q(x)$: $x = -1$, and $x = 1$

420

Step 5:   Since $n < m$, the line $y = 0$ is the horizontal asymptote.

$H(x)$ does not intersect $y = 0$.

Step 6:   Graphing:

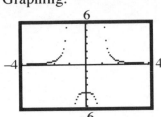

Step 7:   Graphing by hand:

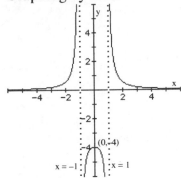

19. $F(x) = \dfrac{x^2 - 3x - 4}{x + 2} = \dfrac{(x + 1)(x - 4)}{x + 2}$ $p(x) = x^2 - 3x - 4; \; q(x) = x + 2; \; n = 2; \; m = 1$

Step 1:   Domain: $\{x \mid x \neq -2\}$

Step 2:   (a)   The x-intercepts are the zeros of $p(x)$: -1 and 4.

(b)   The y-intercept is $F(0) = \dfrac{0^2 - 3(0) - 4}{0 + 2} = \dfrac{-4}{2} = -2$.

Step 3: $F(-x) = \dfrac{(-x)^2 - 3(-x) - 4}{-x + 2} = \dfrac{x^2 + 3x - 4}{-x + 2}$; this is neither $F(x)$ nor $-F(x)$, so there is no symmetry.

Step 4:   The vertical asymptote is the zero of $q(x)$: $x = -2$

Step 5:   Since $n = m + 1$, there is an oblique asymptote. Dividing:

$$\begin{array}{r} x - 5 \\ x + 2 \overline{)\, x^2 - 3x - 4} \\ \underline{x^2 + 2x} \\ -5x - 4 \\ \underline{-5x - 10} \\ 6 \end{array}$$

$F(x) = x - 5 + \dfrac{6}{x + 2}$

The oblique asymptote is $y = x - 5$.

Solve to find intersection points:

$$\dfrac{x^2 - 3x - 4}{x + 2} = x - 5 \rightarrow x^2 - 3x - 4 = x^2 - 3x - 10 \rightarrow -4 = -10$$

Since there is no solution, the oblique asymptote does not intersect $F(x)$.

Step 6:   Graphing:

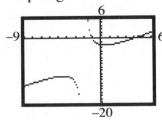

Step 7:   Graphing by hand:

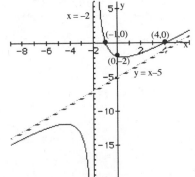

421

20. $F(x) = \dfrac{x^2 + 3x + 2}{x - 1} = \dfrac{(x+2)(x+1)}{x - 1}$ $p(x) = x^2 + 3x + 2;\ q(x) = x - 1;\ n = 2;\ m = 1$

Step 1: Domain: $\{x \mid x \neq 1\}$

Step 2: (a) The x-intercepts are the zeros of $p(x)$: -2 and -1.

  (b) The y-intercept is $F(0) = \dfrac{0^2 + 3(0) + 2}{0 - 1} = \dfrac{2}{-1} = -2$.

Step 3: $F(-x) = \dfrac{(-x)^2 + 3(-x) + 2}{-x - 1} = \dfrac{x^2 - 3x + 2}{-x - 1}$; this is neither $F(x)$ nor $-F(x)$, so there is no symmetry.

Step 4: The vertical asymptote is the zero of $q(x)$: $x = 1$

Step 5: Since $n = m + 1$, there is an oblique asymptote. Dividing:

$$\begin{array}{r} x + 4 \\ x - 1 \overline{\smash{\big)}\, x^2 + 3x + 2} \\ \underline{x^2 - x } \\ 4x + 2 \\ \underline{4x - 4 } \\ 6 \end{array} \qquad F(x) = x + 4 + \dfrac{6}{x - 1}$$

The oblique asymptote is $y = x + 4$.

Solve to find intersection points:

$$\dfrac{x^2 + 3x + 2}{x - 1} = x + 4$$
$$x^2 + 3x + 2 = x^2 + 3x - 4$$
$$2 = -4$$

Since there is no solution, the oblique asymptote does not intersect $F(x)$.

Step 6: Graphing:

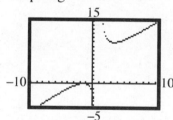

Step 7: Graphing by hand:

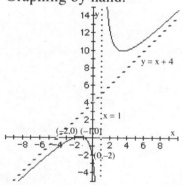

21. $R(x) = \dfrac{x^2 + x - 12}{x - 4} = \dfrac{(x+4)(x-3)}{x - 4}$ $p(x) = x^2 + x - 12;\ q(x) = x - 4;\ n = 2;\ m = 1$

Step 1: Domain: $\{x \mid x \neq 4\}$

Step 2: (a) The x-intercepts are the zeros of $p(x)$: -4 and 3.

  (b) The y-intercept is $R(0) = \dfrac{0^2 + 0 - 12}{0 - 4} = \dfrac{-12}{-4} = 3$.

Step 3: $R(-x) = \dfrac{(-x)^2 + (-x) - 12}{-x - 4} = \dfrac{x^2 - x - 12}{-x - 4}$; this is neither $R(x)$ nor $-R(x)$, so there is no symmetry.

Step 4: The vertical asymptote is the zero of $q(x)$: $x = 4$

Step 5:   Since $n = m + 1$, there is an oblique asymptote. Dividing:

$$
\begin{array}{r}
x + 5 \\
x - 4 \overline{)\; x^2 + \; x - 12} \\
\underline{x^2 - 4x} \\
5x - 12 \\
\underline{5x - 20} \\
8
\end{array}
\qquad R(x) = x + 5 + \dfrac{8}{x - 4}
$$

The oblique asymptote is $y = x + 5$.
Solve to find intersection points:

$$\frac{x^2 + x - 12}{x - 4} = x + 5$$

$$x^2 + x - 12 = x^2 + x - 20$$

$$-12 = -20$$

Since there is no solution, the oblique asymptote does not intersect $R(x)$.

Step 6:   Graphing: Step 7:   Graphing by hand:

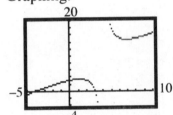 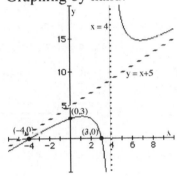

22. $R(x) = \dfrac{x^2 - x - 12}{x + 5} = \dfrac{(x - 4)(x + 3)}{x + 5}$ $p(x) = x^2 - x - 12;\;\; q(x) = x + 5;\;\; n = 2;\;\; m = 1$

Step 1:   Domain: $\{x \mid x \neq -5\}$
Step 2:   (a)   The x-intercepts are the zeros of $p(x)$: -3 and 4.

(b)   The y-intercept is $R(0) = \dfrac{0^2 - 0 - 12}{0 + 5} = -\dfrac{12}{5}$.

Step 3: $R(-x) = \dfrac{(-x)^2 - (-x) - 12}{-x + 5} = \dfrac{x^2 + x - 12}{-x + 5}$; this is neither $R(x)$ nor $-R(x)$, so
there is no symmetry.

Step 4:   The vertical asymptote is the zero of $q(x)$: $x = -5$
Step 5:   Since $n = m + 1$, there is an oblique asymptote. Dividing:

$$
\begin{array}{r}
x - 6 \\
x + 5 \overline{)\; x^2 - \; x - 12} \\
\underline{x^2 + 5x} \\
-6x - 12 \\
\underline{-6x - 30} \\
18
\end{array}
\qquad R(x) = x - 6 + \dfrac{18}{x + 5}
$$

The oblique asymptote is $y = x - 6$.
Solve to find intersection points:

$$\frac{x^2 - x - 12}{x + 5} = x - 6 \rightarrow x^2 - x - 12 = x^2 - x - 30 \rightarrow -12 = -30$$

Since there is no solution, the oblique asymptote does not intersect $R(x)$.

Step 6:   Graphing: Step 7:   Graphing by hand:

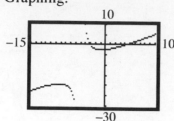   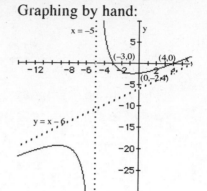

23. $F(x) = \dfrac{x^2 + x - 12}{x + 2} = \dfrac{(x + 4)(x - 3)}{x + 2}$ $p(x) = x^2 + x - 12$; $q(x) = x + 2$; $n = 2$; $m = 1$

Step 1:   Domain: $\left\{x \mid x \neq -2\right\}$

Step 2:   (a)   The x-intercepts are the zeros of $p(x)$: -4 and 3.

          (b)   The y-intercept is $F(0) = \dfrac{0^2 + 0 - 12}{0 + 2} = \dfrac{-12}{2} = -6$.

Step 3: $F(-x) = \dfrac{(-x)^2 + (-x) - 12}{-x + 2} = \dfrac{x^2 - x - 12}{-x + 2}$; this is neither $F(x)$ nor $-F(x)$, so

          there is no symmetry.

Step 4:   The vertical asymptote is the zero of $q(x)$: $x = -2$

Step 5:   Since $n = m + 1$, there is an oblique asymptote. Dividing:

$$\begin{array}{r} x - 1 \\ x + 2 \overline{\smash{)}x^2 + x - 12} \\ \underline{x^2 + 2x} \\ -x - 12 \\ \underline{-x - 2} \\ -10 \end{array}$$

$F(x) = x - 1 + \dfrac{-10}{x + 2}$

The oblique asymptote is $y = x - 1$.

Solve to find intersection points:

$$\frac{x^2 + x - 12}{x + 2} = x - 1 \rightarrow x^2 + x - 12 = x^2 + x - 2 \rightarrow -12 = -2$$

Since there is no solution, the oblique asymptote does not intersect $F(x)$.

Step 6:   Graphing:

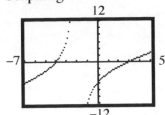

Step 7:   Graphing by hand:

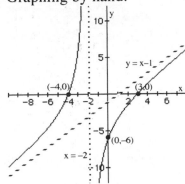

24. $G(x) = \dfrac{x^2 - x - 12}{x + 1} = \dfrac{(x+3)(x-4)}{x+1}$ $p(x) = x^2 - x - 12;\ q(x) = x + 1;\ n = 2;\ m = 1$

Step 1:   Domain: $\{x \mid x \neq -1\}$

Step 2:   (a)   The x-intercepts are the zeros of $p(x)$: -3 and 4.

(b)   The y-intercept is $F(0) = \dfrac{0^2 - 0 - 12}{0 + 1} = \dfrac{-12}{1} = -12$.

Step 3: $G(-x) = \dfrac{(-x)^2 - (-x) - 12}{-x + 1} = \dfrac{x^2 + x - 12}{-x + 1}$; this is neither $G(x)$ nor $-G(x)$, so there is no symmetry.

Step 4:   The vertical asymptote is the zero of $q(x)$: $x = -1$

Step 5:   Since $n = m + 1$, there is an oblique asymptote. Dividing:

$$\begin{array}{r} x - 2 \\ x + 1 \overline{)\, x^2 - x - 12} \\ \underline{x^2 + x} \\ -2x - 12 \\ \underline{-2x - 2} \\ -10 \end{array}$$

$G(x) = x - 2 + \dfrac{-10}{x + 1}$

The oblique asymptote is $y = x - 2$.

Solve to find intersection points: $\dfrac{x^2 - x - 12}{x + 1} = x - 2 \rightarrow x^2 - x - 12 = x^2 - x - 2 \rightarrow -12 = -2$

Since there is no solution, the oblique asymptote does not intersect $G(x)$.

Step 6:   Graphing:

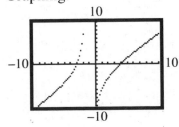

Step 7:   Graphing by hand:

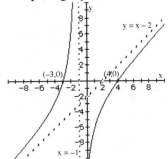

25. $R(x) = \dfrac{x(x-1)^2}{(x+3)^3}$ $p(x) = x(x-1)^2$; $q(x) = (x+3)^3$; $n = 3$; $m = 3$

Step 1:   Domain: $\{x \mid x \neq -3\}$

Step 2:   (a)   The x-intercepts are the zeros of $p(x)$: 0 and 1

(b)   The y-intercept is $R(0) = \dfrac{0(0-1)^2}{(0+3)^3} = \dfrac{0}{27} = 0$.

Step 3: $R(-x) = \dfrac{-x(-x-1)^2}{(-x+3)^3}$; this is neither $R(x)$ nor $-R(x)$, so there is no symmetry.

Step 4:   The vertical asymptote is the zero of $q(x)$: $x = -3$

Step 5:   Since $n = m$, the line $y = 1$ is the horizontal asymptote.

Solve to find intersection points:

$$\frac{x(x-1)^2}{(x+3)^3} = 1$$

$$x^3 - 2x^2 + x = x^3 + 9x^2 + 27x + 27$$

$$0 = 11x^2 + 26x + 27$$

Since there is no real solution, $R(x)$ does not intersect $y = 1$.

Step 6:   Graphing: Step 7:   Graphing by hand:

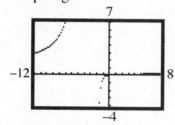

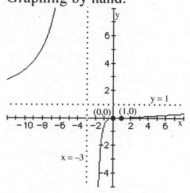

26. $R(x) = \dfrac{(x-1)(x+2)(x-3)}{x(x-4)^2}$ $p(x) = (x-1)(x+2)(x-3)$; $q(x) = x(x-4)^2$;

$n = 3$; $m = 3$

Step 1:   Domain: $\{x \mid x \neq 0, \, x \neq 4\}$

Step 2:   (a)   The x-intercepts are the zeros of $p(x)$: -2, 1, and 3

(b)   The y-intercept is $R(0) = \dfrac{(0-1)(0+2)(0-3)}{0(0-4)^2} = \dfrac{6}{0}$. No y-intercept.

Step 3: $R(-x) = \dfrac{(-x-1)(-x+2)(-x-3)}{-x(-x-4)^2}$; this is neither $R(x)$ nor $-R(x)$, so there is no symmetry.

Step 4:   The vertical asymptotes are the zeros of $q(x)$: $x = 0$ and $x = 4$

Step 5:   Since $n = m$, the line $y = 1$ is the horizontal asymptote.

Solve to find intersection points:

$$\frac{(x-1)(x+2)(x-3)}{x(x-4)^2} = 1$$

$$(x^2 + x - 2)(x-3) = x(x^2 - 8x + 16)$$

$$x^3 - 2x^2 - 5x + 6 = x^3 - 8x^2 + 16x$$

$$6x^2 - 21x + 6 = 0$$

$$2x^2 - 7x + 2 = 0$$

$$x = \frac{7 \pm \sqrt{49 - 4(2)(2)}}{2(2)} = \frac{7 \pm \sqrt{33}}{4}$$

$R(x)$ intersects $y = 1$ at $\left(\dfrac{7-\sqrt{33}}{4}, 1\right)$ and $\left(\dfrac{7+\sqrt{33}}{4}, 1\right)$

Step 6:   Graphing:

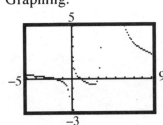

Step 7:   Graphing by hand:

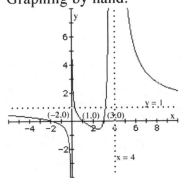

27. $R(x) = \dfrac{x^2 + x - 12}{x^2 - x - 6} = \dfrac{(x+4)(x-3)}{(x-3)(x+2)} = \dfrac{x+4}{x+2}$ $p(x) = x^2 + x - 12;\ q(x) = x^2 - x - 6;$

  $n = 2;\ m = 2$

Step 1:   Domain: $\{x \mid x \neq -2,\ x \neq 3\}$

Step 2:   (a)   The x-intercept is the zero of $p(x)$: -4 (3 is not a zero because reduced form must be used to find the zeros.)

  (b)   The y-intercept is $R(0) = \dfrac{0^2 + 0 - 12}{0^2 - 0 - 6} = \dfrac{-12}{-6} = 2$.

Step 3: $R(-x) = \dfrac{(-x)^2 + (-x) - 12}{(-x)^2 - (-x) - 6} = \dfrac{x^2 - x - 12}{x^2 + x - 6}$; this is neither $R(x)$ nor $-R(x)$, so there is no symmetry.

Step 4:   The vertical asymptote is the zero of $q(x)$: $x = -2$ ($x = 3$ is not a vertical asymptote because reduced form must be used to find the them.)

Step 5:   Since $n = m$, the line $y = 1$ is the horizontal asymptote.

  $R(x)$ does not intersect $y = 1$ because $R(x)$ is not defined at $x = 3$.

$$\frac{x^2 + x - 12}{x^2 - x - 6} = 1$$

$$x^2 + x - 12 = x^2 - x - 6$$

$$2x = 6$$

$$x = 3$$

Step 6: Graphing:

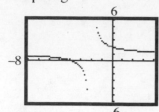

Step 7:   Graphing by hand:

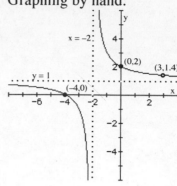

28. $R(x) = \dfrac{x^2 + 3x - 10}{x^2 + 8x + 15} = \dfrac{(x+5)(x-2)}{(x+5)(x+3)} = \dfrac{x-2}{x+3}$ $p(x) = x^2 + 3x - 10;$

$q(x) = x^2 + 8x + 15;$ $n = 2;$ $m = 2$

Step 1: Domain: $\{x \mid x \neq -5, x \neq -3\}$

Step 2: (a)   The x-intercept is the zero of $p(x)$: 2 (–5 is not a zero because reduced form must be used to find the zeros.)

(b)   The y-intercept is $R(0) = \dfrac{0^2 + 3(0) - 10}{0^2 + 8(0) + 15} = \dfrac{-10}{15} = -\dfrac{2}{3}$.

Step 3: $R(-x) = \dfrac{(-x)^2 + 3(-x) - 10}{(-x)^2 + 8(-x) + 15} = \dfrac{x^2 - 3x - 10}{x^2 - 8x + 15}$; this is neither $R(x)$ nor $-R(x)$, so there is no symmetry.

Step 4: The vertical asymptote is the zero of $q(x)$: $x = -3$ ($x = -5$ is not a vertical asymptote because reduced form must be used to find them.)

Step 5: Since $n = m$, the line $y = 1$ is the horizontal asymptote.

$R(x)$ does not intersect $y = 1$ because $R(x)$ is not defined at $x = -5$.

$$\frac{x^2 + 3x - 10}{x^2 + 8x + 15} = 1$$
$$x^2 + 3x - 10 = x^2 + 8x + 15$$
$$-5x = 25$$
$$x = -5$$

Step 6: Graphing:

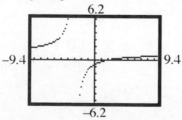

Step 7:   Graphing by hand:

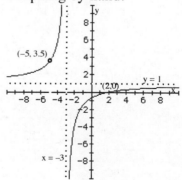

29. $R(x) = \dfrac{6x^2 - 7x - 3}{2x^2 - 7x + 6} = \dfrac{(3x + 1)(2x - 3)}{(2x - 3)(x - 2)} = \dfrac{3x + 1}{x - 2}$ $p(x) = 6x^2 - 7x - 3$;

$q(x) = 2x^2 - 7x + 6$; $n = 2$; $m = 2$

Step 1:   Domain: $\left\{ x \mid x \ne \dfrac{3}{2},\ x \ne 2 \right\}$

Step 2:   (a)   The x-intercept is the zero of $p(x)$: $-\dfrac{1}{3}$ ($\dfrac{3}{2}$ is not a zero because reduced form must be used to find the zeros.)

(b)   The y-intercept is $R(0) = \dfrac{6(0)^2 - 7(0) - 3}{2(0)^2 - 7(0) + 6} = \dfrac{-3}{6} = -\dfrac{1}{2}$.

Step 3: $R(-x) = \dfrac{6(-x)^2 - 7(-x) - 3}{2(-x)^2 - 7(-x) + 6} = \dfrac{6x^2 + 7x - 3}{2x^2 + 7x + 6}$; this is neither $R(x)$ nor $-R(x)$, so there is no symmetry.

Step 4:   The vertical asymptote is the zero of $q(x)$: $x = 2$ ($x = \dfrac{3}{2}$ is not a vertical asymptote because reduced form must be used to find the them.)

Step 5:   Since $n = m$, the line $y = 3$ is the horizontal asymptote.

$R(x)$ does not intersect $y = 3$ because $R(x)$ is not defined at $x = \dfrac{3}{2}$.

$$\frac{6x^2 - 7x - 3}{2x^2 - 7x + 6} = 3$$
$$6x^2 - 7x - 3 = 6x^2 - 21x + 18$$
$$14x = 21$$
$$x = \frac{3}{2}$$

Step 6:   Graphing:

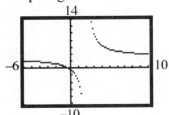

Step 7:   Graphing by hand:

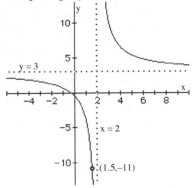

30. $R(x) = \dfrac{8x^2 + 26x + 15}{2x^2 - x - 15} = \dfrac{(4x + 3)(2x + 5)}{(2x + 5)(x - 3)} = \dfrac{4x + 3}{x - 3}$ $p(x) = 8x^2 + 26x + 15$;

$q(x) = 2x^2 - x - 15$; $n = 2$; $m = 2$

Step 1:   Domain: $\left\{ x \mid x \ne -\dfrac{5}{2},\ x \ne 3 \right\}$

Step 2:   (a)   The x-intercept is the zero of $p(x)$: $-\dfrac{3}{4}$ ($-\dfrac{5}{2}$ is not a zero because reduced form must be used to find the zeros.)

429

(b)   The y-intercept is $R(0) = \dfrac{8(0)^2 + 26(0) + 15}{2(0)^2 - (0) - 15} = \dfrac{15}{-15} = -1$.

Step 3: $R(-x) = \dfrac{8(-x)^2 + 26(-x) + 15}{2(-x)^2 - (-x) - 15} = \dfrac{8x^2 - 26x + 15}{2x^2 + x - 15}$; this is neither $R(x)$ nor $-R(x)$,
so there is no symmetry.

Step 4:   The vertical asymptote is the zero of $q(x)$: $x = 3$ ($x = -\dfrac{5}{2}$ is not a vertical
asymptote because reduced form must be used to find them.)

Step 5:   Since $n = m$, the line $y = 4$ is the horizontal asymptote.

$R(x)$ does not intersect $y = 4$ because $R(x)$ is not defined at $x = -\dfrac{5}{2}$.

$$\frac{8x^2 + 26x + 15}{2x^2 - x - 15} = 4$$

$$8x^2 + 26x + 15 = 8x^2 - 4x - 60 \rightarrow 30x = -75 \rightarrow x = -\frac{5}{2}$$

Step 6:   Graphing: Step 7:   Graphing by hand:

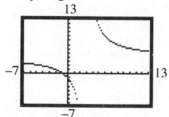

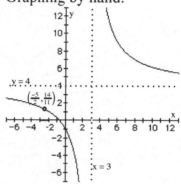

31. $R(x) = \dfrac{x^2 + 5x + 6}{x + 3} = \dfrac{(x + 2)(x + 3)}{x + 3} = x + 2$ $p(x) = x^2 + 5x + 6$; $q(x) = x + 3$;
$n = 2$; $m = 1$

Step 1:   Domain: $\{x \mid x \neq -3\}$

Step 2:   (a)   The x-intercept is the zero of $p(x)$: -2 (-3 is not a zero because reduced
form must be used to find the zeros.)

(b)   The y-intercept is $R(0) = \dfrac{0^2 + 5(0) + 6}{0 + 3} = \dfrac{6}{3} = 2$.

Step 3: $R(-x) = \dfrac{(-x)^2 + 5(-x) + 6}{-x + 3} = \dfrac{x^2 - 5x + 6}{-x + 3}$; this is neither $R(x)$ nor $-R(x)$, so
there is no symmetry.

Step 4:   There are no vertical asymptotes. ($x = -3$ is not a vertical asymptote because
reduced form must be used to find the them.)

Step 5:   Since $n = m + 1$ there is a oblique asymptote. The line $y = x + 2$ is the oblique
asymptote.

The oblique asymptote does not intersect $R(x)$.

Step 6:   Graphing:

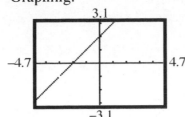

Step 7:   Graphing by hand:

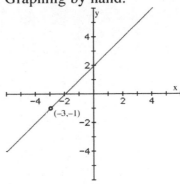

32. $R(x) = \dfrac{x^2 + x - 30}{x + 6} = \dfrac{(x+6)(x-5)}{x+6} = x - 5$ $p(x) = x^2 + x - 30;$ $q(x) = x + 6;$
$n = 2;$ $m = 1$

Step 1:   Domain: $\{x \mid x \neq -6\}$

Step 2:   (a)   The x-intercept is the zero of $p(x)$: 5 (–6 is not a zero because reduced form must be used to find the zeros.)

(b)   The y-intercept is $R(0) = \dfrac{0^2 + (0) - 30}{0 + 6} = \dfrac{-30}{6} = -5$.

Step 3: $R(-x) = \dfrac{(-x)^2 + (-x) - 30}{-x + 6} = \dfrac{x^2 - x - 30}{-x + 6}$; this is neither $R(x)$ nor $-R(x)$, so there is no symmetry.

Step 4:   There are no vertical asymptotes. ($x = -6$ is not a vertical asymptote because reduced form must be used to find them.)

Step 5:   Since $n = m + 1$ there is a oblique asymptote. The line $y = x - 5$ is the oblique asymptote.

The oblique asymptote intersects $R(x)$ at every point of the form $(x, x - 5)$ except $(-6, -11)$.

Step 6:   Graphing:

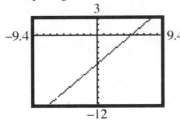

Step 7:   Graphing by hand:

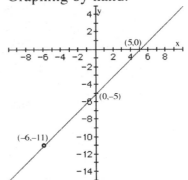

33. $f(x) = x + \dfrac{1}{x} = \dfrac{x^2 + 1}{x}$ $p(x) = x^2 + 1;$ $q(x) = x;$ $n = 2;$ $m = 1$

Step 1:   Domain: $\{x \mid x \neq 0\}$

Step 2:   (a)   There are no x-intercepts.

(b)   There is no y-intercept because 0 is not in the domain.

Step 3: $f(-x) = \dfrac{(-x)^2 + 1}{-x} = \dfrac{x^2 + 1}{-x} = -f(x)$; The graph of $f(x)$ is symmetric to the origin.

431

Step 4:   The vertical asymptote is the zero of $q(x)$: $x = 0$

Step 5:   Since $n = m+1$, there is an oblique asymptote. Dividing:

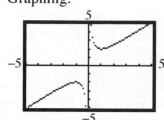

$$f(x) = x + \frac{1}{x}$$

The oblique asymptote is $y = x$.

Solve to find intersection points:

$$\frac{x^2+1}{x} = x \rightarrow x^2 + 1 = x^2 \rightarrow 1 = 0$$

Since there is no solution, the oblique asymptote does not intersect $f(x)$.

Step 6:   Graphing: Step 7:   Graphing by hand:

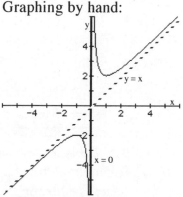

34. $f(x) = 2x + \dfrac{9}{x} = \dfrac{2x^2+9}{x}$ $p(x) = 2x^2 + 9$; $q(x) = x$; $n = 2$; $m = 1$

Step 1:   Domain: $\left\{x \mid x \neq 0\right\}$

Step 2:   (a)   There are no x-intercepts.

(b)   There is no y-intercept because 0 is not in the domain.

Step 3: $f(-x) = \dfrac{2(-x)^2+9}{-x} = \dfrac{2x^2+9}{-x} = -f(x)$; The graph of $f(x)$ is symmetric to the origin.

Step 4:   The vertical asymptote is the zero of $q(x)$: $x = 0$

Step 5:   Since $n = m+1$, there is an oblique asymptote. Dividing:

$$\begin{array}{r} 2x \\ x \overline{)2x^2 + 9} \\ \underline{2x^2} \\ 9 \end{array}$$

$$f(x) = 2x + \frac{9}{x}$$

The oblique asymptote is $y = 2x$.

Solve to find intersection points:

$$\frac{2x^2+9}{x} = 2x \rightarrow 2x^2 + 9 = 2x^2 \rightarrow 9 = 0$$

Since there is no solution, the oblique asymptote does not intersect $f(x)$.

Step 6:   Graphing:

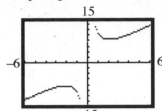

Step 7:   Graphing by hand:

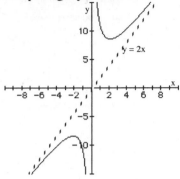

35. $f(x) = x^2 + \dfrac{1}{x} = \dfrac{x^3 + 1}{x}$ $p(x) = x^3 + 1$; $q(x) = x$; $n = 3$; $m = 1$

Step 1:   Domain: $\{x \mid x \neq 0\}$

Step 2:   (a)   The x-intercept is the zero of $p(x)$: -1

   (b)   There is no y-intercept because 0 is not in the domain.

Step 3: $f(-x) = \dfrac{(-x)^3 + 1}{-x} = \dfrac{-x^3 + 1}{-x}$; this is neither $f(x)$ nor $-f(x)$, so there is no symmetry.

Step 4:   The vertical asymptote is the zero of $q(x)$: $x = 0$

Step 5:   Since $n > m + 1$, there is no horizontal or oblique asymptote.

Step 6:   Graphing:

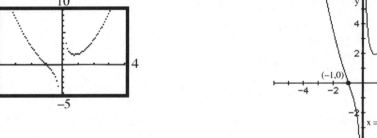

Step 7:   Graphing by hand:

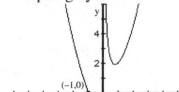

36. $f(x) = 2x^2 + \dfrac{9}{x} = \dfrac{2x^3 + 9}{x}$ $p(x) = 2x^3 + 9$; $q(x) = x$; $n = 3$; $m = 1$

Step 1:   Domain: $\{x \mid x \neq 0\}$

Step 2:   (a)   The x-intercept is the zero of $p(x)$: $-\sqrt[3]{\dfrac{9}{2}} \approx -1.65$

   (b)   There is no y-intercept because 0 is not in the domain.

Step 3: $f(-x) = \dfrac{2(-x)^3 + 9}{-x} = \dfrac{-2x^3 + 9}{-x}$; this is neither $f(x)$ nor $-f(x)$, so there is no symmetry.

Step 4:   The vertical asymptote is the zero of $q(x)$: $x = 0$

Step 5:   Since $n > m + 1$, there is no horizontal or oblique asymptote.

Step 6: Graphing: Step 7:   Graphing by hand:

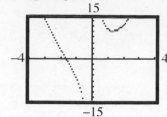

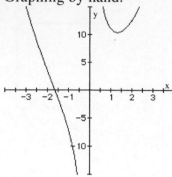

37. $f(x) = x + \dfrac{1}{x^3} = \dfrac{x^4 + 1}{x^3}$ $p(x) = x^4 + 1;$ $q(x) = x^3;$ $n = 4;$ $m = 3$

Step 1: Domain: $\{x \mid x \neq 0\}$

Step 2: (a)   There are no x-intercepts.

        (b)   There is no y-intercept because 0 is not in the domain.

Step 3: $f(-x) = \dfrac{(-x)^4 + 1}{(-x)^3} = \dfrac{x^4 + 1}{-x^3} = -f(x);$ The graph of $f(x)$ is symmetric to the

        origin.

Step 4: The vertical asymptote is the zero of $q(x)$: $x = 0$

Step 5: Since $n = m + 1$, there is an oblique asymptote. Dividing:

$$f(x) = x + \dfrac{1}{x^3}$$

The oblique asymptote is $y = x$.

Solve to find intersection points:

$$\dfrac{x^4 + 1}{x^3} = x \rightarrow x^4 + 1 = x^4 \rightarrow 1 = 0$$

Since there is no solution, the oblique asymptote does not intersect $f(x)$.

Step 6: Graphing: Step 7:   Graphing by hand:

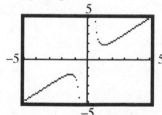

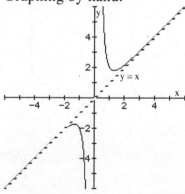

38. $f(x) = 2x + \dfrac{9}{x^3} = \dfrac{2x^4 + 9}{x^3}$ $p(x) = 2x^4 + 9;$ $q(x) = x^3;$ $n = 4;$ $m = 3$

Step 1: Domain: $\{x \mid x \neq 0\}$

Step 2: (a)   There are no x-intercepts.

        (b)   There is no y-intercept because 0 is not in the domain.

Step 3: $f(-x) = \dfrac{2(-x)^4 + 9}{(-x)^3} = \dfrac{2x^4 + 9}{-x^3} = -f(x)$; The graph of $f(x)$ is symmetric to the

origin.

Step 4:   The vertical asymptote is the zero of $q(x)$: $x = 0$

Step 5:   Since $n = m + 1$, there is an oblique asymptote. Dividing:

$$f(x) = 2x + \dfrac{9}{x^3}$$

The oblique asymptote is $y = 2x$.

Solve to find intersection points:

$$\dfrac{2x^4 + 9}{x^3} = 2x \rightarrow 2x^4 + 9 = 2x^4 \rightarrow 9 = 0$$

Since there is no solution, the oblique asymptote does not intersect $f(x)$.

Step 6:   Graphing: Step 7:   Graphing by hand:

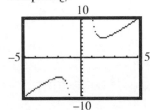

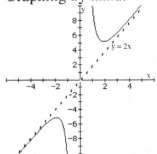

39. $f(x) = \dfrac{x^2}{x^2 - 4}$ 40. $f(x) = \dfrac{-3x}{x^2 - 1}$

41. $f(x) = \dfrac{(x-1)^3(x-3)}{(x+1)^2(x-2)^2}$ 42. $f(x) = \dfrac{3(x+2)(x-1)^2}{(x+3)(x-4)^2}$

43.   (a) $C(t) = \dfrac{t}{2t^2 + 1} \approx \dfrac{t}{2t^2} = \dfrac{1}{2t} \rightarrow 0$ as $t \rightarrow \pm\infty$

therefore the horizontal asymptote is $y = 0$.

The concentration of the drug decreases to 0 as time increases.

(b)   Graphing:

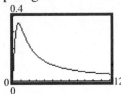

(c)   Using MAXIMUM, the concentration is highest when $t = 0.71$ hours.

44.   (a)   The degree of the numerator is 1 and the degree of the denominator is 2. Thus, the
horizontal asymptote is $C(t) = 0$. The concentration of the drug decreases to 0 as time
increases.

(b)   Graphing:

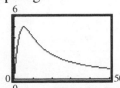

(c)   Using MAXIMUM, the concentration is highest when $t = 5$ minutes.

435

45.   (a)   The average cost function is: $\overline{C}(x) = \dfrac{0.2x^3 - 2.3x^2 + 14.3x + 10.2}{x}$

(b) $\overline{C}(6) = \dfrac{0.2(6)^3 - 2.3(6)^2 + 14.3(6) + 10.2}{6} = \dfrac{56.4}{6} = 9.4$

The average cost of producing 6 Cavaliers per hour is $9400.

(c) $\overline{C}(9) = \dfrac{0.2(9)^3 - 2.3(9)^2 + 14.3(9) + 10.2}{9} = \dfrac{98.4}{9} = 10.933$

The average cost of producing 9 Cavaliers per hour is $10,933.

(d)   Graphing:

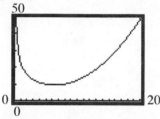

(e)   Using MINIMUM, the number of Cavaliers that should be produced per hour to minimize cost is 6.38.

(f)   The minimum average cost is $9,366.

46.   (a)   The average cost function is: $\overline{C}(x) = \dfrac{0.015x^3 - 0.595x^2 + 9.15x + 98.43}{x}$

(b) $\overline{C}(13) = \dfrac{0.015(13)^3 - 0.595(13)^2 + 9.15(13) + 98.43}{13} = \dfrac{149.78}{13} \approx 11.52$

The average cost of producing 13,000 textbooks per week is $11.52.

(c) $\overline{C}(25) = \dfrac{0.015(25)^3 - 0.595(25)^2 + 9.15(25) + 98.43}{25} = \dfrac{189.68}{25} \approx 7.59$

The average cost of producing 25,000 textbooks per week is $7.59.

(d)   Graphing:

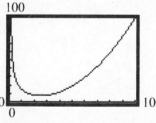

(e)   Using MINIMUM, the number of textbooks that should be produced per week to minimize cost is 25.058 thousand or 25,058 textbooks.

(f)   The minimum average cost is $7.59.

47.   (a)   The surface area is the sum of the areas of the six sides.

$S = xy + xy + xy + xy + x^2 + x^2 = 4xy + 2x^2$

The volume is $x \cdot x \cdot y = x^2 y = 10,000 \quad \rightarrow \quad y = \dfrac{10000}{x^2}$

Thus, $S(x) = 4x\left(\dfrac{10000}{x^2}\right) + 2x^2 = 2x^2 + \dfrac{40000}{x} = \dfrac{2x^3 + 40000}{x}$

(b)   Graphing:

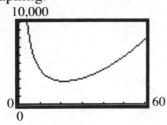

(c)   The minimum surface area (amount of cardboard) is 2,785 square inches.
(d)   The surface area is a minimum when $x = 21.544$.

$$y = \frac{10000}{21.544^2} = 21.545$$

The dimensions of the box are: 21.544 in. by 21.544 in. by 21.545 in.

48.   (a)   The surface area is the sum of the areas of the six sides.

$$S = xy + xy + xy + xy + x^2 + x^2 = 4xy + 2x^2$$

The volume is $x \cdot x \cdot y = x^2 y = 5,000 \quad \rightarrow \quad y = \dfrac{5000}{x^2}$

Thus, $S(x) = 4x\left(\dfrac{5000}{x^2}\right) + 2x^2 = 2x^2 + \dfrac{20000}{x} = \dfrac{2x^3 + 20000}{x}$

(b)   Graphing:

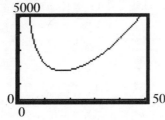

(c)   The minimum surface area (amount of cardboard) is 1,754.41 square inches.
(d)   The surface area is a minimum when $x = 17.1$.

$$y = \frac{5000}{17.1^2} \approx 17.1$$

The dimensions of the box are: 17.1 in. by 17.1 in. by 17.1 in.

49.   (a) $500 = \pi r^2 h \quad \rightarrow \quad h = \dfrac{500}{\pi r^2}$

$$C(r) = 6(2\pi r^2) + 4(2\pi rh) = 12\pi r^2 + 8\pi r\left(\frac{500}{\pi r^2}\right) = 12\pi r^2 + \frac{4000}{r}$$

(b)   Graphing:

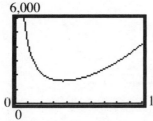

The cost is least for $r = 3.76$ cm.

437

50. (a) $100 = \pi r^2 h \rightarrow h = \dfrac{100}{\pi r^2}$

$$A(r) = 2\pi r^2 + 2\pi rh = 2\pi r^2 + 2\pi r\left(\dfrac{100}{\pi r^2}\right) = 2\pi r^2 + \dfrac{200}{r}$$

(b) $A(3) = 2\pi \cdot 3^2 + \dfrac{200}{3} = 18\pi + \dfrac{200}{3} \approx 123.22$ square feet

(c) $A(2) = 2\pi \cdot 2^2 + \dfrac{200}{2} = 8\pi + 100 \approx 125.13$ square feet

(d) $A(4) = 2\pi \cdot 4^2 + \dfrac{200}{4} = 32\pi + 50 \approx 150.53$ square feet

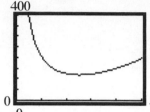

(e) Graphing:　　　　　　　　　　　The area is smallest when $r = 2.52$ feet.

51.

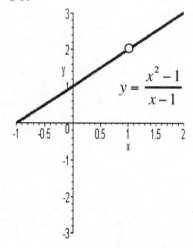

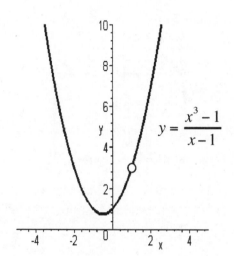

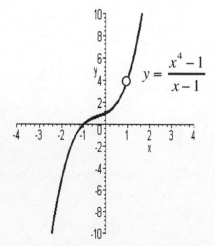

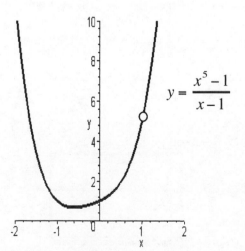

x = 1 is not a vertical asymptote because of the following behavior:

$$y = \frac{x^2-1}{x-1} = \frac{(x+1)(x-1)}{x-1} = x+1 \quad \text{when } x \neq 1$$

$$y = \frac{x^3-1}{x-1} = \frac{(x-1)(x^2+x+1)}{x-1} = x^2+x+1 \quad \text{when } x \neq 1$$

$$y = \frac{x^4-1}{x-1} = \frac{(x^2+1)(x^2-1)}{x-1} = \frac{(x^2+1)(x-1)(x+1)}{x-1} = x^3+x^2+x+1 \quad \text{when } x \neq 1$$

$$y = \frac{x^5-1}{x-1} = \frac{(x^4+x^3+x^2+x+1)(x-1)}{x-1} = x^4+x^3+x^2+x+1 \quad \text{when } x \neq 1$$

In general, the graph of $y = \dfrac{x^n-1}{x-1}, n \geq 1$ an integer will have a "hole" with coordinates $(1, n)$.

52.

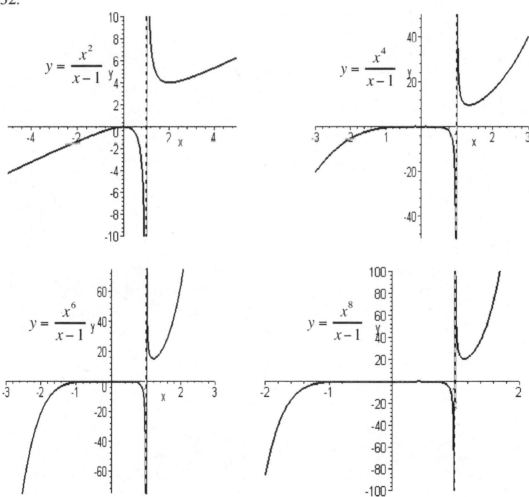

439

53.

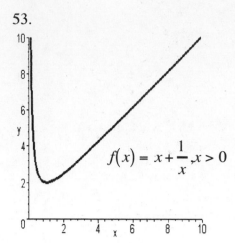

minimum value: $f(1) = 2$

54.

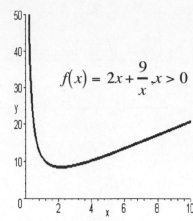

minimum value: $f\left(\sqrt{\dfrac{9}{2}}\right) \approx 6.24$

55.

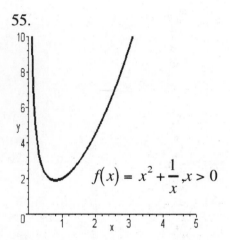

minimum value: $f\left(\sqrt[3]{\dfrac{1}{2}}\right) \approx 1.89$

56.

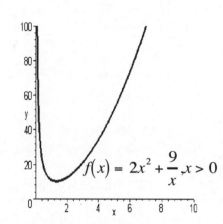

minimum value: $f\left(\sqrt[3]{\dfrac{9}{4}}\right) \approx 10.30$

57.

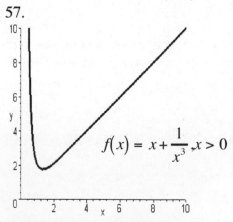

minimum value: $f\left(\sqrt[4]{3}\right) \approx 1.76$

58.

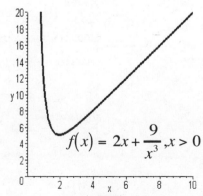

minimum value: $f\left(\sqrt[4]{\dfrac{27}{2}}\right) \approx 5.11$

59.   Answers will vary.

60.   Answers will vary, one example is $R(x) = \dfrac{3(x-2)(x+1)^2}{(x+5)(x-6)^2}$

61.   Answers will vary, one example is $R(x) = \dfrac{2(x-3)(x+2)^2}{(x-1)^3}$

Polynomial and Rational Functions

4.5   Polynomial and Rational Inequalities

1. $(x-5)(x+2) < 0$ $f(x) = (x-5)(x+2)$
     $x = 5, x = -2$ are the zeros.

Interval	Test Number	$f(x)$	Positive/Negative
$-\infty < x < -2$	-3	8	Positive
$-2 < x < 5$	0	-10	Negative
$5 < x < \infty$	6	8	Positive

The solution set is $\left\{ x \mid -2 < x < 5 \right\}$

2. $(x-5)(x+2) > 0$ $f(x) = (x-5)(x+2)$
     $x = 5, x = -2$ are the zeros.

Interval	Test Number	$f(x)$	Positive/Negative
$-\infty < x < -2$	-3	8	Positive
$-2 < x < 5$	0	-10	Negative
$5 < x < \infty$	6	8	Positive

The solution set is $\left\{ x \mid x < -2 \text{ or } x > 5 \right\}$.

3. $x^2 - 4x \geq 0$ $f(x) = x^2 - 4x$
     $x(x-4) \geq 0$
     $x = 0, x = 4$ are the zeros.

Interval	Test Number	$f(x)$	Positive/Negative
$-\infty < x < 0$	-1	5	Positive
$0 < x < 4$	1	-3	Negative
$4 < x < \infty$	5	5	Positive

The solution set is $\left\{ x \mid x \leq 0 \text{ or } x \geq 4 \right\}$.

4. $x^2 + 8x \geq 0$ $f(x) = x^2 + 8x$
     $x(x+8) \geq 0$
     $x = -8, x = 0$ are the zeros.

Interval	Test Number	$f(x)$	Positive/Negative
$-\infty < x < -8$	-9	9	Positive
$-8 < x < 0$	-1	-7	Negative
$0 < x < \infty$	1	9	Positive

The solution set is $\left\{ x \mid x \leq -8 \text{ or } x \geq 0 \right\}$.

5. $$x^2 - 9 < 0 \qquad\qquad f(x) = x^2 - 9$$
    $$(x+3)(x-3) < 0; \qquad x = -3, x = 3 \text{ are the zeros.}$$

Interval	Test Number	$f(x)$	Positive/Negative
$-\infty < x < -3$	-4	7	Positive
$-3 < x < 3$	0	-9	Negative
$3 < x < \infty$	4	7	Positive

    The solution set is $\left\{ x \mid -3 < x < 3 \right\}$.

6. $$x^2 - 1 < 0 \qquad\qquad f(x) = x^2 - 1$$
    $$(x+1)(x-1) < 0; \qquad x = -1, x = 1 \text{ are the zeros.}$$

Interval	Test Number	$f(x)$	Positive/Negative
$-\infty < x < -1$	-2	3	Positive
$-1 < x < 1$	0	-1	Negative
$1 < x < \infty$	2	3	Positive

    The solution set is $\left\{ x \mid -1 < x < 1 \right\}$.

7. $$x^2 + x \geq 2 \qquad\qquad f(x) = x^2 + x - 2$$
    $$x^2 + x - 2 \geq 0 \rightarrow (x+2)(x-1) \geq 0$$
    $$x = -2, x = 1 \text{ are the zeros.}$$

Interval	Test Number	$f(x)$	Positive/Negative
$-\infty < x < -2$	-5	18	Positive
$-2 < x < 1$	0	-2	Negative
$1 < x < \infty$	4	18	Positive

    The solution set is $\left\{ x \mid x \leq -2 \text{ or } x \geq 1 \right\}$.

8. $$x^2 + 7x \leq -12 \qquad\qquad f(x) = x^2 + 7x + 12$$
    $$x^2 + 7x + 12 \leq 0 \rightarrow (x+4)(x+3) \leq 0$$
    $$x = -4, x = -3 \text{ are the zeros.}$$

Interval	Test Number	$f(x)$	Positive/Negative
$-\infty < x < -4$	-5	2	Positive
$-4 < x < -3$	-3.5	-0.25	Negative
$-3 < x < \infty$	0	12	Positive

    The solution set is $\left\{ x \mid -4 \leq x \leq -3 \right\}$.

9. $$2x^2 \leq 5x + 3 \qquad\qquad f(x) = 2x^2 - 5x - 3$$
    $$2x^2 - 5x - 3 \leq 0 \rightarrow (2x+1)(x-3) \leq 0$$
    $$x = -\frac{1}{2}, x = 3 \text{ are the zeros.}$$

Interval	Test Number	$f(x)$	Positive/Negative
$-\infty < x < -1/2$	-1	4	Positive
$-1/2 < x < 3$	0	-3	Negative
$3 < x < \infty$	4	9	Positive

    The solution set is $\left\{ x \mid -\dfrac{1}{2} \leq x \leq 3 \right\}$.

10. $6x^2 \le 6 + 5x$ $f(x) = 6x^2 - 5x - 6$

$6x^2 - 5x - 6 \le 0 \rightarrow (3x + 2)(2x - 3) \le 0$

$x = -\dfrac{2}{3}, x = \dfrac{3}{2}$ are the zeros.

Interval	Test Number	$f(x)$	Positive/Negative
$-\infty < x < -2/3$	-1	5	Positive
$-2/3 < x < 3/2$	0	-6	Negative
$3/2 < x < \infty$	2	8	Positive

The solution set is $\left\{ x \left| -\dfrac{2}{3} \le x \le \dfrac{3}{2} \right. \right\}$.

11. $x(x - 7) > 8$ $f(x) = x^2 - 7x - 8$

$x^2 - 7x > 8 \rightarrow x^2 - 7x - 8 > 0 \rightarrow (x + 1)(x - 8) > 0$

$x = -1, x = 8$ are the zeros.

Interval	Test Number	$f(x)$	Positive/Negative
$-\infty < x < -1$	-2	10	Positive
$-1 < x < 8$	0	-8	Negative
$8 < x < \infty$	9	10	Positive

The solution set is $\left\{ x \left| x < -1 \text{ or } x > 8 \right. \right\}$.

12. $x(x + 1) > 20$ $f(x) = x^2 + x - 20$

$x^2 + x > 20 \rightarrow x^2 + x - 20 > 0 \rightarrow (x + 5)(x - 4) > 0$

$x = -5, x = 4$ are the zeros.

Interval	Test Number	$f(x)$	Positive/Negative
$-\infty < x < -5$	-6	10	Positive
$-5 < x < 4$	0	-20	Negative
$4 < x < \infty$	5	10	Positive

The solution set is $\left\{ x \left| x < -5 \text{ or } x > 4 \right. \right\}$.

13. $4x^2 + 9 < 6x$ $f(x) = 4x^2 - 6x + 9$

$4x^2 - 6x + 9 < 0$

$b^2 - 4ac = (-6)^2 - 4(4)(9) = 36 - 144 = -108$

Since the discriminant is negative, there are no real zeros.

There is only one interval, the entire number line; choose any value and test.

For $x = 0$, $4x^2 - 6x + 9 = 9 > 0$. Thus, there are no real zeros.

14. $25x^2 + 16 < 40x$ $f(x) = 25x^2 - 40x + 16$

$25x^2 - 40x + 16 < 0$

$(5x - 4)^2 < 0$

$x = \dfrac{4}{5}$ is the zero.

Since the square of a quantity is always positive or zero, there are no values of x for which the expression is negative. Thus, there is no solution.

15. $$6(x^2 - 1) > 5x \qquad f(x) = 6x^2 - 5x - 6$$

$$6x^2 - 6 > 5x \rightarrow 6x^2 - 5x - 6 > 0 \rightarrow (3x + 2)(2x - 3) > 0$$

$x = -\dfrac{2}{3}, x = \dfrac{3}{2}$ are the zeros.

Interval	Test Number	$f(x)$	Positive/Negative
$-\infty < x < -2/3$	-1	5	Positive
$-2/3 < x < 3/2$	0	-6	Negative
$3/2 < x < \infty$	2	8	Positive

The solution set is $\left\{ x \middle| x < -\dfrac{2}{3} \text{ or } x > \dfrac{3}{2} \right\}$.

16. $$2(2x^2 - 3x) > -9 \qquad f(x) = 4x^2 - 6x + 9$$

$$4x^2 - 6x > -9 \rightarrow 4x^2 - 6x + 9 > 0$$

$$b^2 - 4ac = (-6)^2 - 4(4)(9) = 36 - 144 = -108$$

$4x^2 - 6x + 9 = 0$ has no real solutions. Therefore it is always positive or always negative. Test at 0: $4(0)^2 - 6(0) + 9 = 9 > 0$ Since it is positive at 0, it will be positive for all real numbers.

17. $$(x - 1)(x^2 + x + 4) \geq 0 \qquad f(x) = (x - 1)(x^2 + x + 4)$$

$x = 1$ is the zero. $x^2 + x + 4 = 0$ has no real zeros.

Interval	Test Number	$f(x)$	Positive/Negative
$-\infty < x < 1$	0	-4	Negative
$1 < x < \infty$	2	10	Positive

The solution set is $\left\{ x \middle| x \geq 1 \right\}$.

18. $$(x + 2)(x^2 - x + 1) \geq 0 \qquad f(x) = (x + 2)(x^2 - x + 1)$$

$x = -2$ is the zero. $x^2 - x + 1 = 0$ has no real zeros.

Interval	Test Number	$f(x)$	Positive/Negative
$-\infty < x < -2$	-3	-13	Negative
$-2 < x < \infty$	0	2	Positive

The solution set is $\left\{ x \middle| x \geq -2 \right\}$.

19. $$(x - 1)(x - 2)(x - 3) \leq 0 \qquad f(x) = (x - 1)(x - 2)(x - 3)$$

$x = 1, x = 2, x = 3$ are the zeros.

Interval	Test Number	$f(x)$	Positive/Negative
$-\infty < x < 1$	0	-6	Negative
$1 < x < 2$	1.5	0.375	Positive
$2 < x < 3$	2.5	-0.375	Negative
$3 < x < \infty$	4	6	Positive

The solution set is $\left\{ x \middle| x \leq 1 \text{ or } 2 \leq x \leq 3 \right\}$.

20.
$$(x+1)(x+2)(x+3) \le 0 \qquad f(x) = (x+1)(x+2)(x+3)$$
$x = -1, x = -2, x = -3$ are the zeros.

Interval	Test Number	$f(x)$	Positive/Negative
$-\infty < x < -3$	-4	-6	Negative
$-3 < x < -2$	-2.5	0.375	Positive
$-2 < x < -1$	-1.5	-0.375	Negative
$-1 < x < \infty$	0	6	Positive

The solution set is $\left\{ x \mid x \le -3 \text{ or } -2 \le x \le -1 \right\}$.

21.
$$x^3 - 2x^2 - 3x > 0 \qquad f(x) = x^3 - 2x^2 - 3x$$
$$x\left(x^2 - 2x - 3\right) > 0 \rightarrow x(x+1)(x-3) > 0$$
$x = -1, x = 0, x = 3$ are the zeros.

Interval	Test Number	$f(x)$	Positive/Negative
$-\infty < x < -1$	-2	-10	Negative
$-1 < x < 0$	-0.5	0.875	Positive
$0 < x < 3$	1	-4	Negative
$3 < x < \infty$	4	20	Positive

The solution set is $\left\{ x \mid -1 < x < 0 \text{ or } x > 3 \right\}$.

22.
$$x^3 + 2x^2 - 3x > 0 \qquad f(x) = x^3 + 2x^2 - 3x$$
$$x\left(x^2 + 2x - 3\right) > 0 \rightarrow x(x-1)(x+3) > 0$$
$x = -3, x = 0, x = 1$ are the zeros.

Interval	Test Number	$f(x)$	Positive/Negative
$-\infty < x < -3$	-4	-20	Negative
$-3 < x < 0$	-1	4	Positive
$0 < x < 1$	0.5	-0.875	Negative
$1 < x < \infty$	2	10	Positive

The solution set is $\left\{ x \mid -3 < x < 0 \text{ or } x > 1 \right\}$.

23.
$$x^4 > x^2 \qquad f(x) = x^4 - x^2$$
$$x^4 - x^2 > 0 \rightarrow x^2\left(x^2 - 1\right) > 0 \rightarrow x^2(x+1)(x-1) > 0$$
$x = -1, x = 0, x = 1$ are the zeros.

Interval	Test Number	$f(x)$	Positive/Negative
$-\infty < x < -1$	-2	12	Positive
$-1 < x < 0$	-0.5	-0.1875	Negative
$0 < x < 1$	0.5	-0.1875	Negative
$1 < x < \infty$	2	12	Positive

The solution set is $\left\{ x \mid x < -1 \text{ or } x > 1 \right\}$.

24. $x^4 < 4x^2$ $f(x) = x^4 - 4x^2$

$x^4 - 4x^2 < 0 \rightarrow x^2(x^2 - 4) < 0 \rightarrow x^2(x+2)(x-2) < 0$

$x = -2, x = 0, x = 2$ are the zeros.

Interval	Test Number	$f(x)$	Positive/Negative
$-\infty < x < -2$	-3	45	Positive
$-2 < x < 0$	-1	-3	Negative
$0 < x < 2$	1	-3	Negative
$2 < x < \infty$	3	45	Positive

The solution set is $\{x | -2 < x < 0 \text{ or } 0 < x < 2\}$.

25. $x^3 \geq 4x^2$ $f(x) = x^3 - 4x^2$

$x^3 - 4x^2 \geq 0 \rightarrow x^2(x-4) \geq 0$

$x = 0, x = 4$ are the zeros.

Interval	Test Number	$f(x)$	Positive/Negative
$-\infty < x < 0$	-1	-3	Negative
$0 < x < 4$	0.5	-0.875	Negative
	5	25	Positive
$4 < x < \infty$			

The solution set is $\{x | x \geq 4\}$.

26. $x^3 \leq 9x^2$ $f(x) = x^3 - 9x^2$

$x^3 - 9x^2 \leq 0 \rightarrow x^2(x-9) \leq 0$

$x = 0, x = 9$ are the zeros.

Interval	Test Number	$f(x)$	Positive/Negative
$-\infty < x < 0$	-1	-10	Negative
$0 < x < 9$	1	-8	Negative
	10	100	Positive
$9 < x < \infty$			

The solution set is $\{x | x < 0 \text{ or } 0 < x < 9\}$.

27. $x^4 > 1$ $f(x) = x^4 - 1$

$x^4 - 1 > 0 \rightarrow (x^2 + 1)(x^2 - 1) > 0 \rightarrow (x^2 + 1)(x+1)(x-1) > 0$

$x = -1, x = 1$ are the zeros.

Interval	Test Number	$f(x)$	Positive/Negative
$-\infty < x < -1$	-2	15	Positive
$-1 < x < 1$	0	-1	Negative
$1 < x < \infty$	2	15	Positive

The solution set is $\{x | x < -1 \text{ or } x > 1\}$.

28. $x^3 > 1$ $f(x) = x^3 - 1$

$x^3 - 1 > 0 \rightarrow (x-1)(x^2 + x + 1) > 0$

$x = 1$ is the zero. $(x^2 + x + 1 = 0$ has no real zeros.)

Interval	Test Number	$f(x)$	Positive/Negative
$-\infty < x < 1$	0	-1	Negative
$1 < x < \infty$	2	7	Positive

The solution set is $\{ x \mid x > 1 \}$

29. $\dfrac{x+1}{x-1} > 0$ $f(x) = \dfrac{x+1}{x-1}$

The zeros and values where the expression is undefined are $x = -1$, and $x = 1$.

Interval	Test Number	$f(x)$	Positive/Negative
$-\infty < x < -1$	-2	$1/3$	Positive
$-1 < x < 1$	0	-1	Negative
$1 < x < \infty$	2	3	Positive

The solution set is $\{ x \mid x < -1 \ \text{ or } \ x > 1 \}$.

30. $\dfrac{x-3}{x+1} > 0$ $f(x) = \dfrac{x-3}{x+1}$

The zeros and values where the expression is undefined are $x = -1$, and $x = 3$.

Interval	Test Number	$f(x)$	Positive/Negative
$-\infty < x < -1$	-2	5	Positive
$-1 < x < 3$	0	-3	Negative
$3 < x < \infty$	4	$1/5$	Positive

The solution set is $\{ x \mid x < -1 \ \text{ or } \ x > 3 \}$.

31. $\dfrac{(x-1)(x+1)}{x} < 0$ $f(x) = \dfrac{(x-1)(x+1)}{x}$

The zeros and values where the expression is undefined are $x = -1$, $x = 0$, and $x = 1$.

Interval	Test Number	$f(x)$	Positive/Negative
$-\infty < x < -1$	-2	-1.5	Negative
$-1 < x < 0$	-0.5	1.5	Positive
$0 < x < 1$	0.5	-1.5	Negative
$1 < x < \infty$	2	1.5	Positive

The solution set is $\{ x \mid x < -1 \ \text{ or } \ 0 < x < 1 \}$.

32. $\dfrac{(x-3)(x+2)}{x-1} \le 0$ $f(x) = \dfrac{(x-3)(x+2)}{x-1}$

The zeros and values where the expression is undefined are $x = -2$, $x = 1$, and $x = 3$.

Interval	Test Number	$f(x)$	Positive/Negative
$-\infty < x < -2$	-3	-1.5	Negative
$-2 < x < 1$	0	6	Positive
$1 < x < 3$	2	-4	Negative
$3 < x < \infty$	4	2	Positive

The solution set is $\{ x \mid x \le -2 \ \text{ or } \ 1 < x \le 3 \}$.

33.
$$\frac{(x-2)^2}{x^2-1} \geq 0 \qquad\qquad f(x) = \frac{(x-2)^2}{x^2-1}$$

$$\frac{(x-2)^2}{(x+1)(x-1)} \geq 0$$

The zeros and values where the expression is undefined are $x = -1$, $x = 1$, and $x = 2$.

Interval	Test Number	$f(x)$	Positive/Negative
$-\infty < x < -1$	-2	$16/3$	Positive
$-1 < x < 1$	0	-4	Negative
$1 < x < 2$	1.5	0.2	Positive
$2 < x < \infty$	3	0.125	Positive

The solution set is $\left\{ x \mid x < -1 \ \text{or} \ x > 1 \right\}$.

34.
$$\frac{(x+5)^2}{x^2-4} \geq 0 \qquad\qquad f(x) = \frac{(x+5)^2}{x^2-4}$$

$$\frac{(x+5)^2}{(x+2)(x-2)} \geq 0$$

The zeros and values where the expression is undefined are $x = -5$, $x = -2$, and $x = 2$.

Interval	Test Number	$f(x)$	Positive/Negative
$-\infty < x < -5$	-6	$1/32$	Positive
$-5 < x < -2$	-3	$4/5$	Positive
$-2 < x < 2$	0	$-25/4$	Negative
$2 < x < \infty$	3	$64/5$	Positive

The solution set is $\left\{ x \mid x < -2 \ \text{or} \ x > 2 \right\}$.

35.
$$6x - 5 < \frac{6}{x} \qquad f(x) = 6x - 5 - \frac{6}{x}$$

$$6x - 5 - \frac{6}{x} < 0 \rightarrow \frac{6x^2 - 5x - 6}{x} < 0 \rightarrow \frac{(2x-3)(3x+2)}{x} < 0$$

The zeros and values where the expression is undefined are $x = -\frac{2}{3}$, $x = 0$, and $x = \frac{3}{2}$.

Interval	Test Number	$f(x)$	Positive/Negative
$-\infty < x < -2/3$	-1	-5	Negative
$-2/3 < x < 0$	-0.5	4	Positive
$0 < x < 3/2$	1	-5	Negative
$3/2 < x < \infty$	2	4	Positive

The solution set is $\left\{ x \mid x < -\frac{2}{3} \ \text{or} \ 0 < x < \frac{3}{2} \right\}$.

36.
$$x + \frac{12}{x} < 7 \qquad f(x) = x + \frac{12}{x} - 7$$

$$x + \frac{12}{x} - 7 < 0 \rightarrow \frac{x^2 - 7x + 12}{x} < 0 \rightarrow \frac{(x-3)(x-4)}{x} < 0$$

The zeros and values where the expression is undefined are $x = 0$, $x = 3$, and $x = 4$.

Interval	Test Number	$f(x)$	Positive/Negative
$-\infty < x < 0$	-1	-20	Negative
$0 < x < 3$	1	6	Positive
$3 < x < 4$	3.5	-0.07	Negative
$4 < x < \infty$	5	0.4	Positive

The solution set is $\left\{ x \mid x < 0 \text{ or } 3 < x < 4 \right\}$.

37. $\quad \dfrac{x+4}{x-2} \leq 1 \qquad f(x) = \dfrac{x+4}{x-2} - 1$

$$\frac{x+4}{x-2} - 1 \leq 0 \rightarrow \frac{x+4-(x-2)}{x-2} \leq 0 \rightarrow \frac{6}{x-2} \leq 0$$

The value where the expression is undefined is $x = 2$.

Interval	Test Number	$f(x)$	Positive/Negative
$-\infty < x < 2$	0	-3	Negative
$2 < x < \infty$	3	6	Positive

The solution set is $\left\{ x \mid x < 2 \right\}$.

38. $\quad \dfrac{x+2}{x-4} \geq 1 \qquad f(x) = \dfrac{x+2}{x-4} - 1$

$$\frac{x+2}{x-4} - 1 \geq 0 \rightarrow \frac{x+2-(x-4)}{x-4} \geq 0 \rightarrow \frac{6}{x-4} \geq 0$$

The value where the expression is undefined is $x = 4$.

Interval	Test Number	$f(x)$	Positive/Negative
$-\infty < x < 4$	0	$-3/2$	Negative
$4 < x < \infty$	5	6	Positive

The solution set is $\left\{ x \mid x > 4 \right\}$.

39. $\quad \dfrac{3x-5}{x+2} \leq 2 \qquad f(x) = \dfrac{3x-5}{x+2} - 2$

$$\frac{3x-5}{x+2} - 2 \leq 0 \rightarrow \frac{3x-5-2(x+2)}{x+2} \leq 0 \rightarrow \frac{x-9}{x+2} \leq 0$$

The zeros and values where the expression is undefined are $x = -2$, and $x = 9$.

Interval	Test Number	$f(x)$	Positive/Negative
$-\infty < x < -2$	-3	12	Positive
$-2 < x < 9$	0	-4.5	Negative
$9 < x < \infty$	10	$1/12$	Positive

The solution set is $\left\{ x \mid -2 < x \leq 9 \right\}$.

40. $\quad \dfrac{x-4}{2x+4} \geq 1 \qquad f(x) = \dfrac{x-4}{2x+4} - 1$

$$\frac{x-4}{2x+4} - 1 \geq 0 \rightarrow \frac{x-4-2x-4}{2x+4} \geq 0 \rightarrow \frac{-x-8}{2x+4} \geq 0$$

The zeros and values where the expression is undefined are $x = -8$, and $x = -2$.

Interval	Test Number	$f(x)$	Positive/Negative
$-\infty < x < -8$	-9	$-1/14$	Negative
$-8 < x < -2$	-3	$5/2$	Positive
$-2 < x < \infty$	0	-2	Negative

The solution set is $\left\{ x \mid -8 \le x < -2 \right\}$.

41.
$$\frac{1}{x-2} < \frac{2}{3x-9} \qquad f(x) = \frac{1}{x+2} - \frac{2}{3x-9}$$

$$\frac{1}{x-2} - \frac{2}{3x-9} < 0 \rightarrow \frac{3x-9-2(x-2)}{(x-2)(3x-9)} < 0 \rightarrow \frac{x-5}{(x-2)(3x-9)} < 0$$

The zeros and values where the expression is undefined are $x = 2$, $x = 3$, and $x = 5$.

Interval	Test Number	$f(x)$	Positive/Negative
$-\infty < x < 2$	0	$-5/18$	Negative
$2 < x < 3$	2.5	$10/3$	Positive
$3 < x < 5$	4	$-1/6$	Negative
$5 < x < \infty$	6	$1/36$	Positive

The solution set is $\left\{ x \mid x < 2 \text{ or } 3 < x < 5 \right\}$.

42.
$$\frac{5}{x-3} > \frac{3}{x+1} \qquad f(x) = \frac{5}{x-3} - \frac{3}{x+1}$$

$$\frac{5}{x-3} - \frac{3}{x+1} > 0 \rightarrow \frac{5x+5-3x+9}{(x-3)(x+1)} > 0 \rightarrow \frac{2x+14}{(x-3)(x+1)} > 0$$

The zeros and values where the expression is undefined are $x = -7$, $x = -1$, and $x = 3$.

Interval	Test Number	$f(x)$	Positive/Negative
$-\infty < x < -7$	-8	$-2/77$	Negative
$-7 < x < -1$	-2	2	Positive
$-1 < x < 3$	0	$-14/3$	Negative
$3 < x < \infty$	4	$22/5$	Positive

The solution set is $\left\{ x \mid -7 < x < -1 \text{ or } x > 3 \right\}$.

43.
$$\frac{2x+5}{x+1} > \frac{x+1}{x-1} \qquad f(x) = \frac{2x+5}{x+1} - \frac{x+1}{x-1}$$

$$\frac{2x+5}{x+1} - \frac{x+1}{x-1} > 0 \rightarrow \frac{(2x+5)(x-1)-(x+1)(x+1)}{(x+1)(x-1)} > 0$$

$$\frac{2x^2+3x-5-\left(x^2+2x+1\right)}{(x+1)(x-1)} > 0 \rightarrow \frac{x^2+x-6}{(x+1)(x-1)} > 0 \rightarrow \frac{(x+3)(x-2)}{(x+1)(x-1)} > 0$$

The zeros and values where the expression is undefined are $x = -3$, $x = -1$, $x = 1$, $x = 2$.

Interval	Test Number	$f(x)$	Positive/Negative
$-\infty < x < -3$	-4	$2/5$	Positive
$-3 < x < -1$	-2	$-4/3$	Negative
$-1 < x < 1$	0	6	Positive
$1 < x < 2$	1.5	$-9/5$	Negative
$2 < x < \infty$	3	$3/4$	Positive

The solution set is $\left\{ x \mid x < -3, \ -1 < x < 1, \ x > 2 \right\}$.

44. $\dfrac{1}{x+2} > \dfrac{3}{x+1}$ $f(x) = \dfrac{1}{x+2} - \dfrac{3}{x+1}$

$\dfrac{1}{x+2} - \dfrac{3}{x+1} > 0 \rightarrow \dfrac{x+1-3(x+2)}{(x+2)(x+1)} > 0 \rightarrow \dfrac{x+1-3x-6}{(x+2)(x+1)} > 0 \rightarrow \dfrac{-2x-5}{(x+2)(x+1)} > 0$

The zeros and values where the expression is undefined are $x = -\dfrac{5}{2}, x = -2,$ and $x = -1$.

Interval	Test Number	$f(x)$	Positive/Negative
$-\infty < x < -5/2$	-3	$1/2$	Positive
$-5/2 < x < -2$	-2.1	-7.27	Negative
$-2 < x < -1$	-1.5	8	Positive
$-1 < x < \infty$	0	$-5/2$	Negative

The solution set is $\left\{ x \mid x < -\dfrac{5}{2} \text{ or } -2 < x < -1 \right\}$.

45. $\dfrac{x^2(3+x)(x+4)}{(x+5)(x-1)} \geq 0$ $f(x) = \dfrac{x^2(3+x)(x+4)}{(x+5)(x-1)}$

The zeros and values where the expression is undefined are
$x = -5, \ x = -4, \ x = -3, \ x = 0$ and $x = 1$.

Interval	Test Number	$f(x)$	Positive/Negative
$-\infty < x < -5$	-6	$216/7$	Positive
$-5 < x < -4$	-4.5	$-243/44$	Negative
$-4 < x < -3$	-3.5	$49/108$	Positive
$-3 < x < 0$	-1	$-3/4$	Negative
$0 < x < 1$	0.5	$-63/44$	Negative
$1 < x < \infty$	2	$120/7$	Positive

The solution set is $\left\{ x \mid x < -5, -4 \leq x \leq -3, x > 1 \right\}$.

46. $\dfrac{x(x^2+1)(x-2)}{(x-1)(x+1)} \geq 0$ $f(x) = \dfrac{x(x^2+1)(x-2)}{(x-1)(x+1)}$

The zeros and values where the expression is undefined are $x = -1, x = 0, x = 1, x = 2$.

Interval	Test Number	$f(x)$	Positive/Negative
$-\infty < x < -1$	-2	$40/3$	Positive
$-1 < x < 0$	-0.5	-2.08	Negative
$0 < x < 1$	0.5	1.25	Positive
$1 < x < 2$	1.5	-1.95	Negative
$2 < x < \infty$	3	3.75	Positive

The solution set is $\left\{ x \mid x < -1, 0 < x < 1, x \geq 2 \right\}$.

47. Let x be the positive number. Then
$$x^3 > 4x^2 \to x^3 - 4x^2 > 0 \to x^2(x-4) > 0$$
The zeros are $x = 0$ and $x = 4$. $f(x) = x^3 - 4x^2$

Interval	Test Number	$f(x)$	Positive/Negative
$-\infty < x < 0$	-1	-5	Negative
$0 < x < 4$	1	-3	Negative
$4 < x < \infty$	5	25	Positive

The solution set is $\{x \mid x > 4\}$. All real numbers larger than 4 satisfy the condition.

48. Let x be the positive number. Then
$$x^2 > 2x \to x^2 - 2x > 0 \to x(x-2) > 0$$
The zeros are $x = 0$ and $x = 2$. $f(x) = x^2 - 2x$

Interval	Test Number	$f(x)$	Positive/Negative
$-\infty < x < 0$	-1	3	Positive
$0 < x < 2$	1	-1	Negative
$2 < x < \infty$	3	3	Positive

The solution set is $\{x \mid x < 0 \text{ or } x > 2\}$. Since x is positive, all real numbers larger than 2 satisfy the condition.

49. The domain of the expression includes all values for which
$$x^2 - 16 \ge 0 \to (x+4)(x-4) \ge 0$$
The zeros are $x = -4$ and $x = 4$. $f(x) = x^2 - 16$

Interval	Test Number	$f(x)$	Positive/Negative
$-\infty < x < -4$	-5	9	Positive
$-4 < x < 4$	0	-16	Negative
$4 < x < \infty$	5	9	Positive

The domain is $\{x \mid x \le -4 \text{ or } x \ge 4\}$.

50. The domain of the expression includes all values for which
$$x^3 - 3x^2 \ge 0 \to x^2(x-3) \ge 0$$
The zeros are $x = 0$ and $x = 3$. $f(x) = x^3 - 3x^2$

Interval	Test Number	$f(x)$	Positive/Negative
$-\infty < x < 0$	-1	-4	Negative
$0 < x < 3$	1	-2	Negative
$3 < x < \infty$	4	16	Positive

The domain is $\{x \mid x = 0 \text{ or } x \ge 3\}$.

51. The domain of the expression includes all values for which
$$\frac{x-2}{x+4} \geq 0$$
The zeros and values where the expression is undefined are $x = -4$ and $x = 2$.
$$f(x) = \frac{x-2}{x+4}$$

Interval	Test Number	$f(x)$	Positive/Negative
$-\infty < x < -4$	-5	7	Positive
$-4 < x < 2$	0	$-1/2$	Negative
$2 < x < \infty$	3	$1/7$	Positive

The domain is $\left\{ x \mid x < -4 \text{ or } x \geq 2 \right\}$.

52. The domain of the expression includes all values for which
$$\frac{x-1}{x+4} \geq 0$$
The zeros and values where the expression is undefined are $x = -4$ and $x = 1$.
$$f(x) = \frac{x-1}{x+4}$$

Interval	Test Number	$f(x)$	Positive/Negative
$-\infty < x < -4$	-5	6	Positive
$-4 < x < 1$	0	$-1/4$	Negative
$1 < x < \infty$	2	$1/6$	Positive

The domain is $\left\{ x \mid x < -4 \text{ or } x \geq 1 \right\}$.

53. Find the values of t for which
$$80t - 16t^2 > 96$$

$-16t^2 + 80t - 96 > 0 \rightarrow 16t^2 - 80t + 96 < 0 \rightarrow 16(t^2 - 5t + 6) < 0 \rightarrow 16(t-2)(t-3) < 0$

The zeros are $t = 2$ and $t = 3$. $s(t) = 16t^2 - 80t + 96$

Interval	Test Number	$s(t)$	Positive/Negative
$-\infty < t < 2$	1	32	Positive
$2 < t < 3$	2.5	-4	Negative
$3 < t < \infty$	4	32	Positive

The solution set is $\left\{ t \mid 2 < t < 3 \right\}$. The ball is more than 96 feet above the ground for times between 2 and 3 seconds.

54. Find the values of t for which
$$96t - 16t^2 > 112$$
$$-16t^2 + 96t - 112 > 0$$
Graph $s(t) = -16t^2 + 96t - 112$.
The zeros are $t = 1.59$ and $t = 4.41$. $s(t) = -16t^2 + 96t - 112$

Interval	Test Number	$s(t)$	Positive/Negative
$-\infty < t < 1.59$	1	-32	Negative
$1.59 < t < 4.41$	2	16	Positive
$4.41 < t < \infty$	5	-32	Negative

The solution set is $\{t \mid 1.59 < t < 4.41\}$. The ball is more than 112 feet above the ground for times between 1.59 and 4.41 seconds.

55.   Profit = Revenue – Cost

The zeros are approximately $x = 7.75$ and $x = 32.25$.

$$f(x) = x^2 - 40x + 250$$

Interval	Test Number	$f(x)$	Positive/Negative
$0 < x < 7.75$	7	19	Positive
$7.75 < x < 32.25$	10	–50	Negative
$32.25 < x < \infty$	40	250	Positive

The profit is at least $50 when at least 8 and no more than 32 watches are sold.

56.   Profit = Revenue – Cost

$$x(5 - 0.05x) - 1.50x \geq 60$$

$$5x - 0.05x^2 - 1.5x \geq 60$$

$$-0.05x^2 + 3.5x - 60 \geq 0$$

$$x^2 - 70x + 1200 \leq 0$$

$$(x - 40)(x - 30) \leq 0$$

The zeros are $x = 30$ and $x = 40$.

$$f(x) = x^2 - 70x + 1200$$

Interval	Test Number	$f(x)$	Positive/Negative
$0 < x < 30$	10	600	Positive
$30 < x < 40$	35	–25	Negative
$40 < x < \infty$	50	200	Positive

The profit is at least $60 when at least 30 and no more than 40 boxes of candy are sold.

57.   The equation $x^2 + kx + 1 = 0$ has no real solutions whenever the discriminant is less than zero.

Solving $b^2 - 4ac = k^2 - 4 < 0 \rightarrow (k + 4)(k - 4) < 0$

The zeros are $k = -4$ and $k = 4$.

$$f(k) = k^2 - 4$$

Interval	Test Number	$f(x)$	Positive/Negative
$-\infty < k < -4$	-5	21	Positive
$-4 < k < 4$	0	–4	Negative
	5	21	Positive
$4 < k < \infty$			

Therefore the equation $x^2 + kx + 1 = 0$ has no real solutions whenever $-4 < k < 4$.

58.   The equation $kx^2 + 2x + 1 = 0$ has two distinct real solutions whenever the discriminant is greater than zero.

Solving $b^2 - 4ac = 4 - 4k > 0 \rightarrow 4(1 - k) > 0$

The zero is $k = 1$.

$$f(k) = 4 - 4k$$

Interval	Test Number	$f(x)$	Positive/Negative
$-\infty < k < 1$	0	4	Positive
$1 < k < \infty$	2	-4	Negative

Therefore the equation $x^2 + kx + 1 = 0$ has two distinct real solutions whenever $-\infty < k < 1$.

59. Answers will vary, for example,

$x^2 < 0$ has no real solution $x^2 \leq 0$ has exactly one real solution

60. $x^2 + 1 < -5$ has no real solution since $x^2 + 1$ always yields a positive number and therefore can never be less than -5.

Polynomial and Rational Functions

4.R Chapter Review

1. $f(x) = (x-2)^2 + 2 = x^2 - 4x + 4 + 2 = x^2 - 4x + 6$

$a = 1, b = -4, c = 6.$ Since $a = 1 > 0,$ the graph opens up.

The x-coordinate of the vertex is $x = \dfrac{-b}{2a} = \dfrac{-(-4)}{2(1)} = \dfrac{4}{2} = 2.$

The y-coordinate of the vertex is $f\left(\dfrac{-b}{2a}\right) = f(2) = (2)^2 - 4(2) + 6 = 2.$

Thus, the vertex is (2, 2).
The axis of symmetry is the line $x = 2.$
The discriminant is:
$$b^2 - 4ac = (-4)^2 - 4(1)(6) = -8 < 0,$$
so the graph has no x-intercepts.
The y-intercept is $f(0) = 6.$

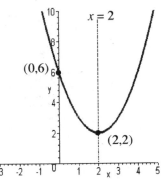

2. $f(x) = (x+1)^2 - 4 = x^2 + 2x + 2 - 4 = x^2 + 2x - 2$
$a = 1, b = 2, c = -2.$ Since $a = 1 > 0,$ the graph opens up.

The x-coordinate of the vertex is $x = \dfrac{-b}{2a} = \dfrac{-2}{2(1)} = -1.$

The y-coordinate of the vertex is $f\left(\dfrac{-b}{2a}\right) = f(-1) = (-1)^2 + 2(-1) - 2 = -3.$

Thus, the vertex is (- 1, - 3).
The axis of symmetry is the line $x = -1.$
The discriminant is:
$$b^2 - 4ac = (2)^2 - 4(1)(-2) = 12 > 0,$$
so the graph has two x-intercepts.
The x-intercepts are found by solving:
$$x^2 + 2x - 2 = 0$$
$$x = \dfrac{-2 \pm \sqrt{12}}{2} = \dfrac{-2 \pm 2\sqrt{3}}{2} = -1 \pm \sqrt{3}$$
The x-intercepts are $-1 - \sqrt{3}$ and $-1 + \sqrt{3}.$
The y-intercept is $f(0) = -2.$

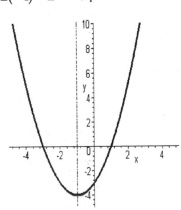

3. $f(x) = \dfrac{1}{4}x^2 - 16$

$a = \dfrac{1}{4}, b = 0, c = -16$. Since $a = \dfrac{1}{4} > 0$, the graph opens up.

The x-coordinate of the vertex is $x = \dfrac{-b}{2a} = \dfrac{-0}{2\left(\dfrac{1}{4}\right)} = \dfrac{0}{\left(\dfrac{1}{2}\right)} = 0$.

The y-coordinate of the vertex is $f\left(\dfrac{-b}{2a}\right) = f(0) = \dfrac{1}{4}(0)^2 - 16 = -16$.

Thus, the vertex is $(0, -16)$.
The axis of symmetry is the line $x = 0$.
The discriminant is:

$$b^2 - 4ac = (0)^2 - 4\left(\dfrac{1}{4}\right)(-16) = 16 > 0,$$

so the graph has two x-intercepts.
The x-intercepts are found by solving:

$$\dfrac{1}{4}x^2 - 16 = 0$$

$$x^2 - 64 = 0 \rightarrow x^2 = 64 \rightarrow x = 8 \ \text{ or } \ x = -8$$

The x-intercepts are -8 and 8.
The y-intercept is $f(0) = -16$.

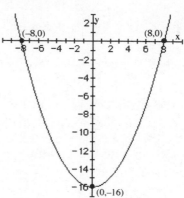

4. $f(x) = -\dfrac{1}{2}x^2 - 2$

$a = -\dfrac{1}{2}, b = 0, c = -2$. Since $a = -\dfrac{1}{2} < 0$, the graph opens down.

The x-coordinate of the vertex is $x = \dfrac{-b}{2a} = \dfrac{-0}{2\left(-\dfrac{1}{2}\right)} = \dfrac{0}{-1} = 0$.

The y-coordinate of the vertex is $f\left(\dfrac{-b}{2a}\right) = f(0) = -\dfrac{1}{2}(0)^2 - 2 = -2$.

Thus, the vertex is $(0, -2)$.
The axis of symmetry is the line $x = 0$.
The discriminant is:

$$b^2 - 4ac = (0)^2 - 4\left(-\dfrac{1}{2}\right)(-2) = -4 < 0,$$

so the graph has no x-intercepts.
The y-intercept is $f(0) = -2$.

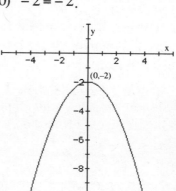

5. $f(x) = -4x^2 + 4x$
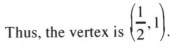
$a = -4, b = 4, c = 0.$ Since $a = -4 < 0$, the graph opens down.

The x-coordinate of the vertex is $x = \dfrac{-b}{2a} = \dfrac{-4}{2(-4)} = \dfrac{-4}{-8} = \dfrac{1}{2}$.

The y-coordinate of the vertex is $f\left(\dfrac{-b}{2a}\right) = f\left(\dfrac{1}{2}\right) = -4\left(\dfrac{1}{2}\right)^2 + 4\left(\dfrac{1}{2}\right) = -1 + 2 = 1$.

Thus, the vertex is $\left(\dfrac{1}{2}, 1\right)$.

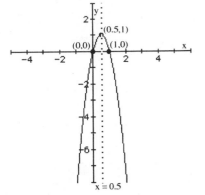

The axis of symmetry is the line $x = \dfrac{1}{2}$.

The discriminant is:
$$b^2 - 4ac = 4^2 - 4(-4)(0) = 16 > 0,$$
so the graph has two x-intercepts.

The x-intercepts are found by solving:
$$-4x^2 + 4x = 0 \rightarrow -4x(x-1) = 0 \rightarrow x = 0 \text{ or } x = 1$$
The x-intercepts are 0 and 1.

The y-intercept is $f(0) = -4(0)^2 + 4(0) = 0$.

6. $f(x) = 9x^2 - 6x + 3$

$a = 9, b = -6, c = 3.$ Since $a = 9 > 0$, the graph opens up.

The x-coordinate of the vertex is $x = \dfrac{-b}{2a} = \dfrac{-(-6)}{2(9)} = \dfrac{6}{18} = \dfrac{1}{3}$.

The y-coordinate of the vertex is $f\left(\dfrac{-b}{2a}\right) = f\left(\dfrac{1}{3}\right) = 9\left(\dfrac{1}{3}\right)^2 - 6\left(\dfrac{1}{3}\right) + 3 = 1 - 2 + 3 = 2$.

Thus, the vertex is $\left(\dfrac{1}{3}, 2\right)$.

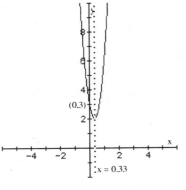

The axis of symmetry is the line $x = \dfrac{1}{3}$.

The discriminant is:
$$b^2 - 4ac = (-6)^2 - 4(9)(3) = -72 < 0,$$
so the graph has no x-intercepts.

The y-intercept is $f(0) = 9(0)^2 - 6(0) + 3 = 3$.

7. $f(x) = \dfrac{9}{2}x^2 + 3x + 1$

$a = \dfrac{9}{2}, b = 3, c = 1.$ Since $a = \dfrac{9}{2} > 0$, the graph opens up.

The x-coordinate of the vertex is 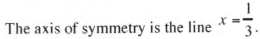 $x = \dfrac{-b}{2a} = \dfrac{-3}{2\left(\dfrac{9}{2}\right)} = \dfrac{-3}{9} = -\dfrac{1}{3}$.

The y-coordinate of the vertex is $f\left(\dfrac{-b}{2a}\right) = f\left(-\dfrac{1}{3}\right) = \dfrac{9}{2}\left(-\dfrac{1}{3}\right)^2 + 3\left(-\dfrac{1}{3}\right) + 1 = \dfrac{1}{2} - 1 + 1 = \dfrac{1}{2}$.

Thus, the vertex is $\left(-\dfrac{1}{3}, \dfrac{1}{2}\right)$.

The axis of symmetry is the line $x = -\dfrac{1}{3}$.

The discriminant is:

$$b^2 - 4ac = 3^2 - 4\left(\dfrac{9}{2}\right)(1) = 9 - 18 = -9 < 0,$$

so the graph has no x-intercepts.

The y-intercept is $f(0) = \dfrac{9}{2}(0)^2 + 3(0) + 1 = 1$.

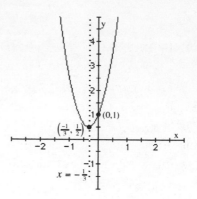

8. $f(x) = -x^2 + x + \dfrac{1}{2}$

$a = -1, b = 1, c = \dfrac{1}{2}.$ Since $a = -1 < 0$, the graph opens down.

The x-coordinate of the vertex is $x = \dfrac{-b}{2a} = \dfrac{-1}{2(-1)} = \dfrac{-1}{-2} = \dfrac{1}{2}$.

The y-coordinate of the vertex is $f\left(\dfrac{-b}{2a}\right) = f\left(\dfrac{1}{2}\right) = -\left(\dfrac{1}{2}\right)^2 + \left(\dfrac{1}{2}\right) + \dfrac{1}{2} = -\dfrac{1}{4} + 1 = \dfrac{3}{4}$.

Thus, the vertex is $\left(\dfrac{1}{2}, \dfrac{3}{4}\right)$.

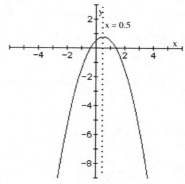

The axis of symmetry is the line $x = \dfrac{1}{2}$.

The discriminant is:

$$b^2 - 4ac = 1^2 - 4(-1)\left(\dfrac{1}{2}\right) = 1 + 2 = 3 > 0,$$

so the graph has two x-intercepts.

The x-intercepts are found by solving:

$$x = \dfrac{-b \pm \sqrt{b^2 - 4ac}}{2a} = \dfrac{-1 \pm \sqrt{3}}{2(-1)}$$

$$= \dfrac{-1 \pm \sqrt{3}}{-2} = \dfrac{1 \pm \sqrt{3}}{2} \approx \dfrac{1 \pm 1.732}{2}$$

The x-intercepts are –0.37 and 1.37.

The y-intercept is $f(0) = -(0)^2 + (0) + \dfrac{1}{2} = \dfrac{1}{2}$.

9. $f(x) = 3x^2 + 4x - 1$

$a = 3, b = 4, c = -1.$ Since $a = 3 > 0$, the graph opens up.

The x-coordinate of the vertex is $x = \dfrac{-b}{2a} = \dfrac{-4}{2(3)} = \dfrac{-4}{6} = -\dfrac{2}{3}$.

The y-coordinate of the vertex is $f\left(\dfrac{-b}{2a}\right) = f\left(-\dfrac{2}{3}\right) = 3\left(-\dfrac{2}{3}\right)^2 + 4\left(-\dfrac{2}{3}\right) - 1 = \dfrac{4}{3} - \dfrac{8}{3} - 1 = -\dfrac{7}{3}$.

Thus, the vertex is $\left(-\dfrac{2}{3}, -\dfrac{7}{3}\right)$.

The axis of symmetry is the line $x = -\dfrac{2}{3}$.

The discriminant is:

$$b^2 - 4ac = (4)^2 - 4(3)(-1) = 16 + 12 = 28 > 0,$$

so the graph has two x-intercepts.

The x-intercepts are found by solving:

$$x = \dfrac{-b \pm \sqrt{b^2 - 4ac}}{2a} = \dfrac{-4 \pm \sqrt{28}}{2(3)}$$

$$= \dfrac{-4 \pm 2\sqrt{7}}{6} = \dfrac{-2 \pm \sqrt{7}}{3} \approx \dfrac{-2 \pm 2.646}{3}$$

The x-intercepts are approximately 0.22 and −1.55.

The y-intercept is $f(0) = 3(0)^2 + 4(0) - 1 = -1$.

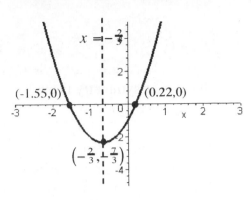

10. $f(x) = -2x^2 - x + 4$

$a = -2, b = -1, c = 4$. Since $a = -2 < 0$, the graph opens down.

The x-coordinate of the vertex is $x = \dfrac{-b}{2a} = \dfrac{-(-1)}{2(-2)} = \dfrac{1}{-4} = -\dfrac{1}{4}$.

The y-coordinate of the vertex is

$$f\left(\dfrac{-b}{2a}\right) = f\left(-\dfrac{1}{4}\right) = -2\left(-\dfrac{1}{4}\right)^2 - \left(-\dfrac{1}{4}\right) + 4 = -\dfrac{1}{8} + \dfrac{1}{4} + 4 = \dfrac{33}{8}.$$

Thus, the vertex is $\left(-\dfrac{1}{4}, \dfrac{33}{8}\right)$.

The axis of symmetry is the line $x = -\dfrac{1}{4}$.

The discriminant is:

$$b^2 - 4ac = (-1)^2 - 4(-2)(4) = 1 + 32 = 33 > 0,$$

so the graph has two x-intercepts.

The x-intercepts are found by solving:

$$x = \dfrac{-b \pm \sqrt{b^2 - 4ac}}{2a} = \dfrac{-(-1) \pm \sqrt{33}}{2(-2)}$$

$$= \dfrac{1 \pm \sqrt{33}}{-4} = \dfrac{-1 \pm \sqrt{33}}{4} \approx \dfrac{-1 \pm 5.745}{4}$$

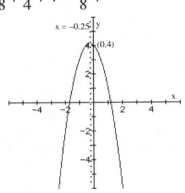

The x-intercepts are −1.69 and 1.19.

The y-intercept is $f(0) = -2(0)^2 - (0) + 4 = 4$.

11. $f(x) = (x+2)^3$

Using the graph of $y = x^3$, shift the graph horizontally, 2 units to the left.

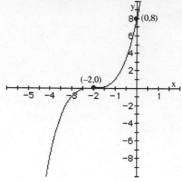

12. $f(x) = -x^3 + 3$

Using the graph of $y = x^3$, reflect the graph about the x-axis, and shift vertically, 3 units up.

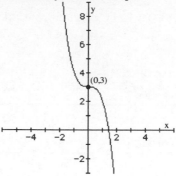

13. $f(x) = -(x-1)^4$

Using the graph of $y = x^4$, shift the graph horizontally, 1 unit right, and reflect about the x-axis.

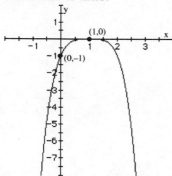

14. $f(x) = (x-1)^4 - 2$

Using the graph of $y = x^4$, shift the graph horizontally, 1 unit right, and shift vertically 2 units down.

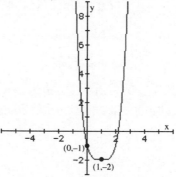

15. $f(x) = (x-1)^4 + 2$

Using the graph of $y = x^4$, shift the graph horizontally, 1 unit to the right, and shift vertically 2 units up.

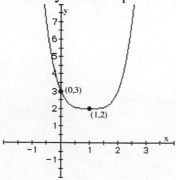

16. $f(x) = (1-x)^3 = -(x-1)^3$

Using the graph of $y = x^3$, shift the graph horizontally, 1 unit to the right, and reflect on the x-axis.

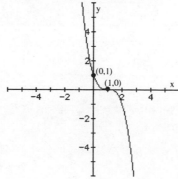

17. $f(x) = 3x^2 - 6x + 4$

$a = 3, b = -6, c = 4$. Since $a = 3 > 0$, the graph opens up, so the vertex is a minimum point. The minimum occurs at $x = \dfrac{-b}{2a} = \dfrac{-(-6)}{2(3)} = \dfrac{6}{6} = 1$. The minimum value is

$f\left(\dfrac{-b}{2a}\right) = f(1) = 3(1)^2 - 6(1) + 4 = 3 - 6 + 4 = 1$.

18. $f(x) = 2x^2 + 8x + 5$

$a = 2, b = 8, c = 5$. Since $a = 2 > 0$, the graph opens up, so the vertex is a minimum point. The minimum occurs at $x = \dfrac{-b}{2a} = \dfrac{-8}{2(2)} = \dfrac{-8}{4} = -2$. The minimum value is

$f\left(\dfrac{-b}{2a}\right) = f(-2) = 2(-2)^2 + 8(-2) + 5 = 8 - 16 + 5 = -3$

19. $f(x) = -x^2 + 8x - 4$

$a = -1, b = 8, c = -4$. Since $a = -1 < 0$, the graph opens down, so the vertex is a maximum point. The maximum occurs at $x = \dfrac{-b}{2a} = \dfrac{-8}{2(-1)} = \dfrac{-8}{-2} = 4$. The maximum value is $f\left(\dfrac{-b}{2a}\right) = f(4) = -(4)^2 + 8(4) - 4 = -16 + 32 - 4 = 12$.

20. $f(x) = -x^2 - 10x - 3$

$a = -1, b = -10, c = -3$. Since $a = -1 < 0$, the graph opens down, so the vertex is a maximum point. The maximum occurs at $x = \dfrac{-b}{2a} = \dfrac{-(-10)}{2(-1)} = \dfrac{10}{-2} = -5$. The maximum value is $f\left(\dfrac{-b}{2a}\right) = f(-5) = -(-5)^2 - 10(-5) - 3 = -25 + 50 - 3 = 22$.

21. $f(x) = -3x^2 + 12x + 4$

$a = -3, b = 12, c = 4$. Since $a = -3 < 0$, the graph opens down, so the vertex is a maximum point. The maximum occurs at $x = \dfrac{-b}{2a} = \dfrac{-12}{2(-3)} = \dfrac{-12}{-6} = 2$. The maximum value is $f\left(\dfrac{-b}{2a}\right) = f(2) = -3(2)^2 + 12(2) + 4 = -12 + 24 + 4 = 16$.

22. $f(x) = -2x^2 + 4$

$a = -2, b = 0, c = 4$. Since $a = -2 < 0$, the graph opens down, so the vertex is a maximum point. The maximum occurs at $x = \dfrac{-b}{2a} = \dfrac{-0}{2(-2)} = 0$. The maximum value is

$f\left(\dfrac{-b}{2a}\right) = f(0) = -2(0)^2 + 4 = 4$

23. $f(x) = x(x + 2)(x + 4)$

(a) x-intercepts: –4, –2, 0;
    y-intercept: 0
(b) crosses x axis at x = –4, –2, 0

(c) $y = x^3$ (d)   2

(e)

	$x < -4$	$-4 < x < -2$	$-2 < x < 0$	$x > 0$
Sign of f	-	+	-	+
Above or below x-axis	below	above	below	above

Graph of f is above the x-axis for $(-4,-2) \cup (0,\infty)$

Graph of f is below the x-axis for $(-\infty,-4) \cup (-2,0)$

(f)

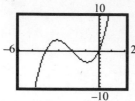

24. $f(x) = x(x-2)(x-4)$

(a)   x-intercepts: 4, 2, 0;
      y-intercept: 0

(b)   crosses x axis at x = 4, 2, 0

(c) $y = x^3$ (d)   2

(e)

	$x < 0$	$0 < x < 2$	$2 < x < 4$	$x > 4$
Sign of f	-	+	-	+
Above or below x-axis	below	above	below	above

Graph of f is above the x-axis for $(0,2) \cup (4,\infty)$

Graph of f is below the x-axis for $(-\infty,0) \cup (2,4)$

(f)

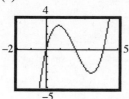

25. $f(x) = (x-2)^2(x+4)$

(a)   x-intercepts: - 4, 2;
      y-intercept: 16

(b)   crosses x axis at x = - 4 and touches the x axis at x = 2

(c) $y = x^3$ (d)   2

(e)

	$x < -4$	$-4 < x < 2$	$2 < x$
Sign of f	-	+	+
Above or below x-axis	below	above	above

Graph of f is above the x-axis for

Graph of f is below the x-axis for $(-\infty,-4)$

(f)

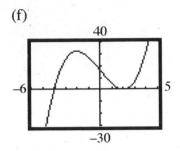

26. $f(x) = (x - 2)(x + 4)^2$
   (a)   x-intercepts: - 4, 2;
         y-intercept: - 32
   (b)   crosses x axis at x = 2 and touches the x axis at x = - 4
   (c) $y = x^3$ (d)   2
   (e)

	$x < -4$	$-4 < x < 2$	$2 < x$
Sign of f	-	-	+
Above or below x-axis	below	below	above

   Graph of f is above the x-axis for $(2, \infty)$
   Graph of f is below the x-axis for $(-\infty, -4) \cup (-4, 2)$

   (f)

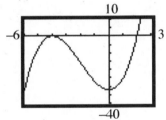

27. $f(x) = -2x^3 + 4x^2 = -2x^2(x - 2)$
   (a)   x-intercepts: 0, 2;
         y-intercept: 0
   (b)   crosses x axis at x = 2 and touches the x axis at x = 0
   (c) $y = -2x^3$ (d)   2
   (e)

	$x < 0$	$0 < x < 2$	$2 < x$
Sign of f	+	+	-
Above or below x-axis	above	above	below

   Graph of f is above the x-axis for $(-\infty, 0) \cup (0, 2)$
   Graph of f is below the x-axis for $(2, \infty)$

(f)

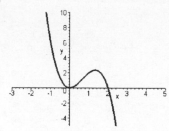

28. $f(x) = -4x^3 + 4x = -4x(x^2 - 1) = -4x(x+1)(x-1)$

    (a)   x-intercepts: 0, - 1, 1;
            y-intercept: 0

    (b)   crosses x axis at x = 0, - 1, 1

    (c) $y = -4x^3$ (d)   2

    (e)

	$x < -1$	$-1 < x < 0$	$0 < x < 1$	$1 < x$
Sign of f	+	-	+	-
Above or below x-axis	above	below	above	below

Graph of f is above the x-axis for $(-\infty, -1) \cup (0, 1)$

Graph of f is below the x-axis for $(-1, 0) \cup (1, \infty)$

    (f)

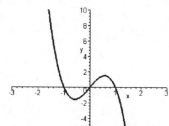

29. $f(x) = (x-1)^2(x+3)(x+1)$

    (a)   x-intercepts: - 3, - 1, 1;
            y-intercept: 3

    (b)   crosses x axis at x = - 3, - 1 and touches x-axis at x = 1

    (c) $y = x^4$(d)   3

    (e)

	$x < -3$	$-3 < x < -1$	$-1 < x < 1$	$1 < x$
Sign of f	+	-	+	+
Above or below x-axis	above	below	above	above

Graph of f is above the x-axis for $(-\infty, -3) \cup (-1, 1) \cup (1, \infty)$

Graph of f is below the x-axis for $(-3, -1)$

(f)

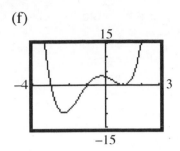

30. $f(x) = (x-4)(x+2)^2(x-2)$
   (a)   x-intercepts: - 2, 2, 4;
         y-intercept: 32
   (b)   crosses x axis at x = 2, 4 and touches x-axis at x = -2
   (c) $y = x^4$ (d)   3
   (e)

	$x < -2$	$-2 < x < 2$	$2 < x < 4$	$4 < x$
Sign of f	+	+	-	+
Above or below x-axis	above	above	below	above

   Graph of f is above the x-axis for $(-\infty, -2) \cup (-2, 2) \cup (4, \infty)$
   Graph of f is below the x-axis for $(2, 4)$

   (f)

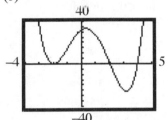

31. $R(x) = \dfrac{2x-6}{x}$ $p(x) = 2x-6$; $q(x) = x$; $n = 1$; $m = 1$

   Step 1:   Domain: $\{x \mid x \neq 0\}$
   Step 2:   (a)   The x-intercept is the zero of $p(x)$: 3
             (b)   There is no y-intercept because 0 is not in the domain.
   Step 3: $R(-x) = \dfrac{2(-x)-6}{-x} = \dfrac{-2x-6}{-x} = \dfrac{2x+6}{x}$; this is neither $R(x)$ nor $-R(x)$, so there
             is no symmetry.
   Step 4:   The vertical asymptote is the zero of $q(x)$: $x = 0$
   Step 5:   Since $n = m$, the line $y = 2$ is the horizontal asymptote.
             $R(x)$ does not intersect $y = 2$.

Step 6:   Graphing: Step 7:   Graphing by hand:

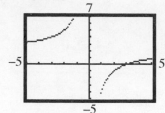   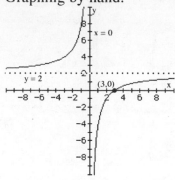

32. $R(x) = \dfrac{4-x}{x}$ $p(x) = 4 - x;\ q(x) = x;\ n = 1;\ m = 1$

Step 1:   Domain: $\{x \mid x \neq 0\}$

Step 2:   (a)   The x-intercept is the zero of $p(x)$: 4
          (b)   There is no y-intercept because 0 is not in the domain.

Step 3: $R(-x) = \dfrac{4-(-x)}{-x} = \dfrac{4+x}{-x}$; this is neither $R(x)$ nor $-R(x)$, so there is no
          symmetry.

Step 4:   The vertical asymptote is the zero of $q(x)$: $x = 0$

Step 5:   Since $n = m$, the line $y = -1$ is the horizontal asymptote.
          $R(x)$ does not intersect $y = -1$.

Step 6:   Graphing: Step 7:   Graphing by hand:

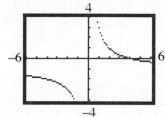   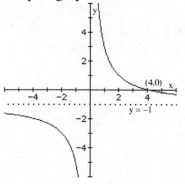

33. $H(x) = \dfrac{x+2}{x(x-2)}$ $p(x) = x + 2;\ q(x) = x(x-2) = x^2 - 2x;\ n = 1;\ m = 2$

Step 1:   Domain: $\{x \mid x \neq 0,\ x \neq 2\}$

Step 2:   (a)   The x-intercept is the zero of $p(x)$: -2
          (b)   There is no y-intercept because 0 is not in the domain.

Step 3: $H(-x) = \dfrac{-x+2}{-x(-x-2)} = \dfrac{-x+2}{x^2+2x}$; this is neither $H(x)$ nor $-H(x)$, so there is no
          symmetry.

Step 4:   The vertical asymptotes are the zeros of $q(x)$: $x = 0$ and $x = 2$

Step 5:   Since $n < m$, the line $y = 0$ is the horizontal asymptote.
          $R(x)$ intersects $y = 0$ at $(-2, 0)$.

Step 6:   Graphing:

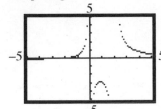

Step 7:   Graphing by hand:

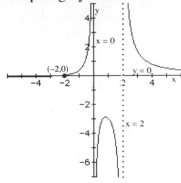

34. $H(x) = \dfrac{x}{x^2 - 1} = \dfrac{x}{(x-1)(x+1)}$ $p(x) = x;\ q(x) = x^2 - 1;\ n = 1;\ m = 2$

Step 1:   Domain: $\{x \mid x \neq -1, x \neq 1\}$

Step 2:   (a)   The x-intercept is the zero of $p(x)$: 0

(b)   The y-intercept is 0.

Step 3: $H(-x) = \dfrac{-x}{(-x)^2 - 1} = \dfrac{-x}{x^2 - 1} = -H(x)$; the graph is symmetric to the origin.

Step 4:   The vertical asymptotes are the zeros of $q(x)$: $x = -1$ and $x = 1$

Step 5:   Since $n < m$, the line $y = 0$ is the horizontal asymptote.

$R(x)$ intersects $y = 0$ at $(0, 0)$.

Step 6:   Graphing:

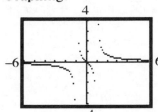

Step 7:   Graphing by hand:

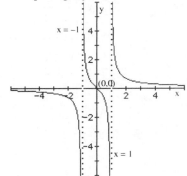

35. $R(x) = \dfrac{x^2 + x - 6}{x^2 - x - 6} = \dfrac{(x+3)(x-2)}{(x-3)(x+2)}$ $p(x) = x^2 + x - 6;\ q(x) = x^2 - x - 6;$

$n = 2;\ m = 2$

Step 1:   Domain: $\{x \mid x \neq -2, x \neq 3\}$

Step 2:   (a)   The x-intercepts are the zeros of $p(x)$: -3 and 2

(b)   The y-intercept is $R(0) = \dfrac{0^2 + 0 - 6}{0^2 - 0 - 6} = \dfrac{-6}{-6} = 1$.

Step 3: $R(-x) = \dfrac{(-x)^2 + (-x) - 6}{(-x)^2 - (-x) - 6} = \dfrac{x^2 - x - 6}{x^2 + x - 6}$; this is neither $R(x)$ nor $-R(x)$, so there

is no symmetry.

Step 4:   The vertical asymptotes are the zeros of $q(x)$: $x = -2$ and $x = 3$

Step 5:   Since $n = m$, the line $y = 1$ is the horizontal asymptote.

$R(x)$ intersects $y = 1$ at $(0, 1)$, since:

$$\frac{x^2 + x - 6}{x^2 - x - 6} = 1$$
$$x^2 + x - 6 = x^2 - x - 6$$
$$2x = 0$$
$$x = 0$$

Step 6:   Graphing:

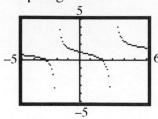

Step 7:   Graphing by hand:

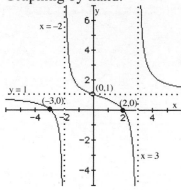

36. $R(x) = \dfrac{x^2 - 6x + 9}{x^2} = \dfrac{(x-3)^2}{x^2}$ $p(x) = x^2 - 6x + 9;$ $q(x) = x^2;$ $n = 2;$ $m = 2$

Step 1:   Domain: $\{x | x \neq 0\}$

Step 2:   (a)   The x-intercept is the zero of $p(x)$: 3

   (b)   There is no y-intercept because 0 is not in the domain.

Step 3: $R(-x) = \dfrac{(-x)^2 - 6(-x) + 9}{(-x)^2} = \dfrac{x^2 + 6x + 9}{x^2}$; this is neither $R(x)$ nor $-R(x)$, so

   there is no symmetry.

Step 4:   The vertical asymptote is the zero of $q(x)$: $x = 0$

Step 5:   Since $n = m$, the line $y = 1$ is the horizontal asymptote.

   $R(x)$ intersects $y = 1$ at $\left(\dfrac{3}{2}, 1\right)$, since:

$$\frac{x^2 - 6x + 9}{x^2} = 1 \rightarrow x^2 - 6x + 9 = x^2 \rightarrow -6x = -9 \rightarrow x = \frac{3}{2}$$

Step 6:   Graphing:

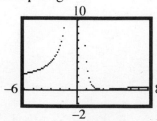

Step 7:   Graphing by hand:

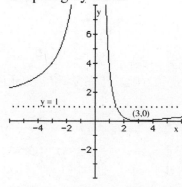

37. $F(x) = \dfrac{x^3}{x^2 - 4}$ $p(x) = x^3$; $q(x) = x^2 - 4$; $n = 3$; $m = 2$

Step 1:   Domain: $\{x \mid x \neq -2, x \neq 2\}$

Step 2:   (a)   The x-intercept is the zero of $p(x)$: 0.

         (b)   The y-intercept is $F(0) = \dfrac{0^3}{0^2 - 4} = \dfrac{0}{-4} = 0$.

Step 3: $F(-x) = \dfrac{(-x)^3}{(-x)^2 - 4} = \dfrac{-x^3}{x^2 - 4} = -F(x)$; $F(x)$ is symmetric to the origin.

Step 4:   The vertical asymptotes are the zeros of $q(x)$: $x = -2$ and $x = 2$

Step 5:   Since $n = m + 1$, there is an oblique asymptote. Dividing:

$$x^2 - 4 \overline{\smash{)}\, x^3 + 0x^2 + 0x + 0} \qquad F(x) = x + \dfrac{4x}{x^2 - 4}$$
$$\underline{x^3 \qquad - 4x}$$
$$4x$$

with quotient x.

The oblique asymptote is $y = x$.

Solve to find intersection points:

$$\dfrac{x^3}{x^2 - 4} = x \rightarrow x^3 = x^3 - 4x \rightarrow 0 = -4x \rightarrow x = 0$$

The oblique asymptote intersects $F(x)$ at $(0, 0)$.

Step 6:   Graphing:

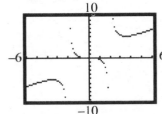

Step 7:   Graphing by hand:

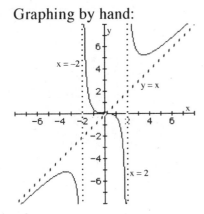

38. $F(x) = \dfrac{3x^3}{(x - 1)^2}$ $p(x) = 3x^3$; $q(x) = (x - 1)^2$; $n = 3$; $m = 2$

Step 1:   Domain: $\{x \mid x \neq 1\}$

Step 2:   (a)   The x-intercept is the zero of $p(x)$: 0.

         (b)   The y-intercept is $F(0) = \dfrac{3 \cdot 0^3}{(0 - 1)^2} = \dfrac{0}{1} = 0$.

Step 3: $F(-x) = \dfrac{3(-x)^3}{(-x - 1)^2} = \dfrac{-3x^3}{(x + 1)^2}$; this is neither $F(x)$ nor $-F(x)$, so there is no symmetry.

Step 4:   The vertical asymptote is the zero of $q(x)$: $x = 1$

Step 5:   Since $n = m + 1$, there is an oblique asymptote. Dividing:

$$\begin{array}{r} 3x + 6 \\ x^2 - 2x + 1{\overline{\smash{\big)}\,3x^3 + 0x^2 + 0x + 0}} \\ \underline{3x^3 - 6x^2 + 3x} \\ 6x^2 - 3x \\ \underline{6x^2 - 12x + 6} \\ 9x - 6 \end{array}$$

$$F(x) = 3x + 6 + \frac{9x - 6}{x^2 - 2x + 1}$$

The oblique asymptote is $y = 3x + 6$.

Solve to find intersection points:

$$\frac{3x^3}{x^2 - 2x + 1} = 3x + 6$$

$$3x^3 = 3x^3 - 9x + 6$$

$$9x = 6$$

$$x = \frac{2}{3}$$

The oblique asymptote intersects $F(x)$ at $\left(\frac{2}{3}, 8\right)$.

Step 6:   Graphing: Step 7:   Graphing by hand:

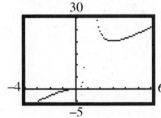
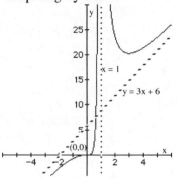

39. $R(x) = \dfrac{2x^4}{(x-1)^2}$ $p(x) = 2x^4$; $q(x) = (x-1)^2$; $n = 4$; $m = 2$

Step 1:   Domain: $\left\{x \mid x \neq 1\right\}$

Step 2:   (a)   The x-intercept is the zero of $p(x)$: 0

          (b)   The y-intercept is $R(0) = \dfrac{2(0)^4}{(0-1)^2} = \dfrac{0}{1} = 0$.

Step 3: $R(-x) = \dfrac{2(-x)^4}{(-x-1)^2} = \dfrac{2x^4}{(x+1)^2}$; this is neither $R(x)$ nor $-R(x)$, so there is no symmetry.

Step 4:   The vertical asymptote is the zero of $q(x)$: $x = 1$

Step 5:   Since $n > m + 1$, there is no horizontal asymptote and no oblique asymptote.

Step 6:   Graphing: Step 7:   Graphing by hand:

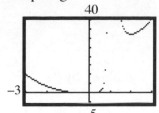

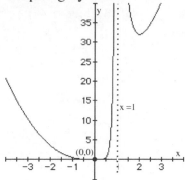

40. $R(x) = \dfrac{x^4}{x^2 - 9} = \dfrac{x^4}{(x + 3)(x - 3)}$ $p(x) = x^4;\; q(x) = x^2 - 9;\; n = 4;\; m = 2$

Step 1:   Domain: $\left\{x \mid x \neq -3,\, x \neq 3\right\}$

Step 2:   (a)   The x-intercept is the zero of $p(x)$: 0

(b)   The y-intercept is $R(0) = \dfrac{(0)^4}{0^2 - 9} = \dfrac{0}{-9} = 0$.

Step 3: $R(-x) = \dfrac{(-x)^4}{(-x)^2 - 9} = \dfrac{x^4}{x^2 - 9} = R(x)$; $R(x)$ is symmetric to the y-axis.

Step 4:   The vertical asymptotes are the zeros of $q(x)$: $x = -3$ and $x = 3$

Step 5:   Since $n > m + 1$, there is no horizontal asymptote and no oblique asymptote.

Step 6:   Graphing: Step 7:   Graphing by hand:

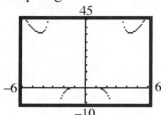

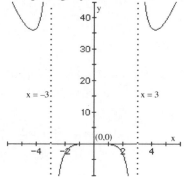

41. $G(x) = \dfrac{x^2 - 4}{x^2 - x - 2} = \dfrac{(x + 2)(x - 2)}{(x - 2)(x + 1)} = \dfrac{x + 2}{x + 1}$ $p(x) = x^2 - 4;\; q(x) = x^2 - x - 2;$
$n = 2;\; m = 2$

Step 1:   Domain: $\left\{x \mid x \neq -1,\, x \neq 2\right\}$

Step 2:   (a)   The x-intercept is the zero of $p(x)$: -2 (2 is not a zero because reduced form must be used to find the zeros.)

(b)   The y-intercept is $G(0) = \dfrac{0^2 - 4}{0^2 - 0 - 2} = \dfrac{-4}{-2} = 2$.

Step 3: $G(-x) = \dfrac{(-x)^2 - 4}{(-x)^2 - (-x) - 2} = \dfrac{x^2 - 4}{x^2 + x - 2}$; this is neither $G(x)$ nor $-G(x)$, so there is no symmetry.

Step 4:   The vertical asymptote is the zero of $q(x)$: $x = -1$ ($x = 2$ is not a vertical asymptote because reduced form must be used to find the them.)

Step 5:   Since $n = m$, the line $y = 1$ is the horizontal asymptote.

$G(x)$ does not intersect $y = 1$ because $G(x)$ is not defined at $x = 2$.

$$\frac{x^2 - 4}{x^2 - x - 2} = 1 \rightarrow x^2 - 4 = x^2 - x - 2 \rightarrow -2 = -x \rightarrow x = 2$$

Step 6:   Graphing: Step 7:   Graphing by hand:

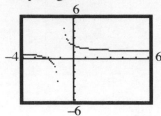   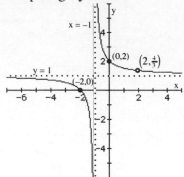

42. $F(x) = \dfrac{(x-1)^2}{x^2 - 1} = \dfrac{(x-1)^2}{(x-1)(x+1)} = \dfrac{x-1}{x+1}$ $p(x) = (x-1)^2;\ \ q(x) = x^2 - 1;$

$n = 2;\ m = 2$

Step 1:   Domain: $\{x \mid x \neq -1,\ x \neq 1\}$

Step 2:   (a)   There is no x-intercept since 1 is not in the domain.

(b)   The y-intercept is $F(0) = \dfrac{(0-1)^2}{0^2 - 1} = \dfrac{1}{-1} = -1$.

Step 3: $F(-x) = \dfrac{(-x-1)^2}{(-x)^2 - 1} = \dfrac{(x+1)^2}{x^2 - 1}$; this is neither $F(x)$ nor $-F(x)$, so there is no symmetry.

Step 4:   The vertical asymptote is the zero of $q(x)$: $x = -1$ ($x = 1$ is not a vertical asymptote because reduced form must be used to find them.)

Step 5:   Since $n = m$, the line $y = 1$ is the horizontal asymptote.

$F(x)$ does not intersect $y = 1$ because $F(x)$ is not defined at $x = 1$.

$$\frac{x^2 - 2x + 1}{x^2 - 1} = 1 \rightarrow x^2 - 2x + 1 = x^2 - 1 \rightarrow -2x = -2 \rightarrow x = 1$$

Step 6:   Graphing: Step 7:   Graphing by hand:

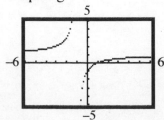   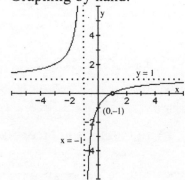

43. $2x^2 + 5x - 12 < 0$ $f(x) = 2x^2 + 5x - 12$
     $(x + 4)(2x - 3) < 0$

     $x = -4, x = \dfrac{3}{2}$ are the zeros.

Interval	Test Number	$f(x)$	Positive/Negative
$-\infty < x < -4$	-5	13	Positive
$-4 < x < 3/2$	0	-12	Negative
$3/2 < x < \infty$	2	6	Positive

     The solution set is $\left\{ x \middle| -4 < x < \dfrac{3}{2} \right\}$.

44. $3x^2 - 2x - 1 \geq 0$ $f(x) = 3x^2 - 2x - 1$
     $(3x + 1)(x - 1) \geq 0$

     $x = -\dfrac{1}{3}, x = 1$ are the zeros.

Interval	Test Number	$f(x)$	Positive/Negative
$-\infty < x < -1/3$	-1	4	Positive
$-1/3 < x < 1$	0	-1	Negative
$1 < x < \infty$	2	7	Positive

     The solution set is $\left\{ x \middle| x \leq -\dfrac{1}{3} \text{ or } x \geq 1 \right\}$.

45. $\dfrac{6}{x + 3} \geq 1$ $f(x) = \dfrac{6}{x + 3} - 1$

     $\dfrac{6}{x + 3} - 1 \geq 0 \rightarrow \dfrac{6 - 1(x + 3)}{x + 3} \geq 0 \rightarrow \dfrac{-x + 3}{x + 3} \geq 0$

     The zeros and values where the expression is undefined are $x = -3$, and $x = 3$.

Interval	Test Number	$f(x)$	Positive/Negative
$-\infty < x < -3$	-4	-7	Negative
$-3 < x < 3$	0	1	Positive
$3 < x < \infty$	4	$-1/7$	Negative

     The solution set is $\left\{ x \middle| -3 < x \leq 3 \right\}$.

46. $\dfrac{-2}{1 - 3x} < 1$ $f(x) = \dfrac{-2}{1 - 3x} - 1$

     $\dfrac{-2}{1 - 3x} - 1 < 0 \rightarrow \dfrac{-2 - 1 + 3x}{1 - 3x} < 0 \rightarrow \dfrac{3x - 3}{1 - 3x} < 0$

     The zeros and values where the expression is undefined are $x = \dfrac{1}{3}$, and $x = 1$.

Interval	Test Number	$f(x)$	Positive/Negative
$-\infty < x < 1/3$	0	-3	Negative
$1/3 < x < 1$	0.5	3	Positive
$1 < x < \infty$	2	$-3/5$	Negative

     The solution set is $\left\{ x \middle| x < \dfrac{1}{3} \text{ or } x > 1 \right\}$.

47.
$$\frac{2x-6}{1-x} < 2 \qquad f(x) = \frac{2x-6}{1-x} - 2$$

$$\frac{2x-6}{1-x} - 2 < 0 \rightarrow \frac{2x-6-2(1-x)}{1-x} < 0 \rightarrow \frac{4x-8}{1-x} < 0$$

The zeros and values where the expression is undefined are $x = 1$, and $x = 2$.

Interval	Test Number	$f(x)$	Positive/Negative
$-\infty < x < 1$	0	–8	Negative
$1 < x < 2$	1.5	4	Positive
$2 < x < \infty$	3	–2	Negative

The solution set is $\left\{ x \mid x < 1 \text{ or } x > 2 \right\}$.

48.
$$\frac{3-2x}{2x+5} \geq 2 \qquad f(x) = \frac{3-2x}{2x+5} - 2$$

$$\frac{3-2x}{2x+5} - 2 \geq 0 \rightarrow \frac{3-2x-4x-10}{2x+5} \geq 0 \rightarrow \frac{-6x-7}{2x+5} \geq 0$$

The zeros and values where the expression is undefined are $x = -\dfrac{7}{6}$, and $x = -\dfrac{5}{2}$.

Interval	Test Number	$f(x)$	Positive/Negative
$-\infty < x < -5/2$	–3	–11	Negative
$-5/2 < x < -7/6$	–2	5	Positive
$-7/6 < x < \infty$	0	–7/5	Negative

The solution set is $\left\{ x \mid -\dfrac{5}{4} < x \leq -\dfrac{7}{6} \right\}$.

49.
$$\frac{(x-2)(x-1)}{x-3} > 0 \qquad f(x) = \frac{(x-2)(x-1)}{x-3}$$

The zeros and values where the expression is undefined are $x = 1$, $x = 2$, and $x = 3$.

Interval	Test Number	$f(x)$	Positive/Negative
$-\infty < x < 1$	0	–2/3	Negative
$1 < x < 2$	1.5	1/6	Positive
$2 < x < 3$	2.5	–3/2	Negative
$3 < x < \infty$	4	6	Positive

The solution set is $\left\{ x \mid 1 < x < 2 \text{ or } x > 3 \right\}$.

50.
$$\frac{x+1}{x(x-5)} \leq 0 \qquad f(x) = \frac{x+1}{x(x-5)}$$

The zeros and values where the expression is undefined are $x = -1$, $x = 0$, and $x = 5$.

Interval	Test Number	$f(x)$	Positive/Negative
$-\infty < x < -1$	–2	–1/14	Negative
$-1 < x < 0$	–0.5	2/11	Positive
$0 < x < 5$	1	–1/2	Negative
$5 < x < \infty$	6	7/6	Positive

The solution set is $\left\{ x \mid x \leq -1 \text{ or } 0 < x < 5 \right\}$.

51. $\dfrac{x^2 - 8x + 12}{x^2 - 16} > 0$ $f(x) = \dfrac{x^2 - 8x + 12}{x^2 - 16}$

$\dfrac{(x-2)(x-6)}{(x+4)(x-4)} > 0$

The zeros and values where the expression is undefined are $x = -4,\, x = 2,\, x = 4,\, x = 6.$

Interval	Test Number	$f(x)$	Positive/Negative
$-\infty < x < -4$	-5	$77/9$	Positive
$-4 < x < 2$	0	$-3/4$	Negative
$2 < x < 4$	3	$3/7$	Positive
$4 < x < 6$	5	$-1/3$	Negative
$6 < x < \infty$	7	$5/33$	Positive

The solution set is $\left\{ x \mid x < -4,\, 2 < x < 4,\, x > 6 \right\}.$

52     $\dfrac{x\left(x^2 + x - 2\right)}{x^2 + 9x + 20} \le 0$ $f(x) = \dfrac{x\left(x^2 + x - 2\right)}{x^2 + 9x + 20}$

$\dfrac{x(x+2)(x-1)}{(x+5)(x+4)} \le 0$

The zeros and values where the expression is undefined are $x = -5,\, x = -4,\, x = -2,\, x = 0,\, x = 1.$

Interval	Test Number	$f(x)$	Positive/Negative
$-\infty < x < -5$	-6	-84	Negative
$-5 < x < -4$	-4.5	247.5	Positive
$-4 < x < -2$	-3	-6	Negative
$-2 < x < 0$	-1	$1/6$	Positive
$0 < x < 1$	0.5	-0.025	Negative
$1 < x < \infty$	2	0.19	Positive

The solution set is $\left\{ x \mid x < -5,\, -4 < x \le -2,\ \text{or}\ 0 \le x \le 1 \right\}$

53.

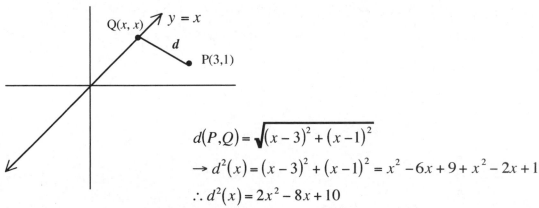

$d(P,Q) = \sqrt{(x-3)^2 + (x-1)^2}$

$\to d^2(x) = (x-3)^2 + (x-1)^2 = x^2 - 6x + 9 + x^2 - 2x + 1$

$\therefore d^2(x) = 2x^2 - 8x + 10$

Since $d^2(x) = 2x^2 - 8x + 10$ is a quadratic function with $a = 2 > 0,$ the vertex corresponds to the minimum value for the function.

The vertex occurs at $x = -\dfrac{b}{2a} = -\dfrac{-8}{2(2)} = 2.$ Therefore the point Q on the line $y = x$ will be closest to the point $P = (3,1)$ when $Q = (2,2).$

54.

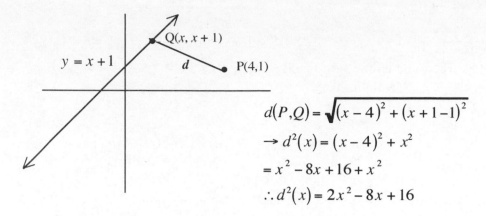

$$d(P,Q) = \sqrt{(x-4)^2 + (x+1-1)^2}$$
$$\rightarrow d^2(x) = (x-4)^2 + x^2$$
$$= x^2 - 8x + 16 + x^2$$
$$\therefore d^2(x) = 2x^2 - 8x + 16$$

Since $d^2(x) = 2x^2 - 8x + 16$ is a quadratic function with $a = 2 > 0$, the vertex corresponds to the minimum value for the function.

The vertex occurs at $x = -\dfrac{b}{2a} = -\dfrac{-8}{2(2)} = 2$. Therefore the point Q on the line $y = x + 1$ will be closest to the point $P = (4,1)$ when $Q = (2,3)$.

55.   Since there are 200 feet of border, we know that $2x + 2y = 200$.
      The area is to be maximized, so $A = x \cdot y$.
      Solving the perimeter formula for y:

$$2x + 2y = 200 \rightarrow 2y = 200 - 2x \rightarrow y = 100 - x$$

The area function is: $A(x) = x(100 - x) = -x^2 + 100x$
The maximum value occurs at the vertex:

$$x = \frac{-b}{2a} = \frac{-100}{2(-1)} = \frac{-100}{-2} = 50$$

The pond should be 50 feet by 50 feet for maximum area.

56.   Let x represent the length and y represent the width of the rectangle.
      $2x + 2y = 20 \rightarrow y = 10 - x$.
      $x \cdot y = 16 \rightarrow x(10 - x) = 16$.
      Solving the area equation:

$$10x - x^2 = 16 \rightarrow x^2 - 10x + 16 = 0$$
$$(x - 8)(x - 2) = 0 \rightarrow x = 8 \text{ or } x = 2$$

The length and width of the rectangle are 8 feet by 2 feet.

57. Consider the diagram

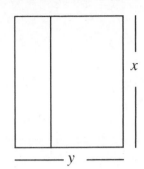

Total amount of fence = $3x + 2y = 10000$

$$\therefore y = \frac{10000 - 3x}{2} = 5000 - \frac{3}{2}x$$

Total enclosed area $= (x)(y) = (x)\left(5000 - \frac{3}{2}x\right)$

$\therefore A(x) = 5000x - \frac{3}{2}x^2 = -\frac{3}{2}x^2 + 5000x$ is a quadratic function with $a = -\frac{3}{2} < 0$.

So the vertex corresponds to the maximum value for this function.
The vertex occurs when

$$x = -\frac{b}{2a} = -\frac{5000}{2\left(-\frac{3}{2}\right)} = \frac{5000}{3} \rightarrow \text{the maximum area is} \quad A\left(\frac{5000}{3}\right) = -\frac{3}{2}\left(\frac{5000}{3}\right)^2 + 5000\left(\frac{5000}{3}\right)$$

$$= -\frac{3}{2}\left(\frac{25000000}{9}\right) + \frac{25000000}{3} = -\frac{12500000}{3} + \frac{25000000}{3}$$

$$= \frac{12500000}{3} \approx 4166666.67 \text{ square meters}$$

58.   The area function is: $A(x) = x(8 - 2x) = -2x^2 + 8x$
The maximum value occurs at the vertex:

$$x = \frac{-b}{2a} = \frac{-8}{2(-2)} = \frac{-8}{-4} = 2$$

The maximum area is:
$A(2) = -2(2)^2 + 8(2) = -8 + 16 = 8$ square units.

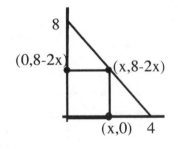

59.   Consider the diagram

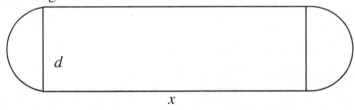

d = diameter of the semicircles = width of the rectangle
x = length of the rectangle
$\therefore$ outside dimension length = $2x + 2$(circumference of a semicircle)

= $2x$ + circumference of a circle = $2x + \pi d = 100$

$$\rightarrow x = \frac{100 - \pi d}{2} = 50 - \frac{1}{2}\pi d$$

Total enclosed area = (area of the rectangle) + 2(area of a semicircle)

= (area of the rectangle) + area of a circle

$$= (x)(d) + \pi r^2 = (x)(d) + \pi\left(\frac{d}{2}\right)^2 = \left(50 - \frac{1}{2}\pi d\right)(d) + \pi\left(\frac{d}{2}\right)^2$$

$$= 50d - \frac{1}{2}\pi d^2 + \frac{1}{4}\pi d^2 = 50d - \frac{1}{4}\pi d^2 = -\frac{1}{4}\pi d^2 + 50d$$

$$\therefore A(d) = -\frac{1}{4}\pi d^2 + 50d \text{ is a quadratic function with } a = -\frac{1}{4}\pi < 0. \text{ Therefore the}$$

vertex corresponds to the maximum value for the function.

The vertex occurs when $x = -\dfrac{b}{2a} = -\dfrac{50}{2\left(-\dfrac{1}{4}\pi\right)} = \dfrac{100}{\pi}$

→ the maximum area is $A\left(\dfrac{100}{\pi}\right) = -\dfrac{1}{4}\pi\left(\dfrac{100}{\pi}\right)^2 + 50\left(\dfrac{100}{\pi}\right) \approx 795.78$ square meters

60. Locate the origin at the point directly under the highest point of the arch. Then the equation is in the form: $y = -ax^2 + k$, where $a > 0$. Since the maximum height is 10 feet, when $x = 0$, $y = k = 10$. Since the point (10, 0) is on the parabola, we can find the constant :

$$0 = -a(10)^2 + 10 \quad \rightarrow \quad a = \frac{10}{10^2} = \frac{1}{10} = 0.10$$

The equation of the parabola is:

$$y = -\frac{1}{10}x^2 + 10 \quad\quad \text{At } x = 8: \quad y = -\frac{1}{10}(8)^2 + 10 = -6.4 + 10 = 3.6 \text{ feet}$$

61. (a) Graphing:

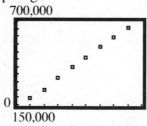

$$A(t) = -212t^3 + 2429t^2 + 59569t + 130003$$

(b) $A(11) = -212(11)^3 + 2429(11)^2 + 59569(11) + 130003 = 796999$ cases

(c) and (d) Graphing the cubic function of best fit:

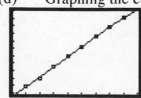

(e) answers will vary

62. (a)   Graphing:

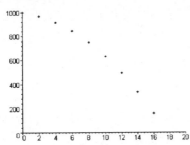

(b) $s(t) = -2.7t^2 - 10t + 1000$

$s(0) = -2.7(0)^2 - 10(0) + 1000 = 1000\, ft/\sec$

(c) $s(t) = -2.7t^2 - 10t + 1000 = 0$

$$t = \frac{-(-10) \pm \sqrt{(-10)^2 - 4(-2.7)(1000)}}{2(-2.7)} = \frac{10 \pm \sqrt{100 + 10800}}{-5.4} = \frac{10 \pm \sqrt{10900}}{-5.4}$$

≈ 17.48 seconds or -21.19 seconds

We discard the negative time value, so the ball hits the ground after approximately 17.48 seconds.

(d) and (e) Graphing the quadratic function of best fit:

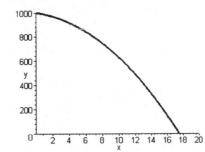

(f) $-\dfrac{1}{2} g = -2.7 \rightarrow g = 5.4\, ft/s^2$

63. Answers will vary, one example is $p(x) = -5(x^2 + 1)(x + 1)^3 \left(x - \dfrac{3}{5} \right)$

64. Answers will vary.

65. (a)   The degree is even.
    (b)   The leading coefficient is positive.
    (c)   The function is even - it is symmetric to the y-axis.
    (d) x^2 is a factor because the curve touches the x-axis at the origin.
    (e)   The minimum degree is 8.
    (f)   Answers will vary, 5 possibilities are:

$$p_1(x) = x^2(x + 3)(x + 2)(x + 1)(x - 1)(x - 2)(x - 3)$$

$$p_2(x) = x^4(x + 3)(x + 2)(x + 1)(x - 1)(x - 2)(x - 3)$$

$$p_3(x) = x^6(x+3)(x+2)(x+1)(x-1)(x-2)(x-3)$$

$$p_4(x) = x^8(x+3)(x+2)(x+1)(x-1)(x-2)(x-3)$$

$$p_5(x) = x^{10}(x+3)(x+2)(x+1)(x-1)(x-2)(x-3)$$

The Zeros of a Polynomial Function

5.1 Synthetic Division

1. Use synthetic division:

$$\begin{array}{r|rrrr} 2 & 1 & -1 & 2 & 4 \\ & & 2 & 2 & 8 \\ \hline & 1 & 1 & 4 & 12 \end{array}$$

Quotient: $x^2 + x + 4$ Remainder: 12

2. Use synthetic division:

$$\begin{array}{r|rrrr} -1 & 1 & 2 & -3 & 1 \\ & & -1 & -1 & 4 \\ \hline & 1 & 1 & -4 & 5 \end{array}$$

Quotient: $x^2 + x - 4$ Remainder: 5

3. Use synthetic division:

$$\begin{array}{r|rrrr} 3 & 3 & 2 & -1 & 3 \\ & & 9 & 33 & 96 \\ \hline & 3 & 11 & 32 & 99 \end{array}$$

Quotient: $3x^2 + 11x + 32$ Remainder: 99

4. Use synthetic division:

$$\begin{array}{r|rrrr} -2 & -4 & 2 & -1 & 1 \\ & & 8 & -20 & 42 \\ \hline & -4 & 10 & -21 & 43 \end{array}$$

Quotient: $-4x^2 + 10x - 21$ Remainder: 43

5. Use synthetic division:

$$\begin{array}{r|rrrrrr} -3 & 1 & 0 & -4 & 0 & 1 & 0 \\ & & -3 & 9 & -15 & 45 & -138 \\ \hline & 1 & -3 & 5 & -15 & 46 & -138 \end{array}$$

Quotient: $x^4 - 3x^3 + 5x^2 - 15x + 46$

Remainder: -138

6. Use synthetic division:

$$\begin{array}{r|rrrrr} 2 & 1 & 0 & 1 & 0 & 2 \\ & & 2 & 4 & 10 & 20 \\ \hline & 1 & 2 & 5 & 10 & 22 \end{array}$$

Quotient: $x^3 + 2x^2 + 5x + 10$ Remainder: 22

7. Use synthetic division:

$$\begin{array}{r|rrrrrr} 1 & 4 & 0 & -3 & 0 & 1 & 0 & 5 \\ & & 4 & 4 & 1 & 1 & 2 & 2 \\ \hline & 4 & 4 & 1 & 1 & 2 & 2 & 7 \end{array}$$

Quotient: $4x^5 + 4x^4 + x^3 + x^2 + 2x + 2$

Remainder: 7

8.   Use synthetic division:

$$-1)\overline{\begin{array}{rrrrrr} 1 & 0 & 5 & 0 & 0 & -10 \\ & -1 & 1 & -6 & 6 & -6 \\ \hline 1 & -1 & 6 & -6 & 6 & -16 \end{array}}$$

Quotient: $x^4 - x^3 + 6x^2 - 6x + 6$ Remainder: -16

9.   Use synthetic division:

$$-1.1)\overline{\begin{array}{rrrr} 0.1 & 0 & 0.2 & 0 \\ & -0.11 & 0.121 & -0.3531 \\ \hline 0.1 & -0.11 & 0.321 & -0.3531 \end{array}}$$

Quotient: $0.1x^2 - 0.11x + 0.321$ Remainder: -0.3531

10.   Use synthetic division:

$$-2.1)\overline{\begin{array}{rrr} 0.1 & 0 & -0.2 \\ & -0.21 & 0.441 \\ \hline 0.1 & -0.21 & 0.241 \end{array}}$$

Quotient: $0.1x - 0.21$ Remainder: 0.241

11.   Use synthetic division:

$$1)\overline{\begin{array}{rrrrrr} 1 & 0 & 0 & 0 & 0 & -1 \\ & 1 & 1 & 1 & 1 & 1 \\ \hline 1 & 1 & 1 & 1 & 1 & 0 \end{array}}$$

Quotient: $x^4 + x^3 + x^2 + x + 1$ Remainder: 0

12.   Use synthetic division:

$$-1)\overline{\begin{array}{rrrrrr} 1 & 0 & 0 & 0 & 0 & 1 \\ & -1 & 1 & -1 & 1 & -1 \\ \hline 1 & -1 & 1 & -1 & 1 & 0 \end{array}}$$

Quotient: $x^4 - x^3 + x^2 - x + 1$ Remainder: 0

13.   Use synthetic division:

$$2)\overline{\begin{array}{rrrr} 4 & -3 & -8 & 4 \\ & 8 & 10 & 4 \\ \hline 4 & 5 & 2 & 8 \end{array}}$$

Remainder $= 8 \neq 0$; therefore $x - 2$ is not a factor of $f(x)$.

14.   Use synthetic division:

$$-3)\overline{\begin{array}{rrrr} -4 & 5 & 0 & 8 \\ & 12 & -51 & 153 \\ \hline -4 & 17 & -51 & 161 \end{array}}$$

Remainder $= 161 \neq 0$; therefore $x + 3$ is not a factor of $f(x)$.

15. Use synthetic division:

$$\begin{array}{r|rrrrr} 2 & 3 & -6 & 0 & -5 & 10 \\ & & 6 & 0 & 0 & -10 \\ \hline & 3 & 0 & 0 & -5 & 0 \end{array}$$

Remainder $= 0$; therefore $x - 2$ is a factor of $f(x)$.

16. Use synthetic division:

$$\begin{array}{r|rrrrr} 2 & 4 & 0 & -15 & 0 & -4 \\ & & 8 & 16 & 2 & 4 \\ \hline & 4 & 8 & 1 & 2 & 0 \end{array}$$

Remainder $= 0$; therefore $x - 2$ is a factor of $f(x)$.

17. Use synthetic division:

$$\begin{array}{r|rrrrrrr} -3 & 3 & 0 & 0 & 82 & 0 & 0 & 27 \\ & & -9 & 27 & -81 & -3 & 9 & -27 \\ \hline & 3 & -9 & 27 & 1 & -3 & 9 & 0 \end{array}$$

Remainder $= 0$; therefore $x + 3$ is a factor of $f(x)$.

18. Use synthetic division:

$$\begin{array}{r|rrrrrrr} -3 & 2 & 0 & -18 & 0 & 1 & 0 & -9 \\ & & -6 & 18 & 0 & 0 & -3 & 9 \\ \hline & 2 & -6 & 0 & 0 & 1 & -3 & 0 \end{array}$$

Remainder $= 0$; therefore $x + 3$ is a factor of $f(x)$.

19. Use synthetic division:

$$\begin{array}{r|rrrrrrr} -4 & 4 & 0 & -64 & 0 & 1 & 0 & -15 \\ & & -16 & 64 & 0 & 0 & -4 & 16 \\ \hline & 4 & -16 & 0 & 0 & 1 & -4 & 1 \end{array}$$

Remainder $= 1 \neq 0$; therefore $x + 3$ is not a factor of $f(x)$.

20. Use synthetic division:

$$\begin{array}{r|rrrrrrr} -4 & 1 & 0 & -16 & 0 & 1 & 0 & -16 \\ & & -4 & 16 & 0 & 0 & -4 & 16 \\ \hline & 1 & -4 & 0 & 0 & 1 & -4 & 0 \end{array}$$

Remainder $= 0$; therefore $x + 4$ is a factor of $f(x)$.

21. Use synthetic division:

$$\begin{array}{r|rrrrr} \frac{1}{2} & 2 & -1 & 0 & 2 & -1 \\ & & 1 & 0 & 0 & 1 \\ \hline & 2 & 0 & 0 & 2 & 0 \end{array}$$

Remainder $= 0$; therefore $x - \frac{1}{2}$ is a factor of $f(x)$.

22. Use synthetic division:

$$-\tfrac{1}{3}\overline{)\begin{array}{rrrrr} 3 & 1 & 0 & -3 & 1 \\ & -1 & 0 & 0 & 1 \\ \hline 3 & 0 & 0 & -3 & 2 \end{array}}$$

Remainder $= 2 \neq 0$; therefore $x + \dfrac{1}{3}$ is not a factor of $f(x)$.

23. Use synthetic division:

$$-2\overline{)\begin{array}{rrrr} 1 & -2 & 3 & 5 \\ & -2 & 8 & -22 \\ \hline 1 & -4 & 11 & -17 \end{array}}$$

$$\frac{x^3 - 2x^2 + 3x + 5}{x + 2} = x^2 - 4x + 11 + \frac{-17}{x + 2}$$

$$a + b + c + d = 1 - 4 + 11 - 17 = -9$$

The Zeros of a Polynomial Function

5.2   The Real Zeros of a Polynomial Function

1. $f(x) = 4x^3 - 3x^2 - 8x + 4;\quad c = 2$
   $f(2) = 4(2)^3 - 3(2)^2 - 8(2) + 4 = 32 - 12 - 16 + 4 = 8 \neq 0$
   Thus, 2 is not a zero of $f \therefore x - 2$ is not a factor of f.

2. $f(x) = -4x^3 + 5x^2 + 8;\quad c = -3$
   $f(-3) = -4(-3)^3 + 5(-3)^2 + 8 = 108 + 45 + 8 = 161 \neq 0$
   Thus, -3 is not a zero of $f \therefore x + 3$ is not a factor of f.

3. $f(x) = 3x^4 - 6x^3 - 5x + 10;\quad c = 2$
   $f(2) = 3(2)^4 - 6(2)^3 - 5(2) + 10 = 48 - 48 - 10 + 10 = 0$
   Thus, 2 is a zero of $f \therefore x - 2$ is a factor of f.

4. $f(x) = 4x^4 - 15x^2 - 4;\quad c = 2$
   $f(2) = 4(2)^4 - 15(2)^2 - 4 = 64 - 60 - 4 = 0$
   Thus, 2 is a zero of $f \therefore x - 2$ is a factor of f.
   Factoring: $f(x) = (4x^2 + 1)(x^2 - 4) = (4x^2 + 1)(x + 2)(x - 2)$

5. $f(x) = 3x^6 + 82x^3 + 27;\quad c = -3$
   $f(-3) = 3(-3)^6 + 82(-3)^3 + 27 = 2187 - 2214 - 27 = 0$
   Thus, -3 is a zero of $f \therefore x + 3$ is a factor of f. Use synthetic division to find the factors.

   $$\begin{array}{r|rrrrrr} -3 & 3 & 0 & 0 & 82 & 0 & 0 & 27 \\ & & -9 & 27 & -81 & -3 & 9 & -27 \\ \hline & 3 & -9 & 27 & 1 & -3 & 9 & 0 \end{array}$$

   The factored form is: $f(x) = (x + 3)(3x^5 - 9x^4 + 27x^3 + x^2 - 3x + 9)$.

6. $f(x) = 2x^6 - 18x^4 + x^2 - 9;\quad c = -3$
   $f(-3) = 2(-3)^6 - 18(-3)^4 + (-3)^2 - 9 = 1458 - 1458 + 9 - 9 = 0$
   Thus, -3 is a zero of $f \therefore x + 3$ is a factor of f.
   Factoring:
   $$f(x) = 2x^4(x^2 - 9) + (x^2 - 9) = (x^2 - 9)(2x^4 + 1) = (x + 3)(x - 3)(2x^4 + 1)$$

7. $f(x) = 4x^6 - 64x^4 + x^2 - 15; \quad c = -4$
    Use synthetic division to determine whether -4 is a zero.

    $$-4 \overline{)\begin{array}{ccccccc} 4 & 0 & -64 & 0 & 1 & 0 & -15 \\ & -16 & 64 & 0 & 0 & -4 & 16 \\ \hline 4 & -16 & 0 & 0 & 1 & -4 & 1 \end{array}}$$

    Thus, -4 is not a zero of $f \therefore x + 4$ is not a factor of f.

8. $f(x) = x^6 - 16x^4 + x^2 - 16; \quad c = -4$
    $f(-4) = (-4)^6 - 16(-4)^4 + (-4)^2 - 16 = 4096 - 4096 + 16 - 16 = 0$
    Thus, -4 is a zero of $f \therefore x + 4$ is a factor of f.
    Factoring:
    $$f(x) = x^4(x^2 - 16) + (x^2 - 16) = (x^2 - 16)(x^4 + 1) = (x + 4)(x - 4)(x^4 + 1)$$

9. $f(x) = 2x^4 - x^3 + 2x - 1; \quad c = \dfrac{1}{2}$

    $$f\left(\frac{1}{2}\right) = 2\left(\frac{1}{2}\right)^4 - \left(\frac{1}{2}\right)^3 + 2\left(\frac{1}{2}\right) - 1 = \frac{1}{8} - \frac{1}{8} + 1 - 1 = 0$$

    Thus, $\dfrac{1}{2}$ is a zero of $f \therefore x - \dfrac{1}{2}$ is a factor of f.
    Factoring:

    $$f(x) = 2x^4 - x^3 + 2x - 1 = 2x^3\left(x - \frac{1}{2}\right) + 2\left(x - \frac{1}{2}\right) = \left(x - \frac{1}{2}\right)(2x^3 + 2)$$

    $$= 2\left(x - \frac{1}{2}\right)(x^3 + 1) = 2\left(x - \frac{1}{2}\right)(x + 1)(x^2 - x + 1)$$

10. $f(x) = 3x^4 + x^3 - 3x + 1; \quad c = -\dfrac{1}{3}$

    $$f\left(-\frac{1}{3}\right) = 3\left(-\frac{1}{3}\right)^4 + \left(-\frac{1}{3}\right)^3 - 3\left(-\frac{1}{3}\right) + 1 = \frac{1}{27} - \frac{1}{27} + 1 + 1 = 2 \neq 0$$

    Thus, $-\dfrac{1}{3}$ is not a zero of $f \therefore x + \dfrac{1}{3}$ is not a factor of f.

11. $f(x) = -4x^7 + x^3 - x^2 + 2$
    The maximum number of zeros is the degree of the polynomial which is 7.
    Examining $f(x) = -4x^7 + x^3 - x^2 + 2$, there are 3 variations in sign; thus, there are 3 or 1 positive real zeros.
    Examining $f(-x) = -4(-x)^7 + (-x)^3 - (-x)^2 + 2 = 4x^7 - x^3 - x^2 + 2$, there are 2 variations in sign; thus, there are 2 or 0 negative real zeros.

12. $f(x) = 5x^4 + 2x^2 - 6x - 5$
    The maximum number of zeros is the degree of the polynomial which is 4.
    Examining $f(x) = 5x^4 + 2x^2 - 6x - 5$, there is 1 variation in sign; thus, there is 1 positive real zero.
    Examining $f(-x) = 5(-x)^4 + 2(-x)^2 - 6(-x) - 5 = 5x^4 + 2x^2 + 6x - 5$, there is 1 variation in sign; thus, there is 1 negative real zero.

13. $f(x) = 2x^6 - 3x^2 - x + 1$
     The maximum number of zeros is the degree of the polynomial which is 6.
     Examining $f(x) = 2x^6 - 3x^2 - x + 1$, there are 2 variations in sign; thus, there are 2 or 0 positive real zeros.
     Examining $f(-x) = 2(-x)^6 - 3(-x)^2 - (-x) + 1 = 2x^6 - 3x^2 + x + 1$, there are 2 variations in sign; thus, there are 2 or 0 negative real zeros.

14. $f(x) = -3x^5 + 4x^4 + 2$
     The maximum number of zeros is the degree of the polynomial which is 5.
     Examining $f(x) = -3x^5 + 4x^4 + 2$, there is 1 variation in sign; thus, there is 1 positive real zero.
     Examining $f(-x) = -3(-x)^5 + 4(-x)^4 + 2 = 3x^5 + 4x^4 + 2$, there is no variation in sign; thus, there are no negative real zeros.

15. $f(x) = 3x^3 - 2x^2 + x + 2$
     The maximum number of zeros is the degree of the polynomial which is 3.
     Examining $f(x) = 3x^3 - 2x^2 + x + 2$, there are 2 variations in sign; thus, there are 2 or 0 positive real zeros.
     Examining $f(-x) = 3(-x)^3 - 2(-x)^2 + (-x) + 2 = -3x^3 - 2x^2 - x + 2$, there is 1 variation in sign; thus, there is 1 negative real zero.

16. $f(x) = -x^3 - x^2 + x + 1$
     The maximum number of zeros is the degree of the polynomial which is 3.
     Examining $f(x) = -x^3 - x^2 + x + 1$, there is 1 variation in sign; thus, there is 1 positive real zero.
     Examining $f(-x) = -(-x)^3 - (-x)^2 + (-x) + 1 = x^3 - x^2 - x + 1$, there are 2 variations in sign; thus, there are 2 or 0 negative real zeros.

17. $f(x) = -x^4 + x^2 - 1$
     The maximum number of zeros is the degree of the polynomial which is 4.
     Examining $f(x) = -x^4 + x^2 - 1$, there are 2 variations in sign; thus, there are 2 or 0 positive real zeros.
     Examining $f(-x) = -(-x)^4 + (-x)^2 - 1 = -x^4 + x^2 - 1$, there are 2 variations in sign; thus, there are 2 or 0 negative real zeros.

18. $f(x) = x^4 + 5x^3 - 2$
     The maximum number of zeros is the degree of the polynomial which is 4.
     Examining $f(x) = x^4 + 5x^3 - 2$, there is 1 variation in sign; thus, there is 1 positive real zero.
     Examining $f(-x) = (-x)^4 + 5(-x)^3 - 2 = x^4 - 5x^3 - 2$, there is 1 variation in sign; thus, there is 1 negative real zero.

19. $f(x) = x^5 + x^4 + x^2 + x + 1$
The maximum number of zeros is the degree of the polynomial which is 5.
Examining $f(x) = x^5 + x^4 + x^2 + x + 1$, there are no variations in sign; thus, there are 0 positive real zeros.
Examining $f(-x) = (-x)^5 + (-x)^4 + (-x)^2 + (-x) + 1 = -x^5 + x^4 + x^2 - x + 1$, there are 3 variations in sign; thus, there are 3 or 1 negative real zeros.

20. $f(x) = x^5 - x^4 + x^3 - x^2 + x - 1$
The maximum number of zeros is the degree of the polynomial which is 5.
Examining $f(x) = x^5 - x^4 + x^3 - x^2 + x - 1$, there are 5 variations in sign; thus, there are 5 or 3 or 1 positive real zeros.
Examining $f(-x) = (-x)^5 - (-x)^4 + (-x)^3 - (-x)^2 + (-x) - 1 = -x^5 - x^4 - x^3 - x^2 - x - 1$, there is no variation in sign; thus, there is no negative real zero.

21. $f(x) = x^6 - 1$
The maximum number of zeros is the degree of the polynomial which is 6.
Examining $f(x) = x^6 - 1$, there is 1 variation in sign; thus, there is 1 positive real zero.
Examining $f(-x) = (-x)^6 - 1 = x^6 - 1$, there is 1 variation in sign; thus, there is 1 negative real zero.

22. $f(x) = x^6 + 1$
The maximum number of zeros is the degree of the polynomial which is 6.
Examining $f(x) = x^6 + 1$, there is no variation in sign; thus, there is no positive real zero.
Examining $f(-x) = (-x)^6 + 1 = x^6 + 1$, there is no variation in sign; thus, there is no negative real zero.

23. $f(x) = 3x^4 - 3x^3 + x^2 - x + 1$
p must be a factor of 1: $p = \pm 1$
q must be a factor of 3: $q = \pm 1, \pm 3$
The possible rational zeros are: $\dfrac{p}{q} = \pm 1, \pm \dfrac{1}{3}$

24. $f(x) = x^5 - x^4 + 2x^2 + 3$
p must be a factor of 3: $p = \pm 1, \pm 3$
q must be a factor of 1: $q = \pm 1$
The possible rational zeros are: $\dfrac{p}{q} = \pm 1, \pm 3$

25. $f(x) = x^5 - 6x^2 + 9x - 3$
p must be a factor of -3: $p = \pm 1, \pm 3$
q must be a factor of 1: $q = \pm 1$
The possible rational zeros are: $\dfrac{p}{q} = \pm 1, \pm 3$

26. $f(x) = 2x^5 - x^4 - x^2 + 1$
 p must be a factor of 1: $p = \pm 1$
 q must be a factor of 2: $q = \pm 1, \pm 2$

 The possible rational zeros are: $\dfrac{p}{q} = \pm 1, \pm \dfrac{1}{2}$

27. $f(x) = -4x^3 - x^2 + x + 2$
 p must be a factor of 2: $p = \pm 1, \pm 2$
 q must be a factor of -4: $q = \pm 1, \pm 2, \pm 4$

 The possible rational zeros are: $\dfrac{p}{q} = \pm 1, \pm 2, \pm \dfrac{1}{2}, \pm \dfrac{1}{4}$

28. $f(x) = 6x^4 - x^2 + 2$
 p must be a factor of 2: $p = \pm 1, \pm 2$
 q must be a factor of 6: $q = \pm 1, \pm 2, \pm 3, \pm 6$

 The possible rational zeros are: $\dfrac{p}{q} = \pm 1, \pm 2, \pm \dfrac{1}{2}, \pm \dfrac{1}{3}, \pm \dfrac{2}{3}, \pm \dfrac{1}{6}$

29. $f(x) = 6x^4 - x^2 + 9$
 p must be a factor of 9: $p = \pm 1, \pm 3, \pm 9$
 q must be a factor of 6: $q = \pm 1, \pm 2, \pm 3, \pm 6$

 The possible rational zeros are: $\dfrac{p}{q} = \pm 1, \pm \dfrac{1}{2}, \pm \dfrac{1}{3}, \pm \dfrac{1}{6}, \pm 3, \pm \dfrac{3}{2}, \pm 9, \pm \dfrac{9}{2}$

30. $f(x) = -4x^3 + x^2 + x + 6$
 p must be a factor of 6: $p = \pm 1, \pm 2, \pm 3, \pm 6$
 q must be a factor of -4: $q = \pm 1, \pm 2, \pm 4$

 The possible rational zeros are: $\dfrac{p}{q} = \pm 1, \pm 2, \pm \dfrac{1}{2}, \pm \dfrac{1}{4}, \pm 3, \pm \dfrac{3}{2}, \pm \dfrac{3}{4}, \pm 6$

31. $f(x) = 2x^5 - x^3 + 2x^2 + 12$
 p must be a factor of 12: $p = \pm 1, \pm 2, \pm 3, \pm 4, \pm 6, \pm 12$
 q must be a factor of 2: $q = \pm 1, \pm 2$

 The possible rational zeros are: $\dfrac{p}{q} = \pm 1, \pm 2, \pm 4, \pm \dfrac{1}{2}, \pm 3, \pm \dfrac{3}{2}, \pm 6, \pm 12$

32. $f(x) = 6x^4 - x^2 + 9$
 p must be a factor of 9: $p = \pm 1, \pm 3, \pm 9$
 q must be a factor of 6: $q = \pm 1, \pm 2, \pm 3, \pm 6$

 The possible rational zeros are: $\dfrac{p}{q} = \pm 1, \pm 3, \pm \dfrac{1}{2}, \pm \dfrac{1}{3}, \pm \dfrac{1}{6}, \pm \dfrac{3}{2}, \pm 9, \pm \dfrac{9}{2}$

33. $f(x) = 6x^4 + 2x^3 - x^2 + 20$

     p must be a factor of 20: $p = \pm 1, \pm 2, \pm 4, \pm 5, \pm 10, \pm 20$

     q must be a factor of 6: $q = \pm 1, \pm 2, \pm 3, \pm 6$

     The possible rational zeros are:

$$\frac{p}{q} = \pm 1, \pm 2, \pm \frac{1}{2}, \pm \frac{1}{3}, \pm \frac{2}{3}, \pm \frac{1}{6}, \pm 4, \pm \frac{4}{3}, \pm 5, \pm \frac{5}{2}, \pm \frac{5}{3}, \pm \frac{5}{6}, \pm 10, \pm \frac{10}{3}, \pm 20, \pm \frac{20}{3}$$

34. $f(x) = -6x^3 - x^2 + x + 10$

     p must be a factor of 10: $p = \pm 1, \pm 2, \pm 5, \pm 10$

     q must be a factor of –6: $q = \pm 1, \pm 2, \pm 3, \pm 6$

     The possible rational zeros are:

$$\frac{p}{q} = \pm 1, \pm 3, \pm \frac{1}{2}, \pm \frac{3}{2}, \pm \frac{1}{3}, \pm \frac{1}{6}, \pm 2, \pm \frac{2}{3}, \pm 5, \pm \frac{5}{2}, \pm \frac{5}{3}, \pm \frac{5}{6}, \pm 10, \pm \frac{10}{3}$$

35. $f(x) = x^3 + 2x^2 - 5x - 6$

    Step 1: $f(x)$ has at most 3 real zeros.

    Step 2:   By Descartes Rule of Signs, there is 1 positive real zero.

             Also because $f(-x) = (-x)^3 + 2(-x)^2 - 5(-x) - 6 = -x^3 + 2x^2 + 5x - 6$, there are 2 or 0 negative real zeros.

    Step 3:   Possible rational zeros:

$$p = \pm 1, \pm 2, \pm 3, \pm 6; \quad q = \pm 1; \quad \frac{p}{q} = \pm 1, \pm 2, \pm 3, \pm 6$$

    Step 4:   Using synthetic division:

```
-3)1    2   -5   -6
       -3    3    6
    _____
    1   -1   -2    0
```

             Since the remainder is 0, $x - (-3) = x + 3$ is a factor. The other factor is the quotient: $x^2 - x - 2$.

             Thus, $f(x) = (x + 3)(x^2 - x - 2) = (x + 3)(x + 1)(x - 2)$.

             The zeros are –3, –1, and 2.

36. $f(x) = x^3 + 8x^2 + 11x - 20$

    Step 1: $f(x)$ has at most 3 real zeros.

    Step 2:   By Descartes Rule of Signs, there is 1 positive real zero.

             Also because $f(-x) = (-x)^3 + 8(-x)^2 + 11(-x) - 20 = -x^3 + 8x^2 - 11x - 20$, there are 2 or 0 negative real zeros.

    Step 3:   Possible rational zeros: $p = \pm 1, \pm 2, \pm 4, \pm 5, \pm 10, \pm 20; \quad q = \pm 1;$

$$\frac{p}{q} = \pm 1, \pm 2, \pm 4, \pm 5, \pm 10, \pm 20$$

    Step 4:   Using synthetic division:

```
-5)1    8   11   -20
       -5  -15    20
    _____
    1    3   -4     0
```

Since the remainder is 0, $x - (-5) = x + 5$ is a factor. The other factor is the quotient: $x^2 + 3x - 4$.

Thus, $f(x) = (x + 5)(x^2 + 3x - 4) = (x + 5)(x + 4)(x - 1)$.

The zeros are –5, –4, and 1.

37. $f(x) = 2x^3 - x^2 + 2x - 1; \ f(-x) = 2(-x)^3 - (-x)^2 + 2(-x) - 1 = -2x^3 - x^2 - 2x - 1$

Step 1: $f(x)$ has at most 3 real zeros.

Step 2:   By Descartes Rule of Signs, there are 3 or 1 positive real zeros; thus, there are no negative real zeros.

Step 3:   Possible rational zeros:

$$p = \pm 1 \quad q = \pm 1, \pm 2; \quad \frac{p}{q} = \pm 1, \pm \frac{1}{2}$$

Step 4:   Using synthetic division:

$$
\begin{array}{r|rrrr}
-1 & 2 & -1 & 2 & -1 \\
   &   & -2 & 3 & -5 \\
\hline
   & 2 & -3 & 5 & \{-6\} \rightarrow
\end{array}
$$

$x + 1$ is **not** a factor

So we try $x - 1$

$$
\begin{array}{r|rrrr}
1 & 2 & -1 & 2 & -1 \\
  &   & 2 & 1 & 3 \\
\hline
  & 2 & 1 & 3 & \{2\} \rightarrow
\end{array}
$$

$x - 1$ is **not** a factor

Let's try $x - \dfrac{1}{2}$

$$
\begin{array}{r|rrrr}
\frac{1}{2} & 2 & -1 & 2 & -1 \\
            &   & 1 & 0 & 1 \\
\hline
            & 2 & 0 & 2 & 0 \rightarrow
\end{array}
$$

$x - \dfrac{1}{2}$ is a factor $\therefore$ the quotient is $2x^2 + 2$.

Thus, $f(x) = 2x^3 - x^2 + 2x - 1 = \left(x - \dfrac{1}{2}\right)(2x^2 + 2)$.

Since $2x^2 + 2 = 0$ has no real solutions, $x = \dfrac{1}{2}$ is the only real zero.

38. $f(x) = 2x^3 + x^2 + 2x + 1$

Step 1: $f(x)$ has at most 3 real zeros.

Step 2:   By Descartes Rule of Signs, there are no positive real zeros.

$f(-x) = 2(-x)^3 + (-x)^2 + 2(-x) + 1 = -2x^3 + x^2 - 2x + 1$; thus, there 3 or 1 negative real zeros.

Step 3:   Possible rational zeros: $p = \pm 1; \quad q = \pm 1, \pm 2;$

$$\frac{p}{q} = \pm 1, \pm \frac{1}{2}$$

Step 4:   Using synthetic division:

$x + 1$ is **not** a factor

$$
\begin{array}{r|rrrr}
-1 & 2 & 1 & 2 & 1 \\
   &   & -2 & 1 & -3 \\
\hline
   & 2 & -1 & 3 & \{-2\} \rightarrow
\end{array}
$$

$$-\tfrac{1}{2}\overline{)\begin{array}{cccc} 2 & 1 & 2 & 1 \\ & -1 & 0 & -1 \\ \hline 2 & 0 & 2 & 0 \to \end{array}}$$

$x + \dfrac{1}{2}$ is a factor

The other factor is the quotient: $2x^2 + 2$.

Thus, $f(x) = 2x^3 + x^2 + 2x + 1 = \left(x + \dfrac{1}{2}\right)(x^2 + 2)$. The only real zero is $-\dfrac{1}{2}$.

39. $f(x) = x^4 + x^2 - 2$

   Step 1: $f(x)$ has at most 4 real zeros.

   Step 2:   By Descartes Rule of Signs, this is one positive real zero.

   $f(-x) = (-x)^4 + (-x)^2 - 2 = x^4 + x^2 - 2$; thus, there is 1 negative real zero.

   Step 3:   Possible rational zeros:

   $$p = \pm 1, \pm 2; \quad q = \pm 1; \quad \dfrac{p}{q} = \pm 1, \pm 2$$

   Step 4:   Using synthetic division:

   $$-1\overline{)\begin{array}{ccccc} 1 & 0 & 1 & 0 & 2 \\ & -1 & 1 & -2 & 2 \\ \hline 1 & -1 & 2 & -2 & 0 \to \end{array}}$$

   Since the remainder is 0, $x - (-1) = x + 1$ is a factor. The other factor is the quotient: $x^3 - x^2 + 2x - 2$.

   Thus, $f(x) = (x+1)(x^3 - x^2 + 2x - 2)$. We can factor $x^3 - x^2 + 2x - 2$ by grouping terms: $x^3 - x^2 + 2x - 2 = x^2(x-1) + 2(x-1) = (x-1)(x^2 + 2)$

   Thus, $f(x) = (x+1)(x-1)(x^2 + 2)$. Since $x^2 + 2 = 0$ has no real solutions, we have two real zeros for f, namely -1 and 1.

40. $f(x) = x^4 - 3x^2 - 4$

   Step 1: $f(x)$ has at most 4 real zeros.

   Step 2:   By Descartes Rule of Signs, there is 1 positive real zero.

   $f(-x) = (-x)^4 - 3(-x)^2 - 4 = x^4 - 3x^2 - 4$; thus, there is one negative real zero.

   Step 3:   Possible rational zeros: $p = \pm 1, \pm 2, \pm 4; \quad q = \pm 1$

   $$\dfrac{p}{q} = \pm 1, \pm 2, \pm 4$$

   We can factor f as follows:

   $$f(x) = x^4 - 3x^2 - 4 = (x^2 - 4)(x^2 + 1) = (x+2)(x-2)(x^2 + 1).$$

   Thus, we have two real zeros, -2 and 2.

41. $f(x) = 4x^4 + 7x^2 - 2$

   Step 1: $f(x)$ has at most 4 real zeros.

   Step 2:   By Descartes Rule of Signs, there is 1 positive real zero.

   $f(-x) = 4(-x)^4 + 7(-x)^2 - 2 = 4x^4 + 7x^2 - 2$; thus, there is one negative real zero.

Step 3:   Possible rational zeros: $p = \pm 1, \pm 2$; $q = \pm 1, \pm 2, \pm 4$

$$\frac{p}{q} = \pm 1, \pm \frac{1}{2}, \pm \frac{1}{4} \pm 2$$

We can factor f as follows:

$$f(x) = 4x^4 + 7x^2 - 2 = (4x^2 - 1)(x^2 + 2) = (2x + 1)(2x - 1)(x^2 + 2).$$

Thus, we have two real zeros, $-\dfrac{1}{2}$ and $\dfrac{1}{2}$.

42. $f(x) = 4x^4 + 15x^2 - 4$

Step 1: $f(x)$ has at most 4 real zeros.

Step 2:   By Descartes Rule of Signs, there is 1 positive real zero.

$f(-x) = 4(-x)^4 + 15(-x)^2 - 4 = 4x^4 + 15x^2 - 4$; thus, there is one negative real zero.

Step 3:   Possible rational zeros: $p = \pm 1, \pm 2, \pm 4$; $q = \pm 1, \pm 2, \pm 4$

$$\frac{p}{q} = \pm 1, \pm \frac{1}{2}, \pm \frac{1}{4} \pm 2, \pm 4$$

We can factor f as follows:

$$f(x) = 4x^4 + 15x^2 - 4 = (4x^2 - 1)(x^2 + 4) = (2x + 1)(2x - 1)(x^2 + 4).$$

Thus, we have two real zeros, $-\dfrac{1}{2}$ and $\dfrac{1}{2}$.

43. $f(x) = x^4 + x^3 - 3x^2 - x + 2$

Step 1: $f(x)$ has at most 4 real zeros.

Step 2:   By Descartes Rule of Signs, there are 2 or 0 positive real zeros.

$f(-x) = (-x)^4 + (-x)^3 - 3(-x)^2 - (-x) + 2 = x^4 - x^3 - 3x^2 + x + 2$; thus, there are 2 or 0 negative real zeros.

Step 3:   Possible rational zeros:

$$p = \pm 1, \pm 2;   q = \pm 1;   \frac{p}{q} = \pm 1, \pm 2$$

Step 4:   Using synthetic division:

```
-2)1   1  -3  -1   2        -1)1  -1  -1   1
     -2   2   2  -2              -1   2  -1
   ─────────────────            ──────────────
    1  -1  -1   1   0            1  -2   1   0
```

Since the remainder is 0, $x + 2$ and $x + 1$ are factors. The other factor is the quotient: $x^2 - 2x + 1$.

Thus, $f(x) = (x + 2)(x + 1)(x - 1)^2$.

The zeros are -2, -1, and 1 (multiplicity 2).

44. $f(x) = x^4 - x^3 - 6x^2 + 4x + 8$

Step 1: $f(x)$ has at most 4 real zeros.

Step 2:   By Descartes Rule of Signs, there are 2 or 0 positive real zeros.

$f(-x) = (-x)^4 - (-x)^3 - 6(-x)^2 + 4(-x) + 8 = x^4 + x^3 - 6x^2 - 4x + 8$; thus, there are 2 or 0 negative real zeros.

Step 3:   Possible rational zeros:

$$p = \pm 1, \pm 2, \pm 4, \pm 8; \quad q = \pm 1; \quad \frac{p}{q} = \pm 1, \pm 2, \pm 4, \pm 8$$

Step 4:   Using synthetic division:

$$-2{\overline{)1 \quad -1 \quad -6 \quad 4 \quad 8}}$$
$$\underline{ -2 \quad 6 \quad 0 \quad -8}$$
$$1 \quad -3 \quad 0 \quad 4 \quad 0$$

$$-1{\overline{)1 \quad -3 \quad 0 \quad 4}}$$
$$\underline{ -1 \quad 4 \quad -4}$$
$$1 \quad -4 \quad 4 \quad 0$$

Since the remainder is 0, $x + 2$ and $x + 1$ are factors. The other factor is the quotient: $x^2 - 4x + 4$.

Thus, $f(x) = (x + 2)(x + 1)(x - 2)^2$.

The zeros are -2, -1, and 2 (multiplicity 2).

45. $f(x) = 4x^5 - 8x^4 - x + 2$

Step 1: $f(x)$ has at most 5 real zeros.

Step 2:   By Descartes Rule of Signs, there are 2 or 0 positive real zeros.
$f(-x) = 4(-x)^5 - 8(-x)^4 - (-x) + 2 = -4x^5 - 8x^4 + x + 2$;
thus, there is 1 negative real zero.

Step 3:   Possible rational zeros:

$$p = \pm 1, \pm 2; \quad q = \pm 1, \pm 2, \pm 4; \quad \frac{p}{q} = \pm 1, \pm 2, \pm \frac{1}{2}, \pm \frac{1}{4}$$

Step 4:   Using synthetic division:

$$2{\overline{)4 \quad -8 \quad 0 \quad 0 \quad -1 \quad 2}}$$
$$\underline{ 8 \quad 0 \quad 0 \quad 0 \quad -2}$$
$$4 \quad 0 \quad 0 \quad 0 \quad -1 \quad 0$$

Since the remainder is 0, $x - 2$ is a factor. The other factor is the quotient: $4x^4 - 1$.

Factoring,

$$f(x) = (x - 2)\left(4x^4 - 1\right) = (x - 2)(2x^2 - 1)(2x^2 + 1)$$

$$= (x - 2)\left(\sqrt{2}x - 1\right)\left(\sqrt{2}x + 1\right)\left(2x^2 + 1\right)$$

The zeros are $\dfrac{-\sqrt{2}}{2}, \dfrac{\sqrt{2}}{2}$, and 2 or $-0.71, -0.71$, and 2.

46. $f(x) = 4x^5 + 12x^4 - x - 3$

Step 1: $f(x)$ has at most 5 real zeros.

Step 2:   By Descartes Rule of Signs, there is 1 positive real zero.
$f(-x) = 4(-x)^5 + 12(-x)^4 - (-x) - 3 = -4x^5 + 12x^4 + x - 3$;
thus, there are 2 or 0 negative real zero.

Step 3:   Possible rational zeros:

$$p = \pm 1, \pm 3; \quad q = \pm 1, \pm 2, \pm 4; \quad \frac{p}{q} = \pm 1, \pm 3, \pm \frac{1}{2}, \pm \frac{3}{2}, \pm \frac{1}{4}, \pm \frac{3}{4}$$

Step 4:   Using synthetic division:

$$-3{\overline{)4 \quad 12 \quad 0 \quad 0 \quad -1 \quad -3}}$$
$$\underline{ -12 \quad 0 \quad 0 \quad 0 \quad 3}$$
$$4 \quad 0 \quad 0 \quad 0 \quad -1 \quad 0$$

Since the remainder is 0, $x + 3$ is a factor. The other factor is the quotient: $4x^4 - 1$.

Factoring,

$$f(x) = (x + 3)\left(4x^4 - 1\right) = (x + 3)(2x^2 - 1)(2x^2 + 1)$$
$$= (x + 3)\left(\sqrt{2}x - 1\right)\left(\sqrt{2}x + 1\right)\left(2x^2 + 1\right)$$

The zeros are $\dfrac{-\sqrt{2}}{2}$, $\dfrac{\sqrt{2}}{2}$, and -3 or -0.71, -0.71, and -3.

47. $x^4 - x^3 + 2x^2 - 4x - 8 = 0$

The solutions of the equation are the zeros of $f(x) = x^4 - x^3 + 2x^2 - 4x - 8$.

Step 1: $f(x)$ has at most 4 real zeros.

Step 2:   By Descartes Rule of Signs, there are 3 or 1 positive real zeros.
$f(-x) = (-x)^4 - (-x)^3 + 2(-x)^2 - 4(-x) - 8 = x^4 + x^3 + 2x^2 + 4x - 8$;
thus, there is 1 negative real zero.

Step 3:   Possible rational zeros:

$$p = \pm 1, \pm 2, \pm 4, \pm 8; \quad q = \pm 1; \quad \frac{p}{q} = \pm 1, \pm 2, \pm 4, \pm 8$$

Step 4:   Using synthetic division:

$$\begin{array}{r|rrrrr} -1 & 1 & -1 & 2 & -4 & -8 \\ & & -1 & 2 & -4 & 8 \\ \hline & 1 & -2 & 4 & -8 & 0 \end{array} \qquad \begin{array}{r|rrrr} 2 & 1 & -2 & 4 & -8 \\ & & 2 & 0 & 8 \\ \hline & 1 & 0 & 4 & 0 \end{array}$$

Since the remainder is 0, $x + 1$ and $x - 2$ are factors. The other factor is the quotient: $x^2 + 4$.

The zeros are -1 and 2. ($x^2 + 4 = 0$ has no real solutions.)

48. $2x^3 + 3x^2 + 2x + 3 = 0$

Solve by factoring:

$$x^2(2x + 3) + (2x + 3) = 0 \rightarrow (2x + 3)\left(x^2 + 1\right) = 0 \rightarrow x = -\frac{3}{2}$$

The zero is $-\dfrac{3}{2}$. ($x^2 + 1 = 0$ has no real solutions.)

49. $3x^3 + 4x^2 - 7x + 2 = 0$

The solutions of the equation are the zeros of $f(x) = 3x^3 + 4x^2 - 7x + 2$.

Step 1: $f(x)$ has at most 3 real zeros.

Step 2:   By Descartes Rule of Signs, there are 2 or 0 positive real zeros.
$f(-x) = 3(-x)^3 + 4(-x)^2 - 7(-x) + 2 = -3x^3 + 4x^2 + 7x + 2$;
thus, there is 1 negative real zero.

Step 3:   Possible rational zeros:

$$p = \pm 1, \pm 2; \quad q = \pm 1, \pm 3; \quad \frac{p}{q} = \pm 1, \pm 2, \pm \frac{1}{3}, \pm \frac{2}{3}$$

Step 4: Using synthetic division:

$$\frac{2}{3})\overline{\begin{array}{cccc} 3 & 4 & -7 & 2 \\ & 2 & 4 & -2 \\ \hline 3 & 6 & -3 & 0 \end{array}}$$

Since the remainder is 0, $x - \dfrac{2}{3}$ is a factor. The other factor is the quotient: $3x^2 + 6x - 3$.

$$f(x) = \left(x - \frac{2}{3}\right)\left(3x^2 + 6x - 3\right) = 3\left(x - \frac{2}{3}\right)\left(x^2 + 2x - 1\right)$$

Using the quadratic formula to solve $x^2 + 2x - 1 = 0$:

$$x = \frac{-2 \pm \sqrt{4 - 4(1)(-1)}}{2(1)} = \frac{-2 \pm \sqrt{8}}{2} = \frac{-2 \pm 2\sqrt{2}}{2} = -1 \pm \sqrt{2}$$

The zeros are $\dfrac{2}{3}$, $-1 + \sqrt{2}$, and $-1 - \sqrt{2}$ or 0.67, 0.41, and –2.41.

50. $2x^3 - 3x^2 - 3x - 5 = 0$
The solutions of the equation are the zeros of $f(x) = 2x^3 - 3x^2 - 3x - 5$.
Step 1: $f(x)$ has at most 3 real zeros.
Step 2: By Descartes Rule of Signs, there is 1 positive real zero.
$f(-x) = 2(-x)^3 - 3(-x)^2 - 3(-x) - 5 = -2x^3 - 3x^2 + 3x - 5$;
thus, there are 2 or 0 negative real zeros.
Step 3: Possible rational zeros:

$$p = \pm 1, \pm 5; \quad q = \pm 1, \pm 2; \quad \frac{p}{q} = \pm 1, \pm 5, \pm \frac{1}{2}, \pm \frac{5}{2}$$

Step 4: Using synthetic division:

$$\frac{5}{2})\overline{\begin{array}{cccc} 2 & -3 & -3 & -5 \\ & 5 & 5 & 5 \\ \hline 2 & 2 & 2 & 0 \end{array}}$$

Since the remainder is 0, $x - \frac{5}{2}$ is a factor. The other factor is the quotient: $2x^2 + 2x + 2$.

$$f(x) = \left(x - \frac{5}{2}\right)\left(2x^2 + 2x + 2\right) = 2\left(x - \frac{5}{2}\right)\left(x^2 + x + 1\right)$$

$x^2 + x + 1 = 0$ has no real zeros.

The zero is $\dfrac{5}{2}$.

51. $3x^3 - x^2 - 15x + 5 = 0$
Solving by factoring:

$$x^2(3x - 1) - 5(3x - 1) = 0 \rightarrow (3x - 1)\left(x^2 - 5\right) = 0 \rightarrow (3x - 1)\left(x - \sqrt{5}\right)\left(x + \sqrt{5}\right) = 0$$

The solutions of the equation are $\dfrac{1}{3}$, $\sqrt{5}$, and $-\sqrt{5}$ or 0.33, 2.24, and –2.24.

52. $2x^3 - 11x^2 + 10x + 8 = 0$

The solutions of the equation are the zeros of $f(x) = 2x^3 - 11x^2 + 10x + 8$.

Step 1: $f(x)$ has at most 3 real zeros.

Step 2:   By Descartes Rule of Signs, there are 2 or 0 positive real zeros.
$f(-x) = 2(-x)^3 - 11(-x)^2 + 10(-x) + 8 = -2x^3 - 11x^2 - 10x + 8$;
thus, there is 1 negative real zero.

Step 3:   Possible rational zeros:

$$p = \pm 1, \pm 2, \pm 4, \pm 8; \quad q = \pm 1, \pm 2; \quad \frac{p}{q} = \pm 1, \pm 2, \pm 4, \pm 8, \pm \frac{1}{2}$$

Step 4:   Using synthetic division:

$$
\begin{array}{r|rrrr}
4 & 2 & -11 & 10 & 8 \\
  &   & 8 & -12 & -8 \\
\hline
  & 2 & -3 & -2 & 0
\end{array}
$$

Since the remainder is 0, $x - 4$ is a factor. The other factor is the quotient: $2x^2 - 3x - 2 = (2x + 1)(x - 2)$.

The zeros are $-\dfrac{1}{2}, 2$, and 4.

53. $x^4 + 4x^3 + 2x^2 - x + 6 = 0$

The solutions of the equation are the zeros of $f(x) = x^4 + 4x^3 + 2x^2 - x + 6$.

Step 1: $f(x)$ has at most 4 real zeros.

Step 2:   By Descartes Rule of Signs, there are 2 or 0 positive real zeros.
$f(-x) = (-x)^4 + 4(-x)^3 + 2(-x)^2 - (-x) + 6 = x^4 - 4x^3 + 2x^2 + x + 6$;
thus, there are 2 or 0 negative real zeros.

Step 3:   Possible rational zeros:

$$p = \pm 1, \pm 2, \pm 3, \pm 6; \quad q = \pm 1; \quad \frac{p}{q} = \pm 1, \pm 2, \pm 3, \pm 6$$

Step 4:   Using synthetic division:

$$
\begin{array}{r|rrrrr}
-3 & 1 & 4 & 2 & -1 & 6 \\
   &   & -3 & -3 & 3 & -6 \\
\hline
   & 1 & 1 & -1 & 2 & 0
\end{array}
\qquad
\begin{array}{r|rrrr}
-2 & 1 & 1 & -1 & 2 \\
   &   & -2 & 2 & -2 \\
\hline
   & 1 & -1 & 1 & 0
\end{array}
$$

Since the remainder is 0, $x + 3$ and $x + 2$ are factors. The other factor is the quotient: $x^2 - x + 1$.

The zeros are -3 and -2. ($x^2 - x + 1 = 0$ has no real solutions.)

54. $x^4 - 2x^3 + 10x^2 - 18x + 9 = 0$

The solutions of the equation are the zeros of $f(x) = x^4 - 2x^3 + 10x^2 - 18x + 9$.

Step 1: $f(x)$ has at most 4 real zeros.

Step 2:   By Descartes Rule of Signs, there are 4 or 2 or 0 positive real zeros.
$f(-x) = (-x)^4 - 2(-x)^3 + 10(-x)^2 - 18(-x) + 9$
$= x^4 + 2x^3 + 10x^2 + 18x + 9$
thus, there are no negative real zeros.

Step 3:   Possible rational zeros:

$$p = \pm1, \pm3, \pm9; \quad q = \pm1; \quad \frac{p}{q} = \pm1, \pm3, \pm9$$

Step 4:   Using synthetic division:

```
1) 1  -2   10  -18    9          1) 1  -1    9   -9
        1   -1    9   -9                 1    0    9
   ─────────────────────            ──────────────────
      1   -1    9   -9    0            1    0    9    0
```

Since the remainder is 0, $x - 1$ and $x - 1$ are factors. The other factor is the quotient: $x^2 + 9$.

The zeros are 1 (multiplicity 2). ($x^2 + 9 = 0$ has no real solutions.)

55. $x^3 - \dfrac{2}{3}x^2 + \dfrac{8}{3}x + 1 = 0$

The solutions of the equation are the zeros of $f(x) = x^3 - \dfrac{2}{3}x^2 + \dfrac{8}{3}x + 1$.

Step 1: $f(x)$ has at most 3 real zeros.

Step 2:   By Descartes Rule of Signs, there are 2 or 0 positive real zeros.

$$f(-x) = (-x)^3 - \frac{2}{3}(-x)^2 + \frac{8}{3}(-x) + 1 = -x^3 - \frac{2}{3}x^2 - \frac{8}{3}x + 1;$$

thus, there is 1 negative real zero.

Step 3:   Use the equivalent equation $3x^3 - 2x^2 + 8x + 3 = 0$ to find the possible rational zeros:

$$p = \pm1, \pm3; \quad q = \pm1, \pm3; \quad \frac{p}{q} = \pm1, \pm3, \pm\frac{1}{3}$$

Step 4:   Using synthetic division:

```
  1 |               2     8
 -─ | 1           -─     ─      1
  3 |               3     3
    |             1      1
    |           -─      ─     -1
    |             3      3
    ──────────────────────────────
        1    -1     3      0
```

Since the remainder is 0, $x + \dfrac{1}{3}$ is a factor. The other factor is the quotient: $x^2 - x + 3$.

The real zero is $-\dfrac{1}{3}$. ($x^2 - x + 3 = 0$ has no real solutions.)

56. $x^3 + \dfrac{3}{2}x^2 + 3x - 2 = 0$

The solutions of the equation are the zeros of $f(x) = x^3 + \dfrac{3}{2}x^2 + 3x - 2$.

Step 1: $f(x)$ has at most 3 real zeros.

Step 2:   By Descartes Rule of Signs, there is 1 positive real zero.

$$f(-x) = (-x)^3 + \frac{3}{2}(-x)^2 + 3(-x) - 2 = -x^3 - \frac{3}{2}x^2 - 3x - 2;$$

thus, there are 2 or no negative real zeros.

Step 3: Use the equivalent equation $2x^3 + 3x^2 + 6x - 4 = 0$ to find the possible rational zeros:

$$p = \pm 1, \pm 2, \pm 4; \quad q = \pm 1, \pm 2; \quad \frac{p}{q} = \pm 1, \pm \frac{1}{2}, \pm 2, \pm 4$$

Step 4: Using synthetic division:

```
1)2   3   6   -4        -1)2   3    6   -4         ½)2   3   6  -4
      2   5   11              -2  -1   -5                 1   2   4
   ─────────────            ───────────────           ──────────────
   2   5   11  {7}          2   1    5  {-9}          2   4   8   0
```

Thus, $x - \dfrac{1}{2}$ is a factor. The other factor is the quotient: $2x^2 + 4x + 8$.

So we have $2x^3 + 3x^2 + 6x - 4 = \left(x - \dfrac{1}{2}\right)(2x^2 + 4x + 8) = 2\left(x - \dfrac{1}{2}\right)(x^2 + 2x + 4)$.

Since $f(x) = x^3 + \dfrac{3}{2}x^2 + 3x - 2 = \dfrac{1}{2}(2x^3 + 3x^2 + 6x - 4)$ we conclude that

$$f(x) = x^3 + \frac{3}{2}x^2 + 3x - 2 = \frac{1}{2}(2x^3 + 3x^2 + 6x - 4) = \frac{1}{2}\left(2\left(x - \frac{1}{2}\right)(x^2 + 2x + 4)\right) = \left(x - \frac{1}{2}\right)(x^2 + 2x + 4)$$

and since $x^2 + 2x + 4 = 0$ has no real solutions, the only real zero for f is $\dfrac{1}{2}$.

57. $2x^4 - 19x^3 + 57x^2 - 64x + 20 = 0$

The solutions of the equation are the zeros of $f(x) = 2x^4 - 19x^3 + 57x^2 - 64x + 20$.

Step 1: $f(x)$ has at most 4 real zeros.

Step 2: By Descartes Rule of Signs, there are 4, 2 or 0 positive real zeros.

$$f(-x) = 2(-x)^4 - 19(-x)^3 + 57(-x)^2 - 64(-x) + 20$$

$$= 2x^4 + 19x^3 + 57x^2 + 64x + 20$$

thus, there are no negative real zeros.

Step 3: To find the possible rational zeros:

$$p = \pm 1, \pm 2, \pm 4, \pm 5, \pm 10, \pm 20; \quad q = \pm 1, \pm 2;$$

$$\frac{p}{q} = \pm 1, \pm \frac{1}{2}, \pm 2, \pm 4, \pm 5, \pm \frac{5}{2}, \pm 10, \pm 20$$

Step 4: Using synthetic division:

```
1)2  -19   57  -64    20          ½)2  -19   57   -64     20
      2   -17   40   -24                1   -9        24  -20
   ─────────────────────             ──────────────────────────
   2  -17   40   -24  {-4}           2  -18   48   -40      0
```

Thus, $x - \dfrac{1}{2}$ is a factor.

So :

$$f(x) = 2x^4 - 19x^3 + 57x^2 - 64x + 20 = \left(x - \frac{1}{2}\right)(2x^3 - 18x^2 + 48x - 40)$$

$$= 2\left(x - \frac{1}{2}\right)(x^3 - 9x^2 + 24x - 20)$$

Now try $x = 2$ as a solution to the equation $x^3 - 9x^2 + 24x - 20 = 0$.

$$\begin{array}{r|rrrr} 2) & 1 & -9 & 24 & -20 \\ & & 2 & -14 & 20 \\ \hline & 1 & -7 & 10 & 0 \end{array}$$

Thus, $x^3 - 9x^2 + 24x - 20 = (x-2)(x^2 - 7x + 10) = (x-2)(x-2)(x-5)$

So we have

$$f(x) = 2x^4 - 19x^3 + 57x^2 - 64x + 20 = 2\left(x - \frac{1}{2}\right)(x-2)^2(x-5).$$

Therefore, f has real zeros $\frac{1}{2}, 2, 5$, and 2 is a zero of multiplicity 2.

58. $2x^4 + x^3 - 24x^2 + 20x + 16 = 0$

The solutions of the equation are the zeros of $f(x) = 2x^4 + x^3 - 24x^2 + 20x + 16$.

Step 1: $f(x)$ has at most 4 real zeros.

Step 2:   By Descartes Rule of Signs, there are 2 or 0 positive real zeros.

$$f(-x) = 2(-x)^4 + (-x)^3 - 24(-x)^2 + 20(-x) + 16 = 2x^4 - x^3 - 24x^2 - 20x + 16;$$

thus, there are 2 or 0 negative real zeros.

Step 3:   To find the possible rational zeros:

$$p = \pm 1, \pm 2, \pm 4, \pm 8, \pm 16; \quad q = \pm 1, \pm 2;$$

$$\frac{p}{q} = \pm 1, \pm \frac{1}{2}, \pm 2, \pm 4, \pm 8, \pm 16$$

Step 4:   Using synthetic division:

$$\begin{array}{r|rrrrr} 2) & 2 & 1 & -24 & 20 & 16 \\ & & 4 & 10 & -28 & -16 \\ \hline & 2 & 5 & -14 & -8 & 0 \end{array}$$

Thus, $x - 2$ is a factor.

So : $f(x) = 2x^4 + x^3 - 24x^2 + 20x + 16 = (x-2)(2x^3 + 5x^2 - 14x - 8)$.

Now try $x = -4$ as a solution to the equation $2x^3 + 5x^2 - 14x - 8 = 0$.

$$\begin{array}{r|rrrr} -4) & 2 & 5 & -14 & -8 \\ & & -8 & 12 & 8 \\ \hline & 2 & -3 & -2 & 0 \end{array}$$

Thus, $2x^3 + 5x^2 - 14x - 8 = (x+4)(2x^2 - 3x - 2) = (x+4)(2x+1)(x-2)$

So we have

$$f(x) = 2x^4 + x^3 - 24x^2 + 20x + 16 = (x-2)(x+4)(2x+1)(x-2)$$

$$= (x-2)^2(x+4)(2x+1)$$

Therefore, f has real zeros $-\frac{1}{2}, -4, 2$, and 2 is a zero of multiplicity 2.

59. $f(x) = x^3 + 2x^2 + 5x - 6 = (x + 3)(x + 1)(x - 2)\cdot$

x-intercepts: $-3, -1, 2$;   y-intercept: -6;   crosses x axis at $x = -3, -1, 2$

	$x < -3$	$-3 < x < -1$	$-1 < x < 2$	$x > 2$
Sign of f	-	+	-	+
Above or below x-axis	below	above	below	above

Graph of f is above the x-axis for $(-3, -1) \cup (2, \infty)$

Graph of f is below the x-axis for $(-\infty, -3) \cup (-1, -2)$

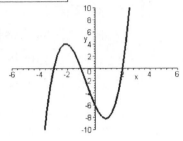

60. $f(x) = x^3 + 8x^2 + 11x - 20 = (x + 5)(x + 4)(x - 1)\cdot$

x-intercepts: $-5, -4, 1$;   y-intercept: -20;   crosses x axis at $x = -5, -4, 1$

	$x < -5$	$-5 < x < -4$	$-4 < x < 1$	$x > 1$
Sign of f	-	+	-	+
Above or below x-axis	below	above	below	above

Graph of f is above the x-axis for $(-5, -4) \cup (1, \infty)$

Graph of f is below the x-axis for $(-\infty, -5) \cup (-4, 1)$

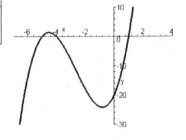

61. $f(x) = 2x^3 - x^2 + 2x - 1 = \left(x - \dfrac{1}{2}\right)\left(2x^2 + 2\right)$.

x-intercepts: $\dfrac{1}{2}$;   y-intercept: -1;   crosses x axis at $x = \dfrac{1}{2}$

	$x < \dfrac{1}{2}$	$x > \dfrac{1}{2}$
Sign of f	-	+
Above or below x-axis	below	above

Graph of f is above the x-axis for $\left(\dfrac{1}{2}, \infty\right)$

Graph of f is below the x-axis for $\left(-\infty, \dfrac{1}{2}\right)$

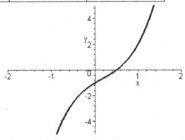

62. $f(x) = 2x^3 + x^2 + 2x + 1 = \left(x + \dfrac{1}{2}\right)\left(x^2 + 2\right)$.

x-intercepts: $-\dfrac{1}{2}$;   y-intercept: 1;   crosses x axis at $x = -\dfrac{1}{2}$

	$x < -\dfrac{1}{2}$	$x > -\dfrac{1}{2}$
Sign of f	-	+
Above or below x-axis	below	above

Graph of f is above the x-axis for $\left(-\dfrac{1}{2}, \infty\right)$

Graph of f is below the x-axis for $\left(-\infty, -\dfrac{1}{2}\right)$

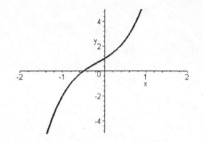

63. $f(x) = x^4 + x^2 - 2 = (x + 1)(x - 1)\left(x^2 + 2\right)$.

x-intercepts: −1, 1;   y-intercept: -2;   crosses x axis at $x = -1, 1$

	$x < -1$	$-1 < x < 1$	$x > 1$
Sign of f	+	-	+
Above or below x-axis	above	below	above

Graph of f is above the x-axis for $(-\infty, -1) \cup (1, \infty)$

Graph of f is below the x-axis for $(-1, -1)$

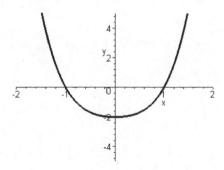

64. $f(x) = x^4 - 3x^2 - 4 = (x + 2)(x - 2)\left(x^2 + 1\right)$.

x-intercepts: −2, 2;   y-intercept: -4;   crosses x axis at $x = -2, 2$

	$x < -2$	$-2 < x < -2$	$x > 2$
Sign of f	+	-	+
Above or below x-axis	above	below	above

Graph of f is above the x-axis for $(-\infty, -2) \cup (2, \infty)$
Graph of f is below the x-axis for $(-2, 2)$

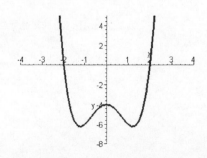

65. $f(x) = 4x^4 + 7x^2 - 2 = (2x+1)(2x-1)(x^2+2)$.

x-intercepts: $-\dfrac{1}{2}, \dfrac{1}{2}$;   y-intercept: -2;   crosses x axis at $x = -\dfrac{1}{2}, \dfrac{1}{2}$

	$x < -\dfrac{1}{2}$	$-\dfrac{1}{2} < x < \dfrac{1}{2}$	$x > \dfrac{1}{2}$
Sign of f	+	-	+
Above or below x-axis	above	below	above

Graph of f is above the x-axis for $\left(-\infty, -\dfrac{1}{2}\right) \cup \left(\dfrac{1}{2}, \infty\right)$

Graph of f is below the x-axis for $\left(-\dfrac{1}{2}, \dfrac{1}{2}\right)$

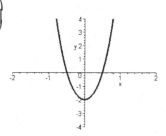

66. $f(x) = 4x^4 + 15x^2 - 4 = (2x+1)(2x-1)(x^2+4)$.

x-intercepts: $-\dfrac{1}{2}, \dfrac{1}{2}$;   y-intercept: -4;   crosses x axis at $x = -\dfrac{1}{2}, \dfrac{1}{2}$

	$x < -\dfrac{1}{2}$	$-\dfrac{1}{2} < x < \dfrac{1}{2}$	$x > \dfrac{1}{2}$
Sign of f	+	-	+
Above or below x-axis	above	below	above

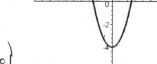

Graph of f is above the x-axis for $\left(-\infty, -\dfrac{1}{2}\right) \cup \left(\dfrac{1}{2}, \infty\right)$

Graph of f is below the x-axis for $\left(-\dfrac{1}{2}, \dfrac{1}{2}\right)$

67. $f(x) = x^4 + x^3 - 3x^2 - x + 2 = (x+2)(x+1)(x-1)^2$.

x-intercepts: $-2, -1, 1$;   y-intercept: 2

crosses x axis at $x = -2, -1$;   touches x axis at $x = 1$

	$x < -2$	$-2 < x < -1$	$-1 < x < 1$	$x > 1$
Sign of f	+	-	+	+
Above or below x-axis	above	below	above	above

Graph of f is above the x-axis for $(-\infty, -2) \cup (-1, 1) \cup (1, \infty)$

Graph of f is below the x-axis for $(-2, -1)$

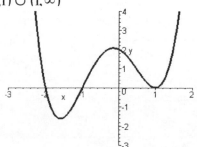

68. $f(x) = x^4 - 3x^3 - 6x^2 + 4x + 8 = (x+2)(x+1)(x-2)^2$.

x-intercepts: –2, –1, 2;   y-intercept: 8

crosses x axis at x = –2, –1;   touches x axis at x = 2

	$x < -2$	$-2 < x < -1$	$-1 < x < 2$	$x > 2$
Sign of f	+	-	+	+
Above or below x-axis	above	below	above	above

Graph of f is above the x-axis for $(-\infty, -2) \cup (-1, 2) \cup (2, \infty)$

Graph of f is below the x-axis for $(-2, -1)$

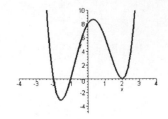

69. $f(x) = 4x^5 - 8x^4 - x + 2 = (x-2)(\sqrt{2}x - 1)(\sqrt{2}x + 1)(2x^2 + 1)$

x-intercepts: $-\dfrac{1}{\sqrt{2}}, \dfrac{1}{\sqrt{2}}, 2$;   y-intercept: 2

crosses x axis at x = $-\dfrac{1}{\sqrt{2}}, \dfrac{1}{\sqrt{2}}, 2$

	$x < -\dfrac{1}{\sqrt{2}}$	$-\dfrac{1}{\sqrt{2}} < x < \dfrac{1}{\sqrt{2}}$	$\dfrac{1}{\sqrt{2}} < x < 2$	$x > 2$
Sign of f	-	+	-	+
Above or below x-axis	below	above	below	above

Graph of f is above the x-axis for $\left(-\dfrac{1}{\sqrt{2}}, \dfrac{1}{\sqrt{2}}\right) \cup (2, \infty)$

Graph of f is below the x-axis for $\left(-\infty, -\dfrac{1}{\sqrt{2}}\right) \cup \left(\dfrac{1}{\sqrt{2}}, 2\right)$

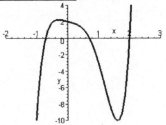

70.

$f(x) = 4x^5 + 12x^4 - x - 3 = (x+3)(\sqrt{2}x - 1)(\sqrt{2}x + 1)(2x^2 + 1)$

x-intercepts: $-3, -\dfrac{1}{\sqrt{2}}, \dfrac{1}{\sqrt{2}}$;   y-intercept: -3

crosses x axis at x = $-3, -\dfrac{1}{\sqrt{2}}, \dfrac{1}{\sqrt{2}}$

	$x < -3$	$-3 < x < -\dfrac{1}{\sqrt{2}}$	$-\dfrac{1}{\sqrt{2}} < x < \dfrac{1}{\sqrt{2}}$	$x > \dfrac{1}{\sqrt{2}}$
Sign of f	-	+	-	+
Above or below x-axis	below	above	below	above

Graph of f is above the x-axis for $\left(-3, -\frac{1}{\sqrt{2}}\right) \cup \left(\frac{1}{\sqrt{2}}, \infty\right)$

Graph of f is below the x-axis for $(-\infty, -3) \cup \left(-\frac{1}{\sqrt{2}}, \frac{1}{\sqrt{2}}\right)$

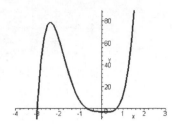

71. $f(x) = x^4 - 3x^2 - 4$
$a_3 = 0, a_2 = -3, a_1 = 0, a_0 = -4$

$Max\{1, |-4| + |0| + |-3| + |0|\} = Max\{1, 4 + 0 + 3 + 0\} = Max\{1, 7\} = 7$

$1 + Max\{|-4|, |0|, |-3|, |0|\} = 1 + Max\{4, 0, 3, 0\} = 1 + 4 = 5$
The smaller of the two numbers is 5. Thus, every zero of f lies between -5 and 5.

72. $f(x) = x^4 - 5x^2 - 36$
$a_3 = 0, a_2 = -5, a_1 = 0, a_0 = -36$

$Max\{1, |-36| + |0| + |-5| + |0|\} = Max\{1, 36 + 0 + 5 + 0\} = Max\{1, 41\} = 41$

$1 + Max\{|-36|, |0|, |-5|, |0|\} = 1 + Max\{36, 0, 5, 0\} = 1 + 36 = 37$
The smaller of the two numbers is 37. Thus, every zero of f lies between -37 and 37.

73. $f(x) = x^4 + x^3 - x - 1$
$a_3 = 1, a_2 = 0, a_1 = -1, a_0 = -1$

$Max\{1, |-1| + |-1| + |0| + |1|\} = Max\{1, 1 + 1 + 0 + 1\} = Max\{1, 3\} = 3$

$1 + Max\{|-1|, |-1|, |0|, |1|\} = 1 + Max\{1, 1, 0, 1\} = 1 + 1 = 2$
The smaller of the two numbers is 2. Thus, every zero of f lies between -2 and 2.

74. $f(x) = x^4 + x^3 + x - 1$
$a_3 = 1, a_2 = 0, a_1 = 1, a_0 = -1$

$Max\{1, |-1| + |1| + |0| + |1|\} = Max\{1, 1 + 1 + 0 + 1\} = Max\{1, 3\} = 3$

$1 + Max\{|-1|, |1|, |0|, |1|\} = 1 + Max\{1, 1, 0, 1\} = 1 + 1 = 2$
The smaller of the two numbers is 2. Thus, every zero of f lies between -2 and 2.

75. $f(x) = 3x^4 + 3x^3 - x^2 - 12x - 12 = 3\left(x^4 + x^3 - \frac{1}{3}x^2 - 4x - 4\right)$

Note: The leading coefficient must be 1.

$a_3 = 1, a_2 = -\frac{1}{3}, a_1 = -4, a_0 = -4$

$$Max\left\{1, \left|-4\right| + \left|-4\right| + \left|-\frac{1}{3}\right| + \left|1\right|\right\} = Max\left\{1, 4 + 4 + \frac{1}{3} + 1\right\} = Max\left\{1, \frac{28}{3}\right\} = \frac{28}{3}$$

$$1 + Max\left\{\left|-4\right|, \left|-4\right|, \left|-\frac{1}{3}\right|, \left|1\right|\right\} = 1 + Max\left\{4, 4, \frac{1}{3}, 1\right\} = 1 + 4 = 5$$

The smaller of the two numbers is 5. Thus, every zero of f lies between -5 and 5.

76. $f(x) = 3x^4 - 3x^3 - 5x^2 + 27x - 36 = 3\left(x^4 + x^3 - \frac{5}{3}x^2 + 9x - 12\right)$

Note: The leading coefficient must be 1.

$a_3 = 1, a_2 = -\frac{5}{3}, a_1 = 9, a_0 = -12$

$$Max\left\{1, \left|-12\right| + \left|9\right| + \left|-\frac{5}{3}\right| + \left|1\right|\right\} = Max\left\{1, 12 + 9 + \frac{5}{3} + 1\right\} = Max\left\{1, \frac{71}{3}\right\} = \frac{71}{3}$$

$$1 + Max\left\{\left|-12\right|, \left|9\right|, \left|-\frac{5}{3}\right|, \left|1\right|\right\} = 1 + Max\left\{12, 9, \frac{5}{3}, 1\right\} = 1 + 12 = 13$$

The smaller of the two numbers is 13. Thus, every zero of f lies between -13 and 13.

77. $f(x) = 4x^5 - x^4 + 2x^3 - 2x^2 + x - 1 = 4\left(x^5 - \frac{1}{4}x^4 + \frac{1}{2}x^3 - \frac{1}{2}x^2 + \frac{1}{4}x - \frac{1}{4}\right)$

Note: The leading coefficient must be 1. $a_4 = -\frac{1}{4}, a_3 = \frac{1}{2}, a_2 = -\frac{1}{2}, a_1 = \frac{1}{4}, a_0 = -\frac{1}{4}$

$$Max\left\{1, \left|-\frac{1}{4}\right| + \left|\frac{1}{4}\right| + \left|-\frac{1}{2}\right| + \left|\frac{1}{2}\right| + \left|-\frac{1}{4}\right|\right\} = Max\left\{1, \frac{1}{4} + \frac{1}{4} + \frac{1}{2} + \frac{1}{2} + \frac{1}{4}\right\} = Max\left\{1, \frac{7}{4}\right\} = \frac{7}{4}$$

$$1 + Max\left\{\left|-\frac{1}{4}\right|, \left|\frac{1}{4}\right|, \left|-\frac{1}{2}\right|, \left|\frac{1}{2}\right|, \left|-\frac{1}{4}\right|\right\} = 1 + Max\left\{\frac{1}{4}, \frac{1}{4}, \frac{1}{2}, \frac{1}{2}, \frac{1}{4}\right\} = 1 + \frac{1}{2} = \frac{3}{2}$$

The smaller of the two numbers is $\frac{3}{2}$. Thus, every zero of f lies between $-\frac{3}{2}$ and $\frac{3}{2}$.

78. $f(x) = 4x^5 + x^4 + x^3 + x^2 - 2x - 2 = 4\left(x^5 + \frac{1}{4}x^4 + \frac{1}{4}x^3 + \frac{1}{4}x^2 - \frac{1}{2}x - \frac{1}{2}\right)$

Note: The leading coefficient must be 1. $a_4 = \frac{1}{4}, a_3 = \frac{1}{4}, a_2 = \frac{1}{4}, a_1 = -\frac{1}{2}, a_0 = -\frac{1}{2}$

$$Max\left\{1, \left|-\frac{1}{2}\right| + \left|-\frac{1}{2}\right| + \left|\frac{1}{4}\right| + \left|\frac{1}{4}\right| + \left|\frac{1}{4}\right|\right\} = Max\left\{1, \frac{1}{2} + \frac{1}{2} + \frac{1}{4} + \frac{1}{4} + \frac{1}{4}\right\} = Max\left\{1, \frac{7}{4}\right\} = \frac{7}{4}$$

$$1 + Max\left\{\left|-\frac{1}{2}\right|, \left|-\frac{1}{2}\right|, \left|\frac{1}{4}\right|, \left|\frac{1}{4}\right|, \left|\frac{1}{4}\right|\right\} = 1 + Max\left\{\frac{1}{2}, \frac{1}{2}, \frac{1}{4}, \frac{1}{4}, \frac{1}{4}\right\} = 1 + \frac{1}{2} = \frac{3}{2}$$

The smaller of the two numbers is $\frac{3}{2}$. Thus, every zero of f lies between $-\frac{3}{2}$ and $\frac{3}{2}$.

79. $f(x) = 8x^4 - 2x^2 + 5x - 1;\ [0, 1]$
$f(0) = -1 < 0$ and $f(1) = 10 > 0$
Since one is positive and one is negative, there is a zero in the interval.

80. $f(x) = x^4 + 8x^3 - x^2 + 2;\ [-1, 0]$
$f(-1) = -6 < 0$ and $f(0) = 2 > 0$
Since one is positive and one is negative, there is a zero in the interval.

81. $f(x) = 2x^3 + 6x^2 - 8x + 2;\ [-5, -4]$
$f(-5) = -58 < 0$ and $f(-4) = 2 > 0$
Since one is positive and one is negative, there is a zero in the interval.

82. $f(x) = 3x^3 - 10x + 9;\ [-3, -2]$
$f(-3) = -42 < 0$ and $f(-2) = 5 > 0$
Since one is positive and one is negative, there is a zero in the interval.

83. $f(x) = x^5 - x^4 + 7x^3 - 7x^2 - 18x + 18;\ [1.4, 1.5]$
$f(1.4) = -0.1754 < 0$ and $f(1.5) = 1.4063 > 0$
Since one is positive and one is negative, there is a zero in the interval.

84. $f(x) = x^5 - 3x^4 - 2x^3 + 6x^2 + x + 2;\ [1.7, 1.8]$
$f(1.7) = 0.35627 > 0$ and $f(1.8) = -1.021 < 0$
Since one is positive and one is negative, there is a zero in the interval.

85. $8x^4 - 2x^2 + 5x - 1 = 0;\quad 0 \le r \le 1$

Consider the function $f(x) = 8x^4 - 2x^2 + 5x - 1$
Subdivide the interval [0,1] into 10 equal subintervals:

[0,0.1]; [0.1,0.2]; [0.2,0.3]; [0.3,0.4]; [0.4,0.5]; [0.5,0.6]; [0.6,0.7]; [0.7,0.8]; [0.8,0.9]; [0.9,1]

$f(0) = -1; f(0.1) = -0.5192$
$f(0.1) = -0.5192; f(0.2) = -0.0672$
$f(0.2) = -0.0672; f(0.3) = 0.3848$ so f has a real zero on the interval [0.2,0.3].
Subdivide the interval [0.2,0.3] into 10 equal subintervals:

[0.2,0.21]; [0.21,0.22]; [0.22,0.23]; [0.23,0.24]; [0.24,0.25]; [0.25,0.26];[0.26,0.27]; [0.27,0.28]; [0.28,0.29]; [0.29,0.3]

$f(0.2) = -0.0672; f(0.21) = -0.02264$
$f(0.21) = -0.02264; f(0.22) = 0.0219$ so f has a real zero on the interval [0.21,0.22], therefore $r = 0.21$, correct to 2 decimal places.

86. $x^4 + 8x^3 - x^2 + 2 = 0; \quad -1 \le r \le 0$

Consider the function $f(x) = x^4 + 8x^3 - x^2 + 2$
Subdivide the interval [- 1, 0] into 10 equal subintervals:

[-1,-0.9]; [-0.9,-0.8]; [-0.8,-0.7]; [-0.7,-0.6]; [-0.6,-0.5]; [-0.5,-0.4]; [-0.4,-0.3];
[-0.3,-0.2]; [-0.2,-0.1]; [-0.1,0]

$f(-1) = -6; f(-0.9) = -3.9859$
$f(-0.9) = -3.9859; f(-0.8) = -2.3264$
$f(-0.8) = -2.3264; f(-0.7) = -0.9939$
$f(-0.7) = -0.9939; f(-0.6) = 0.0416$ so f has a real zero on the interval
                                                [-0.7,-0.6].
Subdivide the interval [-0.7,-0.6] into 10 equal subintervals:

[-0.7,-0.69]; [-0.69,-0.68]; [-0.68,-0.67]; [-0.67,-0.66]; [-0.66,-0.65]; [-0.65,-0.64];
[-0.64,-0.63]; [-0.63,-0.62]; [-0.62,-0.61]; [-0.61,-0.6]

$f(-0.7) = -0.9939; f(-0.69) = -0.8775$
$f(-0.69) = -0.8775; f(-0.68) = -0.7640$
$f(-0.68) = -0.7640; f(-0.67) = -0.6535$
$f(-0.67) = -0.6535; f(-0.66) = -0.5458$
$f(-0.66) = -0.5458; f(-0.65) = -0.4410$
$f(-0.65) = -0.4410; f(-0.64) = -0.3390$
$f(-0.64) = -0.3390; f(-0.63) = -0.2397$
$f(-0.63) = -0.2397; f(-0.62) = -0.1433$
$f(-0.62) = -0.1433; f(-0.61) = -0.0495$
$f(-0.61) = -0.0495; f(-0.60) = 0.0416$ so f has a real zero on the interval
                                                  [-0.61,-0.6], therefore $r = -0.61$,
                                                  correct to 2 decimal places.

87. $2x^3 + 6x^2 - 8x + 2 = 0; \quad -5 \le r \le -4$

Consider the function $f(x) = 2x^3 + 6x^2 - 8x + 2$
Subdivide the interval [-5,-4] into 10 equal subintervals:

[-5,-4.9]; [-4.9,-4.8]; [-4.8,-4.7]; [-4.7,-4.6]; [-4.6,-4.5]; [-4.5,-4.4]; [-4.4,-4.3];
[-4.3,-4.2]; [-4.2,-4.1]; [-4.1,-4]

$f(-5) = -58; f(-4.9) = -50.038$
$f(-4.9) = -50.038; f(-4.8) = -42.544$
$f(-4.8) = -42.544; f(-4.7) = -35.506$
$f(-4.7) = -35.506; f(-4.6) = -28.912$
$f(-4.6) = -28.912; f(-4.5) = -22.75$

$f(-4.5) = -22.75; f(-4.4) = -17$
$f(-4.4) = -17; f(-4.3) = -11.674$
$f(-4.3) = -11.674; f(-4.2) = -6.736$
$f(-4.2) = -6.736; f(-4.1) = -2.182$
$f(-4.1) = -2.182; f(-4) = 2$ so f has a real zero on the interval $[-4.1,-4]$.
Subdivide the interval $[-4.1,-4]$ into 10 equal subintervals:

$[-4.1,-4.09]$; $[-4.09,-4.08]$; $[-4.08,-4.07]$; $[-4.07,-4.06]$; $[-4.06,-4.05]$; $[-4.05,-4.04]$;
$[-4.04,-4.03]$; $[-4.03,-4.02]$; $[-4.02,-4.01]$; $[-4.01,-4]$

$f(-4.1) = -2.182; f(-4.09) = -1.7473$
$f(-4.09) = -1.7473; f(-4.08) = -1.3162$
$f(-4.08) = -1.3162; f(-4.07) = -0.8889$
$f(-4.07) = -0.8889; f(-4.06) = -0.4652$
$f(-4.06) = -0.4652; f(-4.05) = -0.0452$
$f(-4.05) = -0.4652; f(-4.04) = 0.3711$ so f has a real zero on the interval
                                                 $[-4.05,-4.04]$, therefore $r = -4.05$,
                                                 correct to 2 decimal places.

88. $3x^3 - 10x + 9 = 0$; $-3 \le r \le -2$
Consider the function $f(x) = 3x^3 - 10x + 9$
Subdivide the interval $[-3,-2]$ into 10 equal subintervals:

$[-3,-2.9]$; $[-2.9,-2.8]$; $[-2.8,-2.7]$; $[-2.7,-2.6]$; $[-2.6,-2.5]$; $[-2.5,-2.4]$; $[-2.4,-2.3]$;
$[-2.3,-2.2]$; $[-2.2,-2.1]$; $[-2.1,-2]$

$f(-3) = -42; f(-2.9) = -35.167$
$f(-2.9) = -35.167; f(-2.8) = -28.856$
$f(-2.8) = -28.856; f(-2.7) = -23.049$
$f(-2.7) = -23.049; f(-2.6) = -17.728$
$f(-2.6) = -17.728; f(-2.5) = -12.875$
$f(-2.5) = -12.875; f(-2.4) = -8.472$
$f(-2.4) = -8.472; f(-2.3) = -4.501$
$f(-2.3) = -4.501; f(-2.2) = -0.944$ so f has a real zero on the interval
$f(-2.2) = -0.944; f(-2.1) = 2.217$ $[-2.2,-2.1]$.
Subdivide the interval $[-2.2,-2.1]$ into 10 equal subintervals:

$[-2.2,-2.19]$; $[-2.19,-2.18]$; $[-2.18,-2.17]$; $[-2.17,-2.16]$; $[-2.16,-2.15]$; $[-2.15,-2.14]$;
$[-2.14,-2.13]$; $[-2.13,-2.12]$; $[-2.12,-2.11]$; $[-2.11,-2.1]$

$f(-2.2) = -0.944; f(-2.19) = -0.6104$ so f has a real zero on the interval
$f(-2.19) = -0.6104; f(-2.18) = -0.2807$ $[-2.18,-2.17]$, therefore $r = -2.18$,
$f(-2.18) = -0.2807; f(-2.17) = 0.0451$ correct to 2 decimal places.

89. $f(x) = x^3 + x^2 + x - 4$

$f(1) = -1; f(2) = 10$ so f has a real zero on the interval
                                                 [1,2],
Subdivide the interval [1,2] into 10 equal subintervals:

[1,1.1]; [1.1,1.2]; [1.2,1.3]; [1.3,1.4]; [1.4,1.5]; [1.5,1.6]; [1.6,1.7]; [1.7,1.8]; [1.8,1.9]; [1.9,2]

$f(1) = -1; f(1.1) = -0.359$
$f(1.1) = -0.359; f(1.2) = 0.368$ so f has a real zero on the interval [1.1,1.2].
Subdivide the interval [1,1.2] into 10 equal subintervals:

[1,1.11]; [1.11,1.12]; [1.12,1.13]; [1.13,1.14]; [1.14,1.15]; [1.15,1.16];[1.16,1.17]; [1.17,1.18]; [1.18,1.19]; [1.19,1.2]

$f(1) = -1; f(1.11) = -0.2903$ so f has a real zero on the interval
$f(1.11) = -0.2903; f(1.12) = -0.2207$ [1.15,1.16], therefore $r = 1.15$, correct
$f(1.12) = -0.2207; f(1.13) = -0.1502$ to 2 decimal places.
$f(1.13) = -0.1502; f(1.14) = -0.0789$
$f(1.14) = -0.0789; f(1.15) = -0.0066$
$f(1.15) = -0.0066; f(1.16) = 0.0665$

90. $f(x) = 2x^4 + x^2 - 1$

$f(0) = -1; f(1) = 2$ so f has a real zero on the interval [0,1],
Subdivide the interval [0,1] into 10 equal subintervals:

[0,0.1]; [0.1,0.2]; [0.2,0.3]; [0.3,0.4]; [0.4,0.5]; [0.5,0.6]; [0.6,0.7]; [0.7,0.8]; [0.8,0.9]; [0.9,1]

$f(0) = -1; f(0.1) = -0.9898$
$f(0.1) = -0.9898; f(0.2) = -0.9568$
$f(0.2) = -0.9568; f(0.3) = -0.8938$
$f(0.3) = -0.8938; f(0.4) = -0.7888$
$f(0.4) = -0.7888; f(0.5) = -0.625$
$f(0.5) = -0.625; f(0.6) = -0.3808$
$f(0.6) = -0.3808; f(0.7) = -0.0298$
$f(0.7) = -0.0298; f(0.8) = 0.4592$ so f has a real zero on the interval [0.7,0.8].
Subdivide the interval [0.7,0.8] into 10 equal subintervals:

[0.7,0.71]; [0.71,0.72]; [0.72,0.73]; [0.73,0.74]; [0.74,0.75]; [0.75,0.76];[0.76,0.77]; [0.77,0.78]; [0.78,0.79]; [0.79,0.8]

$f(0.7) = -0.298; f(0.71) = 0.123$ so f has a real zero on the interval $[0.7, 0.71]$, therefore $r = 0.70$, correct to 2 decimal places.

91. $f(x) = 2x^4 - 3x^3 - 4x^2 - 8$
$f(2) = -16; f(3) = 37$ so f has a real zero on the interval $[2,3]$,
Subdivide the interval $[2,3]$ into 10 equal subintervals:

$[2, 2.1]$; $[2.1, 2.2]$; $[2.2, 2.3]$; $[2.3, 2.4]$; $[2.4, 2.5]$; $[2.5, 2.6]$; $[2.6, 2.7]$; $[2.7, 2.8]$; $[2.8, 2.9]$; $[2.9, 3]$

$f(2) = -16; f(2.1) = -14.5268$
$f(2.1) = -14.5268; f(2.2) = -12.4528$
$f(2.2) = -12.4528; f(2.3) = -9.6928$
$f(2.3) = -9.6928; f(2.4) = -6.1568$
$f(2.4) = -6.1568; f(2.5) = -1.75$
$f(2.5) = -1.75; f(2.6) = 3.6272$ so f has a real zero on the interval $[2.5, 2.6]$.
Subdivide the interval $[2.5, 2.6]$ into 10 equal subintervals:

$[2.5, 2.51]$; $[2.51, 2.52]$; $[2.52, 2.53]$; $[2.53, 2.54]$; $[2.54, 2.55]$; $[2.55, 2.56]$; $[2.56, 2.57]$; $[2.57, 2.58]$; $[2.58, 2.59]$; $[2.59, 2.6]$

$f(2.5) = -1.75; f(2.51) = -1.2576$
$f(2.51) = -1.2576; f(2.52) = -0.7555$
$f(2.52) = -0.7555; f(2.53) = -0.2434$
$f(2.53) = -0.2434; f(2.54) = 0.2787$ so f has a real zero on the interval $[2.53, 2.54]$, therefore $r = 2.53$, correct to 2 decimal places.

92. $f(x) = 3x^3 - 2x^2 - 20$

$f(2) = -4; f(3) = 43$ so f has a real zero on the interval $[2,3]$,
Subdivide the interval $[2,3]$ into 10 equal subintervals:

$[2, 2.1]$; $[2.1, 2.2]$; $[2.2, 2.3]$; $[2.3, 2.4]$; $[2.4, 2.5]$; $[2.5, 2.6]$; $[2.6, 2.7]$; $[2.7, 2.8]$; $[2.8, 2.9]$; $[2.9, 3]$

$f(2) = -4; f(2.1) = -1.037$
$f(2.1) = -1.037; f(2.2) = 2.264$ so f has a real zero on the interval $[2.1, 2.2]$.
Subdivide the interval $[2.1, 2.2]$ into 10 equal subintervals:

$[2.1, 2.11]$; $[2.11, 2.12]$; $[2.12, 2.13]$; $[2.13, 2.14]$; $[2.14, 2.15]$; $[2.15, 2.16]$; $[2.16, 2.17]$; $[2.17, 2.18]$; $[2.18, 2.19]$; $[2.19, 2.2]$

$f(2.1) = -1.037; f(2.11) = -0.7224$
$f(2.11) = -0.7224; f(2.12) = -0.4044$
$f(2.12) = -0.4044; f(2.13) = -0.0830$
$f(2.13) = -0.0830; f(2.14) = 0.2418$ so f has a real zero on the interval
[2.13,2.14], therefore $r = 2.13$, correct
to 2 decimal places.

93. $x - 2$ is a factor of $f(x) = x^3 - kx^2 + kx + 2$ only if the remainder that results when $f(x)$ is divided by $x - 2$ is 0. Dividing, we have:

$$
\begin{array}{r|rrrr}
2 & 1 & -k & k & 2 \\
  &   & 2 & -2k+4 & -2k+8 \\
\hline
  & 1 & -k+2 & -k+4 & -2k+10
\end{array}
$$

Since we want the remainder to equal 0, set the remainder equal to zero and solve:
$$-2k + 10 = 0 \rightarrow -2k = -10 \rightarrow k = 5$$

94. $x + 2$ is a factor of $f(x) = x^4 - kx^3 + kx^2 + 1$ only if the remainder that results when $f(x)$ is divided by $x + 2$ is 0. Dividing, we have:

$$
\begin{array}{r|rrrrr}
-2 & 1 & -k & k & 0 & 1 \\
   &   & -2 & 2k+4 & -6k-8 & 12k+16 \\
\hline
   & 1 & -k-2 & 3k+4 & -6k-8 & 12k+17
\end{array}
$$

Since we want the remainder to equal 0, set the remainder equal to zero and solve:
$$12k + 17 = 0 \rightarrow 12k = -17 \rightarrow k = -\frac{17}{12}$$

95.   By the Remainder Theorem we know that the remainder from synthetic division by c is equal to $f(c)$. Thus the easiest way to find the remainder is to evaluate:
$$f(1) = 2(1)^{20} - 8(1)^{10} + 1 - 2 = 2 - 8 + 1 - 2 = -7$$
The remainder is –7.

96.   By the Remainder Theorem we know that the remainder from synthetic division by c is equal to $f(c)$. Thus the easiest way to find the remainder is to evaluate:
$$f(-1) = -3(-1)^{17} + (-1)^9 - (-1)^5 + 2(-1) = 3 - 1 + 1 - 2 = 1$$
The remainder is 1.

97.   We want to prove that $x - c$ is a factor of $x^n - c^n$, for any positive integer n. By the Factor Theorem, $x - c$ will be a factor of $f(x)$ provided $f(c) = 0$. Here, $f(x) = x^n - c^n$, so that $f(c) = c^n - c^n = 0$. Therefore, $x - c$ is a factor of $x^n - c^n$.

98.   We want to prove that $x + c$ is a factor of $x^n + c^n$, if $n \geq 1$ is an odd integer. By the Factor Theorem, $x + c$ will be a factor of $f(x)$ provided $f(-c) = 0$. Here, $f(x) = x^n + c^n$, so that $f(-c) = (-c)^n + c^n = -c^n + c^n = 0$ if $n \geq 1$ is an odd integer. Therefore, $x + c$ is a factor of $x^n + c^n$ if $n \geq 1$ is an odd integer.

99. $x^3 - 8x^2 + 16x - 3 = 0$ has solution $x = 3$, so $x - 3$ is a factor of
$f(x) = x^3 - 8x^2 + 16x - 3$.
Using synthetic division

$$3)\overline{1 \quad -8 \quad 16 \quad -3}$$
$$\underline{\quad\quad 3 \; -15 \quad 3}$$
$$1 \;\; -5 \;\; 1 \quad\; 0$$

$\therefore f(x) = x^3 - 8x^2 + 16x - 3 = (x - 3)(x^2 - 5x + 1)$.
Solving $x^2 - 5x + 1 = 0$

$$x = \frac{5 \pm \sqrt{25 - 4}}{2} = \frac{5 \pm \sqrt{21}}{2}$$

The sum of these two roots is $\dfrac{5 + \sqrt{21}}{2} + \dfrac{5 - \sqrt{21}}{2} = \dfrac{10}{2} = 5$.

100. $x^3 + 5x^2 + 5x - 2 = 0$ has solution $x = -2$, so $x + 2$ is a factor of
$f(x) = x^3 + 5x^2 + 5x - 2$.
Using synthetic division

$$-2)\overline{1 \quad 5 \quad 5 \quad -2}$$
$$\underline{\quad\quad -2 \; -6 \quad 2}$$
$$1 \;\; 3 \;\; -1 \quad\; 0$$

$\therefore f(x) = x^3 + 5x^2 + 5x - 2 = (x + 2)(x^2 + 3x - 1)$.

Solving $x^2 + 3x - 1 = 0$, $x = \dfrac{-3 \pm \sqrt{9 + 4}}{2} = \dfrac{-3 \pm \sqrt{13}}{2}$

The sum of these two roots is $\dfrac{-3 + \sqrt{13}}{2} + \dfrac{-3 - \sqrt{13}}{2} = \dfrac{-6}{2} = -3$.

101. $f(x) = 2x^3 + 3x^2 - 6x + 7$
By the Rational Zero Theorem, the only possible rational zeros are:

$\dfrac{p}{q} = \pm 1, \pm 7, \pm \dfrac{1}{2}, \pm \dfrac{7}{2}$ Since $\dfrac{1}{3}$ is not in the list of possible rational zeros, it is not a

zero of $f(x)$.

102. $f(x) = 4x^3 - 5x^2 - 3x + 1$
By the Rational Zero Theorem, the only possible rational zeros are:
$\dfrac{p}{q} = \pm 1, \pm \dfrac{1}{2}, \pm \dfrac{1}{4}$

Since $\dfrac{1}{3}$ is not in the list of possible rational zeros, it is not a zero of $f(x)$.

103. $f(x) = 2x^6 - 5x^4 + x^3 - x + 1$

By the Rational Zero Theorem, the only possible rational zeros are:

$\dfrac{p}{q} = \pm 1, \pm \dfrac{1}{2}$ Since $\dfrac{3}{5}$ is not in the list of possible rational zeros, it is not a zero

of $f(x)$.

104. $f(x) = x^7 + 6x^5 - x^4 + x + 2$

By the Rational Zero Theorem, the only possible rational zeros are:

$\dfrac{p}{q} = \pm 1, \pm 2$ Since $\dfrac{2}{3}$ is not in the list of possible rational zeros, it is not a zero

of $f(x)$.

105. Let x be the length of a side of the original cube.

After removing the 1 inch slice, one dimension will be $x - 1$.

The volume of the new solid will be:

$$(x-1) \cdot x \cdot x = 294 \rightarrow x^3 - x^2 = 294 \rightarrow x^3 - x^2 - 294 = 0$$

By Descartes Rule of Signs, we know that there is one positive real solution.

The possible rational zeros are:

$p = \pm 1, \pm 2, \pm 3, \pm 6, \pm 7, \pm 14, \pm 21, \pm 42, \pm 49, \pm 98, \pm 147, \pm 294; \quad q = \pm 1$

The rational zeros are the same as the values for p.

Using synthetic division:

$$
\begin{array}{r|rrrr}
7 & 1 & -1 & 0 & -294 \\
  &   & 7 & 42 & 294 \\
\hline
  & 1 & 6 & 42 & 0
\end{array}
$$

7 is a zero, so the length of the original edge of the cube was 7 inches.

106. Let x be the length of a side of the original cube.

The volume is x^3.

The dimensions are changed to $x + 6$, $x + 12$, and $x - 4$.

The volume of the new solid will be $(x + 6)(x + 12)(x - 4)$

Solve the volume equation:

$$(x + 6)(x + 12)(x - 4) = 2x^3$$

$$\left(x^2 + 18x + 72\right)(x - 4) = 2x^3 \rightarrow x^3 + 14x^2 - 288 = 2x^3 \rightarrow x^3 - 14x^2 + 288 = 0$$

By Descartes Rule of Signs, we know that there are 2 or 0 positive real solutions.

The possible rational zeros are:

$p = \pm 1, \pm 2, \pm 3, \pm 4, \pm 6, \pm 8, \pm 9, \pm 12, \pm 16, \pm 18, \pm 24, \pm 32, \pm 36, \pm 48,$
$\pm 72, \pm 96, \pm 144, \pm 288; \quad q = \pm 1$

The rational zeros are the same as the values for p.

Using synthetic division:

$$
\begin{array}{r|rrrr}
6 & 1 & -14 & 0 & 288 \\
  &   & 6 & -48 & -288 \\
\hline
  & 1 & -8 & -48 & 0
\end{array}
$$

Therefore, 6 is a zero; the other factor is $x^2 - 8x - 48 = (x - 12)(x + 4)$. The other zeros are 12 and -4. The length of the original edge of the cube was 6 inches or 12 inches.

107. $f(x) = x^n + a_{n-1}x^{n-1} + a_{n-2}x^{n-2} + ... + a_1 x + a_0;$ where $a_{n-1}, a_{n-2}, ... a_1, a_0$ are integers

If r is a real zero of f, then r is either rational or irrational. We know that the rational roots of f must be of the form $\dfrac{p}{q}$ where p is a divisor of a_0 and q is a divisor of 1. This means that $q = \pm 1$. So if r is rational , then $r = \dfrac{p}{q} = \pm p$. Therefore, r is an integer or r is irrational.

108.   Let $\dfrac{p}{q}$ be a root for the polynomial $f(x) = a_n x^n + a_{n-1}x^{n-1} + a_{n-2}x^{n-2} + ... + a_1 x + a_0$ where $a_n, a_{n-1}, a_{n-2}, ... a_1, a_0$ are integers. Suppose also that p and q have no common factors other than 1 and -1.

Then

$$ f\left(\frac{p}{q}\right) = a_n\left(\frac{p}{q}\right)^n + a_{n-1}\left(\frac{p}{q}\right)^{n-1} + a_{n-2}\left(\frac{p}{q}\right)^{n-2} + ... + a_1\left(\frac{p}{q}\right) + a_0 = 0 $$

$$ \rightarrow \frac{1}{q^n}\left(a_n p^n + a_{n-1}p^{n-1}q + a_{n-2}p^{n-2}q^2 + ... + a_1 pq^{n-1} + a_0 q^n\right) = 0 $$

Because p is a factor of the first n terms of this equation, p must also be a factor of $a_0 q^n$. Since p is not a factor of q, p must be a factor of a_0. Similarly, q must be a factor of a_n

109. (a) $f(x) = 8x^4 - 2x^2 + 5x - 1 \quad 0 \le r \le 1$

At Step 0 we have the interval $[0,1]$.

$f(0) = -1; \quad f(1) = 10$

Let m = the midpoint of the interval being considered.

So $m_0 = 0.5$

n	m_{n-1}	$f(m_{n-1})$	New interval
1	0.5	$f(0.5) = 1.5 > 0$	$[0,0.5]$
2	0.25	$f(0.25) = 0.15625 > 0$	$[0,0.25]$
3	0.125	$f(0.125) = -0.4043 < 0$	$[0.125,0.25]$
4	0.1875	$f(0.1875) = -0.1229 < 0$	$[0.1875,0.25]$
5	0.21875	$f(0.21875) = 0.0164 > 0$	$[0.1875,0.21875]$
6	0.203125	$f(0.203125) = -0.0533 < 0$	$[0.203125,0.21875]$
7	0.2109375	$f(0.2109375) = -0.0185 < 0$	$[0.2109375,0.21875]$
8	0.21484375		

Since the midpoint value at Step 8 agrees with the midpoint value at Step 7 to two decimal places, $r = 0.21$, correct to 2 decimal places.

(b) $f(x) = x^4 + 8x^3 - x^2 + 2; \quad -1 \le r \le 0$

At Step 0 we have the interval [-1,0].

$f(-1) = -6; \quad f(0) = 2$

Let m = the midpoint of the interval being considered.

So $m_0 = -0.5$

n	m_{n-1}	$f(m_{n-1})$	New interval
1	- 0.5	$f(-0.5) = 0.8125 > 0$	[-1,- 0.5]
2	- 0.75	$f(-0.75) = -1.6211 < 0$	[-0.75,- 0.5]
3	-0.625	$f(-0.625) = -0.1912 < 0$	[-0.625,-0.5]
4	-0.5625	$f(-0.5625) = 0.3599 > 0$	[-0.625,-0.5625]
5	-0.59375	$f(-0.59375) = 0.0972 > 0$	[-0.625,-0.59375]
6	-0.609375	$f(-0.609375) = -0.04372 < 0$	[-0.609375,-0.59375]
7	-0.6015625		

Since the midpoint value at Step 7 agrees with the midpoint value at Step 6 to two decimal places, $r = - 0.60$, correct to 2 decimal places.

(c) $f(x) = 2x^3 + 6x^2 - 8x + 2; \quad -5 \le r \le -4$

At Step 0 we have the interval [-5,-4].

$f(-5) = -58; \quad f(-4) = 2$

Let m = the midpoint of the interval being considered.

So $m_0 = -4.5$

n	m_{n-1}	$f(m_{n-1})$	New interval
1	- 4.5	$f(-4.5) = -22.75 < 0$	[-4.5,- 4]
2	- 4.25	$f(-4.25) = -9.1562 < 0$	[-4.25,- 4]
3	-4.125	$f(-4.125) = -3.2852 < 0$	[-4.125,-4]
4	-4.0625	$f(-4.0625) = -0.5708 < 0$	[-4.0625,-4]
5	-4.03125	$f(-4.03125) = 0.7324 > 0$	[-4.0625, -4.03125]
6	-4.046875	$f(-4.046875) = 0.0852 > 0$	[-4.0625, -4.046875]
7	-4.0546875	$f(-4.0546875) = -0.2417 < 0$	[-4.0546875, -4.046875]
8	-4.05078125		

Since the midpoint value at Step 8 agrees with the midpoint value at Step 7 to two decimal places, $r = - 4.05$, correct to 2 decimal places.

(d) $f(x) = 3x^3 - 10x + 9;$ $-3 \le r \le -2$

At Step 0 we have the interval [-3,-2].

$f(-3) = -42;$ $f(-2) = 5$

Let m = the midpoint of the interval being considered.

So $m_0 = -2.5$

n	m_{n-1}	$f(m_{n-1})$	New interval
1	- 2.5	$f(-2.5) = -12.875 < 0$	[-2.5,- 2]
2	- 2.25	$f(-2.25) = -2.6719 < 0$	[-2.25,- 2]
3	-2.125	$f(-2.125) = 1.4629 > 0$	[-2.25,- 2.125]
4	-2.1875	$f(-2.1875) = -0.5276 < 0$	[-2.1875,- 2.125]
5	-2.15625	$f(-2.15625) = 0.4866 > 0$	[-2.1875,-2.15625]
6	-2.171875	$f(-2.171875) = -0.0157 < 0$	[-2.171875,-2.15625]
7	-2.1640625	$f(-2.1640625) = 0.2366 > 0$	[-2.171875,- 2.1640625]
8	-2.16796875		

Since the midpoint value at Step 8 agrees with the midpoint value at Step 7 to two decimal places, $r = -2.16$, correct to 2 decimal places.

(e) $f(x) = x^3 + x^2 + x - 4;$ $1 \le r \le 2$

At Step 0 we have the interval [1,2].

$f(1) = -1;$ $f(2) = 10$

Let m = the midpoint of the interval being considered.

So $m_0 = 1.5$

n	m_{n-1}	$f(m_{n-1})$	New interval
1	1.5	$f(1.5) = 3.125 > 0$	[1,1.5]
2	1.25	$f(1.25) = 0.7656 > 0$	[1,1.25]
3	1.125	$f(1.125) = -0.1855 < 0$	[1.125,1.25]
4	1.1875	$f(1.1875) = 0.2722 > 0$	[1.125,1.1875]
5	1.15625	$f(1.15625) = 0.0390 > 0$	[1.125,1.15625]
6	1.140625	$f(1.140625) = -0.0744 < 0$	[1.140625,1.15625]
7	1.1484375		

Since the midpoint value at Step 7 agrees with the midpoint value at Step 6 to two decimal places, $r = 1.14$, correct to 2 decimal places.

(f) $f(x) = 2x^4 + x^2 - 1;$ $0 \le r \le 1$

At Step 0 we have the interval [0,1].

$$f(0) = -1; \quad f(1) = 2$$

Let m = the midpoint of the interval being considered.

So $m_0 = 0.5$

n	m_{n-1}	$f(m_{n-1})$	New interval
1	0.5	$f(0.5) = -0.625 < 0$	[0.5,1]
2	0.75	$f(0.75) = 0.1593 > 0$	[0.5,0.75]
3	0.625	$f(0.625) = -0.3042 < 0$	[0.625,0.75]
4	0.6875	$f(0.6875) = -0.0805 < 0$	[0.6875,0.75]
5	0.71875	$f(0.71875) = 0.0504 > 0$	[0.6875,0.71875]
6	0.703125	$f(0.703125) = -0.0168 < 0$	[0.703125,0.71875]
7	0.7109375	$f(0.7109375) = 0.0164 > 0$	[0.703125, 0.7109375]
8	0.70703125	$f(0.70703125) = -0.0032 < 0$	[0.70703125, 0.7109375]
9	0.708984375		

Since the midpoint value at Step 9 agrees with the midpoint value at Step 8 to two decimal places, $r = 0.70$, correct to 2 decimal places.

(g) $f(x) = 2x^4 - 3x^3 - 4x^2 - 8;$ $2 \le r \le 3$

At Step 0 we have the interval [2,3]

$$f(2) = -16; \quad f(3) = 37$$

Let m = the midpoint of the interval being considered.

So $m_0 = 2.5$

n	m_{n-1}	$f(m_{n-1})$	New interval
1	2.5	$f(2.5) = -1.75 < 0$	[2.5,3]
2	2.75	$f(2.75) = 13.7422 > 0$	[2.5,2.75]
3	2.625	$f(2.625) = 5.1352 > 0$	[2.5,2.625]
4	2.5625	$f(2.5625) = 1.4905 > 0$	[2.5,2.5625]
5	2.53125	$f(2.53125) = -0.1787 < 0$	[2.53125,2.5625]
6	2.546875	$f(2.546875) = 0.6435 > 0$	[2.53125, 2.546875]
7	2.5390625	$f(2.5390625) = 0.2293 > 0$	[2.53125, 2.5390625]
8	2.53515625		

Since the midpoint value at Step 8 agrees with the midpoint value at Step 7 to two decimal places, $r = 2.53$, correct to 2 decimal places.

(h) $f(x) = 3x^3 - 2x^2 - 20;$ $2 \le r \le 3$

At Step 0 we have the interval [2,3].

$f(2) = -4;$ $f(3) = 43$

Let m = the midpoint of the interval being considered.

So $m_0 = 2.5$

n	m_{n-1}	$f(m_{n-1})$	New interval
1	2.5	$f(2.5) = 14.375 > 0$	[2,2.5]
2	2.25	$f(2.25) = 4.0469 > 0$	[2,2.25]
3	2.125	$f(2.125) = -0.2441 < 0$	[2.125,2.25]
4	2.1875	$f(2.1875) = 1.8323 > 0$	[2.125,2.1875]
5	2.15625	$f(2.15625) = 0.7771 > 0$	[2.125,2.15625]
6	2.140625	$f(2.140625) = 0.2622 > 0$	[2.125, 2.140625]
7	2.1328125	$f(2.1328125) = 0.0080 > 0$	[2.125, 2.1328125]
8	2.1315625		

Since the midpoint value at Step 8 agrees with the midpoint value at Step 7 to two decimal places, $r = 2.13$, correct to 2 decimal places.

The Zeros of a Polynomial Function

5.3   Complex Numbers; Quadratic Equations with a Negative Discriminant

1. $(2 - 3i) + (6 + 8i) = (2 + 6) + (-3 + 8)i = 8 + 5i$

2. $(4 + 5i) + (-8 + 2i) = (4 + (-8)) + (5 + 2)i = -4 + 7i$

3. $(-3 + 2i) - (4 - 4i) = (-3 - 4) + (2 - (-4))i = -7 + 6i$

4. $(3 - 4i) - (-3 - 4i) = (3 - (-3)) + (-4 - (-4))i = 6 + 0i = 6$

5. $(2 - 5i) - (8 + 6i) = (2 - 8) + (-5 - 6)i = -6 - 11i$

6. $(-8 + 4i) - (2 - 2i) = (-8 - 2) + (4 - (-2))i = -10 + 6i$

7. $3(2 - 6i) = 6 - 18i$

8. $-4(2 + 8i) = -8 - 32i$

9. $2i(2 - 3i) = 4i - 6i^2 = 4i - 6(-1) = 6 + 4i$

10. $3i(-3 + 4i) = -9i + 12i^2 = -9i + 12(-1) = -12 - 9i$

11. $(3 - 4i)(2 + i) = 6 + 3i - 8i - 4i^2 = 6 - 5i - 4(-1) = 10 - 5i$

12. $(5 + 3i)(2 - i) = 10 - 5i + 6i - 3i^2 = 10 + i - 3(-1) = 13 + i$

13. $(-6 + i)(-6 - i) = 36 + 6i - 6i - i^2 = 36 - (-1) = 37$

14. $(-3 + i)(3 + i) = -9 - 3i + 3i + i^2 = -9 + (-1) = -10$

15. $\dfrac{10}{3 - 4i} = \dfrac{10}{3 - 4i} \cdot \dfrac{3 + 4i}{3 + 4i} = \dfrac{30 + 40i}{9 + 12i - 12i - 16i^2} = \dfrac{30 + 40i}{9 - 16(-1)} = \dfrac{30 + 40i}{25}$

$\qquad = \dfrac{30}{25} + \dfrac{40}{25}i = \dfrac{6}{5} + \dfrac{8}{5}i$

16. $\dfrac{13}{5-12i} = \dfrac{13}{5-12i} \cdot \dfrac{5+12i}{5+12i} = \dfrac{65+156i}{25+60i-60i-144i^2} = \dfrac{65+156i}{25-144(-1)} = \dfrac{65+156i}{169}$

$= \dfrac{65}{169} + \dfrac{156}{169}i = \dfrac{5}{13} + \dfrac{12}{13}i$

17. $\dfrac{2+i}{i} = \dfrac{2+i}{i} \cdot \dfrac{-i}{-i} = \dfrac{-2i-i^2}{-i^2} = \dfrac{-2i-(-1)}{-(-1)} = \dfrac{1-2i}{1} = 1-2i$

18. $\dfrac{2-i}{-2i} = \dfrac{2-i}{-2i} \cdot \dfrac{i}{i} = \dfrac{2i-i^2}{-2i^2} = \dfrac{2i-(-1)}{-2(-1)} = \dfrac{1+2i}{2} = \dfrac{1}{2}+i$

19. $\dfrac{6-i}{1+i} = \dfrac{6-i}{1+i} \cdot \dfrac{1-i}{1-i} = \dfrac{6-6i-i+i^2}{1-i+i-i^2} = \dfrac{6-7i+(-1)}{1-(-1)} = \dfrac{5-7i}{2} = \dfrac{5}{2}-\dfrac{7}{2}i$

20. $\dfrac{2+3i}{1-i} = \dfrac{2+3i}{1-i} \cdot \dfrac{1+i}{1+i} = \dfrac{2+2i+3i+3i^2}{1+i-i-i^2} = \dfrac{2+5i+3(-1)}{1-(-1)} = \dfrac{-1+5i}{2} = -\dfrac{1}{2}+\dfrac{5}{2}i$

21. $\left(\dfrac{1}{2}+\dfrac{\sqrt{3}}{2}i\right)^2 = \dfrac{1}{4}+2\left(\dfrac{1}{2}\right)\left(\dfrac{\sqrt{3}}{2}i\right)+\dfrac{3}{4}i^2 = \dfrac{1}{4}+\dfrac{\sqrt{3}}{2}i+\dfrac{3}{4}(-1) = -\dfrac{1}{2}+\dfrac{\sqrt{3}}{2}i$

22. $\left(\dfrac{\sqrt{3}}{2}-\dfrac{1}{2}i\right)^2 = \dfrac{3}{4}-2\left(\dfrac{\sqrt{3}}{2}\right)\left(\dfrac{1}{2}i\right)+\dfrac{1}{4}i^2 = \dfrac{3}{4}-\dfrac{\sqrt{3}}{2}i+\dfrac{1}{4}(-1) = \dfrac{1}{2}-\dfrac{\sqrt{3}}{2}i$

23. $(1+i)^2 = 1+2i+i^2 = 1+2i+(-1) = 2i$

24. $(1-i)^2 = 1-2i+i^2 = 1-2i+(-1) = -2i$

25. $i^{23} = i^{22+1} = i^{22} \cdot i = \left(i^2\right)^{11} \cdot i = (-1)^{11}i = -i$

26. $i^{14} = \left(i^2\right)^7 = (-1)^7 = -1$

27. $i^{-15} = \dfrac{1}{i^{15}} = \dfrac{1}{i^{14+1}} = \dfrac{1}{i^{14} \cdot i} = \dfrac{1}{\left(i^2\right)^7 \cdot i} = \dfrac{1}{(-1)^7 i} = \dfrac{1}{-i} = \dfrac{1}{-i} \cdot \dfrac{i}{i} = \dfrac{i}{-i^2} = \dfrac{i}{-(-1)} = i$

28. $i^{-23} = \dfrac{1}{i^{23}} = \dfrac{1}{i^{22+1}} = \dfrac{1}{i^{22} \cdot i} = \dfrac{1}{\left(i^2\right)^{11} \cdot i} = \dfrac{1}{(-1)^{11} i} = \dfrac{1}{-i} = \dfrac{1}{-i} \cdot \dfrac{i}{i} = \dfrac{i}{-i^2} = \dfrac{i}{-(-1)} = i$

29. $i^6 - 5 = \left(i^2\right)^3 - 5 = (-1)^3 - 5 = -1 - 5 = -6$

30. $4 + i^3 = 4 + i^2 \cdot i = 4 + (-1)i = 4 - i$

31. $6i^3 - 4i^5 = i^3(6 - 4i^2) = i^2 \cdot i(6 - 4(-1)) = -1 \cdot i(10) = -10i$

32. $4i^3 - 2i^2 + 1 = 4i^2 \cdot i - 2i^2 + 1 = 4(-1)i - 2(-1) + 1 = -4i + 2 + 1 = 3 - 4i$

33. $(1+i)^3 = (1+i)(1+i)(1+i) = (1 + 2i + i^2)(1+i) = (1 + 2i - 1)(1+i) = 2i(1+i)$
         $= 2i + 2i^2 = 2i + 2(-1) = -2 + 2i$

34. $(3i)^4 + 1 = 81i^4 + 1 = 81(1) + 1 = 82$

35. $i^7(1 + i^2) = i^7(1 + (-1)) = i^7(0) = 0$

36. $2i^4(1 + i^2) = 2(1)(1 + (-1)) = 2(0) = 0$

37. $i^6 + i^4 + i^2 + 1 = \left(i^2\right)^3 + \left(i^2\right)^2 + i^2 + 1 = (-1)^3 + (-1)^2 + (-1) + 1 = -1 + 1 - 1 + 1 = 0$

38. $i^7 + i^5 + i^3 + i = \left(i^2\right)^3 \cdot i + \left(i^2\right)^2 \cdot i + i^2 \cdot i + i = (-1)^3 \cdot i + (-1)^2 \cdot i + (-1) \cdot i + i$
         $= -i + i - i + i = 0$

39. $\sqrt{-4} = 2i$ 40. $\sqrt{-9} = 3i$ 41. $\sqrt{-25} = 5i$ 42. $\sqrt{-64} = 8i$

43. $\sqrt{(3 + 4i)(4i - 3)} = \sqrt{12i - 9 + 16i^2 - 12i} = \sqrt{-9 + 16(-1)} = \sqrt{-25} = 5i$

44. $\sqrt{(4 + 3i)(3i - 4)} = \sqrt{12i - 16 + 9i^2 - 12i} = \sqrt{-16 + 9(-1)} = \sqrt{-25} = 5i$

45. $x^2 + 4 = 0$
     $a = 1, b = 0, c = 4, \quad b^2 - 4ac = 0^2 - 4(1)(4) = -16$

     $x = \dfrac{-0 \pm \sqrt{-16}}{2(1)} = \dfrac{\pm 4i}{2} = \pm 2i \rightarrow$ The solution set is $\{\pm 2i\}$.

46. $x^2 - 4 = 0$
     $(x + 2)(x - 2) = 0 \rightarrow x = -2$ or $x = 2 \rightarrow$ The solution set is $\{\pm 2\}$.

47. $x^2 - 16 = 0$
     $a = 1, b = 0, c = -16, \quad b^2 - 4ac = 0^2 - 4(1)(-16) = 64$

     $x = \dfrac{-0 \pm \sqrt{64}}{2(1)} = \dfrac{\pm 8}{2} = \pm 4 \rightarrow$ The solution set is $\{\pm 4\}$.

48. $x^2 + 25 = 0$
       $x^2 = -25 \rightarrow x = \pm\sqrt{-25} = \pm 5i \rightarrow$ The solution set is $\{\pm 5i\}$.

49. $x^2 - 6x + 13 = 0$
$a = 1, b = -6, c = 13,\quad b^2 - 4ac = (-6)^2 - 4(1)(13) = 36 - 52 = -16$

$x = \dfrac{-(-6) \pm \sqrt{-16}}{2(1)} = \dfrac{6 \pm 4i}{2} = 3 \pm 2i \quad \rightarrow$ The solution set is $\{3 - 2i, 3 + 2i\}$.

50. $x^2 + 4x + 8 = 0$
$a = 1, b = 4, c = 8,\quad b^2 - 4ac = 4^2 - 4(1)(8) = 16 - 32 = -16$

$x = \dfrac{-4 \pm \sqrt{-16}}{2(1)} = \dfrac{-4 \pm 4i}{2} = -2 \pm 2i$
The solution set is $\{-2 - 2i, -2 + 2i\}$.

51. $x^2 - 6x + 10 = 0$
$a = 1, b = -6, c = 10,\quad b^2 - 4ac = (-6)^2 - 4(1)(10) = 36 - 40 = -4$

$x = \dfrac{-(-6) \pm \sqrt{-4}}{2(1)} = \dfrac{6 \pm 2i}{2} = 3 \pm i$
The solution set is $\{3 - i, 3 + i\}$.

52. $x^2 - 2x + 5 = 0$
$a = 1, b = -2, c = 5,\quad b^2 - 4ac = (-2)^2 - 4(1)(5) = 4 - 20 = -16$

$x = \dfrac{-(-2) \pm \sqrt{-16}}{2(1)} = \dfrac{2 \pm 4i}{2} = 1 + 2i$
The solution set is $\{1 - 2i, 1 + 2i\}$.

53. $8x^2 - 4x + 1 = 0$
$a = 8, b = -4, c = 1,\quad b^2 - 4ac = (-4)^2 - 4(8)(1) = 16 - 32 = -16$

$x = \dfrac{-(-4) \pm \sqrt{-16}}{2(8)} = \dfrac{4 \pm 4i}{16} = \dfrac{1}{4} \pm \dfrac{1}{4}i$
The solution set is $\left\{ \dfrac{1}{4} - \dfrac{1}{4}i, \dfrac{1}{4} + \dfrac{1}{4}i \right\}$.

54. $10x^2 + 6x + 1 = 0$
$a = 10, b = 6, c = 1,\quad b^2 - 4ac = 6^2 - 4(10)(1) = 36 - 40 = -4$

$x = \dfrac{-6 \pm \sqrt{-4}}{2(10)} = \dfrac{-6 \pm 2i}{20} = -\dfrac{3}{10} \pm \dfrac{1}{10}i$
The solution set is $\left\{ -\dfrac{3}{10} - \dfrac{1}{10}i, -\dfrac{3}{10} + \dfrac{1}{10}i \right\}$.

55. $5x^2 + 1 = 2x \rightarrow 5x^2 - 2x + 1 = 0$

$a = 5, b = -2, c = 1, \quad b^2 - 4ac = (-2)^2 - 4(5)(1) = 4 - 20 = -16$

$$x = \frac{-(-2) \pm \sqrt{-16}}{2(5)} = \frac{2 \pm 4i}{10} = \frac{1}{5} \pm \frac{2}{5}i$$

The solution set is $\left\{ \dfrac{1}{5} - \dfrac{2}{5}i, \ \dfrac{1}{5} + \dfrac{2}{5}i \right\}$.

56. $13x^2 + 1 = 6x \rightarrow 13x^2 - 6x + 1 = 0$

$a = 13, b = -6, c = 1, \quad b^2 - 4ac = (-6)^2 - 4(13)(1) = 36 - 52 = -16$

$$x = \frac{-(-6) \pm \sqrt{-16}}{2(13)} = \frac{6 \pm 4i}{26} = \frac{3}{13} \pm \frac{2}{13}i$$

The solution set is $\left\{ \dfrac{3}{13} - \dfrac{2}{13}i, \ \dfrac{3}{13} + \dfrac{2}{13}i \right\}$.

57. $x^2 + x + 1 = 0$

$a = 1, b = 1, c = 1, \quad b^2 - 4ac = 1^2 - 4(1)(1) = 1 - 4 = -3$

$$x = \frac{-1 \pm \sqrt{-3}}{2(1)} = \frac{-1 \pm \sqrt{3}i}{2} = -\frac{1}{2} \pm \frac{\sqrt{3}}{2}i$$

The solution set is $\left\{ -\dfrac{1}{2} - \dfrac{\sqrt{3}}{2}i, \ -\dfrac{1}{2} + \dfrac{\sqrt{3}}{2}i \right\}$.

58. $x^2 - x + 1 = 0$

$a = 1, b = -1, c = 1, \quad b^2 - 4ac = (-1)^2 - 4(1)(1) = 1 - 4 = -3$

$$x = \frac{-(-1) \pm \sqrt{-3}}{2(1)} = \frac{1 \pm \sqrt{3}i}{2} = \frac{1}{2} \pm \frac{\sqrt{3}}{2}i$$

The solution set is $\left\{ \dfrac{1}{2} - \dfrac{\sqrt{3}}{2}i, \ \dfrac{1}{2} + \dfrac{\sqrt{3}}{2}i \right\}$.

59. $x^3 - 8 = 0$

$(x - 2)(x^2 + 2x + 4) = 0$

$$x - 2 = 0 \rightarrow x = 2$$

$$x^2 + 2x + 4 = 0$$

$a = 1, b = 2, c = 4, \quad b^2 - 4ac = 2^2 - 4(1)(4) = 4 - 16 = -12$

$$x = \frac{-2 \pm \sqrt{-12}}{2(1)} = \frac{-2 \pm 2\sqrt{3}i}{2} = -1 \pm \sqrt{3}i$$

The solution set is $\left\{ 2, \ -1 - \sqrt{3}i, \ -1 + \sqrt{3}i \right\}$.

60. $x^3 + 27 = 0$

$(x+3)(x^2 - 3x + 9) = 0$

$x + 3 = 0 \rightarrow x = -3$

or $x^2 - 3x + 9 = 0$

$a = 1, b = -3, c = 9, \quad b^2 - 4ac = (-3)^2 - 4(1)(9) = 9 - 36 = -27$

$x = \dfrac{-(-3) \pm \sqrt{-27}}{2(1)} = \dfrac{3 \pm 3\sqrt{3}\,i}{2} = \dfrac{3}{2} \pm \dfrac{3\sqrt{3}}{2}i$

The solution set is $\left\{-3, \ \dfrac{3}{2} - \dfrac{3\sqrt{3}}{2}i, \ \dfrac{3}{2} + \dfrac{3\sqrt{3}}{2}i\right\}$.

61. $x^4 = 16 \rightarrow x^4 - 16 = 0$

$(x^2 - 4)(x^2 + 4) = 0$

$(x - 2)(x + 2)(x^2 + 4) = 0$

$x - 2 = 0 \rightarrow x = 2$

$x + 2 = 0 \rightarrow x = -2$

$x^2 + 4 = 0 \rightarrow x = \pm 2i$

The solution set is $\{-2, \ 2, \ -2i, \ 2i\}$.

62. $x^4 = 1 \rightarrow x^4 - 1 = 0$

$(x^2 - 1)(x^2 + 1) = 0$

$(x - 1)(x + 1)(x^2 + 1) = 0$

$x - 1 = 0 \rightarrow x = 1$

$x + 1 = 0 \rightarrow x = -1$

$x^2 + 1 = 0 \rightarrow x = \pm i$

The solution set is $\{-1, \ 1, \ -i, \ i\}$.

63. $x^4 + 13x^2 + 36 = 0$

$(x^2 + 9)(x^2 + 4) = 0$

$x^2 + 9 = 0 \rightarrow x = \pm 3i$

$x^2 + 4 = 0 \rightarrow x = \pm 2i$

The solution set is $\{-3i, \ 3i, \ -2i, \ 2i\}$.

64. $x^4 + 3x^2 - 4 = 0$

$(x^2 - 1)(x^2 + 4) = 0$

$(x - 1)(x + 1)(x^2 + 4) = 0$

$x - 1 = 0 \rightarrow x = 1$

$x + 1 = 0 \rightarrow x = -1$

$x^2 + 4 = 0 \rightarrow x = \pm 2i$

The solution set is $\{-1,\ 1,\ -2i,\ 2i\}$.

65. $3x^2 - 3x + 4 = 0$
$a = 3, b = -3, c = 4,\quad b^2 - 4ac = (-3)^2 - 4(3)(4) = 9 - 48 = -39$
The equation has two complex conjugate solutions.

66. $2x^2 - 4x + 1 = 0$
$a = 2, b = -4, c = 1,\quad b^2 - 4ac = (-4)^2 - 4(2)(1) = 16 - 8 = 8$
The equation has two unequal real number solutions.

67. $2x^2 + 3x - 4 = 0$
$a = 2, b = 3, c = -4,\quad b^2 - 4ac = 3^2 - 4(2)(-4) = 9 + 32 = 41$
The equation has two unequal real solutions.

68. $x^2 + 6 = 2x \rightarrow x^2 - 2x + 6 = 0$
$a = 1, b = -2, c = 6,\quad b^2 - 4ac = (-2)^2 - 4(1)(6) = 4 - 24 = -20$
The equation has two complex conjugate solutions.

69. $9x^2 - 12x + 4 = 0$
$a = 9, b = -12, c = 4,\quad b^2 - 4ac = (-12)^2 - 4(9)(4) = 144 - 144 = 0$
The equation has a repeated real solution.

70. $4x^2 + 12x + 9 = 0$
$a = 4, b = 12, c = 9,\quad b^2 - 4ac = 12^2 - 4(4)(9) = 144 - 144 = 0$
The equation has a repeated real solution.

71. The other solution is the conjugate of $2 + 3i$, or $2 - 3i$.

72. The other solution is the conjugate of $4 - i$, or $4 + i$.

73. $z + \bar{z} = 3 - 4i + \overline{3 - 4i} = 3 - 4i + 3 + 4i = 6$

74. $w - \bar{w} = 8 + 3i - \left(\overline{8 + 3i}\right) = 8 + 3i - (8 - 3i) = 8 + 3i - 8 + 3i = 0 + 6i = 6i$

75. $z \cdot \bar{z} = (3 - 4i)(\overline{3 - 4i}) = (3 - 4i)(3 + 4i) = 9 + 12i - 12i - 16i^2 = 9 - 16(-1) = 25$

76. $\overline{z - w} = \overline{3 - 4i - (8 + 3i)} = \overline{3 - 4i - 8 - 3i} = \overline{-5 - 7i} = -5 + 7i$

77. $z + \bar{z} = a + bi + \overline{a + bi} = a + bi + a - bi = 2a$
$z - \bar{z} = a + bi - (\overline{a + bi}) = a + bi - (a - bi) = a + bi - a + bi = 2bi$

78. $\bar{\bar{z}} = \overline{\overline{a + bi}} = \overline{a - bi} = a + bi = z$

79. $\overline{z + w} = \overline{(a + bi) + (c + di)} = \overline{(a + c) + (b + d)i} = (a + c) - (b + d)i$
$= (a - bi) + (c - di) = \overline{a + bi} + \overline{c + di} = \bar{z} + \bar{w}$

80. $\overline{z \cdot w} = \overline{(a + bi) \cdot (c + di)} = \overline{ac + adi + bci + bd\,i^2} = \overline{(ac - bd) + (ad + bc)i}$
     $= (ac - bd) - (ad + bc)i$

     $\overline{z} \cdot \overline{w} = \overline{a + bi} \cdot \overline{c + di} = (a - bi)(c - di) = ac - ad\,i - bc\,i + bd\,i^2$
     $= (ac - bd) - (ad + bc)i$

81. Answers will vary.   82. Answers will vary.

Chapter 5

The Zeros of a Polynomial Function

5.4   Complex Zeros; Fundamental Theorem of Algebra

1.   Since complex zeros appear in conjugate pairs, $4 + i$, the conjugate of $4 - i$, is the remaining zero of f.

2.   Since complex zeros appear in conjugate pairs, $3 - i$, the conjugate of $3 + i$, is the remaining zero of f.

3.   Since complex zeros appear in conjugate pairs, $-i$, the conjugate of i, and $1 - i$, the conjugate of $1 + i$, are the remaining zeros of f.

4.   Since complex zeros appear in conjugate pairs, $2 - i$, the conjugate of $2 + i$, is the remaining zero of f.

5.   Since complex zeros appear in conjugate pairs, $-i$, the conjugate of i, and $-2i$, the conjugate of $2i$, are the remaining zeros of f.

6.   Since complex zeros appear in conjugate pairs, $-i$, the conjugate of i, is the remaining zero of f.

7.   Since complex zeros appear in conjugate pairs, $-i$, the conjugate of i, is the remaining zero of f.

8.   Since complex zeros appear in conjugate pairs, $2 + i$, the conjugate of $2 - i$, and i, the conjugate of $-i$, are the remaining zeros of f.

9.   Since complex zeros appear in conjugate pairs, $2 - i$, the conjugate of $2 + i$, and $-3 + i$, the conjugate of $-3 - i$, are the remaining zeros of f.

10.   Since complex zeros appear in conjugate pairs, $-i$, the conjugate of i, $3 + 2i$, the conjugate of $3 - 2i$, and $-2 - i$, the conjugate of $-2 + i$, are the remaining zeros of f.

11.   Since $3 + 2i$ is a zero, its conjugate $3 - 2i$ is also a zero of f. Finding the function:

$$\begin{aligned} f(x) &= (x - 4)(x - 4)(x - (3 + 2i))(x - (3 - 2i)) \\ &= \left(x^2 - 8x + 16\right)((x - 3) - 2i)((x - 3) + 2i) \\ &= \left(x^2 - 8x + 16\right)\left(x^2 - 6x + 9 - 4i^2\right) \\ &= \left(x^2 - 8x + 16\right)\left(x^2 - 6x + 13\right) \\ &= x^4 - 6x^3 + 13x^2 - 8x^3 + 48x^2 - 104x + 16x^2 - 96x + 208 \\ &= x^4 - 14x^3 + 77x^2 - 200x + 208 \end{aligned}$$

12.   Since $1 + 2i$ and i are zeros, their conjugates $1 - 2i$ and $-i$ are also zeros of f. Finding the function:

$$\begin{aligned} f(x) &= (x - i)(x - (-i))(x - (1 + 2i))(x - (1 - 2i)) \\ &= (x - i)(x + i)((x - 1) - 2i)((x - 1) + 2i) \\ &= \left(x^2 - i^2\right)\left(x^2 - 2x + 1 - 4i^2\right) = \left(x^2 + 1\right)\left(x^2 - 2x + 5\right) \\ &= x^4 - 2x^3 + 5x^2 + 1x^2 - 2x + 5 = x^4 - 2x^3 + 6x^2 - 2x + 5 \end{aligned}$$

13.   Since $-i$ is a zero, its conjugate i is also a zero, and since $1 + i$ is a zero, its conjugate $1 - i$ is also a zero of f. Finding the function:

$$\begin{aligned} f(x) &= (x - 2)(x + i)(x - i)(x - (1 + i))(x - (1 - i)) \\ &= (x - 2)\left(x^2 - i^2\right)((x - 1) - i)((x - 1) + i) \\ &= (x - 2)\left(x^2 + 1\right)\left(x^2 - 2x + 1 - i^2\right) \\ &= \left(x^3 - 2x^2 + x - 2\right)\left(x^2 - 2x + 2\right) \\ &= x^5 - 2x^4 + 2x^3 - 2x^4 + 4x^3 - 4x^2 + x^3 - 2x^2 + 2x - 2x^2 + 4x - 4 \\ &= x^5 - 4x^4 + 7x^3 - 8x^2 + 6x - 4 \end{aligned}$$

14.   Since i is a zero, its conjugate $-i$ is also a zero; since $4 - i$ is a zero, its conjugate $4 + i$ is also a zero; and since $2 + i$ is a zero, its conjugate $2 - i$ is also a zero of f. Finding the function:

$$\begin{aligned} f(x) &= (x + i)(x - i)(x - (4 + i))(x - (4 - i))(x - (2 + i))(x - (2 - i)) \\ &= \left(x^2 - i^2\right)((x - 4) - i)((x - 4) + i)((x - 2) - i)((x - 2) + i) \\ &= \left(x^2 + 1\right)\left(x^2 - 8x + 16 - i^2\right)\left(x^2 - 4x + 4 - i^2\right) \\ &= \left(x^2 + 1\right)\left(x^2 - 8x + 17\right)\left(x^2 - 4x + 5\right) \\ &= \left(x^4 - 8x^3 + 17x^2 + x^2 - 8x + 17\right)\left(x^2 - 4x + 5\right) \\ &= \left(x^4 - 8x^3 + 18x^2 - 8x + 17\right)\left(x^2 - 4x + 5\right) \\ &= x^6 - 4x^5 + 5x^4 - 8x^5 + 32x^4 - 40x^3 + 18x^4 - 72x^3 + 90x^2 - 8x^3 \\ &\qquad\qquad\qquad\qquad + 32x^2 - 40x + 17x^2 - 68x + 85 \\ &= x^6 - 12x^5 + 55x^4 - 120x^3 + 139x^2 - 108x + 85 \end{aligned}$$

15. Since $-i$ is a zero, its conjugate i is also a zero of f. Finding the function:
$$f(x) = (x-3)(x-3)(x+i)(x-i)$$
$$= \left(x^2 - 6x + 9\right)\left(x^2 - i^2\right)$$
$$= \left(x^2 - 6x + 9\right)\left(x^2 + 1\right)$$
$$= x^4 + x^2 - 6x^3 - 6x + 9x^2 + 9$$
$$= x^4 - 6x^3 + 10x^2 - 6x + 9$$

16. Since $1 + i$ is a zero, its conjugate $1 - i$ is also a zero of f. Finding the function:
$$f(x) = (x-1)^3(x-(1+i))(x-(1-i))$$
$$= \left(x^3 - 3x^2 + 3x - 1\right)((x-1)-i)((x-1)+i)$$
$$= \left(x^3 - 3x^2 + 3x - 1\right)\left(x^2 - 2x + 1 - i^2\right)$$
$$= \left(x^3 - 3x^2 + 3x - 1\right)\left(x^2 - 2x + 2\right)$$
$$= x^5 - 2x^4 + 2x^3 - 3x^4 + 6x^3 - 6x^2 + 3x^3 - 6x^2 + 6x - x^2 + 2x - 2$$
$$= x^5 - 5x^4 + 11x^3 - 13x^2 + 8x - 2$$

17. Since $2i$ is a zero, its conjugate $-2i$ is also a zero of f. $x - 2i$ and $x + 2i$ are factors of f.
Thus, $(x - 2i)(x + 2i) = x^2 + 4$ is a factor of f. Using division to find the other factor:

$$
\begin{array}{r}
x - 4 \\
x^2 + 4 \overline{\smash{)}\, x^3 - 4x^2 + 4x - 16} \\
\underline{x^3 \qquad\quad + 4x} \\
-4x^2 \qquad - 16 \\
\underline{-4x^2 \qquad - 16}
\end{array}
$$

$x - 4$ is a factor and the remaining zero is 4. The zeros of f are $4, 2i, -2i$.

18. Since $-5i$ is a zero, its conjugate $5i$ is also a zero of g. $x + 5i$ and $x - 5i$ are factors of g.
Thus, $(x + 5i)(x - 5i) = x^2 + 25$ is a factor of g. Using division to find the other factor:

$$
\begin{array}{r}
x + 3 \\
x^2 + 25 \overline{\smash{)}\, x^3 + 3x^2 + 25x + 75} \\
\underline{x^3 \qquad\quad + 25x} \\
3x^2 \qquad + 75 \\
\underline{3x^2 \qquad + 75}
\end{array}
$$

$x + 3$ is a factor and the remaining zero is -3. The zeros of g are $-3, 5i, -5i$.

19. Since $-2i$ is a zero, its conjugate $2i$ is also a zero of f. $x - 2i$ and $x + 2i$ are factors of f. Thus, $(x - 2i)(x + 2i) = x^2 + 4$ is a factor of f. Using division to find the other factor:

$$
\begin{array}{r}
2x^2 + 5x - 3 \\
x^2 + 4 \overline{\smash{\big)}\ 2x^4 + 5x^3 + 5x^2 + 20x - 12} \\
\underline{2x^4 \qquad\quad + 8x^2} \\
5x^3 - 3x^2 + 20x \\
\underline{5x^3 \qquad\quad + 20x} \\
-3x^2 \qquad\quad - 12 \\
\underline{-3x^2 \qquad\quad - 12}
\end{array}
$$

$2x^2 + 5x - 3 = (2x - 1)(x + 3)$ are factors and the remaining zeros are $\dfrac{1}{2}$ and -3. The zeros of f are $2i, -2i, -3, \dfrac{1}{2}$.

20. Since $3i$ is a zero, its conjugate $-3i$ is also a zero of h. $x - 3i$ and $x + 3i$ are factors of h. Thus, $(x - 3i)(x + 3i) = x^2 + 9$ is a factor of h. Using division to find the other factor:

$$
\begin{array}{r}
3x^2 + 5x - 2 \\
x^2 + 9 \overline{\smash{\big)}\ 3x^4 + 5x^3 + 25x^2 + 45x - 18} \\
\underline{3x^4 \qquad\quad + 27x^2} \\
5x^3 - 2x^2 + 45x \\
\underline{5x^3 \qquad\quad + 45x} \\
-2x^2 \qquad\quad - 18 \\
\underline{-2x^2 \qquad\quad - 18}
\end{array}
$$

$3x^2 + 5x - 2 = (3x - 1)(x + 2)$ are factors and the remaining zeros are $\dfrac{1}{3}$ and -2. The zeros of h are $3i, -3i, -2, \dfrac{1}{3}$.

21. Since $3 - 2i$ is a zero, its conjugate $3 + 2i$ is also a zero of h. $x - (3 - 2i)$ and $x - (3 + 2i)$ are factors of h. Thus,
$(x - (3 - 2i))(x - (3 + 2i)) = ((x - 3) + 2i)((x - 3) - 2i) = x^2 - 6x + 9 - 4i^2 = x^2 - 6x + 13$ is a factor of h. Using division to find the other factor:

$$
\begin{array}{r}
x^2 - 3x - 10 \\
x^2 - 6x + 13 \overline{\smash{\big)}\ x^4 - 9x^3 + 21x^2 + 21x - 130} \\
\underline{x^4 - 6x^3 + 13x^2} \\
-3x^3 + 8x^2 + 21x \\
\underline{-3x^3 + 18x^2 - 39x} \\
-10x^2 + 60x - 130 \\
\underline{-10x^2 + 60x - 130}
\end{array}
$$

$x^2 - 3x - 10 = (x + 2)(x - 5)$ are factors and the remaining zeros are –2 and 5. The zeros of h are $3 - 2i, 3 + 2i, -2, 5$.

22. Since $1 + 3i$ is a zero, its conjugate $1 - 3i$ is also a zero of f. $x - (1 + 3i)$ and $x - (1 - 3i)$ are factors of f. Thus,

$(x - (1 + 3i))(x - (1 - 3i)) = ((x - 1) - 3i)((x - 1) + 3i) = x^2 - 2x + 1 - 9i^2 = x^2 - 2x + 10$ is a factor of f. Using division to find the other factor:

$$
\begin{array}{r}
x^2 - 5x - 6 \\
x^2 - 2x + 10 \overline{\smash{)}\, x^4 - 7x^3 + 14x^2 - 38x - 60} \\
\underline{x^4 - 2x^3 + 10x^2} \\
-5x^3 + 4x^2 - 38x \\
\underline{-5x^3 + 10x^2 - 50x} \\
-6x^2 + 12x - 60 \\
\underline{-6x^2 + 12x - 60}
\end{array}
$$

$x^2 - 5x - 6 = (x + 1)(x - 6)$ are factors and the remaining zeros are –1 and 6. The zeros of f are $1 + 3i, 1 - 3i, -1, 6$.

23. Since $-4i$ is a zero, its conjugate $4i$ is also a zero of h. $x - 4i$ and $x + 4i$ are factors of h. Thus, $(x - 4i)(x + 4i) = x^2 + 16$ is a factor of h. Using division to find the other factor:

$$
\begin{array}{r}
3x^3 + 2x^2 - 33x - 22 \\
x^2 + 16 \overline{\smash{)}\, 3x^5 + 2x^4 + 15x^3 + 10x^2 - 528x - 352} \\
\underline{3x^5 + 48x^3} \\
2x^4 - 33x^3 + 10x^2 \\
\underline{2x^4 + 32x^2} \\
-33x^3 - 22x^2 - 528x \\
\underline{-33x^3 - 528x} \\
-22x^2 - 352 \\
\underline{-22x^2 - 352}
\end{array}
$$

$3x^3 + 2x^2 - 33x - 22 = x^2(3x + 2) - 11(3x + 2) = (3x + 2)(x^2 - 11)$

$= (3x + 2)\left(x - \sqrt{11}\right)\left(x + \sqrt{11}\right)$ are factors and the remaining zeros are $-\dfrac{2}{3}, \sqrt{11}$, and $-\sqrt{11}$.

The zeros of h are $4i, -4i, -\sqrt{11}, \sqrt{11}, -\dfrac{2}{3}$.

24. Since $3i$ is a zero, its conjugate $-3i$ is also a zero of g. $x - 3i$ and $x + 3i$ are factors of g. Thus, $(x - 3i)(x + 3i) = x^2 + 9$ is a factor of g. Using division to find the other factor:

$$
\begin{array}{r}
2x^3 - 3x^2 - 23x + 12 \\
x^2 + 9\overline{)2x^5 - 3x^4 - 5x^3 - 15x^2 - 207x + 108} \\
\underline{2x^5 \qquad\quad + 18x^3} \\
-3x^4 - 23x^3 - 15x^2 \\
\underline{-3x^4 \qquad\quad - 27x^2} \\
-23x^3 + 12x^2 - 207x \\
\underline{-23x^3 \qquad\quad - 207x} \\
12x^2 \qquad + 108 \\
\underline{12x^2 \qquad + 108}
\end{array}
$$

Graph: $y = 2x^3 - 3x^2 - 23x + 12$ It appears that -3 is a zero.

$$
\begin{array}{r|rrrr}
-3) & 2 & -3 & -23 & 12 \\
    &   & -6 & 27 & -12 \\
\hline
    & 2 & -9 & 4 & 0
\end{array}
$$

$x + 3$ is a factor. The remaining factor is $2x^2 - 9x + 4 = (2x - 1)(x - 4)$.

The zeros of g are $3i, -3i, -3, \dfrac{1}{2}, 4$.

25. $f(x) = x^3 - 1 = (x - 1)\left(x^2 + x + 1\right)$ The zeros of $x^2 + x + 1 = 0$ are:

$$x = \frac{-1 \pm \sqrt{1^2 - 4(1)(1)}}{2(1)} = \frac{-1 \pm \sqrt{-3}}{2} = -\frac{1}{2} + \frac{\sqrt{3}}{2}i \text{ or } -\frac{1}{2} - \frac{\sqrt{3}}{2}i$$

The zeros are: $1, -\dfrac{1}{2} + \dfrac{\sqrt{3}}{2}i, -\dfrac{1}{2} - \dfrac{\sqrt{3}}{2}i$.

26. $f(x) = x^4 - 1 = \left(x^2 - 1\right)\left(x^2 + 1\right) = (x - 1)(x + 1)\left(x^2 + 1\right)$
The zeros of $x^2 + 1 = 0$ are $x = \pm i$.
The zeros are: $-1, 1, -i, i$.

27. $f(x) = x^3 - 8x^2 + 25x - 26$
Step 1: $f(x)$ has 3 complex zeros.
Step 2:   By Descartes Rule of Signs, there are 3 or 1 positive real zeros.
$f(-x) = (-x)^3 - 8(-x)^2 + 25(-x) - 26 = -x^3 - 8x^2 - 25x - 26$; thus, there are no negative real zeros.
Step 3:   Possible rational zeros:

$$p = \pm 1, \pm 2, \pm 13, \pm 26; \quad q = \pm 1; \quad \frac{p}{q} = \pm 1, \pm 2, \pm 13, \pm 26$$

Step 4:   Using synthetic division:

$$2\overline{)1 \quad -8 \quad 25 \quad -26}$$
$$\underline{\quad\quad 2 \quad -12 \quad 26}$$
$$1 \quad -6 \quad 13 \quad 0$$

Since the remainder is 0, $x - 2$ is a factor. The other factor is the quotient:
$x^2 - 6x + 13$.

Using the quadratic formula to find the zeros of $x^2 - 6x + 13 = 0$:

$$x = \frac{-(-6) \pm \sqrt{(-6)^2 - 4(1)(13)}}{2(1)} = \frac{6 \pm \sqrt{-16}}{2} = \frac{6 \pm 4i}{2} = 3 \pm 2i.$$

The complex zeros are $2,\ 3 - 2i,\ 3 + 2i$.

28. $f(x) = x^3 + 13x^2 + 57x + 85$

Step 1: $f(x)$ has 3 complex zeros.

Step 2:   By Descartes Rule of Signs, there are no positive real zeros.
$f(-x) = (-x)^3 + 13(-x)^2 + 57(-x) + 85 = -x^3 + 13x^2 - 57x + 85$; thus, there are 3 or 1 negative real zeros.

Step 3:   Possible rational zeros:

$$p = \pm 1, \pm 5, \pm 17, \pm 85; \quad q = \pm 1; \quad \frac{p}{q} = \pm 1, \pm 5, \pm 17, \pm 85$$

Step 4:   Using synthetic division:

$$-5\overline{)1 \quad 13 \quad 57 \quad 85}$$
$$\underline{\quad\quad -5 \quad -40 \quad -85}$$
$$1 \quad 8 \quad 17 \quad 0$$

Since the remainder is 0, $x + 5$ is a factor. The other factor is the quotient:
$x^2 + 8x + 17$.

Using the quadratic formula to find the zeros of $x^2 + 8x + 17 = 0$:

$$x = \frac{-8 \pm \sqrt{8^2 - 4(1)(17)}}{2(1)} = \frac{-8 \pm \sqrt{-4}}{2} = \frac{-8 \pm 2i}{2} = -4 \pm i.$$

The complex zeros are $-5,\ -4 - i,\ -4 + i$.

29. $f(x) = x^4 + 5x^2 + 4 = \left(x^2 + 4\right)\left(x^2 + 1\right) = (x + 2i)(x - 2i)(x + i)(x - i)$

The zeros are: $-2i,\ -i,\ i,\ 2i$.

30. $f(x) = x^4 + 13x^2 + 36 = \left(x^2 + 4\right)\left(x^2 + 9\right) = (x + 2i)(x - 2i)(x + 3i)(x - 3i)$

The zeros are: $-3i,\ -2i,\ 2i,\ 3i$.

31. $f(x) = x^4 + 2x^3 + 22x^2 + 50x - 75$

Step 1: $f(x)$ has 4 complex zeros.

Step 2:   By Descartes Rule of Signs, there is 1 positive real zero.
$$f(-x) = (-x)^4 + 2(-x)^3 + 22(-x)^2 + 50(-x) - 75$$
$$= x^4 - 2x^3 + 22x^2 - 50x - 75$$
thus, there are 3 or 1 negative real zeros.

Step 3:   Possible rational zeros:
$$p = \pm 1, \pm 3, \pm 5, \pm 15, \pm 25, \pm 75; \quad q = \pm 1;$$
$$\frac{p}{q} = \pm 1, \pm 3, \pm 5, \pm 15, \pm 25, \pm 75$$

Step 4:   Using synthetic division:

$$-3\overline{)1 \quad 2 \quad 22 \quad 50 \quad -75}$$
$$\underline{\quad -3 \quad 3 \quad -75 \quad 75}$$
$$1 \quad -1 \quad 25 \quad -25 \quad 0$$

Since the remainder is 0, $x + 3$ is a factor. The other factor is the quotient:
$$x^3 - x^2 + 25x - 25 = x^2(x-1) + 25(x-1) = (x-1)\left(x^2 + 25\right)$$
$$= (x-1)(x+5i)(x-5i)$$
The complex zeros are $-3,\ 1,\ -5i,\ 5i$.

32. $f(x) = x^4 + 3x^3 - 19x^2 + 27x - 252$

Step 1: $f(x)$ has 4 complex zeros.

Step 2:   By Descartes Rule of Signs, there are 3 or 1 positive real zeros.
$$f(-x) = (-x)^4 + 3(-x)^3 - 19(-x)^2 + 27(-x) - 252$$
$$= x^4 - 3x^3 - 19x^2 - 27x - 252$$
thus, there is 1 negative real zero.

Step 3:   Possible rational zeros:
$$p = \pm 1, \pm 2, \pm 3, \pm 4, \pm 6, \pm 7, \pm 9, \pm 12, \pm 14, \pm 18, \pm 21, \pm 28, \pm 36,$$
$$\pm 42, \pm 63, \pm 84, \pm 126, \pm 252; \quad q = \pm 1;$$
The possible rational zeros are the same as the values of p.

Step 4:   Using synthetic division:

$$-7\overline{)1 \quad 3 \quad -19 \quad 27 \quad -252}$$
$$\underline{\quad -7 \quad 28 \quad -63 \quad 252}$$
$$1 \quad -4 \quad 9 \quad -36 \quad 0$$

Since the remainder is 0, $x + 7$ is a factor. The other factor is the quotient:
$$x^3 - 4x^2 + 9x - 36 = x^2(x-4) + 9(x-4) = (x-4)\left(x^2 + 9\right)$$
$$= (x-4)(x+3i)(x-3i)$$
The complex zeros are $-7,\ 4,\ -3i,\ 3i$.

33. $f(x) = 3x^4 - x^3 - 9x^2 + 159x - 52$

Step 1: $f(x)$ has 4 complex zeros.

Step 2:   By Descartes Rule of Signs, there are 3 or 1 positive real zeros.
$$f(-x) = 3(-x)^4 - (-x)^3 - 9(-x)^2 + 159(-x) - 52$$
$$= 3x^4 + x^3 - 9x^2 - 159x - 52$$
thus, there is 1 negative real zero.

Step 3:   Possible rational zeros:

$$p = \pm 1, \pm 2, \pm 4, \pm 13, \pm 26, \pm 52; \quad q = \pm 1, \pm 3;$$
$$\frac{p}{q} = \pm 1, \pm 2, \pm 4, \pm 13, \pm 26, \pm 52, \pm \frac{1}{3}, \pm \frac{2}{3}, \pm \frac{4}{3}, \pm \frac{13}{3}, \pm \frac{26}{3}, \pm \frac{52}{3}$$

Step 4:   Using synthetic division:

$$-4\overline{)\,3 \quad -1 \quad -9 \quad 159 \quad -52\,}$$

$$\underline{\quad\quad -12 \quad 52 \quad -172 \quad 52\,}$$

$$3 \quad -13 \quad 43 \quad -13 \quad 0$$

$$\tfrac{1}{3}\overline{)\,3 \quad -13 \quad 43 \quad -13\,}$$

$$\underline{\quad\quad 1 \quad -4 \quad 13\,}$$

$$3 \quad -12 \quad 39 \quad 0$$

Since the remainder is 0, $x+4$ and $x-\dfrac{1}{3}$ are factors. The other factor is the quotient: $3x^2 - 12x + 39 = 3(x^2 - 4x + 13)$.

Using the quadratic formula to find the zeros of $x^2 - 4x + 13 = 0$:

$$x = \frac{-(-4) \pm \sqrt{(-4)^2 - 4(1)(13)}}{2(1)} = \frac{4 \pm \sqrt{-36}}{2} = \frac{4 \pm 6i}{2} = 2 \pm 3i.$$

The complex zeros are $-4,\ \dfrac{1}{3},\ 2-3i,\ 2+3i$.

34. $f(x) = 2x^4 + x^3 - 35x^2 - 113x + 65$

Step 1: $f(x)$ has 4 complex zeros.

Step 2:   By Descartes Rule of Signs, there are 2 or 0 positive real zeros.

$$f(-x) = 2(-x)^4 + (-x)^3 - 35(-x)^2 - 113(-x) + 65 = 2x^4 - x^3 - 35x^2 + 113x + 65$$

thus, there are 2 or 0 negative real zeros.

Step 3:   Possible rational zeros:

$$p = \pm 1,\ \pm 5,\ \pm 13,\ \pm 65; \quad q = \pm 1,\ \pm 2;$$

$$\frac{p}{q} = \pm 1,\ \pm 5,\ \pm 13,\ \pm 65,\ \pm \frac{1}{2},\ \pm \frac{5}{2},\ \pm \frac{13}{2},\ \pm \frac{65}{2}$$

Step 4:   Using synthetic division:

$$5\overline{)\,2 \quad 1 \quad -35 \quad -113 \quad 65\,}$$

$$\underline{\quad\quad 10 \quad 55 \quad 100 \quad -65\,}$$

$$2 \quad 11 \quad 20 \quad -13 \quad 0$$

$$\tfrac{1}{2}\overline{)\,2 \quad 11 \quad 20 \quad -13\,}$$

$$\underline{\quad\quad 1 \quad 6 \quad 13\,}$$

$$2 \quad 12 \quad 26 \quad 0$$

Since the remainder is 0, $x-5$ and $x-\dfrac{1}{2}$ are factors. The other factor is the quotient: $2x^2 + 12x + 26 = 2(x^2 + 6x + 13)$.

Using the quadratic formula to find the zeros of $x^2 + 6x + 13 = 0$:

$$x = \frac{-6 \pm \sqrt{6^2 - 4(1)(13)}}{2(1)} = \frac{-6 \pm \sqrt{-16}}{2} = \frac{-6 \pm 4i}{2} = -3 \pm 2i.$$

The complex zeros are $5,\ \dfrac{1}{2},\ -3-2i,\ -3+2i$.

35.   If the coefficients are real numbers and $2+i$ is a zero, then $2-i$ would also be a zero. This would then require a polynomial of degree 4.

36.   Three zeros are given. If the coefficients are real numbers, then the complex zeros would also have their conjugates as zeros. This would mean that there are 5 zeros which would require a polynomial of degree 5.

37. If the coefficients are real numbers, then complex zeros must appear in conjugate pairs. We have a conjugate pair and one real zero. Thus, there is only one remaining zero and it must be real because a complex zero would require a pair and the polynomial would then have to be of degree 5.

38. One of the remaining zeros must be $4 + i$, the conjugate of $4 - i$. The third zero is a real number. Thus the fourth zero must also be a real number in order to have a degree 4 polynomial.

The Zeros of a Polynomial Function

5.R   Chapter Review

1.
$$\begin{array}{r|rrrr} 1) & 8 & -3 & 1 & 4 \\ & & 8 & 5 & 6 \\ \hline & 8 & 5 & 6 & 10 \end{array}$$

$$\therefore 8x^3 - 3x^2 + x + 4 = (x-1)(8x^2 + 5x + 6) + \frac{10}{x-1}$$

$$q(x) = 8x^2 + 5x + 6; \qquad R = \frac{10}{x-1}$$

2.
$$\begin{array}{r|rrrr} 2) & 2 & 8 & -5 & 5 \\ & & 4 & 24 & 38 \\ \hline & 2 & 12 & 19 & 43 \end{array}$$

$$\therefore 2x^3 + 8x^2 - 5x + 5 = (x-2)(2x^2 + 12x + 19) + \frac{43}{x-2}$$

$$q(x) = 2x^2 + 12x + 19; \qquad R = \frac{43}{x-2}$$

3.
$$\begin{array}{r|rrrrr} -2) & 1 & -2 & 0 & 1 & -1 \\ & & -2 & 8 & -16 & 30 \\ \hline & 1 & -4 & 8 & -15 & 29 \end{array}$$

$$\therefore x^4 - 2x^3 + x - 1 = (x+2)(x^3 - 4x^2 + 8x - 15) + \frac{29}{x+2}$$

$$q(x) = x^3 - 4x^2 + 8x - 15; \qquad R = \frac{29}{x+2}$$

4.
$$\begin{array}{r|rrrrr} -1) & 1 & 0 & -1 & 3 & 0 \\ & & -1 & 1 & 0 & -3 \\ \hline & 1 & -1 & 0 & 3 & -3 \end{array}$$

$$\therefore x^4 - x^2 + 3x = (x+1)(x^3 - x^2 + 3) + \frac{-3}{x+1}$$

$$q(x) = x^3 - x^2 + 3; \qquad R = \frac{-3}{x+1}$$

5. $f(x) = 12x^6 - 8x^4 + 1$ at $x = 4$

```
4) 12   0    -8     0       0       0       1
        48   192    736    2944    11776   47104
   ──────────────────────────────────────────────
   12   48   184    736    2944    11776   47105
```

$f(4) = 47105$

6. $f(x) = -16x^3 + 18x^2 - x + 2$ at $x = -2$

```
-2) -16   18    -1     2
          32   -100   202
   ──────────────────────────
   -16   50   -101   204
```

$f(-2) = 204$

7. $f(x) = 12x^8 - x^7 + 8x^4 - 2x^3 + x + 3$
      Examining $f(x)$, there are 4 variations in sign; thus, there are 4 or 2 or 0 positive real
      zeros.
      Examining $f(-x) = 12(-x)^8 - (-x)^7 + 8(-x)^4 - 2(-x)^3 + (-x) + 3$
      $= 12x^8 + x^7 + 8x^4 + 2x^3 - x + 3$, there are 2 variations in sign; thus, there are 2 or 0
      negative real zeros.

8. $f(x) = -6x^5 + x^4 + 5x^3 + x + 1$
      Examining $f(x)$, there is 1 variation in sign; thus, there is 1 positive real zero.
      Examining $f(-x) = -6(-x)^5 + (-x)^4 + 5(-x)^3 + (-x) + 1 = 6x^5 + x^4 - 5x^3 - x + 1$, there are
      2 variations in sign; thus, there are 2 or 0 negative real zeros.

9. $f(x) = 12x^8 - x^7 + 6x^4 - x^3 + x - 3$
      p must be a factor of -3: $p = \pm 1, \pm 3$
      q must be a factor of 12: $q = \pm 1, \pm 2, \pm 3, \pm 4, \pm 6, \pm 12$

      The possible rational zeros are: $\dfrac{p}{q} = \pm 1, \pm 3, \pm \dfrac{1}{2}, \pm \dfrac{3}{2}, \pm \dfrac{1}{3}, \pm \dfrac{1}{4}, \pm \dfrac{3}{4}, \pm \dfrac{1}{6}, \pm \dfrac{1}{12}$

10. $f(x) = -6x^5 + x^4 + 2x^3 - x + 1$
      p must be a factor of 1: $p = \pm 1$
      q must be a factor of -6: $q = \pm 1, \pm 2, \pm 3, \pm 6$

      The possible rational zeros are: $\dfrac{p}{q} = \pm 1, \pm \dfrac{1}{2}, \pm \dfrac{1}{3}, \pm \dfrac{1}{6}$

11. $f(x) = x^3 - 3x^2 - 6x + 8$

Step 1: $f(x)$ has at most 3 real zeros.

Step 2:   By Descartes Rule of Signs, there are 2 or 0 positive real zeros.

Also because $f(-x) = (-x)^3 - 3(-x)^2 - 6(-x) + 8 = -x^3 - 3x^2 + 6x + 8$, there is 1 negative real zero.

Step 3:   Possible rational zeros:

$$p = \pm 1, \pm 2, \pm 4, \pm 8; \quad q = \pm 1; \quad \frac{p}{q} = \pm 1, \pm 2, \pm 4, \pm 8$$

Step 4:   Using the Bounds on Zeros Theorem:

$a_2 = -3, \quad a_1 = -6, \quad a_0 = 8$

$\text{Max} \left\{ 1, |8| + |-6| + |-3| \right\} = \text{Max} \left\{ 1, 17 \right\} = 17$

$1 + \text{Max} \left\{ |8|, |-6|, |-3| \right\} = 1 + 8 = 9$

The smaller of the two numbers is 9. Thus, every zero of f lies between -9 and 9.

Step 5:   Using synthetic division:

$$
\begin{array}{r|rrrr}
-2) & 1 & -3 & -6 & 8 \\
    &   & -2 & 10 & -8 \\
\hline
    & 1 & -5 & 4 & 0
\end{array}
$$

Since the remainder is 0, $x - (-2) = x + 2$ is a factor. The other factor is the quotient: $x^2 - 5x + 4$.

Thus, $f(x) = (x + 2)(x^2 - 5x + 4) = (x + 2)(x - 1)(x - 4)$.

The zeros are -2, 1, and 4.

12. $f(x) = x^3 - x^2 - 10x - 8$

Step 1: $f(x)$ has at most 3 real zeros.

Step 2:   By Descartes Rule of Signs, there is 1 positive real zero.

Also because $f(-x) = (-x)^3 - (-x)^2 - 10(-x) - 8 = -x^3 - x^2 + 10x - 8$, there are 2 or 0 negative real zeros.

Step 3:   Possible rational zeros:

$$p = \pm 1, \pm 2, \pm 4, \pm 8; \quad q = \pm 1; \quad \frac{p}{q} = \pm 1, \pm 2, \pm 4, \pm 8$$

Step 4:   Using the Bounds on Zeros Theorem:

$a_2 = -1, \quad a_1 = -10, \quad a_0 = -8$

$\text{Max} \left\{ 1, |-8| + |-10| + |-1| \right\} = \text{Max} \left\{ 1, 19 \right\} = 19$

$1 + \text{Max} \left\{ |-8|, |-10|, |-1| \right\} = 1 + 10 = 11$

The smaller of the two numbers is 11. Thus, every zero of f lies between -11 and 11.

Step 5:   Using synthetic division:

$$
\begin{array}{r|rrrr}
-2) & 1 & -1 & -10 & -8 \\
    &   & -2 & 6   & 8 \\
\hline
    & 1 & -3 & -4 & 0
\end{array}
$$

Since the remainder is 0, $x - (-2) = x + 2$ is a factor. The other factor is the quotient: $x^2 - 3x - 4$.

Thus, $f(x) = (x + 2)(x^2 - 3x - 4) = (x + 2)(x + 1)(x - 4)$.

The zeros are -2, -1, and 4.

13. $f(x) = 4x^3 + 4x^2 - 7x + 2$

Step 1: $f(x)$ has at most 3 real zeros.

Step 2: By Descartes Rule of Signs, there are 2 or 0 positive real zeros.

$f(-x) = 4(-x)^3 + 4(-x)^2 - 7(-x) + 2 = -4x^3 + 4x^2 + 7x + 2$; thus, there is 1 negative real zero.

Step 3: Possible rational zeros:

$$p = \pm 1, \pm 2; \quad q = \pm 1, \pm 2, \pm 4; \quad \frac{p}{q} = \pm 1, \pm 2, \pm \frac{1}{2}, \pm \frac{1}{4}$$

Step 4: Using the Bounds on Zeros Theorem:

$$f(x) = 4\left(x^3 + x^2 - \frac{7}{4}x + \frac{1}{2}\right) \rightarrow a_2 = 1, \quad a_1 = -\frac{7}{4}, \quad a_0 = \frac{1}{2}$$

$$\text{Max}\left\{1, \left|\frac{1}{2}\right| + \left|-\frac{7}{4}\right| + |1|\right\} = \text{Max}\left\{1, \frac{13}{4}\right\} = \frac{13}{4} = 3.25$$

$$1 + \text{Max}\left\{\left|\frac{1}{2}\right|, \left|-\frac{7}{4}\right|, |1|\right\} = 1 + \frac{7}{4} = \frac{11}{4} = 2.75$$

The smaller of the two numbers is 2.75. Thus, every zero of f lies between –2.75 and 2.75.

Step 5: Using synthetic division:

```
-2)4    4   -7    2
       -8    8   -2
    ─────────────────
    4   -4    1    0
```

Since the remainder is 0, $x - (-2) = x + 2$ is a factor. The other factor is the quotient: $4x^2 - 4x + 1$. Thus,

$$f(x) = (x + 2)\left(4x^2 - 4x + 1\right) = (x + 2)(2x - 1)(2x - 1).$$

The zeros are –2 and $\dfrac{1}{2}$ (multiplicity 2).

14. $f(x) = 4x^3 - 4x^2 - 7x - 2$

Step 1: $f(x)$ has at most 3 real zeros.

Step 2: By Descartes Rule of Signs, there is 1 positive real zero.

$f(-x) = 4(-x)^3 - 4(-x)^2 - 7(-x) - 2 = -4x^3 - 4x^2 + 7x - 2$; thus, there are 2 or 0 negative real zeros.

Step 3: Possible rational zeros:

$$p = \pm 1, \pm 2; \quad q = \pm 1, \pm 2, \pm 4; \quad \frac{p}{q} = \pm 1, \pm 2, \pm \frac{1}{2}, \pm \frac{1}{4}$$

Step 4: Using the Bounds on Zeros Theorem:

$$f(x) = 4\left(x^3 - x^2 - \frac{7}{4}x - \frac{1}{2}\right) \rightarrow a_2 = -1, \quad a_1 = -\frac{7}{4}, \quad a_0 = -\frac{1}{2}$$

$$\text{Max}\left\{1, \left|-\frac{1}{2}\right| + \left|-\frac{7}{4}\right| + |-1|\right\} = \text{Max}\left\{1, \frac{13}{4}\right\} = \frac{13}{4} = 3.25$$

$$1 + \text{Max}\left\{\left|-\frac{1}{2}\right|, \left|-\frac{7}{4}\right|, |-1|\right\} = 1 + \frac{7}{4} = \frac{11}{4} = 2.75$$

The smaller of the two numbers is 2.75. Thus, every zero of f lies between –2.75 and 2.75.

Step 5:   Using synthetic division:

$$2)\overline{\begin{array}{cccc} 4 & -4 & -7 & -2 \end{array}}$$
$$\begin{array}{ccc} 8 & 8 & 2 \end{array}$$
$$\overline{\begin{array}{cccc} 4 & 4 & 1 & 0 \end{array}}$$

Since the remainder is 0, $x-2$ is a factor. The other factor is the quotient:
$4x^2 + 4x + 1$.
Thus, $f(x) = (x-2)\left(4x^2 + 4x + 1\right) = (x-2)(2x+1)(2x+1)$.

The zeros are 2 and $-\dfrac{1}{2}$ (multiplicity 2).

15. $f(x) = x^4 - 4x^3 + 9x^2 - 20x + 20$
Step 1: $f(x)$ has at most 4 real zeros.
Step 2:   By Descartes Rule of Signs, there are 4 or 2 or 0 positive real zeros.
$$f(-x) = (-x)^4 - 4(-x)^3 + 9(-x)^2 - 20(-x) + 20$$
$$= x^4 + 4x^3 + 9x^2 + 20x + 20;$$
thus, there are no negative real zeros.
Step 3:   Possible rational zeros:
$$p = \pm 1, \pm 2, \pm 4, \pm 5, \pm 10, \pm 20; \quad q = \pm 1;$$
$$\frac{p}{q} = \pm 1, \pm 2, \pm 4, \pm 5, \pm 10, \pm 20$$
Step 4:   Using the Bounds on Zeros Theorem:
$$a_3 = -4, \ a_2 = 9, \ a_1 = -20, \ a_0 = 20$$
$$\text{Max}\left\{1, |20| + |-20| + |9| + |-4|\right\} = \text{Max}\left\{1, 53\right\} = 53$$
$$1 + \text{Max}\left\{|20|, |-20|, |9|, |-4|\right\} = 1 + 20 = 21$$
The smaller of the two numbers is 21. Thus, every zero of f lies between –21 and 21.
Step 5:   Using synthetic division:

$$2)\overline{\begin{array}{cccc} 1 & -4 & 9 & -20 & 20 \end{array}} \qquad 2)\overline{\begin{array}{cccc} 1 & -2 & 5 & -10 \end{array}}$$

Since the remainder is 0, $x-2$ is a factor twice. The other factor is the quotient: $x^2 + 5$.
Thus, $f(x) = (x-2)(x-2)\left(x^2 + 5\right) = (x-2)^2\left(x^2 + 5\right)$.
The zero is 2 (multiplicity 2). ($x^2 + 5 = 0$ has no real solutions.)

16. $f(x) = x^4 + 6x^3 + 11x^2 + 12x + 18$
Step 1: $f(x)$ has at most 4 real zeros.
Step 2:   By Descartes Rule of Signs, there are no positive real zeros.
$$f(-x) = (-x)^4 + 6(-x)^3 + 11(-x)^2 + 12(-x) + 18$$
$$= x^4 - 6x^3 + 11x^2 - 12x + 18;$$
thus, there are 4 or 2 or 0 negative real zeros.

Step 3:   Possible rational zeros:
$$p = \pm 1, \pm 2, \pm 3, \pm 6, \pm 9, \pm 18; \quad q = \pm 1;$$

$$\frac{p}{q} = \pm 1, \pm 2, \pm 3, \pm 6, \pm 9, \pm 18$$

Step 4:   Using the Bounds on Zeros Theorem:
$$a_3 = 6, \quad a_2 = 11, \quad a_1 = 12, \quad a_0 = 18$$

$$\text{Max} \left\{ 1, |18| + |12| + |11| + |6| \right\} = \text{Max} \left\{ 1, 47 \right\} = 47$$

$$1 + \text{Max} \left\{ |18|, |12|, |11|, |6| \right\} = 1 + 18 = 19$$

The smaller of the two numbers is 19. Thus, every zero of f lies between -19 and 19.

Step 5:   Using synthetic division:

```
-3) 1   6   11   12   18        -3) 1   3   2   6
      -3  -9   -6  -18                -3   0  -6
    ─────────────────────            ──────────────
    1   3    2    6    0            1   0   2   0
```

Since the remainder is 0, $x - (-3) = x + 3$ is a factor twice. The other factor is the quotient: $x^2 + 2$.

Thus, $f(x) = (x + 3)(x + 3)\left(x^2 + 2\right) = (x + 3)^2\left(x^2 + 2\right)$.

The zero is -3 (multiplicity 2). ($x^2 + 2 = 0$ has no real solutions.)

17. $2x^4 + 2x^3 - 11x^2 + x - 6 = 0$

The solutions of the equation are the zeros of $f(x) = 2x^4 + 2x^3 - 11x^2 + x - 6$.

Step 1: $f(x)$ has at most 4 real zeros.

Step 2:   By Descartes Rule of Signs, there are 3 or 1 positive real zeros.
$$f(-x) = 2(-x)^4 + 2(-x)^3 - 11(-x)^2 + (-x) - 6 = 2x^4 - 2x^3 - 11x^2 - x - 6;$$
thus, there is 1 negative real zero.

Step 3:   Possible rational zeros:

$$p = \pm 1, \pm 2, \pm 3, \pm 6; \quad q = \pm 1, \pm 2; \quad \frac{p}{q} = \pm 1, \pm 2, \pm 3, \pm 6, \pm \frac{1}{2}, \pm \frac{3}{2}$$

Step 4:   Using the Bounds on Zeros Theorem:

$$f(x) = 2\left(x^4 + x^3 - \frac{11}{2}x^2 + \frac{1}{2}x - 3 \right) \rightarrow a_3 = 1, \quad a_2 = -\frac{11}{2}, \quad a_1 = \frac{1}{2}, \quad a_0 = -3$$

$$\text{Max} \left\{ 1, |-3| + \left|\frac{1}{2}\right| + \left|-\frac{11}{2}\right| + |1| \right\} = \text{Max} \left\{ 1, 10 \right\} = 10$$

$$1 + \text{Max} \left\{ |-3|, \left|\frac{1}{2}\right|, \left|-\frac{11}{2}\right|, |1| \right\} = 1 + \frac{11}{2} = \frac{13}{2} = 6.5$$

The smaller of the two numbers is 6.5. Thus, every zero of f lies between -6.5 and 6.5.

Step 5:   Using synthetic division:

```
-3) 2   2  -11   1  -6        2) 2  -4   1  -2
      -6   12  -3   6              4   0   2
    ──────────────────────        ──────────────
    2  -4    1  -2   0          2   0   1   0
```

Since the remainder is 0, $x + 3$ and $x - 2$ are factors. The other factor is the quotient: $2x^2 + 1$. The zeros are -3 and 2. ($2x^2 + 1 = 0$ has no real solutions.)

18. $3x^4 + 3x^3 - 17x^2 + x - 6 = 0$

The solutions of the equation are the zeros of $f(x) = 3x^4 + 3x^3 - 17x^2 + x - 6$.

Step 1: $f(x)$ has at most 4 real zeros.

Step 2:   By Descartes Rule of Signs, there are 3 or 1 positive real zeros.

$f(-x) = 3(-x)^4 + 3(-x)^3 - 17(-x)^2 + (-x) - 6 = 3x^4 - 3x^3 - 17x^2 - x - 6$;

thus, there is 1 negative real zero.

Step 3:   Possible rational zeros:

$$p = \pm 1, \pm 2, \pm 3, \pm 6; \quad q = \pm 1, \pm 3; \quad \frac{p}{q} = \pm 1, \pm 2, \pm 3, \pm 6, \pm \frac{1}{3}, \pm \frac{2}{3}$$

Step 4:   Using the Bounds on Zeros Theorem:

$$f(x) = 3\left(x^4 + x^3 - \frac{17}{3}x^2 + \frac{1}{3}x - 2 \right) \to a_3 = 1,\ a_2 = -\frac{17}{3},\ a_1 = \frac{1}{3},\ a_0 = -2$$

$$\text{Max}\left\{ 1, |-2| + \left|\frac{1}{3}\right| + \left|-\frac{17}{3}\right| + |1| \right\} = \text{Max}\ \{1, 9\} = 9$$

$$1 + \text{Max}\left\{ |-2|, \left|\frac{1}{3}\right|, \left|-\frac{17}{3}\right|, |1| \right\} = 1 + \frac{17}{3} = \frac{20}{3}$$

The smaller of the two numbers is 6.67. Thus, every zero of f lies between -6.67 and 6.67.

Step 5:   Using synthetic division:

```
-3)3    3   -17    1   -6          2)3   -6    1   -2
      -9    18   -3    6                6    0    2
   ─────────────────────             ─────────────────
    3   -6    1   -2    0             3    0    1    0
```

Since the remainder is 0, $x + 3$ and $x - 2$ are factors. The other factor is the quotient: $3x^2 + 1$.

The zeros are -3 and 2. ($3x^2 + 1 = 0$ has no real solutions.)

19. $2x^4 + 7x^3 + x^2 - 7x - 3 = 0$

The solutions of the equation are the zeros of $f(x) = 2x^4 + 7x^3 + x^2 - 7x - 3$.

Step 1: $f(x)$ has at most 4 real zeros.

Step 2:   By Descartes Rule of Signs, there is 1 positive real zero.

$f(-x) = 2(-x)^4 + 7(-x)^3 + (-x)^2 - 7(-x) - 3 = 2x^4 - 7x^3 + x^2 + 7x - 3$;

thus, there are 3 or 1 negative real zeros.

Step 3:   Possible rational zeros:

$$p = \pm 1, \pm 3; \quad q = \pm 1, \pm 2; \quad \frac{p}{q} = \pm 1, \pm 3, \pm \frac{1}{2}, \pm \frac{3}{2}$$

Step 4:   Using the Bounds on Zeros Theorem:

$$f(x) = 2\left(x^4 + \frac{7}{2}x^3 + \frac{1}{2}x^2 - \frac{7}{2}x - \frac{3}{2} \right) \to a_3 = \frac{7}{2},\ a_2 = \frac{1}{2},\ a_1 = -\frac{7}{2},\ a_0 = -\frac{3}{2}$$

$$\text{Max}\left\{ 1, \left|-\frac{3}{2}\right| + \left|-\frac{7}{2}\right| + \left|\frac{1}{2}\right| + \left|\frac{7}{2}\right| \right\} = \text{Max}\ \{1, 9\} = 9$$

$$1 + \text{Max}\left\{ \left|-\frac{3}{2}\right|, \left|-\frac{7}{2}\right|, \left|\frac{1}{2}\right|, \left|\frac{7}{2}\right| \right\} = 1 + \frac{7}{2} = \frac{9}{2} = 4.5$$

The smaller of the two numbers is 4.5. Thus, every zero of f lies between -4.5 and 4.5.

Step 5:   Using synthetic division:

$$-3\overline{)\begin{array}{rrrrr} 2 & 7 & 1 & -7 & -3 \\ & -6 & -3 & 6 & 3 \\ \hline 2 & 1 & -2 & -1 & 0 \end{array}}$$

$$-1\overline{)\begin{array}{rrrr} 2 & 1 & -2 & -1 \\ & -2 & 1 & 1 \\ \hline 2 & -1 & -1 & 0 \end{array}}$$

Since the remainder is 0, $x+3$ and $x+1$ are factors. The other factor is the quotient: $2x^2 - x - 1$.

Thus, $f(x) = (x+3)(x+1)\left(2x^2 - x - 1\right) = (x+3)(x+1)(2x+1)(x-1)$.

The zeros are $-3, -1, -\dfrac{1}{2}$, and 1.

20. $2x^4 + 7x^3 - 5x^2 - 28x - 12 = 0$

The solutions of the equation are the zeros of $f(x) = 2x^4 + 7x^3 - 5x^2 - 28x - 12$.

Step 1: $f(x)$ has at most 4 real zeros.

Step 2:   By Descartes Rule of Signs, there is 1 positive real zero.

$$f(-x) = 2(-x)^4 + 7(-x)^3 - 5(-x)^2 - 28(-x) - 12$$

$$= 2x^4 - 7x^3 - 5x^2 + 28x - 12;$$

thus, there are 3 or 1 negative real zeros.

Step 3:   Possible rational zeros:

$$p = \pm 1, \pm 2, \pm 3, \pm 4, \pm 6, \pm 12; \quad q = \pm 1, \pm 2;$$

$$\frac{p}{q} = \pm 1, \pm 2, \pm 3, \pm 4, \pm 6, \pm 12, \pm \frac{1}{2}, +\frac{3}{2}$$

Step 4:   Using the Bounds on Zeros Theorem:

$$f(x) = 2\left(x^4 + \frac{7}{2}x^3 - \frac{5}{2}x^2 - 14x - 6\right)$$

$$a_3 = \frac{7}{2}, \quad a_2 = -\frac{5}{2}, \quad a_1 = -14, \quad a_0 = -6$$

$$\text{Max}\left\{1, |-6| + |-14| + \left|-\frac{5}{2}\right| + \left|\frac{7}{2}\right|\right\} = \text{Max}\{1, 26\} = 26$$

$$1 + \text{Max}\left\{|-6|, |-14|, \left|-\frac{5}{2}\right|, \left|\frac{7}{2}\right|\right\} = 1 + 14 = 15$$

The smaller of the two numbers is 15. Thus, every zero of f lies between -15 and 15.

Step 5:   Using synthetic division:

$$-3\overline{)\begin{array}{rrrrr} 2 & 7 & -5 & -28 & -12 \\ & -6 & -3 & 24 & 12 \\ \hline 2 & 1 & -8 & -4 & 0 \end{array}}$$

$$-2\overline{)\begin{array}{rrrr} 2 & 1 & -8 & -4 \\ & -4 & 6 & 4 \\ \hline 2 & -3 & -2 & 0 \end{array}}$$

Since the remainder is 0, $x+3$ and $x+2$ are factors. The other factor is the quotient: $2x^2 - 3x - 2$.

Thus, $f(x) = (x+3)(x+2)\left(2x^2 - 3x - 2\right) = (x+3)(x+2)(2x+1)(x-2)$.

The zeros are $-3, -2, -\dfrac{1}{2}$, and 2.

21. $f(x) = x^3 - 3x^2 - 6x + 8$.

Step 1: $f(x)$ has at most 3 real zeros.

Step 2:   By Descartes Rule of Signs, there are 2 or no positive real zeros.

$$f(-x) = (-x)^3 - 3(-x)^2 - 6(-x) + 8 = -x^3 - 3x^2 + 6x + 8;$$

thus, there is 1 negative real zero.

Step 3:   Possible rational zeros:

$$p = \pm 1, \pm 2, \pm 4, \pm 8; \quad q = \pm 1;$$

$$\frac{p}{q} = \pm 1, \pm 2, \pm 4, \pm 8$$

Step 4:   Using synthetic division:

$$\begin{array}{r|rrrr} -1 & 1 & -3 & -6 & 8 \\ & & -1 & 4 & 2 \\ \hline & 1 & -4 & -2 & \{10\} \end{array}$$

$\rightarrow x + 1$ is not a factor

$$\begin{array}{r|rrrr} 1 & 1 & -3 & -6 & 8 \\ & & 1 & -2 & -8 \\ \hline & 1 & -2 & -8 & 0 \end{array}$$

$\rightarrow x - 1$ is a factor

Thus, $f(x) = (x - 1)(x^2 - 2x - 8) = (x - 1)(x - 4)(x + 2)$.

The zeros are 1, 4, and - 2.

22. $f(x) = x^3 - x^2 - 10x - 8$.

Step 1: $f(x)$ has at most 3 real zeros.

Step 2:   By Descartes Rule of Signs, there is 1 positive real zero.

$$f(-x) = (-x)^3 - (-x)^2 - 10(-x) - 8 = -x^3 + x^2 + 10x - 8;$$

thus, there are 2 or no negative real zeros.

Step 3:   Possible rational zeros:

$$p = \pm 1, \pm 2, \pm 4, \pm 8; \quad q = \pm 1;$$

$$\frac{p}{q} = \pm 1, \pm 2, \pm 4, \pm 8$$

Step 4:   Using synthetic division:

$$\begin{array}{r|rrrr} -1 & 1 & -1 & -10 & -8 \\ & & -1 & 2 & 8 \\ \hline & 1 & -2 & -8 & 0 \end{array}$$

$\rightarrow x + 1$ is a factor

Thus, $f(x) = (x + 1)(x^2 - 2x - 8) = (x - 1)(x - 4)(x + 2)$.

The zeros are - 1, 4, and - 2.

23. $f(x) = 4x^3 + 4x^2 - 7x + 2.$
  Step 1: $f(x)$ has at most 3 real zeros.
  Step 2:   By Descartes Rule of Signs, there are 2 or no positive real zeros.
$$f(-x) = 4(-x)^3 + 4(-x)^2 - 7(-x) + 2 = -4x^3 + 4x^2 + 7x + 2;$$
  thus, there is 1 negative real zero.
  Step 3:   Possible rational zeros:
$$p = \pm 1, \pm 2; \quad q = \pm 1, \pm 2, \pm 4;$$
$$\frac{p}{q} = \pm 1, \pm \frac{1}{2}, \pm \frac{1}{4}, \pm 2$$

  Step 4:   Using synthetic division:

$$\begin{array}{r|rrr} -1 & 4 & 4 & -7 & 2 \\ & & -4 & 0 & 7 \\ \hline & 4 & 0 & -7 & \{9\} \end{array}$$ $\rightarrow x + 1$ is not a factor

$$\begin{array}{r|rrr} 1 & 4 & 4 & -7 & 2 \\ & & 4 & 8 & 1 \\ \hline & 4 & 8 & 1 & \{3\} \end{array}$$ $\rightarrow x - 1$ is not a factor

$$\begin{array}{r|rrr} -2 & 4 & 4 & -7 & 2 \\ & & -8 & 8 & -2 \\ \hline & 4 & -4 & 1 & 0 \end{array}$$ $\rightarrow x + 2$ is a factor

Thus, $f(x) = (x + 2)(4x^2 - 4x + 1) = (x + 2)(4x - 2)\left(x - \frac{1}{2}\right) = 4(x + 2)\left(x - \frac{1}{2}\right)^2.$

The zeros are -2, and $\frac{1}{2}$ (with multiplicity 2).

24. $f(x) = 4x^3 - 4x^2 - 7x - 2.$
  Step 1: $f(x)$ has at most 3 real zeros.
  Step 2:   By Descartes Rule of Signs, there is 1 positive real zero.
$$f(-x) = 4(-x)^3 - 4(-x)^2 - 7(-x) - 2 = -4x^3 - 4x^2 + 7x - 2;$$
  thus, there are 2 or no negative real zeros.
  Step 3:   Possible rational zeros:
$$p = \pm 1, \pm 2; \quad q = \pm 1, \pm 2, \pm 4;$$
$$\frac{p}{q} = \pm 1, \pm \frac{1}{2}, \pm \frac{1}{4}, \pm 2$$

Step 4:   Using synthetic division:

$$1)\overline{)4\quad -4\quad -7\quad -2}$$
$$ 4\quad 0\quad -7$$
$$\overline{ 4\quad 0\quad -7\quad \{-9\}}$$

$\rightarrow x-1$ is not a factor

$$-1)\overline{)4\quad -4\quad -7\quad -2}$$
$$ -4\quad 8\quad -1$$
$$\overline{ 4\quad -8\quad 1\quad \{-3\}}$$

$\rightarrow x+1$ is not a factor

$$2)\overline{)4\quad -4\quad -7\quad -2}$$
$$ 8\quad 8\quad 2$$
$$\overline{ 4\quad 4\quad 1\quad 0}$$

$\rightarrow x-2$ is a factor

Thus, $f(x) = (x-2)(4x^2 + 4x + 1) = (x-2)(2x+1)(2x+1) = (x-2)(2x+1)^2$.

The zeros are 2, and $-\dfrac{1}{2}$ (with multiplicity 2).

25. $f(x) = x^4 - 4x^3 + 9x^2 - 20x + 20$.

Step 1: $f(x)$ has at most 4 real zeros.

Step 2:   By Descartes Rule of Signs, there are 4, 2 or no positive real zeros.
$$f(-x) = (-x)^4 - 4(-x)^3 + 9(-x)^2 - 20(-x) + 20 = x^4 + 4x^3 + 9x^2 + 20x + 20;$$
thus, there are no negative real zeros.

Step 3:   Possible rational zeros:
$$p = \pm 1, \pm 2, \pm 4, \pm 5, \pm 10, \pm 20;\quad q = \pm 1;$$

$$\frac{p}{q} = \pm 1, \pm 2, \pm 4, \pm 5, \pm 10, \pm 20$$

Step 4:   Using synthetic division:

$$1)\overline{)1\quad -4\quad 9\quad -20\quad 20}$$
$$ 1\quad -3\quad 6\quad -14$$
$$\overline{ 1\quad -3\quad 6\quad -14\quad \{6\}}$$

$\rightarrow x-1$ is not a factor

$$2)\overline{)1\quad -4\quad 9\quad -20\quad 20}$$
$$ 2\quad -4\quad 10\quad -20$$
$$\overline{ 2\quad -2\quad 5\quad -10\quad 0}$$

$\rightarrow x-2$ is a factor

Thus, $f(x) = (x-2)(x^3 - 2x^2 + 5x - 10)$. We can factor $x^3 - 2x^2 + 5x - 10$ by grouping

$$x^3 - 2x^2 + 5x - 10 = x^2(x-2) + 5(x-2) = (x-2)(x^2 + 5)$$

$$= (x-2)(x + \sqrt{5}i)(x - \sqrt{5}i) \rightarrow f(x) = (x-2)^2(x + \sqrt{5}i)(x - \sqrt{5}i)$$

The zeros are 2 (multiplicity 2), $\sqrt{5}i$, and $-\sqrt{5}i$.

26. $f(x) = x^4 + 6x^3 + 11x^2 + 12x + 18$.

Step 1: $f(x)$ has at most 4 real zeros.

Step 2:   By Descartes Rule of Signs, there are no positive real zeros.
$$f(-x) = (-x)^4 + 6(-x)^3 + 11(-x)^2 + 12(-x) + 18$$
$$= x^4 - 6x^3 + 11x^2 - 12x + 18;$$
thus, there are 4,2 or no negative real zeros.

Step 3:   Possible rational zeros:
$$p = \pm 1, \pm 2, \pm 3, \pm 6, \pm 9, \pm 18; \quad q = \pm 1;$$

$$\frac{p}{q} = \pm 1, \pm 2, \pm 3, \pm 6, \pm 9, \pm 18$$

Step 4:   Using synthetic division:

$$1 \overline{)\, 1 \quad 6 \quad 11 \quad 12 \quad 18 \,}$$
$$ 1 \quad 7 \quad 18 \quad 30$$
$$\overline{ 1 \quad 7 \quad 18 \quad 30 \quad \{48\}}$$

$\rightarrow x - 1$ is not a factor

$$-1 \overline{)\, 1 \quad 6 \quad 11 \quad 12 \quad 18 \,}$$
$$ -1 \quad -5 \quad -6 \quad -6$$
$$\overline{ 1 \quad 5 \quad 6 \quad 6 \quad \{12\}}$$

$\rightarrow x + 1$ is not a factor

$$2 \overline{)\, 1 \quad 6 \quad 11 \quad 12 \quad 18 \,}$$
$$ 2 \quad 16 \quad 54 \quad 132$$
$$\overline{ 1 \quad 8 \quad 27 \quad 66 \quad \{150\}}$$

$\rightarrow x - 2$ is not a factor

$$-2 \overline{)\, 1 \quad 6 \quad 11 \quad 12 \quad 18 \,}$$
$$ -2 \quad -8 \quad -6 \quad -12$$
$$\overline{ 1 \quad 4 \quad 3 \quad 6 \quad \{6\}}$$

$\rightarrow x + 2$ is not a factor

$$3 \overline{)\, 1 \quad 6 \quad 11 \quad 12 \quad 18 \,}$$
$$ 3 \quad 27 \quad 114 \quad 378$$
$$\overline{ 1 \quad 9 \quad 38 \quad 126 \quad \{396\}}$$

$\rightarrow x + 2$ is not a factor

$$-3 \overline{)\, 1 \quad 6 \quad 11 \quad 12 \quad 18 \,}$$
$$ -3 \quad -9 \quad -6 \quad -18$$
$$\overline{ 1 \quad 3 \quad 2 \quad 6 \quad 0}$$

$\rightarrow x + 3$ is a factor

Thus, $f(x) = (x + 3)(x^3 + 3x^2 + 2x + 6)$. We can factor $x^3 + 3x^2 + 2x + 6$ by grouping

$$x^3 + 3x^2 + 2x + 6 = x^2(x + 3) + 2(x + 3) = (x + 3)(x^2 + 2)$$

$$= (x + 3)(x + \sqrt{2}i)(x - \sqrt{2}i) \rightarrow f(x) = (x + 3)^2(x + \sqrt{2}i)(x - \sqrt{2}i)$$

The zeros are -3 (multiplicity 2), $\sqrt{2}i$, and $-\sqrt{2}i$.

27. $f(x) = 2x^4 + 2x^3 - 11x^2 + x - 6$.

Step 1: $f(x)$ has at most 4 real zeros.

Step 2:   By Descartes Rule of Signs, there are 3 or 1 positive real zeros.

$$f(-x) = 2(-x)^4 + 2(-x)^3 - 11(-x)^2 + (-x) - 6 = 2x^4 - 2x^3 - 11x^2 - x - 6;$$

thus, there is 1 negative real zero.

Step 3:   Possible rational zeros:

$$p = \pm 1, \pm 2, \pm 3, \pm 6; \quad q = \pm 1, \pm 2;$$

$$\frac{p}{q} = \pm 1, \pm \frac{1}{2}, \pm 2, \pm 3, \pm \frac{3}{2} \pm 6$$

Step 4:   Using synthetic division:

```
-1)2   2  -11    1   -6
      -2    0   11  -12          → x + 1 is not a factor
    ─────────────────────
     2    0  -11   12  {-18}
```

```
 1)2   2  -11    1   -6
       2    4   -7   -6          → x - 1 is not a factor
    ─────────────────────
     2    4   -7   -6  {-12}
```

```
-2)2   2  -11    1   -6
      -4    4   14  -30          → x + 2 is not a factor
    ─────────────────────
     2   -2   -7   15  {-36}
```

```
 2)2   2  -11    1   -6
       4   12    2    6          → x - 2 is a factor
    ─────────────────────
     2    6    1    3    0
```

Thus, $f(x) = (x - 2)(2x^3 + 6x^2 + x + 3)$.

We can factor $2x^3 + 6x^2 + x + 3$ by grouping

$$2x^3 + 6x^2 + x + 3 = 2x^2(x + 3) + (x + 3) = (x + 3)(2x^2 + 1)$$

$$= (x + 3)(\sqrt{2}x + i)(\sqrt{2}x - i) \rightarrow f(x) = (x - 2)(x + 3)(\sqrt{2}x + i)(\sqrt{2}x - i)$$

The zeros are 2, -3, $-\dfrac{\sqrt{2}}{2}i$, and $\dfrac{\sqrt{2}}{2}i$.

28. $f(x) = 3x^4 + 3x^3 - 17x^2 + x - 6$.

Step 1: $f(x)$ has at most 4 real zeros.

Step 2:   By Descartes Rule of Signs, there are 3 or 1 positive real zeros.

$$f(-x) = 3(-x)^4 + 3(-x)^3 - 17(-x)^2 + (-x) - 6 = 3x^4 - 3x^3 - 17x^2 - x - 6;$$

thus, there is 1 negative real zero.

Step 3: Possible rational zeros:
$$p = \pm 1, \pm 2, \pm 3, \pm 6; \quad q = \pm 1, \pm 3;$$

$$\frac{p}{q} = \pm 1, \pm \frac{1}{3}, \pm 2, \pm \frac{2}{3}, \pm 3, \pm 6$$

Step 4: Using synthetic division:

$$
\begin{array}{r|rrrr}
1) & 3 & 3 & -17 & 1 & -6 \\
   &   & 3 & 6 & -11 & -10 \\
\hline
   & 3 & 6 & -11 & -10 & \{-16\}
\end{array}
$$ $\rightarrow x - 1$ is not a factor

$$
\begin{array}{r|rrrr}
-1) & 3 & 3 & -17 & 1 & -6 \\
    &   & -3 & 0 & 17 & -18 \\
\hline
    & 3 & 0 & -17 & 18 & \{-24\}
\end{array}
$$ $\rightarrow x + 1$ is not a factor

$$
\begin{array}{r|rrrr}
2) & 3 & 3 & -17 & 1 & -6 \\
   &   & 6 & 18 & 2 & 6 \\
\hline
   & 3 & 9 & 1 & 3 & 0
\end{array}
$$ $\rightarrow x - 2$ is a factor

Thus, $f(x) = (x-2)(3x^3 + 9x^2 + x + 3)$.

We can factor $3x^3 + 9x^2 + x + 3$ by grouping
$$3x^3 + 9x^2 + x + 3 = 3x^2(x+3) + (x+3) = (x+3)(3x^2+1)$$

$$= (x+3)(\sqrt{3}x + i)(\sqrt{3}x - i) \rightarrow f(x) = (x-2)(x+3)(\sqrt{3}x + i)(\sqrt{3}x - i)$$

The zeros are 2, -3, $-\dfrac{\sqrt{3}}{3}i$, and $\dfrac{\sqrt{3}}{3}i$.

29. $f(x) = 2x^4 + 7x^3 + x^2 - 7x - 3$.
Step 1: $f(x)$ has at most 4 real zeros.
Step 2: By Descartes Rule of Signs, there is 1 positive real zero.
$$f(-x) = 2(-x)^4 + 7(-x)^3 + (-x)^2 - 7(-x) - 3 = 2x^4 - 7x^3 + x^2 + 7x - 3;$$
thus, there are 3 or 1 negative real zeros.
Step 3: Possible rational zeros:
$$p = \pm 1, \pm 3; \quad q = \pm 1, \pm 2;$$

$$\frac{p}{q} = \pm 1, \pm \frac{1}{2}, \pm 3, \pm \frac{3}{2}$$

Step 4: Using synthetic division:

$$
\begin{array}{r|rrrr}
1) & 2 & 7 & 1 & -7 & -3 \\
   &   & 2 & 9 & 10 & 3 \\
\hline
   & 2 & 9 & 10 & 3 & 0
\end{array}
$$ $\rightarrow x - 1$ is a factor

Thus, $f(x) = (x-1)(2x^3 + 9x^2 + 10x + 3)$.

Note: $g(x) = 2x^3 + 9x^2 + 10x + 3$ has the same possible rational roots as f. However, since we have already found the only positive real zero for f, so we only need to look at the possible negative zeros, $\dfrac{p}{q} = -1, -\dfrac{1}{2}, -3, -\dfrac{3}{2}$.

$$
\begin{array}{r|rrrr}
-1 & 2 & 9 & 10 & 3 \\
   &   & -2 & -7 & -3 \\
\hline
   & 2 & 7 & 3 & 0
\end{array}
$$

$\rightarrow x + 1$ is a factor

$2x^3 + 9x^2 + 10x + 3 = (x+1)(2x^2 + 7x + 3)$

$= (x+1)(2x+1)(x+3) \rightarrow f(x) = (x-1)(x+1)(2x+1)(x+3)$

The zeros are 1, -1, $-\dfrac{1}{2}$, and -3.

30. $f(x) = 2x^4 + 7x^3 - 5x^2 - 28x - 12$.

Step 1: $f(x)$ has at most 4 real zeros.

Step 2:   By Descartes Rule of Signs, there is 1 positive real zero.

$f(-x) = 2(-x)^4 + 7(-x)^3 - 5(-x)^2 - 28(-x) - 12 = 2x^4 - 7x^3 - 5x^2 + 28x - 12$;

thus, there are 3 or 1 negative real zeros.

Step 3:   Possible rational zeros:

$p = \pm 1, \pm 2, \pm 3, \pm 4, \pm 6, \pm 12; \quad q = \pm 1, \pm 2;$

$\dfrac{p}{q} = \pm 1, \pm \dfrac{1}{2}, \pm 3, \pm 4, \pm \dfrac{3}{2}, \pm 6, \pm 12$

Step 4:   Using synthetic division:

$$
\begin{array}{r|rrrrr}
1 & 2 & 7 & -5 & -28 & -12 \\
  &   & 2 & 9 & 4 & -24 \\
\hline
  & 2 & 9 & 4 & -24 & \{-36\}
\end{array}
$$

$\rightarrow x - 1$ is not a factor

$$
\begin{array}{r|rrrrr}
-1 & 2 & 7 & -5 & -28 & -12 \\
   &   & -2 & -5 & 10 & 18 \\
\hline
   & 2 & 5 & -10 & -18 & \{6\}
\end{array}
$$

$\rightarrow x + 1$ is not a factor

$$
\begin{array}{r|rrrrr}
2 & 2 & 7 & -5 & -28 & -12 \\
  &   & 4 & 22 & 34 & 12 \\
\hline
  & 2 & 11 & 17 & 6 & 0
\end{array}
$$

$\rightarrow x - 2$ is a factor

Thus, $f(x) = (x-2)(2x^3 + 11x^2 + 17x + 6)$.

Note: $g(x) = 2x^3 + 11x^2 + 17x + 6$ has the same possible rational roots as f. However, since we have already found the only positive real zero for f, so

we only need to look at the possible negative zeros, $\dfrac{p}{q} = -1, -\dfrac{1}{2}, -3, -4, -\dfrac{3}{2}, -6, -12$.

$$-2\overline{)2 \quad 11 \quad 17 \quad 6} \quad \to x+2 \text{ is a factor}$$
$$\underline{\quad -4 \quad -14 \quad 6}$$
$$2 \quad 7 \quad 3 \quad 0$$

$$2x^3 + 11x^2 + 17x + 6 = (x+2)(2x^2 + 7x + 3)$$
$$= (x+2)(2x+1)(x+3) \to f(x) = (x-2)(x+2)(2x+1)(x+3)$$

The zeros are 2, -2, $-\dfrac{1}{2}$, and -3.

31. $f(x) = x^3 - x^2 - 4x + 2$
$a_2 = -1, \quad a_1 = -4, \quad a_0 = 2$
$\text{Max}\left\{1, |2| + |-4| + |-1|\right\} = \text{Max}\left\{1, 7\right\} = 7$
$1 + \text{Max}\left\{|2|, |-4|, |-1|\right\} = 1 + 4 = 5$
The smaller of the two numbers is 5, $\therefore$ every zero of f lies between -5 and 5.

32. $f(x) = x^3 + x^2 - 10x - 5$
$a_2 = 1, \quad a_1 = -10, \quad a_0 = -5$
$\text{Max}\left\{1, |-5| + |-10| + |1|\right\} = \text{Max}\left\{1, 16\right\} = 16$
$1 + \text{Max}\left\{|-5|, |-10|, |1|\right\} = 1 + 10 = 11$
The smaller of the two numbers is 11, $\therefore$ every zero of f lies between -11 and 11.

33. $f(x) = 2x^3 - 7x^2 - 10x + 35 = 2\left(x^3 - \dfrac{7}{2}x^2 - 5x + \dfrac{35}{2}\right)$

$a_2 = -\dfrac{7}{2}, \quad a_1 = -5, \quad a_0 = \dfrac{35}{2}$

$\text{Max}\left\{1, \left|\dfrac{35}{2}\right| + |-5| + \left|-\dfrac{7}{2}\right|\right\} = \text{Max}\left\{1, 26\right\} = 26$

$1 + \text{Max}\left\{\left|\dfrac{35}{2}\right|, |-5|, \left|-\dfrac{7}{2}\right|\right\} = 1 + \dfrac{35}{2} = \dfrac{37}{2} = 18.5$

The smaller of the two numbers is 18.5, $\therefore$ every zero of f lies between -18.5 and 18.5.

34. $f(x) = 3x^3 - 7x^2 - 6x + 14 = 3\left(x^3 - \dfrac{7}{3}x^2 - 2x + \dfrac{14}{3}\right)$

$a_2 = -\dfrac{7}{3}, \quad a_1 = -2, \quad a_0 = \dfrac{14}{3}$

$\text{Max}\left\{1, \left|\dfrac{14}{3}\right| + |-2| + \left|-\dfrac{7}{3}\right|\right\} = \text{Max}\left\{1, 9\right\} = 9$

$1 + \text{Max}\left\{\left|\dfrac{14}{3}\right|, |-2|, \left|-\dfrac{7}{3}\right|\right\} = 1 + \dfrac{14}{3} = \dfrac{17}{3} = 5.\overline{66}$

The smaller of the two numbers is $5.\overline{66}$, $\therefore$ every zero of f lies between $-5.\overline{66}$ and $5.\overline{66}$.

35. $f(x) = 3x^3 - x - 1;\ [0, 1]$
$f(0) = -1 < 0$ and $f(1) = 1 > 0$
Since one is positive and one is
negative, there is a zero in the
interval.

36. $f(x) = 2x^3 - x^2 - 3;\ [1, 2]$
$f(1) = -2 < 0$ and $f(2) = 9 > 0$
Since one is positive and one is
negative, there is a zero in the
interval.

37. $f(x) = 8x^4 - 4x^3 - 2x - 1;\ [0, 1]$
$f(0) = -1 < 0$ and $f(1) = 1 > 0$
Since one is positive and one is
negative, there is a zero in the
interval.

38. $f(x) = 3x^4 + 4x^3 - 8x - 2;\ [1, 2]$
$f(1) = -3 < 0$ and $f(2) = 62 > 0$
Since one is positive and one is
negative, there is a zero in the
interval.

39. $f(x) = x^3 - x - 2$
$f(1) = -2;\ f(2) = 4$,   so by the Intermediate Value Theorem, f has a zero on the
interval [1,2].
Subdivide the interval [1,2] into 10 equal subintervals:

[1,1.1]; [1.1,1.2]; [1.2,1.3]; [1.3,1.4]; [1.4,1.5]; [1.5,1.6]; [1.6,1.7]; [1.7,1.8];
[1.8,1.9]; [1.9,2]

$f(1) = -2; f(1.1) = -1.769$
$f(1.1) = -1.769; f(1.2) = -1.472$
$f(1.2) = -1.472; f(1.3) = -1.103$
$f(1.3) = -1.103; f(1.4) = -0.656$
$f(1.4) = -0.656; f(1.5) = -0.125$
$f(1.5) = -0.125; f(1.6) = 0.496$ so f has a real zero on the interval [1.5,1.6].
Subdivide the interval [1.5,1.6] into 10 equal subintervals:

[1.5,1.51]; [1.51,1.52]; [1.52,1.53]; [1.53,1.54]; [1.54,1.55]; [1.55,1.56];[1.56,1.57];
[1.57,1.58]; [1.58,1.59]; [1.59,1.6]

$f(1.5) = -0.125; f(1.51) = -0.0670$
$f(1.51) = -0.0670; f(1.52) = -0.0082$
$f(1.52) = -0.0082; f(1.53) = 0.0516$ so f has a real zero on the interval
[1.52,1.53], therefore $r = 1.52$,
correct to 2 decimal places.

40. $f(x) = 2x^3 - x^2 - 3$
$f(1) = -2;\ f(2) = 9$,   so by the Intermediate Value Theorem, f has a zero on the
interval [1,2].

Subdivide the interval [1,2] into 10 equal subintervals:

[1,1.1]; [1.1,1.2]; [1.2,1.3]; [1.3,1.4]; [1.4,1.5]; [1.5,1.6]; [1.6,1.7]; [1.7,1.8];
[1.8,1.9]; [1.9,2]

$f(1) = -2; f(1.1) = -1.548$

$f(1.1) = -1.548; f(1.2) = -0.984$

$f(1.2) = -0.984; f(1.3) = -0.296$

$f(1.3) = -0.296; f(1.4) = 0.528$ so f has a real zero on the interval $[1.3,1.4]$.

Subdivide the interval $[1.3,1.4]$ into 10 equal subintervals:

$[1.3,1.31]; [1.31,1.32]; [1.32,1.33]; [1.33,1.34]; [1.34,1.35]; [1.35,1.36];[1.36,1.37];$
$[1.37,1.38]; [1.38,1.39]; [1.39,1.4]$

$f(1.3) = -0.296; f(1.31) = -0.2200$

$f(1.31) = -0.2200; f(1.32) = -0.1425$

$f(1.32) = -0.1425; f(1.33) = -0.0636$

$f(1.33) = -0.0636; f(1.34) = 0.0166$ so f has a real zero on the interval
$[1.33,01.34]$, therefore $r = 1.33$,
correct to 2 decimal places.

41. $f(x) = 8x^4 - 4x^3 - 2x - 1$

$f(0) = -1; \quad f(1) = 1$,   so by the Intermediate Value Theorem, f has a zero on the
interval $[0,1]$.

Subdivide the interval $[0,1]$ into 10 equal subintervals:

$[0,0.1]; [0.1,0.2]; [0.2,0.3]; [0.3,0.4]; [0.4,0.5]; [0.5,0.6]; [0.6,0.7]; [0.7,0.8];$
$[0.8,0.9]; [0.9,1]$

$f(0) = -1; f(0.1) = -1.2032$

$f(0.1) = -1.2032; f(0.2) = -1.4192$

$f(0.2) = -1.4192; f(0.3) = -1.6432$

$f(0.3) = -1.6432; f(0.4) = -1.8512$

$f(0.4) = -1.8512; f(0.5) = -2$

$f(0.5) = -2; f(0.6) = -2.0272$

$f(0.6) = -2.0272; f(0.7) = -1.8512$

$f(0.7) = -1.8512; f(0.8) = -1.3712$

$f(0.8) = -1.3712; f(0.9) = -0.4672$

$f(0.9) = -0.4672; f(1) = 1$ so f has a real zero on the interval $[0.9,1]$.

Subdivide the interval $[0.9,1]$ into 10 equal subintervals:

$[0.9,0.91]; [0.91,0.92]; [0.92,0.93]; [0.93,0.94]; [0.94,0.95]; [0.95,0.96];[0.96,0.97];$
$[0.97,0.98]; [0.98,0.99]; [0.99,1]$

$f(0.9) = -0.4672; f(0.91) = -0.3483$ so f has a real zero on the

$f(0.91) = -0.3483; f(0.92) = -0.2236$ interval $[0.93,0.94]$, therefore

$f(0.92) = -0.2236; f(0.93) = -0.0930$ $r = 0.93$, correct to 2 decimal

$f(0.93) = -0.0930; f(0.94) = 0.0437$ places.

42.　$f(x) = 3x^4 + 4x^3 - 8x - 2$

　　$f(1) = -3;\ f(2) = 62,$　so by the Intermediate Value Theorem, f has a zero on the interval [1,2].

Subdivide the interval [1,2] into 10 equal subintervals:

[1,1.1]; [1.1,1.2]; [1.2,1.3]; [1.3,1.4]; [1.4,1.5]; [1.5,1.6]; [1.6,1.7]; [1.7,1.8]; [1.8,1.9]; [1.9,2]

$f(1) = -3; f(1.1) = -1.0837$

$f(1.1) = -1.0837; f(1.2) = 1.5328$　　　so f has a real zero on the interval [1.1,1.2].

Subdivide the interval [1.1,1.2] into 10 equal subintervals:

[1.1,1.11]; [1.11,1.12]; [1.12,1.13]; [1.13,1.14]; [1.14,1.15]; [1.15,1.16]; [1.16,1.17]; [1.17,1.18]; [1.18,1.19]; [1.19,1.2]

$f(1.1) = -1.0837; f(1.11) = -0.8553$

$f(1.11) = -0.8553; f(1.12) = -0.6197$

$f(1.12) = -0.6197; f(1.13) = -0.3770$

$f(1.13) = -0.3770; f(1.14) = -0.1269$

$f(1.14) = -0.1269; f(1.15) = 0.1305$　　　so f has a real zero on the interval [1.14,1.15], therefore $r = 1.14$, correct to 2 decimal places.

43.　$(6 + 3i) - (2 - 4i) = (6 - 2) + (3 - (-4))i = 4 + 7i$

44.　$(8 - 3i) + (-6 + 2i) = (8 - 6) + (-3 + 2)i = 2 - i$

45.　$4(3 - i) + 3(-5 + 2i) = 12 - 4i - 15 + 6i = -3 + 2i$

46.　$2(1 + i) - 3(2 - 3i) = 2 + 2i - 6 + 9i = -4 + 11i$

47.　$\dfrac{3}{3+i} = \dfrac{3}{3+i} \cdot \dfrac{3-i}{3-i} = \dfrac{9-3i}{9-3i+3i-i^2} = \dfrac{9-3i}{10} = \dfrac{9}{10} - \dfrac{3}{10}i$

48.　$\dfrac{4}{2-i} = \dfrac{4}{2-i} \cdot \dfrac{2+i}{2+i} = \dfrac{8+4i}{4+2i-2i-i^2} = \dfrac{8+4i}{5} = \dfrac{8}{5} + \dfrac{4}{5}i$

49.　$i^{50} = i^{48} \cdot i^2 = (i^4)^{12} \cdot i^2 = 1^{12}(-1) = -1$

50.　$i^{29} = i^{28} \cdot i = (i^4)^7 \cdot i = 1^7 \cdot i = i$

51.　$(2 + 3i)^3 = (2 + 3i)^2(2 + 3i) = (4 + 12i + 9i^2)(2 + 3i) = (-5 + 12i)(2 + 3i)$

　　　　　　$= -10 - 15i + 24i + 36i^2 = -46 + 9i$

52. $(3-2i)^3 = (3-2i)^2(3-2i) = (9-12i+4i^2)(3-2i) = (5-12i)(3-2i)$
$= 15-10i-36i+24i^2 = -9-46i$

53.   Since complex zeros appear in conjugate pairs, $4-i$, the conjugate of $4+i$, is the remaining zero of f.

54.   Since complex zeros appear in conjugate pairs, $3-4i$, the conjugate of $3+4i$, is the remaining zero of f.

55.   Since complex zeros appear in conjugate pairs, $-i$, the conjugate of i, and $1-i$, the conjugate of $1+i$, are the remaining zeros of f.

56.   Since complex zeros appear in conjugate pairs, $1-i$, the conjugate of $1+i$, is the remaining zero of f.

57. $x^2+x+1=0$
$a=1, b=1, c=1, \quad b^2-4ac = 1^2-4(1)(1) = 1-4 = -3$
$x = \dfrac{-1\pm\sqrt{-3}}{2(1)} = \dfrac{-1\pm\sqrt{3}\,i}{2} = -\dfrac{1}{2}\pm\dfrac{\sqrt{3}}{2}i \rightarrow$ The solution set is $\left\{-\dfrac{1}{2}-\dfrac{\sqrt{3}}{2}i,\ -\dfrac{1}{2}+\dfrac{\sqrt{3}}{2}i\right\}$.

58. $x^2-x+1=0$
$a=1, b=-1, c=1, \quad b^2-4ac = (-1)^2-4(1)(1) = 1-4 = -3$
$x = \dfrac{-(-1)\pm\sqrt{-3}}{2(1)} = \dfrac{1\pm\sqrt{3}\,i}{2} = \dfrac{1}{2}\pm\dfrac{\sqrt{3}}{2}i \rightarrow$ The solution set is $\left\{\dfrac{1}{2}-\dfrac{\sqrt{3}}{2}i,\ \dfrac{1}{2}+\dfrac{\sqrt{3}}{2}i\right\}$.

59. $2x^2+x-2=0$
$a=2, b=1, c=-2, \quad b^2-4ac = 1^2-4(2)(-2) = 1+16 = 17$
$x = \dfrac{-1\pm\sqrt{17}}{2(2)} = \dfrac{-1\pm\sqrt{17}}{4} \rightarrow$ The solution set is $\left\{\dfrac{-1-\sqrt{17}}{4},\ \dfrac{-1+\sqrt{17}}{4}\right\}$.

60. $3x^2-2x-1=0$
$(3x+1)(x-1)=0 \rightarrow x=-\dfrac{1}{3}$ or $x=1 \rightarrow$ The solution set is $\left\{-\dfrac{1}{3},\ 1\right\}$.

61. $x^2+3=x$
$x^2-x+3=0$
$a=1, b=-1, c=3, \quad b^2-4ac = (-1)^2-4(1)(3) = 1-12 = -11$
$x = \dfrac{-(-1)\pm\sqrt{-11}}{2(1)} = \dfrac{1\pm\sqrt{11}\,i}{2} = \dfrac{1}{2}\pm\dfrac{\sqrt{11}}{2}i \rightarrow$ The solution set is $\left\{\dfrac{1}{2}-\dfrac{\sqrt{11}}{2}i,\ \dfrac{1}{2}+\dfrac{\sqrt{11}}{2}i\right\}$.

62. $2x^2 + 1 = 2x$

$2x^2 - 2x + 1 = 0$

$a = 2, b = -2, c = 1, \quad b^2 - 4ac = (-2)^2 - 4(2)(1) = 4 - 8 = -4$

$x = \dfrac{-(-2) \pm \sqrt{-4}}{2(2)} = \dfrac{2 \pm 2i}{4} = \dfrac{1}{2} \pm \dfrac{1}{2}i \rightarrow$ The solution set is $\left\{ \dfrac{1}{2} - \dfrac{1}{2}i, \ \dfrac{1}{2} + \dfrac{1}{2}i \right\}$.

63. $x(1 - x) = 6$

$-x^2 + x - 6 = 0$

$a = -1, b = 1, c = -6, \quad b^2 - 4ac = 1^2 - 4(-1)(-6) = 1 - 24 = -23$

$x = \dfrac{-1 \pm \sqrt{-23}}{2(-1)} = \dfrac{-1 \pm \sqrt{23}\,i}{-2} = \dfrac{1}{2} \pm \dfrac{\sqrt{23}}{2}i \rightarrow$ The solution set is $\left\{ \dfrac{1}{2} - \dfrac{\sqrt{23}}{2}i, \ \dfrac{1}{2} + \dfrac{\sqrt{23}}{2}i \right\}$.

64. $x(1 + x) = 2$

$x^2 + x - 2 = 0$

$(x + 2)(x - 1) = 0 \rightarrow x = -2$ or $x = 1 \rightarrow$ The solution set is $\{-2, 1\}$.

65. $x^4 + 2x^2 - 8 = 0$

$\left(x^2 + 4 \right)\left(x^2 - 2 \right) = 0 \rightarrow x^2 + 4 = 0$ or $x^2 - 2 = 0$

$x^2 = -4 \rightarrow x = \pm 2i$

$x^2 = 2 \rightarrow x = \pm \sqrt{2}$

The solution set is $\left\{ -2i, \ 2i, \ -\sqrt{2}, \ \sqrt{2} \right\}$.

66. $x^4 + 8x^2 - 9 = 0$

$\left(x^2 + 9 \right)\left(x^2 - 1 \right) = 0 \rightarrow \left(x^2 + 9 \right)(x - 1)(x + 1) = 0$

$x^2 + 9 = 0 \rightarrow x = \pm 3i$

$x - 1 = 0 \rightarrow x = 1$

$x + 1 = 0 \rightarrow x = -1$

The solution set is $\left\{ -3i, \ 3i, \ -1, \ 1 \right\}$.

67. $x^3 - x^2 - 8x + 12 = 0$

The solutions of the equation are the zeros of the function $f(x) = x^3 - x^2 - 8x + 12$.

Step 1: $f(x)$ has 3 complex zeros.

Step 2:   By Descartes Rule of Signs, there are 2 or 0 positive real zeros.

$f(-x) = (-x)^3 - (-x)^2 - 8(-x) + 12 = -x^3 - x^2 + 8x + 12$; thus, there is 1 negative real zero.

Step 3:   Possible rational zeros:

$p = \pm 1, \pm 2, \pm 3, \pm 4, \pm 6, \pm 12; \quad q = \pm 1; \quad \dfrac{p}{q} = \pm 1, \pm 2, \pm 3, \pm 4, \pm 6, \pm 12$

Step 4:   Using synthetic division:

$$2\overline{)\begin{array}{cccc} 1 & -1 & -8 & 12 \\ & 2 & 2 & -12 \end{array}}$$
$$\begin{array}{cccc} 1 & 1 & -6 & 0 \end{array}$$

Since the remainder is 0, $x - 2$ is a factor. The other factor is the quotient:
$x^2 + x - 6 = (x + 3)(x - 2)$.
The complex zeros are $-3, 2$ (multiplicity 2).

68. $x^3 - 3x^2 - 4x + 12 = 0$

$x^2(x - 3) - 4(x - 3) = 0 \rightarrow (x - 3)(x^2 - 4) = 0$

$(x - 3)(x - 2)(x + 2) = 0 \rightarrow x = 3$ or $x = 2$ or $x = -2$
The solution set is $\{-2, 2, 3\}$

69. $3x^4 - 4x^3 + 4x^2 - 4x + 1 = 0$
The solutions of the equation are the zeros of the function $f(x) = 3x^4 - 4x^3 + 4x^2 - 4x + 1$
Step 1: $f(x)$ has 4 complex zeros.
Step 2:   By Descartes Rule of Signs, there are 4 or 2 or 0 positive real zeros.
$f(-x) = 3(-x)^4 - 4(-x)^3 + 4(-x)^2 - 4(-x) + 1 = 3x^4 + 4x^3 + 4x^2 + 4x + 1;$
thus, there are no negative real zeros.
Step 3:   Possible rational zeros:

$$p = \pm 1; \quad q = \pm 1, \pm 3; \quad \frac{p}{q} = \pm 1, \pm\frac{1}{3}$$

Step 4:   Using synthetic division:

$$1\overline{)\begin{array}{ccccc} 3 & -4 & 4 & -4 & 1 \\ & 3 & -1 & 3 & -1 \end{array}} \qquad \frac{1}{3}\overline{)\begin{array}{cccc} 3 & -1 & 3 & -1 \\ & & 1 & 0 & 1 \end{array}}$$
$$\begin{array}{ccccc} 3 & -1 & 3 & -1 & 0 \end{array} \qquad \begin{array}{cccc} 3 & 0 & 3 & 0 \end{array}$$

Since the remainder is 0, $x - 1$ and $x - \dfrac{1}{3}$ are factors. The other factor is the
quotient: $3x^2 + 3 = 3(x^2 + 1)$.
Solving $x^2 + 1 = 0 \rightarrow x^2 = -1 \rightarrow x = \pm i$

The complex zeros are $1, \dfrac{1}{3}, -i, i$.

70. $x^4 + 4x^3 + 2x^2 - 8x - 8 = 0$
The solutions of the equation are the zeros of the function $f(x) = x^4 + 4x^3 + 2x^2 - 8x - 8$
Step 1: $f(x)$ has 4 complex zeros.
Step 2:   By Descartes Rule of Signs, there is 1 positive real zero.
$f(-x) = (-x)^4 + 4(-x)^3 + 2(-x)^2 - 8(-x) - 8 = x^4 - 4x^3 + 2x^2 + 8x - 8;$
thus, there are 3 or 1 negative real zeros.
Step 3:   Possible rational zeros:

$$p = \pm 1, \pm 2, \pm 4, \pm 8; \quad q = \pm 1; \quad \frac{p}{q} = \pm 1, \pm 2, \pm 4, \pm 8$$

Step 4:   Using synthetic division:

$$-2)\overline{\begin{matrix} 1 & 4 & 2 & -8 & -8 \\ & -2 & -4 & 4 & 8 \\ \hline 1 & 2 & -2 & -4 & 0 \end{matrix}} \qquad -2)\overline{\begin{matrix} 1 & 2 & -2 & -4 \\ & -2 & 0 & 4 \\ \hline 1 & 0 & -2 & 0 \end{matrix}}$$

Since the remainder is 0, $x + 2$ is a factor twice. The other factor is the quotient: $x^2 - 2$.

Solving $x^2 - 2 = 0 \rightarrow x^2 = 2 \rightarrow x = \pm\sqrt{2}$:

The solutions are -2 (multiplicity 2), $-\sqrt{2}, \sqrt{2}$.

Chapter 6

Exponential and Logarithmic Functions

6.1 One-to-One Functions; Inverse Functions

1. (a)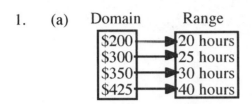

   (b) Inverse is a function.

2. (a)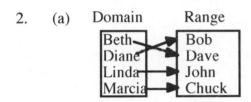

   (b) Inverse is a function.

3. (a)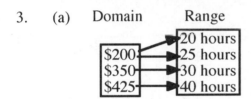

   (b) Inverse is not a function since $200 corresponds to two elements in the range.

4. (a)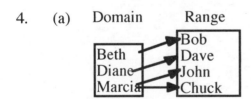

   (b) Inverse is not a function since Marcia corresponds to two elements in the range.

5. (a) $\{(6,2), (6,-3), (9,4), (10,1)\}$

   (b) Inverse is not a function since 6 corresponds to 2 and –3.

6. (a) $\{(5,-2), (3,-1), (7,3), (12,4)\}$

   (b) Inverse is a function.

7. (a) $\{(0,0), (1,1), (16,2), (81,3)\}$

   (b) Inverse is a function.

8. (a) $\{(2,1), (8,2), (18,3), (32,4)\}$

   (b) Inverse is a function.

9. Every horizontal line intersects the graph of f at exactly one point. One-to-One.

10. Every horizontal line intersects the graph of f at exactly one point. One-to-One.

11.   There are horizontal lines that intersect the graph of f at more than one point. Not One-to-One.

12.   There are horizontal lines that intersect the graph of f at more than one point. Not One-to-One.

13.   Every horizontal line intersects the graph of f at exactly one point. One-to-One.

14.   The horizontal line $y = 2$ intersects the graph of f at every point. Not One-to-One.

15.   Graphing the inverse:

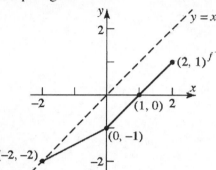

16.   Graphing the inverse:

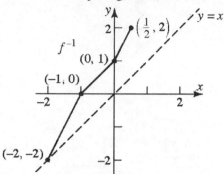

17.   Graphing the inverse:

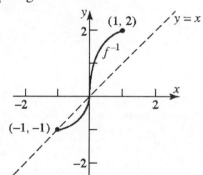

18.   Graphing the inverse:

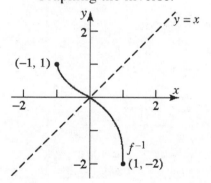

19.   Graphing the inverse:

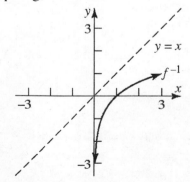

20.   Graphing the inverse:

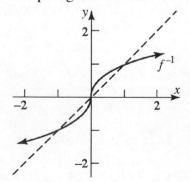

21. $f(x) = 3x + 4, \qquad g(x) = \frac{1}{3}(x - 4)$

$f(g(x)) = f\left(\frac{1}{3}(x - 4)\right) = 3\left(\frac{1}{3}(x - 4)\right) + 4 = (x - 4) + 4 = x$

$g(f(x)) = g(3x + 4) = \frac{1}{3}((3x + 4) - 4) = \frac{1}{3}(3x) = x$

22. $f(x) = 3 - 2x, \qquad g(x) = -\frac{1}{2}(x - 3)$

$f(g(x)) = f\left(-\frac{1}{2}(x - 3)\right) = 3 - 2\left(-\frac{1}{2}(x - 3)\right) = 3 + (x - 3) = x$

$g(f(x)) = g(3 - 2x) = -\frac{1}{2}((3 - 2x) - 3) = -\frac{1}{2}(-2x) = x$

23. $f(x) = 4x - 8, \qquad g(x) = \frac{x}{4} + 2$

$f(g(x)) = f\left(\frac{x}{4} + 2\right) = 4\left(\frac{x}{4} + 2\right) - 8 = (x + 8) - 8 = x$

$g(f(x)) = g(4x - 8) = \frac{4x - 8}{4} + 2 = x - 2 + 2 = x$

24. $f(x) = 2x + 6, \qquad g(x) = \frac{1}{2}x - 3$

$f(g(x)) = f\left(\frac{1}{2}x - 3\right) = 2\left(\frac{1}{2}x - 3\right) + 6 = (x - 6) + 6 = x$

$g(f(x)) = g(2x + 6) = \frac{1}{2}(2x + 6) - 3 = x + 3 - 3 = x$

25. $f(x) = x^3 - 8, \qquad g(x) = \sqrt[3]{x + 8}$

$f(g(x)) = f\left(\sqrt[3]{x + 8}\right) = \left(\sqrt[3]{x + 8}\right)^3 - 8 = (x + 8) - 8 = x$

$g(f(x)) = g(x^3 - 8) = \sqrt[3]{(x^3 - 8) + 8} = \sqrt[3]{x^3} = x$

26. $f(x) = (x - 2)^2, \; x \geq 2; \; g(x) = \sqrt{x} + 2, \; x \geq 0$

$f(g(x)) = f\left(\sqrt{x} + 2\right) = \left(\sqrt{x} + 2 - 2\right)^2 = \left(\sqrt{x}\right)^2 = x$

$g(f(x)) = g\left((x - 2)^2\right) = \sqrt{(x - 2)^2} + 2 = x - 2 + 2 = x$

27. $f(x) = \dfrac{1}{x}, \qquad g(x) = \dfrac{1}{x}$

$f(g(x)) = f\left(\dfrac{1}{x}\right) = \dfrac{1}{\left(\dfrac{1}{x}\right)} = x$

$g(f(x)) = g\left(\dfrac{1}{x}\right) = \dfrac{1}{\left(\dfrac{1}{x}\right)} = x$

28. $f(x) = x, \qquad g(x) = x$
$f(g(x)) = f(x) = x$
$g(f(x)) = g(x) = x$

29. $f(x) = \dfrac{2x+3}{x+4}, \qquad g(x) = \dfrac{4x-3}{2-x}$

$f(g(x)) = f\left(\dfrac{4x-3}{2-x}\right) = \dfrac{2\left(\dfrac{4x-3}{2-x}\right)+3}{\left(\dfrac{4x-3}{2-x}\right)+4} = \dfrac{\left(\dfrac{8x-6+6-3x}{2-x}\right)}{\left(\dfrac{4x-3+8-4x}{2-x}\right)} = \dfrac{\left(\dfrac{5x}{2-x}\right)}{\left(\dfrac{5}{2-x}\right)}$

$= \dfrac{5x}{2-x} \cdot \dfrac{2-x}{5} = x$

$g(f(x)) = g\left(\dfrac{2x+3}{x+4}\right) = \dfrac{4\left(\dfrac{2x+3}{x+4}\right)-3}{2-\left(\dfrac{2x+3}{x+4}\right)} = \dfrac{\left(\dfrac{8x+12-3x-12}{x+4}\right)}{\left(\dfrac{2x+8-2x-3}{x+4}\right)} = \dfrac{\left(\dfrac{5x}{x+4}\right)}{\left(\dfrac{5}{x+4}\right)}$

$= \dfrac{5x}{x+4} \cdot \dfrac{x+4}{5} = x$

30. $f(x) = \dfrac{x-5}{2x+3}, \qquad g(x) = \dfrac{3x+5}{1-2x}$

$f(g(x)) = f\left(\dfrac{3x+5}{1-2x}\right) = \dfrac{\left(\dfrac{3x+5}{1-2x}\right)-5}{2\left(\dfrac{3x+5}{1-2x}\right)+3} = \dfrac{\left(\dfrac{3x+5-5+10x}{1-2x}\right)}{\left(\dfrac{6x+10+3-6x}{1-2x}\right)} = \dfrac{\left(\dfrac{13x}{1-2x}\right)}{\left(\dfrac{13}{1-2x}\right)}$

$= \dfrac{13x}{1-2x} \cdot \dfrac{1-2x}{13} = x$

$g(f(x)) = g\left(\dfrac{x-5}{2x+3}\right) = \dfrac{3\left(\dfrac{x-5}{2x+3}\right)+5}{1-2\left(\dfrac{x-5}{2x+3}\right)} = \dfrac{\left(\dfrac{3x-15+10x+15}{2x+3}\right)}{\left(\dfrac{2x+3-2x+10}{2x+3}\right)} = \dfrac{\left(\dfrac{13x}{2x+3}\right)}{\left(\dfrac{13}{2x+3}\right)}$

$= \dfrac{13x}{2x+3} \cdot \dfrac{2x+3}{13} = x$

31. $f(x) = 3x$

$y = 3x$

$x = 3y$ Inverse

$y = \dfrac{x}{3} \rightarrow f^{-1}(x) = \dfrac{x}{3}$

Verify: $f\big(f^{-1}(x)\big) = f\left(\dfrac{x}{3}\right) = 3\left(\dfrac{x}{3}\right) = x$

$\qquad f^{-1}(f(x)) = f^{-1}(3x) = \dfrac{3x}{3} = x$

Domain of f = range of f^{-1} = $(-\infty, \infty)$

Range of f = domain of f^{-1} = $(-\infty, \infty)$

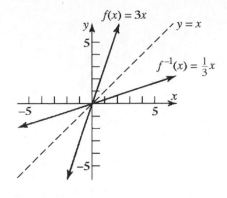

32. $f(x) = -4x$

$y = -4x$

$x = -4y$ Inverse

$y = \dfrac{x}{-4} \rightarrow f^{-1}(x) = -\dfrac{x}{4}$

Verify: $f\big(f^{-1}(x)\big) = f\left(-\dfrac{x}{4}\right) = -4\left(-\dfrac{x}{4}\right) = x$

$\qquad f^{-1}(f(x)) = f^{-1}(-4x) = -\dfrac{-4x}{4} = x$

Domain of f = range of f^{-1} = $(-\infty, \infty)$

Range of f = domain of f^{-1} = $(-\infty, \infty)$

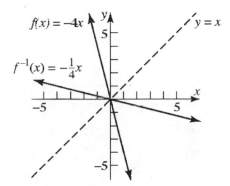

33. $f(x) = 4x + 2$

$y = 4x + 2$

$x = 4y + 2$ Inverse

$4y = x - 2 \rightarrow y = \dfrac{x-2}{4} \rightarrow f^{-1}(x) = \dfrac{x-2}{4}$

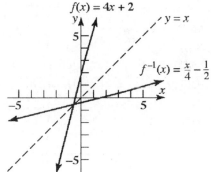

Verify: $f\big(f^{-1}(x)\big) = f\left(\dfrac{x-2}{4}\right) = 4\left(\dfrac{x-2}{4}\right) + 2 = x - 2 + 2 = x$

$\qquad f^{-1}(f(x)) = f^{-1}(4x+2) = \dfrac{(4x+2)-2}{4} = \dfrac{4x}{4} = x$

Domain of f = range of f^{-1} = $(-\infty, \infty)$

Range of f = domain of f^{-1} = $(-\infty, \infty)$

34. $f(x) = 1 - 3x$

$\quad y = 1 - 3x$

$\quad x = 1 - 3y$ Inverse

$\quad 3y = 1 - x \rightarrow y = \dfrac{1-x}{3} \rightarrow f^{-1}(x) = \dfrac{1-x}{3}$

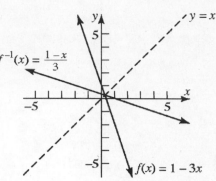

Verify: $f\left(f^{-1}(x)\right) = f\left(\dfrac{1-x}{3}\right) = 1 - 3\left(\dfrac{1-x}{3}\right) = 1 - (1-x) = x$

$\qquad f^{-1}\left(f(x)\right) = f^{-1}(1-3x) = \dfrac{1-(1-3x)}{3} = \dfrac{3x}{3} = x$

Domain of f = range of $f^{-1} = (-\infty, \infty)$

Range of f = domain of $f^{-1} = (-\infty, \infty)$

35. $f(x) = x^3 - 1$

$\quad y = x^3 - 1$

$\quad x = y^3 - 1$ Inverse

$\quad y^3 = x + 1 \rightarrow y = \sqrt[3]{x+1} \rightarrow f^{-1}(x) = \sqrt[3]{x+1}$

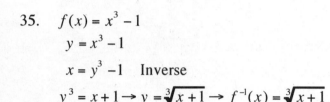
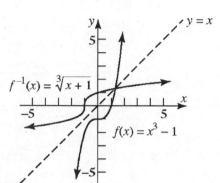

Verify: $f\left(f^{-1}(x)\right) = f\left(\sqrt[3]{x+1}\right) = \left(\sqrt[3]{x+1}\right)^3 - 1 = x + 1 - 1 = x$

$\qquad f^{-1}\left(f(x)\right) = f^{-1}\left(x^3 - 1\right) = \sqrt[3]{\left(x^3-1\right)+1} = \sqrt[3]{x^3} = x$

Domain of f = range of $f^{-1} = (-\infty, \infty)$

Range of f = domain of $f^{-1} = (-\infty, \infty)$

36. $f(x) = x^3 + 1$

$\quad y = x^3 + 1$

$\quad x = y^3 + 1$ Inverse

$\quad y^3 = x - 1 \rightarrow y = \sqrt[3]{x-1} \rightarrow f^{-1}(x) = \sqrt[3]{x-1}$

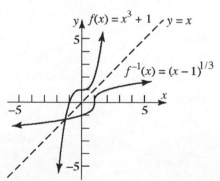

Verify: $f\left(f^{-1}(x)\right) = f\left(\sqrt[3]{x-1}\right) = \left(\sqrt[3]{x-1}\right)^3 + 1 = x - 1 + 1 = x$

$\qquad f^{-1}\left(f(x)\right) = f^{-1}\left(x^3 + 1\right) = \sqrt[3]{\left(x^3+1\right)-1} = \sqrt[3]{x^3} = x$

Domain of f = range of $f^{-1} = (-\infty, \infty)$

Range of f = domain of $f^{-1} = (-\infty, \infty)$

37. $f(x) = x^2 + 4, \ x \geq 0$

     $y = x^2 + 4 \quad x \geq 0$

     $x = y^2 + 4 \quad y \geq 0 \quad$ Inverse

     $y^2 = x - 4 \quad y \geq 0$

     $y = \sqrt{x - 4} \rightarrow f^{-1}(x) = \sqrt{x - 4}$

Verify:

  $f\left(f^{-1}(x)\right) = f\left(\sqrt{x - 4}\right) =$

  $\left(\sqrt{x - 4}\right)^2 + 4 = x - 4 + 4 = x$

    $f^{-1}(f(x)) = f^{-1}\left(x^2 + 4\right) = \sqrt{\left(x^2 + 4\right) - 4}$

    $= \sqrt{x^2} = |x| = x, \ x \geq 0$

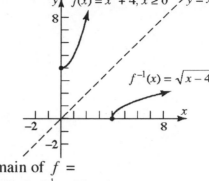

Domain of $f =$
range of $f^{-1} = [0, \infty)$

Range of $f =$
domain of $f^{-1} = [4, \infty)$

38. $f(x) = x^2 + 9, \ x \geq 0$

     $y = x^2 + 9 \quad x \geq 0$

     $x = y^2 + 9 \quad y \geq 0 \quad$ Inverse

     $y^2 = x - 9 \quad y \geq 0$

     $y = \sqrt{x - 9} \rightarrow f^{-1}(x) = \sqrt{x - 9}$

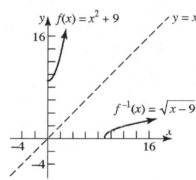

Verify: $f\left(f^{-1}(x)\right) = f\left(\sqrt{x - 9}\right) = \left(\sqrt{x - 9}\right)^2 + 9 = x - 9 + 9 = x$

     $f^{-1}(f(x)) = f^{-1}\left(x^2 + 9\right) = \sqrt{\left(x^2 + 9\right) - 9} = \sqrt{x^2} = |x| = x, \ x \geq 0$

Domain of $f =$ range of $f^{-1} = [0, \infty)$; Range of $f =$ domain of $f^{-1} = [9, \infty)$

39. $f(x) = \dfrac{4}{x}$

    $y = \dfrac{4}{x}$

    $x = \dfrac{4}{y} \quad$ Inverse

    $xy = 4 \rightarrow y = \dfrac{4}{x} \rightarrow f^{-1}(x) = \dfrac{4}{x}$

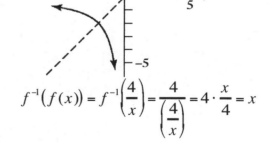

Verify: $f\left(f^{-1}(x)\right) = f\left(\dfrac{4}{x}\right) = \dfrac{4}{\left(\dfrac{4}{x}\right)} = 4 \cdot \dfrac{x}{4} = x$; $f^{-1}(f(x)) = f^{-1}\left(\dfrac{4}{x}\right) = \dfrac{4}{\left(\dfrac{4}{x}\right)} = 4 \cdot \dfrac{x}{4} = x$

Domain of $f =$ range of $f^{-1} =$ all real numbers except 0
Range of $f =$ domain of $f^{-1} =$ all real numbers except 0

40. $f(x) = -\dfrac{3}{x}$

$y = -\dfrac{3}{x}$

$x = -\dfrac{3}{y}$ Inverse

$xy = -3 \rightarrow y = -\dfrac{3}{x} \rightarrow f^{-1}(x) = -\dfrac{3}{x}$

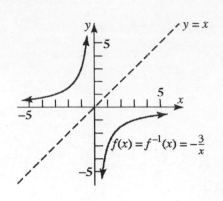

Verify: $f\left(f^{-1}(x)\right) = f\left(-\dfrac{3}{x}\right) = -\dfrac{3}{\left(-\dfrac{3}{x}\right)} = 3 \cdot \dfrac{x}{3} = x$

$f^{-1}\left(f(x)\right) = f^{-1}\left(-\dfrac{3}{x}\right) = -\dfrac{3}{\left(-\dfrac{3}{x}\right)} = 3 \cdot \dfrac{x}{3} = x$

Domain of f = range of f^{-1} = all real numbers except 0
Range of f = domain of f^{-1} = all real numbers except 0

41. $f(x) = \dfrac{1}{x-2}$

$y = \dfrac{1}{x-2} \rightarrow x = \dfrac{1}{y-2}$ Inverse

$x(y-2) = 1 \rightarrow xy - 2x = 1 \rightarrow xy = 2x + 1$

$y = \dfrac{2x+1}{x} \rightarrow f^{-1}(x) = \dfrac{2x+1}{x}$

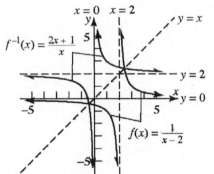

Verify: $f\left(f^{-1}(x)\right) = f\left(\dfrac{2x+1}{x}\right) = \dfrac{1}{\left(\dfrac{2x+1}{x} - 2\right)} = \dfrac{1}{\left(\dfrac{2x+1-2x}{x}\right)} = \dfrac{1}{\left(\dfrac{1}{x}\right)} = x$

$f^{-1}\left(f(x)\right) = f^{-1}\left(\dfrac{1}{x-2}\right) = \dfrac{2\left(\dfrac{1}{x-2}\right) + 1}{\left(\dfrac{1}{x-2}\right)} = \dfrac{\left(\dfrac{2+x-2}{x-2}\right)}{\left(\dfrac{1}{x-2}\right)} = \dfrac{x}{x-2} \cdot \dfrac{x-2}{1} = x$

Domain of f = range of f^{-1} = all real numbers except 2
Range of f = domain of f^{-1} = all real numbers except 0

42. $f(x) = \dfrac{4}{x+2}$

$y = \dfrac{4}{x+2}$

$x = \dfrac{4}{y+2}$ Inverse

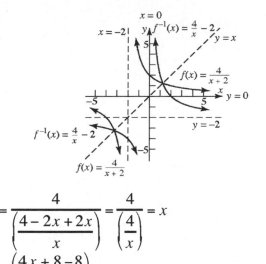

$x(y+2) = 4 \rightarrow xy + 2x = 4 \rightarrow xy = 4 - 2x$

$y = \dfrac{4-2x}{x} \rightarrow f^{-1}(x) = \dfrac{4-2x}{x}$

Verify: $f\left(f^{-1}(x)\right) = f\left(\dfrac{4-2x}{x}\right) = \dfrac{4}{\left(\dfrac{4-2x}{x}\right)+2} = \dfrac{4}{\left(\dfrac{4-2x+2x}{x}\right)} = \dfrac{4}{\left(\dfrac{4}{x}\right)} = x$

$f^{-1}\left(f(x)\right) = f^{-1}\left(\dfrac{4}{x+2}\right) = \dfrac{4-2\left(\dfrac{4}{x+2}\right)}{\left(\dfrac{4}{x+2}\right)} = \dfrac{\left(\dfrac{4x+8-8}{x+2}\right)}{\left(\dfrac{4}{x+2}\right)} = \dfrac{4x}{x+2} \cdot \dfrac{x+2}{4} = x$

Domain of f = range of f^{-1} = all real numbers except -2
Range of f = domain of f^{-1} = all real numbers except 0

43. $f(x) = \dfrac{2}{3+x}$

$y = \dfrac{2}{3+x}$

$x = \dfrac{2}{3+y}$ Inverse

Domain of f =
range of f^{-1} = all real numbers except -3

Range of f =
domain of f^{-1} = all real numbers except 0

$x(3+y) = 2$

$3x + xy = 2 \rightarrow xy = 2 - 3x$

$y = \dfrac{2-3x}{x} \rightarrow f^{-1}(x) = \dfrac{2-3x}{x}$

Verify: $f\left(f^{-1}(x)\right) = f\left(\dfrac{2-3x}{x}\right) = \dfrac{2}{3+\left(\dfrac{2-3x}{x}\right)} = \dfrac{2}{\left(\dfrac{3x+2-3x}{x}\right)} = \dfrac{2}{\left(\dfrac{2}{x}\right)} = 2 \cdot \dfrac{x}{2} = x$

$f^{-1}\left(f(x)\right) = f^{-1}\left(\dfrac{2}{3+x}\right) = \dfrac{2-3\left(\dfrac{2}{3+x}\right)}{\left(\dfrac{2}{3+x}\right)} = \dfrac{\left(\dfrac{6+2x-6}{3+x}\right)}{\left(\dfrac{2}{3+x}\right)} = \dfrac{2x}{3+x} \cdot \dfrac{3+x}{2} = x$

44. $f(x) = \dfrac{4}{2-x}$

Domain of $f =$
range of f^{-1} = all real numbers except 2

$y = \dfrac{4}{2-x}$

$x = \dfrac{4}{2-y}$ Inverse

Range of $f =$
domain of f^{-1} = all real numbers except 0

$x(2-y) = 4 \to 2x - xy = 4$

$xy = 2x - 4 \to y = \dfrac{2x-4}{x}$

$f^{-1}(x) = \dfrac{2x-4}{x}$

Verify: $f\left(f^{-1}(x)\right) = f\left(\dfrac{2x-4}{x}\right) = \dfrac{4}{2 - \left(\dfrac{2x-4}{x}\right)} = \dfrac{4}{\left(\dfrac{2x-2x+4}{x}\right)} = \dfrac{4}{\left(\dfrac{4}{x}\right)} = 4 \cdot \dfrac{x}{4} = x$

$f^{-1}(f(x)) = f^{-1}\left(\dfrac{4}{2-x}\right) = \dfrac{2\left(\dfrac{4}{2-x}\right) - 4}{\left(\dfrac{4}{2-x}\right)} = \dfrac{\left(\dfrac{8-8+4x}{2-x}\right)}{\left(\dfrac{4}{2-x}\right)} = \dfrac{4x}{2-x} \cdot \dfrac{2-x}{4} = x$

45. $f(x) = \dfrac{3x}{x+2}$

Domain of $f =$
range of f^{-1} = all real numbers except -2

$y = \dfrac{3x}{x+2}$

$x = \dfrac{3y}{y+2}$ Inverse

Range of $f =$
domain of f^{-1} = all real numbers except 3

$x(y+2) = 3y$

$xy + 2x = 3y$

$2x = 3y - xy$

$2x = y(3-x)$

$\dfrac{2x}{3-x} = y \to f^{-1}(x) = \dfrac{2x}{3-x}$

Verify: $f\left(f^{-1}(x)\right) = f\left(\dfrac{2x}{3-x}\right) = \dfrac{3\left(\dfrac{2x}{3-x}\right)}{\left(\dfrac{2x}{3-x}\right) + 2} = \dfrac{\left(\dfrac{6x}{3-x}\right)}{\left(\dfrac{2x + 2(3-x)}{3-x}\right)} = \dfrac{\left(\dfrac{6x}{3-x}\right)}{\left(\dfrac{2x+6-2x}{3-x}\right)}$

$= \dfrac{\left(\dfrac{6x}{3-x}\right)}{\left(\dfrac{6}{3-x}\right)} = \left(\dfrac{6x}{3-x}\right) \cdot \left(\dfrac{3-x}{6}\right) = x$

$$f^{-1}(f(x)) = f^{-1}\left(\frac{3x}{x+2}\right) = \frac{2\left(\frac{3x}{x+2}\right)}{3-\left(\frac{3x}{x+2}\right)} = \frac{\left(\frac{6x}{x+2}\right)}{\left(\frac{3(x+2)-3x}{x+2}\right)} = \frac{\left(\frac{6x}{x+2}\right)}{\left(\frac{3x+6-3x}{x+2}\right)}$$

$$= \frac{\left(\frac{6x}{x+2}\right)}{\left(\frac{6}{x+2}\right)} = \left(\frac{6x}{x+2}\right) \cdot \left(\frac{x+2}{6}\right) = x$$

46. $f(x) = \dfrac{-2x}{x-1}$

$y = \dfrac{-2x}{x-1}$

$x = \dfrac{-2y}{y-1}$ Inverse

$x(y-1) = -2y$

$xy - x = -2y \rightarrow xy + 2y = x$

$y(x+2) = x \rightarrow y = \dfrac{x}{x+2}$

$f^{-1}(x) = \dfrac{x}{x+2}$

Domain of f =
range of f^{-1} = all real numbers except 1

Range of f =
domain of f^{-1} = all real numbers except -2

Verify:

$$f(f^{-1}(x)) = f\left(\frac{x}{x+2}\right) = \frac{-2\left(\frac{x}{x+2}\right)}{\left(\frac{x}{x+2}\right)-1} = \frac{\left(\frac{-2x}{x+2}\right)}{\left(\frac{x-1(x+2)}{x+2}\right)} = \frac{\left(\frac{-2x}{x+2}\right)}{\left(\frac{x-x-2}{x+2}\right)}$$

$$= \frac{\left(\frac{-2x}{x+2}\right)}{\left(\frac{-2}{x+2}\right)} = \left(\frac{-2x}{x+2}\right) \cdot \left(\frac{x+2}{-2}\right) = x$$

$$f^{-1}(f(x)) = f^{-1}\left(\frac{-2x}{x-1}\right) = \frac{\left(\frac{-2x}{x-1}\right)}{\left(\left(\frac{-2x}{x-1}\right)+2\right)} = \frac{\left(\frac{-2x}{x-1}\right)}{\left(\frac{-2x+2(x-1)}{x-1}\right)} = \frac{\left(\frac{-2x}{x-1}\right)}{\left(\frac{-2x+2x-2}{x-1}\right)}$$

$$= \frac{\left(\frac{-2x}{x-1}\right)}{\left(\frac{-2}{x-1}\right)} = \left(\frac{-2x}{x-1}\right) \cdot \left(\frac{x-1}{-2}\right) = x$$

47. $f(x) = \dfrac{2x}{3x-1}$

    $y = \dfrac{2x}{3x-1}$

    $x = \dfrac{2y}{3y-1}$ Inverse

    $x(3y-1) = 2y$

    $3xy - x = 2y$

    $3xy - 2y = x$

    $y(3x-2) = x \rightarrow y = \dfrac{x}{3x-2}$

    $f^{-1}(x) = \dfrac{x}{3x-2}$

Domain of f =

range of f^{-1} = all real numbers except $\dfrac{1}{3}$

Range of f =

domain of f^{-1} = all real numbers except $\dfrac{2}{3}$

Verify:

$$f\left(f^{-1}(x)\right) = f\left(\dfrac{x}{3x-2}\right) = \dfrac{2\left(\dfrac{x}{3x-2}\right)}{3\left(\dfrac{x}{3x-2}\right)-1} = \dfrac{\left(\dfrac{2x}{3x-2}\right)}{\left(\dfrac{3x-1(3x-2)}{3x-2}\right)} = \dfrac{\left(\dfrac{2x}{3x-2}\right)}{\left(\dfrac{3x-3x+2}{3x-2}\right)} = \dfrac{2x}{3x-2}\cdot\dfrac{3x-2}{2} = x$$

$$f^{-1}\left(f(x)\right) = f^{-1}\left(\dfrac{2x}{3x-1}\right) = \dfrac{\left(\dfrac{2x}{3x-1}\right)}{3\left(\dfrac{2x}{3x-1}\right)-2} = \dfrac{\left(\dfrac{2x}{3x-1}\right)}{\left(\dfrac{6x-2(3x-1)}{3x-1}\right)} = \dfrac{\left(\dfrac{2x}{3x-1}\right)}{\left(\dfrac{6x-6x+2}{3x-1}\right)} = \dfrac{2x}{3x-1}\cdot\dfrac{3x-1}{2} = x$$

48. $f(x) = \dfrac{3x+1}{-x}$

    $y = \dfrac{3x+1}{-x}$

    $x = \dfrac{3y+1}{-y}$ Inverse

    $-xy = 3y+1$

    $-xy - 3y = 1$

    $y(-x-3) = 1 \rightarrow y = \dfrac{1}{-x-3}$

    $f^{-1}(x) = \dfrac{1}{-x-3}$

Domain of f =

range of f^{-1} = all real numbers except 0

Range of f =

domain of f^{-1} = all real numbers except - 3

Verify: $$f\left(f^{-1}(x)\right) = f\left(\dfrac{1}{-x-3}\right) = \dfrac{3\left(\dfrac{1}{-x-3}\right)+1}{-\left(\dfrac{1}{-x-3}\right)} = \dfrac{\left(\dfrac{3-x-3}{-x-3}\right)}{\left(\dfrac{-1}{-x-3}\right)} = \dfrac{\left(\dfrac{-x}{-x-3}\right)}{\left(\dfrac{-1}{-x-3}\right)} = \dfrac{-x}{-x-3}\cdot\dfrac{-x-3}{-1} = x$$

$$f^{-1}(f(x)) = f^{-1}\left(\frac{3x+1}{x}\right) = \frac{1}{-\left(\frac{3x+1}{-x}\right)-3} = \frac{1}{\left(\frac{3x+1-3x}{x}\right)} = 1 \cdot \frac{x}{1} = x$$

49. $f(x) = \dfrac{3x+4}{2x-3}$

$y = \dfrac{3x+4}{2x-3}$

$x = \dfrac{3y+4}{2y-3}$ Inverse

$x(2y-3) = 3y+4$

$2xy - 3x = 3y + 4$

$2xy - 3y = 3x + 4$

$y(2x-3) = 3x+4$

$y = \dfrac{3x+4}{2x-3}$

$f^{-1}(x) = \dfrac{3x+4}{2x-3}$

Domain of f =

range of f^{-1} = all real numbers except $\dfrac{3}{2}$

Range of f =

domain of f^{-1} = all real numbers except $\dfrac{3}{2}$

Verify:

$$f(f^{-1}(x)) = f\left(\frac{3x+4}{2x-3}\right) = \frac{3\left(\frac{3x+4}{2x-3}\right)+4}{2\left(\frac{3x+4}{2x-3}\right)-3} = \frac{\left(\frac{9x+12+8x-12}{2x-3}\right)}{\left(\frac{6x+8-6x+9}{2x-3}\right)} = \frac{\left(\frac{17x}{2x-3}\right)}{\left(\frac{17}{2x-3}\right)}$$

$$= \frac{17x}{2x-3} \cdot \frac{2x-3}{17} = x$$

$$f^{-1}(f(x)) = f^{-1}\left(\frac{3x+4}{2x-3}\right) = \frac{3\left(\frac{3x+4}{2x-3}\right)+4}{2\left(\frac{3x+4}{2x-3}\right)-3} = \frac{\left(\frac{9x+12+8x-12}{2x-3}\right)}{\left(\frac{6x+8-6x+9}{2x-3}\right)} = \frac{\left(\frac{17x}{2x-3}\right)}{\left(\frac{17}{2x-3}\right)}$$

$$= \frac{17x}{2x-3} \cdot \frac{2x-3}{17} = x$$

50. $f(x) = \dfrac{2x-3}{x+4}$

$y = \dfrac{2x-3}{x+4}$

$x = \dfrac{2y-3}{y+4}$ Inverse

$x(y+4) = 2y-3$

$xy + 4x = 2y - 3$

$xy - 2y = -4x - 3$

$y(x-2) = -4x-3$

$y = \dfrac{-4x-3}{x-2}$

$f^{-1}(x) = \dfrac{-4x-3}{x-2}$

Domain of f =
range of f^{-1} = all real numbers except -4

Range of f =
domain of f^{-1} = all real numbers except 2

Verify:

$$f\left(f^{-1}(x)\right) = f\left(\frac{-4x-3}{x-2}\right) = \frac{2\left(\frac{-4x-3}{x-2}\right)-3}{\left(\frac{-4x-3}{x-2}\right)+4} = \frac{\left(\frac{-8x-6-3x+6}{x-2}\right)}{\left(\frac{-4x-3+4x-8}{x-2}\right)} = \frac{\left(\frac{-11x}{x-2}\right)}{\left(\frac{-11}{x-2}\right)}$$

$$= \frac{-11x}{x-2} \cdot \frac{x-2}{-11} = x$$

$$f^{-1}\left(f(x)\right) = f^{-1}\left(\frac{2x-3}{x+4}\right) = \frac{-4\left(\frac{2x-3}{x+4}\right)-3}{\left(\frac{2x-3}{x+4}\right)-2} = \frac{\left(\frac{-8x+12-3x-12}{x+4}\right)}{\left(\frac{2x-3-2x-8}{x+4}\right)} = \frac{\left(\frac{-11x}{x+4}\right)}{\left(\frac{-11}{x+4}\right)}$$

$$= \frac{-11x}{x+4} \cdot \frac{x+4}{-11} = x$$

51. $f(x) = \dfrac{2x+3}{x+2}$

$y = \dfrac{2x+3}{x+2}$

$x = \dfrac{2y+3}{y+2}$ Inverse

$x(y+2) = 2y+3$

$xy + 2x = 2y + 3$

$xy - 2y = -2x + 3$

$y(x-2) = -2x + 3$

$y = \dfrac{-2x+3}{x-2}$

$f^{-1}(x) = \dfrac{-2x+3}{x-2}$

Domain of f =
range of f^{-1} = all real numbers except –2

Range of f =
domain of f^{-1} = all real numbers except 2

Verify:

$$f\left(f^{-1}(x)\right) = f\left(\frac{-2x+3}{x-2}\right) = \frac{2\left(\frac{-2x+3}{x-2}\right)+3}{\left(\frac{-2x+3}{x-2}\right)+2} = \frac{\left(\frac{-4x+6+3x-6}{x-2}\right)}{\left(\frac{-2x+3+2x-4}{x-2}\right)} = \frac{\left(\frac{-x}{x-2}\right)}{\left(\frac{-1}{x-2}\right)}$$

$$= \frac{-x}{x-2} \cdot \frac{x-2}{-1} = x$$

$$f^{-1}\left(f(x)\right) = f^{-1}\left(\frac{2x+3}{x+2}\right) = \frac{-2\left(\frac{2x+3}{x+2}\right)+3}{\left(\frac{2x+3}{x+2}\right)-2} = \frac{\left(\frac{-4x-6+3x+6}{x+2}\right)}{\left(\frac{2x+3-2x-4}{x+2}\right)} = \frac{\left(\frac{-x}{x+2}\right)}{\left(\frac{-1}{x+2}\right)}$$

$$= \frac{-x}{x+2} \cdot \frac{x+2}{-1} = x$$

52. $f(x) = \dfrac{-3x-4}{x-2}$

$y = \dfrac{-3x-4}{x-2}$

$x = \dfrac{-3y-4}{y-2}$ Inverse

$x(y-2) = -3y-4$

$xy - 2x = -3y-4$

$xy + 3y = 2x - 4$

$y(x+3) = 2x-4$

$y = \dfrac{2x-4}{x+3}$

$f^{-1}(x) = \dfrac{2x-4}{x+3}$

Domain of f =
range of f^{-1} = all real numbers except 2

Range of f =
domain of f^{-1} = all real numbers except –3

Verify:

$f\left(f^{-1}(x)\right) = f\left(\dfrac{2x-4}{x+3}\right) = \dfrac{-3\left(\dfrac{2x-4}{x+3}\right)-4}{\left(\dfrac{2x-4}{x+3}\right)-2} = \dfrac{\left(\dfrac{-6x+12-4x-12}{x+3}\right)}{\left(\dfrac{2x-4-2x-6}{x+3}\right)} = \dfrac{\left(\dfrac{-10x}{x+3}\right)}{\left(\dfrac{-10}{x+3}\right)}$

$= \dfrac{-10x}{x+3} \cdot \dfrac{x+3}{-10} = x$

$f^{-1}\left(f(x)\right) = f^{-1}\left(\dfrac{-3x-4}{x-2}\right) = \dfrac{2\left(\dfrac{-3x-4}{x-2}\right)-4}{\left(\dfrac{-3x-4}{x-2}\right)+3} = \dfrac{\left(\dfrac{-6x-8-4x+8}{x-2}\right)}{\left(\dfrac{-3x-4+3x-6}{x-2}\right)} = \dfrac{\left(\dfrac{-10x}{x-2}\right)}{\left(\dfrac{-10}{x-2}\right)}$

$= \dfrac{-10x}{x-2} \cdot \dfrac{x-2}{-10} = x$

53. $f(x) = \dfrac{x^2-4}{2x^2}, x > 0$

$y = \dfrac{x^2-4}{2x^2}, x > 0$

$x = \dfrac{y^2-4}{2y^2}, y > 0$ Inverse

$2xy^2 = y^2 - 4, y > 0$

$2xy^2 - y^2 = -4, y > 0$

$y^2(2x-1) = -4, y > 0$

$y^2 = \dfrac{-4}{2x-1} \rightarrow y = \sqrt{\dfrac{-4}{2x-1}}$

$f^{-1}(x) = \sqrt{\dfrac{-4}{2x-1}}, x > 0$

Domain of f =
range of f^{-1} = $(0, \infty)$

Range of f =
domain of = $f^{-1} = \left(0, \dfrac{1}{2}\right)$

Verify:

$$f\left(f^{-1}(x)\right)=f\left(\sqrt{\frac{-4}{2x-1}}\right)=\frac{\left(\sqrt{\frac{-4}{2x-1}}\right)^2-4}{2\left(\sqrt{\frac{-4}{2x-1}}\right)^2}=\frac{\left(\frac{-4}{2x-1}-4\right)}{2\left(\frac{-4}{2x-1}\right)}=\frac{\left(\frac{-4-4(2x-1)}{2x-1}\right)}{\left(\frac{-8}{2x-1}\right)}=\frac{\left(\frac{-4-8x+4}{2x-1}\right)}{\left(\frac{-8}{2x-1}\right)}$$

$$=\frac{\left(\frac{-8x}{2x-1}\right)}{\left(\frac{-8}{2x-1}\right)}=\left(\frac{-8x}{2x-1}\right)\cdot\left(\frac{2x-1}{-8}\right)=x$$

$$f^{-1}\left(f(x)\right)=f^{-1}\left(\frac{x^2-4}{2x^2}\right)=\sqrt{\frac{-4}{2\left(\frac{x^2-4}{2x^2}\right)-1}}=\sqrt{\frac{-4}{\left(\frac{x^2-4}{x^2}\right)-1}}=\sqrt{\frac{-4}{\left(\frac{x^2-4-x^2}{x^2}\right)}}=\sqrt{\frac{-4}{\left(\frac{-4}{x^2}\right)}}$$

$$=\sqrt{\frac{-4}{1}\cdot\frac{x^2}{-4}}=\sqrt{x^2}=|x|=x \text{ when } x>0$$

54. $f(x)=\dfrac{x^2+3}{3x^2}, x>0$ Domain of $f=$
                                               range of $f^{-1}=(0,\infty)$

$\qquad y=\dfrac{x^2+3}{3x^2}, y>0$

$\qquad x=\dfrac{y^2+3}{3y^2}, y>0$ Inverse   Range of $f=$
                                               domain of $=f^{-1}=\left(\dfrac{1}{3},\infty\right)$

$\qquad 3xy^2=y^2+3, y>0$

$3xy^2-y^2=3, y>0$

$y^2(3x-1)=3, y>0$

$\qquad y^2=\dfrac{3}{3x-1}\rightarrow y=\sqrt{\dfrac{3}{3x-1}}$

$\qquad f^{-1}(x)=\sqrt{\dfrac{3}{3x-1}}, y>0$

Verify: $f\left(f^{-1}(x)\right)=f\left(\sqrt{\dfrac{3}{3x-1}}\right)=\dfrac{\left(\sqrt{\dfrac{3}{3x-1}}\right)^2+3}{3\left(\sqrt{\dfrac{3}{3x-1}}\right)^2}=\dfrac{\left(\dfrac{3}{3x-1}+3\right)}{3\left(\dfrac{3}{3x-1}\right)}=\dfrac{\left(\dfrac{3+3(3x-1)}{3x-1}\right)}{\left(\dfrac{9}{3x-1}\right)}=\dfrac{\left(\dfrac{3+9x-3}{3x-1}\right)}{\left(\dfrac{9}{3x-1}\right)}$

$=\dfrac{\left(\dfrac{9x}{3x-1}\right)}{\left(\dfrac{9}{3x-1}\right)}=\left(\dfrac{9x}{3x-1}\right)\cdot\left(\dfrac{3x-1}{9}\right)=x$

$$f^{-1}(f(x)) = f^{-1}\left(\frac{x^2+3}{3x^2}\right) = \sqrt{\frac{3}{3\left(\frac{x^2+3}{3x^2}\right)-1}} = \sqrt{\frac{3}{\left(\frac{x^2+3}{x^2}\right)-1}} = \sqrt{\frac{3}{\left(\frac{x^2+3-x^2}{x^2}\right)}} = \sqrt{\frac{3}{\left(\frac{3}{x^2}\right)}}$$

$$= \sqrt{\frac{3}{1} \cdot \frac{x^2}{3}} = \sqrt{x^2} = x$$

55. $f(x) = mx + b, \quad m \neq 0$
$y = mx + b$
$x = my + b$ Inverse
$x - b = my$
$y = \frac{x-b}{m}$
$f^{-1}(x) = \frac{x-b}{m}, \quad m \neq 0$

56. $f(x) = \sqrt{r^2 - x^2}, \quad 0 \le x \le r$
$y = \sqrt{r^2 - x^2}$
$x = \sqrt{r^2 - y^2}$ Inverse
$x^2 = r^2 - y^2$
$y^2 = r^2 - x^2$
$y = \sqrt{r^2 - x^2}$
$f^{-1}(x) = \sqrt{r^2 - x^2}, \quad 0 \le x \le r$

57. f^{-1} lies in quadrant I. Whenever (a,b) is on f, then (b,a) is on f^{-1}. Since both coordinates of (a,b) are positive, both coordinates of (b,a) are positive and it is in quadrant I.

58. f^{-1} lies in quadrant IV. Whenever (a,b) is on f, then (b,a) is on f^{-1}. Since a is negative and b is positive, (b,a) must be a point in quadrant IV.

59. $f(x) = |x|, x \ge 0$ is one-to-one. Thus, $f(x) = x, x \ge 0$ and $f^{-1}(x) = x, x \ge 0$.

60. $f(x) = x^4, x \ge 0$ is one-to-one.
$y = x^4 \quad x \ge 0$
$x = y^4$ Inverse
$y = \sqrt[4]{x}$
$f^{-1}(x) = \sqrt[4]{x}$

61. $f(x) = \frac{9}{5}x + 32 \qquad g(x) = \frac{5}{9}(x-32)$

$f(g(x)) = f\left(\frac{5}{9}(x-32)\right) = \frac{9}{5}\left(\frac{5}{9}(x-32)\right) + 32 = x - 32 + 32 = x$

$g(f(x)) = g\left(\frac{9}{5}x + 32\right) = \frac{5}{9}\left(\frac{9}{5}x + 32 - 32\right) = \frac{5}{9}\left(\frac{9}{5}x\right) = x$

62. $p(x) = 300 - 50x$
$\quad\quad p = 300 - 50x$

$\quad 50x = 300 - p \rightarrow x = \dfrac{300 - p}{50}$

$\quad x(p) = \dfrac{300 - p}{50}$

63. $T(l) = 2\pi\sqrt{\dfrac{l}{g}}, \quad g \approx 32.2$

$\quad T = 2\pi\sqrt{\dfrac{l}{g}} \quad \rightarrow \quad \dfrac{T}{2\pi} = \sqrt{\dfrac{l}{g}}$

$\quad \rightarrow \quad \dfrac{T^2}{4\pi^2} = \dfrac{l}{g} \quad \rightarrow \quad l = \dfrac{gT^2}{4\pi^2}$

$\quad l(T) = \dfrac{gT^2}{4\pi^2}$

64. $f(x) = \dfrac{ax + b}{cx + d}$

(a) domain of f all real numbers except $-\dfrac{d}{c}$.

(b) $y = \dfrac{ax + b}{cx + d}$

$\quad x = \dfrac{ay + b}{cy + d} \quad$ Inverse

$\quad x(cy + d) = ay + b$

$\quad cxy + dx = ay + b$

$\quad cxy - ay = b - dx$

$\quad y(cx - a) = b - dx$

$\quad\quad y = \dfrac{b - dx}{cx - a}$

$\quad f^{-1}(x) = \dfrac{-dx + b}{cx - a}$

(c) range of f all real numbers except $\dfrac{a}{c}$.

(d)

$\quad f = f^{-1} \quad$ if $\dfrac{ax + b}{cx + d} = \dfrac{-dx + b}{cx - a}$

This is true if $a = -d$.

65. An even function cannot be one-to-one. When a function is even, $f(-x) = f(x)$. Thus, both x and $-x$ produce the same y value.

66. An odd function may not be one-to-one. Consider a function such as $f(x) = x^3 - x$.

67. If the graph of a function and its inverse intersect, they must intersect at a point on the line $y = x$. However, the graphs do not have to intersect.

68.   Yes, consider the function $f(x) = \dfrac{1}{x}$. In general the graph of f must have symmetry across the line $y = x$.

69. Answers will vary.

70. $f(x) = \begin{cases} x, & \text{if } x \text{ is rational} \\ -x, & \text{if } x \text{ is irrational} \end{cases}$

Chapter 6

Exponential and Logarithmic Functions

6.2 Exponential Functions

1. (a) $3^{2.2} \approx 11.212$ (b) $3^{2.23} \approx 11.587$ (c) $3^{2.236} \approx 11.664$ (d) $3^{\sqrt{5}} \approx 11.665$

2. (a) $5^{1.7} \approx 15.426$ (b) $5^{1.73} \approx 16.189$ (c) $5^{1.732} \approx 16.241$ (d) $5^{\sqrt{3}} \approx 16.242$

3. (a) $2^{3.14} \approx 8.815$ (b) $2^{3.141} \approx 8.821$ (c) $2^{3.1415} \approx 8.824$ (d) $2^{\pi} \approx 8.825$

4. (a) $2^{2.7} \approx 6.498$ (b) $2^{2.71} \approx 6.543$ (c) $2^{2.718} \approx 6.580$ (d) $2^{e} \approx 6.581$

5. (a) $3.1^{2.7} \approx 21.217$ (b) $3.14^{2.71} \approx 22.217$
   (c) $3.141^{2.718} \approx 22.440$ (d) $\pi^{e} \approx 22.459$

6. (a) $2.7^{3.1} \approx 21.738$ (b) $2.71^{3.14} \approx 22.884$
   (c) $2.718^{3.141} \approx 23.119$ (d) $e^{\pi} \approx 23.141$

7. $e^{1.2} \approx 3.320$ 8. $e^{-1.3} \approx 0.273$

9. $e^{-0.85} \approx 0.427$ 10. $e^{2.1} \approx 8.166$

11. B   12. F   13. D   14. H   15. A   16. C   17. E   18. G

19. $f(x) = 2^x + 1$
    Using the graph of $y = 2^x$, shift the graph
    up 1 unit.
    Domain: $(-\infty, \infty)$
    Range: $(1, \infty)$
    Horizontal Asymptote: $y = 1$

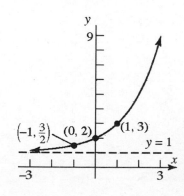

582

20. $f(x) = 2^{x+2}$
Using the graph of $y = 2^x$, shift the graph
left 2 units.
Domain: $(-\infty, \infty)$
Range: $(0, \infty)$
Horizontal Asymptote: $y = 0$

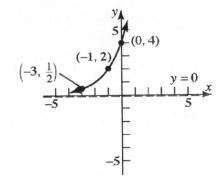

21. $f(x) = 3^{-x} - 2$
Using the graph of $y = 3^x$, reflect the
graph about the y-axis, and shift down 2
units.
Domain: $(-\infty, \infty)$
Range: $(-2, \infty)$
Horizontal Asymptote: $y = -2$

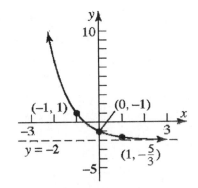

22. $f(x) = -3^x + 1$
Using the graph of $y = 3^x$, reflect the
graph about the x-axis, and shift up 1
unit.
Domain: $(-\infty, \infty)$
Range: $(-\infty, 1)$
Horizontal Asymptote: $y = 1$

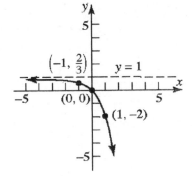

23. $f(x) = 2 + 3\left(4^x\right)$
Using the graph of $y = 4^x$, stretch the
graph vertically by a factor of 3, and shift
up 2 units.
Domain: $(-\infty, \infty)$
Range: $(2, \infty)$
Horizontal Asymptote: $y = 2$

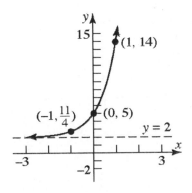

24. $f(x) = 1 - 3(2^x)$

Using the graph of $y = 2^x$, stretch the graph vertically by a factor of 3, reflect about the x-axis, and shift up 1 unit.
Domain: $(-\infty, \infty)$
Range: $(-\infty, 1)$
Horizontal Asymptote: $y = 1$

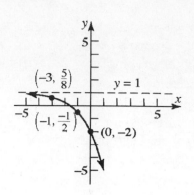

25. $f(x) = 2 + 3^{x/2}$

Using the graph of $y = 3^x$, stretch the graph horizontally by a factor of 2, and shift up 2 units.
Domain: $(-\infty, \infty)$
Range: $(2, \infty)$
Horizontal Asymptote: $y = 2$

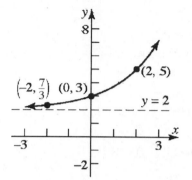

26. $f(x) = 1 - 2^{-x/3}$

Using the graph of $y = 2^x$, stretch the graph horizontally by a factor of 3, reflect about the y-axis, reflect about the x-axis, and shift up 1 unit.
Domain: $(-\infty, \infty)$
Range: $(-\infty, 1)$
Horizontal Asymptote: $y = 1$

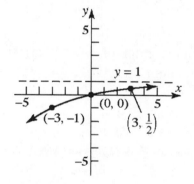

27. $f(x) = e^{-x}$

Using the graph of $y = e^x$, reflect the graph about the y-axis.
Domain: $(-\infty, \infty)$
Range: $(0, \infty)$
Horizontal Asymptote: $y = 0$

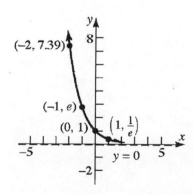

28. $f(x) = -e^x$
Using the graph of $y = e^x$, reflect the
graph about the x-axis.
Domain: $(-\infty, \infty)$
Range: $(-\infty, 0)$
Horizontal Asymptote: $y = 0$

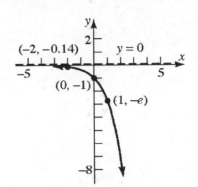

29. $f(x) = e^{x+2}$
Using the graph of $y = e^x$, shift the graph
2 units to the left.
Domain: $(-\infty, \infty)$
Range: $(0, \infty)$
Horizontal Asymptote: $y = 0$

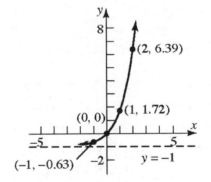

30. $f(x) = e^x - 1$
Using the graph of $y = e^x$, shift the graph
down 1 unit.
Domain: $(-\infty, \infty)$
Range: $(-1, \infty)$
Horizontal Asymptote: $y = -1$

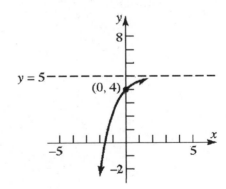

31. $f(x) = 5 - e^{-x}$
Using the graph of $y = e^x$, reflect the
graph about the y-axis, reflect about the
x-axis, and shift up 5 units.
Domain: $(-\infty, \infty)$
Range: $(-\infty, 5)$
Horizontal Asymptote: $y = 5$

32. $f(x) = 9 - 3e^{-x}$
      Using the graph of $y = e^x$, reflect the
      graph about the y-axis, stretch vertically
      by a factor of 3, reflect about the x-axis,
      and shift up 9 units.
      Domain: $(-\infty, \infty)$
      Range: $(-\infty, 9)$
      Horizontal Asymptote: $y = 9$

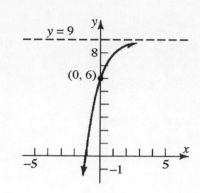

33. $f(x) = 2 - e^{-x/2}$
      Using the graph of $y = e^x$, reflect the
      graph about the y-axis, stretch
      horizontally by a factor of 2, reflect about
      the x-axis, and shift up 2 units.
      Domain: $(-\infty, \infty)$
      Range: $(-\infty, 2)$
      Horizontal Asymptote: $y = 2$

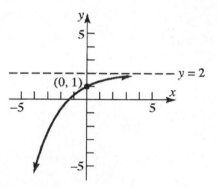

34. $f(x) = 7 - 3e^{-2x}$
      Using the graph of $y = e^x$, reflect the
      graph about the y-axis, shrink

      horizontally by a factor of $\dfrac{1}{2}$, stretch
      vertically by a factor of 3, reflect about
      the x-axis, and shift up 7 units.
      Domain: $(-\infty, \infty)$
      Range: $(-\infty, 7)$
      Horizontal Asymptote: $y = 7$

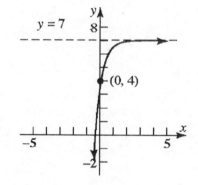

35. $2^{2x+1} = 4$
      $2^{2x+1} = 2^2$

      $2x + 1 = 2 \rightarrow 2x = 1 \rightarrow x = \dfrac{1}{2}$

      The solution is $\left\{\dfrac{1}{2}\right\}$.

36. $5^{1-2x} = \dfrac{1}{5}$
      $5^{1-2x} = 5^{-1}$

      $1 - 2x = -1 \rightarrow -2x = -2 \rightarrow x = 1$
      The solution is $\{1\}$.

37.
$$3^{x^3} = 9^x$$
$$3^{x^3} = \left(3^2\right)^x$$
$$3^{x^3} = 3^{2x}$$
$$x^3 = 2x \rightarrow x^3 - 2x = 0 \rightarrow x(x^2 - 2) = 0$$
$$x = 0 \ \text{ or } \ x^2 = 2$$
$$x = 0 \ \text{ or } \ x = \pm\sqrt{2}$$
The solution is $\left\{-\sqrt{2}, \ 0, \ \sqrt{2}\right\}$.

38.
$$4^{x^2} = 2^x$$
$$\left(2^2\right)^{x^2} = 2^x$$
$$2^{2x^2} = 2^x$$
$$2x^2 = x \rightarrow 2x^2 - x = 0 \rightarrow x(2x - 1) = 0$$
$$x = 0 \ \text{ or } \ x = \frac{1}{2}$$
The solution is $\left\{0, \frac{1}{2}\right\}$.

39.
$$8^{x^2 - 2x} = \frac{1}{2}$$
$$\left(2^3\right)^{x^2 - 2x} = 2^{-1}$$
$$2^{3x^2 - 6x} = 2^{-1}$$
$$3x^2 - 6x = -1 \rightarrow 3x^2 - 6x + 1 = 0$$
$$x = \frac{-(-6) \pm \sqrt{(-6)^2 - 4(3)(1)}}{2(3)} = \frac{6 \pm \sqrt{24}}{6} = \frac{6 \pm 2\sqrt{6}}{6} = \frac{3 \pm \sqrt{6}}{3}$$
The solution is $\left\{\dfrac{3 - \sqrt{6}}{3}, \ \dfrac{3 + \sqrt{6}}{3}\right\}$.

40.
$$9^{-x} = \frac{1}{3}$$
$$\left(3^2\right)^{-x} = 3^{-1}$$
$$3^{-2x} = 3^{-1}$$
$$-2x = -1 \rightarrow x = \frac{1}{2}$$
The solution is $\left\{\dfrac{1}{2}\right\}$.

41.
$$2^x \cdot 8^{-x} = 4^x$$
$$2^x \cdot \left(2^3\right)^{-x} = \left(2^2\right)^x$$
$$2^x \cdot 2^{-3x} = 2^{2x}$$
$$2^{-2x} = 2^{2x}$$
$$-2x = 2x \rightarrow -4x = 0 \rightarrow x = 0$$
The solution is $\{0\}$.

42.
$$\left(\frac{1}{2}\right)^{1-x} = 4$$
$$\left(2^{-1}\right)^{1-x} = 2^2$$
$$2^{-1+x} = 2^2$$
$$-1 + x = 2 \rightarrow x = 3$$
The solution is $\{3\}$.

43.
$$\left(\frac{1}{5}\right)^{2-x} = 25$$
$$\left(5^{-1}\right)^{2-x} = 5^2$$
$$5^{x-2} = 5^2$$
$$x - 2 = 2 \rightarrow x = 4$$
The solution is $\{4\}$.

44. $4^x - 2^x = 0$

$\left(2^2\right)^x = 2^x$

$2^{2x} = 2^x$

$2x = x \to x = 0$

The solution is $\{0\}$.

45. $4^x = 8$

$\left(2^2\right)^x = 2^3$

$2^{2x} = 2^3$

$2x = 3 \to x = \dfrac{3}{2}$

The solution is $\left\{ \dfrac{3}{2} \right\}$.

46. $9^{2x} = 27$

$\left(3^2\right)^{2x} = 3^3$

$3^{4x} = 3^3$

$4x = 3 \to x = \dfrac{3}{4}$

The solution is $\left\{ \dfrac{3}{4} \right\}$.

47. $e^{x^2} = e^{3x} \cdot \dfrac{1}{e^2}$

$e^{x^2} = e^{3x-2}$

$x^2 = 3x - 2$

$x^2 - 3x + 2 = 0$

$(x-1)(x-2) = 0 \to x = 1$ or $x = 2$

The solution is $\{1, 2\}$.

48. $\left(e^4\right)^x \cdot e^{x^2} = e^{12}$

$e^{4x} \cdot e^{x^2} = e^{12}$

$e^{4x+x^2} = e^{12}$

$x^2 + 4x = 12 \to x^2 + 4x - 12 = 0 \to (x+6)(x-2) = 0$

$x = -6$ or $x = 2$

The solution is $\{-6, 2\}$.

49. $4^x = 7$

$\left(4^x\right)^{-2} = 7^{-2} \quad \to \quad 4^{-2x} = \dfrac{1}{7^2} = \dfrac{1}{49}$

50. $2^x = 3$

$4^{-x} = \left(2^2\right)^{-x} = 2^{-2x} = \left(2^x\right)^{-2} = 3^{-2} = \dfrac{1}{9}$

51. $3^{-x} = 2$

$(3^{-x})^{-2} = 2^{-2} \quad \to \quad 3^{2x} = \dfrac{1}{2^2} = \dfrac{1}{4}$

52. $5^{-x} = 3$

$5^{3x} = \left(5^{-x}\right)^{-3} = 3^{-3} = \dfrac{1}{27}$

53. $f(x) = \begin{cases} e^{-x} & \text{if } x < 0 \\ e^x & \text{if } x \geq 0 \end{cases}$

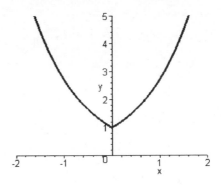

domain $= (-\infty, \infty)$
range $= [1, \infty)$
y-intercept (0, 1)

54. $f(x) = \begin{cases} e^x & \text{if } x < 0 \\ e^{-x} & \text{if } x \geq 0 \end{cases}$

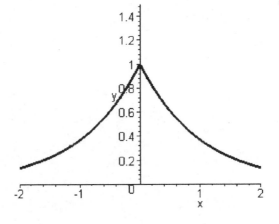

domain $= (-\infty, \infty)$
range $= (0, 1]$
y-intercept (0, 1)
horizontal asymptote $y = 0$

55. $f(x) = \begin{cases} -e^x & \text{if } x < 0 \\ -e^{-x} & \text{if } x \geq 0 \end{cases}$

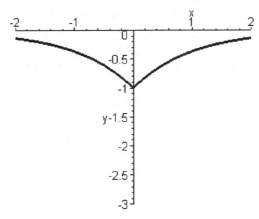

domain $= (-\infty, \infty)$
range $= [-1, 0)$
y-intercept (0, - 1)
horizontal asymptote $y = 0$

56. $f(x) = \begin{cases} -e^{-x} & \text{if } x < 0 \\ -e^x & \text{if } x \geq 0 \end{cases}$

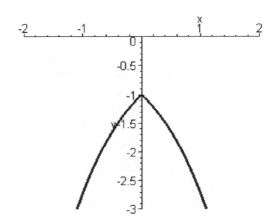

domain $= (-\infty, \infty)$
range $= (-\infty, -1]$
y-intercept (0, - 1)

57. $p = 100e^{-0.03n}$

    (a) $p = 100e^{-0.03(10)} = 100e^{-0.3} \approx 100(0.741) = 74.1\%$ of light

    (b) $p = 100e^{-0.03(25)} = 100e^{-0.75} \approx 100(0.472) = 47.2\%$ of light

58. $p(h) = 760e^{-0.145h}$

    (a) $p(2) = 760e^{-0.145(2)} = 760e^{-0.290} \approx 760(0.748) = 568.68$ mm of mercury

    (b) $p(10) = 760e^{-0.145(10)} = 760e^{-1.45} \approx 760(0.235) = 178.27$ mm of mercury

59. $w(d) = 50e^{-0.004d}$

    (a) $w(30) = 50e^{-0.004(30)} = 50e^{-0.12} \approx 50(0.887) = 44.35$ watts

    (b) $w(365) = 50e^{-0.004(365)} = 50e^{-1.46} \approx 50(0.232) = 11.61$ watts

60. $A(n) = A_0 e^{-0.35n}$

    (a) $A(3) = 100e^{-0.35(3)} = 100e^{-1.05} \approx 100(0.350) = 35$ square millimeters

    (b) $A(10) = 100e^{-0.35(10)} = 100e^{-3.5} \approx 100(0.030) = 3$ square millimeters

61. $D(h) = 5e^{-0.4h}$

        $D(1) = 5e^{-0.4(1)} = 5e^{-0.4} \approx 5(0.670) = 3.35$ milligrams

        $D(6) = 5e^{-0.4(6)} = 5e^{-2.4} \approx 5(0.091) = 0.45$ milligrams

62. $N = P\left(1 - e^{-0.15d}\right)$

    $N = 1000\left(1 - e^{-0.15(3)}\right) = 1000\left(1 - e^{-0.45}\right) \approx 1000(1 - 0.638) = 1000(0.362) = 362$

    362 students will have heard the rumor after 3 days.

63. $F(t) = 1 - e^{-0.1t}$

    (a) $F(10) = 1 - e^{-0.1(10)} = 1 - e^{-1} \approx 1 - 0.368 = 0.632 = 63.2\%$

    (b) $F(40) = 1 - e^{-0.1(40)} = 1 - e^{-4} \approx 1 - 0.018 = 0.982 = 98.2\%$

    (c) as $t \to +\infty$, $F(t) = 1 - e^{-0.1t} \to 1 - 0 = 1$

    (d) Graphing the function:

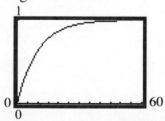

    (e) $F(7) \approx 50$, so 7 minutes are needed for the probability to reach 50%.

64. $F(t) = 1 - e^{-0.15t}$

    (a) $F(15) = 1 - e^{-0.15(15)} = 1 - e^{-2.25} \approx 1 - 0.105 = 0.895 = 89.5\%$

    (b) $F(30) = 1 - e^{-0.15(30)} = 1 - e^{-4.5} \approx 1 - 0.011 = 0.989 = 98.9\%$

    (c) as $t \to +\infty$, $F(t) = 1 - e^{-0.15t} \to 1 - 0 = 1$

(d)   Graphing the function:

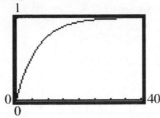

(e) $F(6) \approx 60$, so 6 minutes are needed for the probability to reach 60%.

65. $P(x) = \dfrac{20^x e^{-20}}{x!}$

(a) $P(15) = \dfrac{20^{15} e^{-20}}{15!} \approx 0.0516 = 5.16\%$ The probability that 15 cars will arrive between 5:00 p.m. and 6:00 p.m. is 5.16%.

(b) $P(20) = \dfrac{20^{20} e^{-20}}{20!} \approx 0.0888 = 8.88\%$ The probability that 20 cars will arrive between 5:00 p.m. and 6:00 p.m. is 8.88%.

66. $P(x) = \dfrac{4^x e^{-4}}{x!}$

(a) $P(5) = \dfrac{4^5 e^{-4}}{5!} \approx 0.156 = 15.6\%$ The probability that 5 people will arrive within the next minute is 15.6%.

(b) $P(8) = \dfrac{4^8 e^{-4}}{8!} \approx 0.030 = 3.0\%$ The probability that 8 people will arrive within the next minute is 3.0%.

67. $R = 10^{\left(\frac{2345}{T} - \frac{2345}{D} + 2\right)}$

(a) $R = 10^{\left(\frac{2345}{283} - \frac{2345}{278} + 2\right)} \approx 10^{1.851} \approx 70.96\%$

(b) $R = 10^{\left(\frac{2345}{293} - \frac{2345}{288} + 2\right)} \approx 10^{1.861} \approx 72.61\%$

(c) $R = 10^{\left(\frac{2345}{x} - \frac{2345}{x} + 2\right)} = 10^2 = 100\%$

68. $L(t) = 500\left(1 - e^{-0.0061\,t}\right)$

(a) $L(30) = 500\left(1 - e^{-0.0061(30)}\right) = 500\left(1 - e^{-0.183}\right) \approx 500(1 - 0.833) \approx 83.5$ words

(b) $L(60) = 500\left(1 - e^{-0.0061(60)}\right) = 500\left(1 - e^{-0.366}\right) \approx 500(1 - 0.694) \approx 153$ words

69. $I = \dfrac{E}{R}\left[1 - e^{-\left(\frac{R}{L}\right)t}\right]$

(a) $I = \dfrac{120}{10}\left[1 - e^{-\left(\frac{10}{5}\right)0.3}\right] = 12\left[1 - e^{-0.6}\right] \approx 5.414$ amperes after 0.3 second

$$I = \frac{120}{10}\left[1 - e^{-\left(\frac{10}{5}\right)0.5}\right] = 12\left[1 - e^{-1}\right] \approx 7.585 \text{ amperes after 0.5 second}$$

$$I = \frac{120}{10}\left[1 - e^{-\left(\frac{10}{5}\right)1}\right] = 12\left[1 - e^{-2}\right] \approx 10.376 \text{ amperes after 1 second}$$

(b)   As $t \to \infty$, $e^{-\left(\frac{10}{5}\right)t} \to 0$. Therefore, the maximum current is 12 amperes.

(c)   Graphing the function:

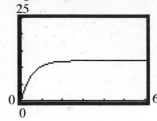

(d) $I = \frac{120}{5}\left[1 - e^{-\left(\frac{5}{10}\right)0.3}\right] = 24\left[1 - e^{-0.15}\right] \approx 3.343 \text{ amperes after 0.3 second}$

$$I = \frac{120}{5}\left[1 - e^{-\left(\frac{5}{10}\right)0.5}\right] = 24\left[1 - e^{-0.25}\right] \approx 5.309 \text{ amperes after 0.5 second}$$

$$I = \frac{120}{5}\left[1 - e^{-\left(\frac{5}{10}\right)1}\right] = 24\left[1 - e^{-0.5}\right] \approx 9.443 \text{ amperes after 1 second}$$

(e)   As $t \to \infty$, $e^{-\left(\frac{5}{10}\right)t} \to 0$. Therefore, the maximum current is 24 amperes.

(f)   Graphing the function:

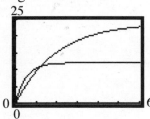

70. $I = \frac{E}{R} \cdot e^{\left(\frac{-t}{RC}\right)}$

(a) $I = \frac{120}{2000} \cdot e^{\left(\frac{-0}{2000 \cdot 1}\right)} = \frac{120}{2000} e^0 = 0.06 \text{ amperes initially.}$

$$I = \frac{120}{2000} \cdot e^{\left(\frac{-1000}{2000 \cdot 1}\right)} = \frac{120}{2000} e^{-1/2} \approx 0.0364 \text{ amperes after 1000 microseconds}$$

$$I = \frac{120}{2000} \cdot e^{\left(\frac{-3000}{2000 \cdot 1}\right)} = \frac{120}{2000} e^{-1.5} \approx 0.0134 \text{ amperes after 3000 microseconds}$$

(b)   The maximum current occurs at $t = 0$. Therefore, the maximum current is 0.06 amperes.

(c)   Graphing the function:

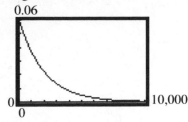

(d) $I = \dfrac{120}{1000} \cdot e^{\left(\frac{-0}{1000 \cdot 2}\right)} = \dfrac{120}{1000} e^{0} = 0.12$ amperes initially.

$I = \dfrac{120}{1000} \cdot e^{\left(\frac{-1000}{1000 \cdot 2}\right)} = \dfrac{120}{1000} e^{-1/2} \approx 0.0728$ amperes after 1000 microseconds

$I = \dfrac{120}{1000} \cdot e^{\left(\frac{-3000}{1000 \cdot 2}\right)} = \dfrac{120}{1000} e^{-1.5} \approx 0.0268$ amperes after 3000 microseconds

(e)   The maximum current occurs at $t = 0$. Therefore, the maximum current is 0.12 amperes.

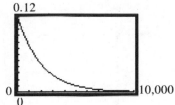

(f)   Graphing the function:

71. $2 + \dfrac{1}{2!} + \dfrac{1}{3!} + \dfrac{1}{4!} + \ldots + \dfrac{1}{n!}$

$n = 4;\quad 2 + \dfrac{1}{2!} + \dfrac{1}{3!} + \dfrac{1}{4!} = 2.7083$

$n = 6;\quad 2 + \dfrac{1}{2!} + \dfrac{1}{3!} + \dfrac{1}{4!} + \dfrac{1}{5!} + \dfrac{1}{6!} = 2.7181$

$n = 8;\quad 2 + \dfrac{1}{2!} + \dfrac{1}{3!} + \dfrac{1}{4!} + \dfrac{1}{5!} + \dfrac{1}{6!} + \dfrac{1}{7!} + \dfrac{1}{8!} = 2.7182788$

$n = 10;\quad 2 + \dfrac{1}{2!} + \dfrac{1}{3!} + \dfrac{1}{4!} + \dfrac{1}{5!} + \dfrac{1}{6!} + \dfrac{1}{7!} + \dfrac{1}{8!} + \dfrac{1}{9!} + \dfrac{1}{10!} = 2.7182818$

$e = 2.718281828$

72.   For $n = 2$ $2 + \dfrac{1}{1 + \dfrac{1}{2}} = 2.66667$

$n = 3$ $2 + \dfrac{1}{1 + \dfrac{1}{2 + \dfrac{2}{3}}} = 2.72727$

$n = 4 \qquad \approx 2.71698$

$n = 5 \qquad \approx 2.71845$

$n = 6 \qquad \approx 2.71826$

$e = 2.718281828$

73. $f(x) = a^{x}$

$\dfrac{f(x+h) - f(x)}{h} = \dfrac{a^{x+h} - a^{x}}{h} = \dfrac{a^{x}a^{h} - a^{x}}{h} = \dfrac{a^{x}\left(a^{h} - 1\right)}{h} = a^{x}\left(\dfrac{a^{h} - 1}{h}\right)$

74. $f(x) = a^x$

$f(A+B) = a^{A+B} = a^A \cdot a^B = f(A) \cdot f(B)$

75. $f(x) = a^x$

$f(-x) = a^{-x} = \dfrac{1}{a^x} = \dfrac{1}{f(x)}$

76. $f(x) = a^x$

$f(\alpha x) = a^{\alpha x} = \left(a^x\right)^\alpha = \left[f(x)\right]^\alpha$

77. (a) $y = \dfrac{6}{1+e^{-(5.085-0.1156(100))}} \approx 0.0092$ O - rings

(b) $y = \dfrac{6}{1+e^{-(5.085-0.1156(60))}} \approx 0.8145$ O - rings

(c) $y = \dfrac{6}{1+e^{-(5.085-0.1156(30))}} \approx 5.0063$ O - rings

(d) Graphing:

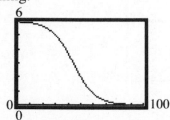

At 58°F, there would be 1 leaky O-ring.
At 44°F, there would be 3 leaky O-rings.
At 30°F, there would be 5 leaky O-rings.

78. $f(x) = 2^{\left(2^x\right)} + 1$

$f(1) = 2^{\left(2^1\right)} + 1 = 2^2 + 1 = 4 + 1 = 5$

$f(2) = 2^{\left(2^2\right)} + 1 = 2^4 + 1 = 16 + 1 = 17$

$f(3) = 2^{\left(2^3\right)} + 1 = 2^8 + 1 = 256 + 1 = 257$

$f(4) = 2^{\left(2^4\right)} + 1 = 2^{16} + 1 = 65536 + 1 = 65537$

$f(5) = 2^{\left(2^5\right)} + 1 = 2^{32} + 1 = 4,294,967,296 + 1 = 4,294,967,297$

$\qquad 4,294,967,297 = 641 \times 6,700,417$

79. We can use the function $f(t) = f(0)e^{kt}$

the number of bacteria doubles
every minute means

$f(1) = 2f(0)$

$f(0)e^{k \cdot (1)} = 2f(0)$

$e^{k} = 2$

the container is full after
60 minutes means

$f(60) = 4$

$f(0)e^{k(60)} = 4$

$f(0)\left(e^{k}\right)^{(60)} = 4$

$f(0)(2)^{(60)} = 4$

$\rightarrow f(0) = \dfrac{4}{2^{60}} = \dfrac{2^2}{2^{60}} = \dfrac{1}{2^{58}}$

We want to find t so that $f(t) = 2$.

$f(t) = f(0)e^{kt} = 2$

$f(0)\left(e^{k}\right)^{t} = 2$

$f(0)(2)^{t} = 2$

$\left(\dfrac{1}{2^{58}}\right)(2)^{t} = 2 \rightarrow 2^{t} = 2 \cdot 2^{58} = 2^{59} \rightarrow t = 59 \ \text{minutes}$

80. Answers will vary.

81. Answers will vary.

Chapter 6

Exponential and Logarithmic Functions

6.3 Logarithmic Functions

1. $9 = 3^2$ is equivalent to $2 = \log_3 9$

2. $16 = 4^2$ is equivalent to $2 = \log_4 16$

3. $a^2 = 1.6$ is equivalent to $2 = \log_a 1.6$

4. $a^3 = 2.1$ is equivalent to $3 = \log_a 2.1$

5. $1.1^2 = M$ is equivalent to $2 = \log_{1.1} M$

6. $2.2^3 = N$ is equivalent to $3 = \log_{2.2} N$

7. $2^x = 7.2$ is equivalent to $x = \log_2 7.2$

8. $3^x = 4.6$ is equivalent to $x = \log_3 4.6$

9. $x^{\sqrt{2}} = \pi$ is equivalent to $\sqrt{2} = \log_x \pi$

10. $x^{\pi} = e$ is equivalent to $\pi = \log_x e$

11. $e^x = 8$ is equivalent to $x = \ln 8$

12. $e^{2.2} = M$ is equivalent to $2.2 = \ln M$

13. $\log_2 8 = 3$ is equivalent to $2^3 = 8$

14. $\log_3\left(\dfrac{1}{9}\right) = -2$ is equivalent to $3^{-2} = \dfrac{1}{9}$

15. $\log_a 3 = 6$ is equivalent to $a^6 = 3$

16. $\log_b 4 = 2$ is equivalent to $b^2 = 4$

17. $\log_3 2 = x$ is equivalent to $3^x = 2$

18. $\log_2 6 = x$ is equivalent to $2^x = 6$

19. $\log_2 M = 1.3$ is equivalent to $2^{1.3} = M$

20. $\log_3 N = 2.1$ is equivalent to $3^{2.1} = N$

21. $\log_{\sqrt{2}} \pi = x$ is equivalent to $\left(\sqrt{2}\right)^x = \pi$

22. $\log_\pi x = \dfrac{1}{2}$ is equivalent to $\pi^{1/2} = x$

23. $\ln 4 = x$ is equivalent to $e^x = 4$

24. $\ln x = 4$ is equivalent to $e^4 = x$

25. $\log_2 1 = 0$ since $2^0 = 1$

26. $\log_8 8 = 1$ since $8^1 = 8$

27. $\log_5 25 = 2$ since $5^2 = 25$

28. $\log_3\left(\dfrac{1}{9}\right) = -2$ since $3^{-2} = \dfrac{1}{9}$

29. $\log_{\frac{1}{2}} 16 = -4$ since $\left(\dfrac{1}{2}\right)^{-4} = 2^4 = 16$

30. $\log_{\frac{1}{3}} 9 = -2$ since $\left(\dfrac{1}{3}\right)^{-2} = 3^2 = 9$

31. $\log_{10}\sqrt{10} = \dfrac{1}{2}$ since $10^{1/2} = \sqrt{10}$

32. $\log_5\sqrt[3]{25} = \dfrac{2}{3}$ since $5^{2/3} = 25^{1/3} = \sqrt[3]{25}$

33. $\log_{\sqrt{2}} 4 = 4$ since $\left(\sqrt{2}\right)^4 = 4$

34. $\log_{\sqrt{3}} 9 = 4$ since $\left(\sqrt{3}\right)^4 = 9$

35. $\ln\sqrt{e} = \dfrac{1}{2}$ since $e^{1/2} = \sqrt{e}$

36. $\ln e^3 = 3$ since $e^3 = e^3$

37. The domain of $f(x) = \ln(x-3)$ is:
$x - 3 > 0 \rightarrow x > 3$
$\{x \mid x > 3\}$

38. The domain of $g(x) = \ln(x-1)$ is:
$x - 1 > 0 \rightarrow x > 1$
$\{x \mid x > 1\}$

39. The domain of $F(x) = \log_2 x^2$ is:
$x^2 > 0$
$\{x \mid x \neq 0\}$

40. The domain of $H(x) = \log_5 x^3$ is:
$x^3 > 0 \rightarrow x > 0$
$\{x \mid x > 0\}$

41. The domain of $h(x) = \log_{\frac{1}{2}}\left(x^2 - 2x + 1\right)$ is:
$x^2 - 2x + 1 > 0 \rightarrow (x-1)^2 > 0$
$\{x \mid x \neq 1\}$

42. The domain of $G(x) = \log_{\frac{1}{2}}\left(x^2 - 1\right)$ is:
$x^2 - 1 > 0 \rightarrow (x+1)(x-1) > 0$
$x < -1$ or $x > 1$
$\{x \mid x < -1 \text{ or } x > 1\}$

43. The domain of $f(x) = \ln\left(\dfrac{1}{x+1}\right)$ is:
$\dfrac{1}{x+1} > 0 \rightarrow x + 1 > 0$
$x > -1$
$\{x \mid x > -1\}$

44. The domain of $g(x) = \ln\left(\dfrac{1}{x-5}\right)$ is:
$\dfrac{1}{x-5} > 0 \rightarrow x - 5 > 0$
$x > 5$
$\{x \mid x > 5\}$

45. The domain of $g(x) = \log_5\left(\dfrac{x+1}{x}\right)$ requires that $\dfrac{x+1}{x} > 0$.

The expression is zero or undefined when $x = -1$ or $x = 0$.

$$f(x) = \dfrac{x+1}{x}$$

Interval	Test Number	$f(x) = \dfrac{x+1}{x}$	Positive/Negative
$-\infty < x < -1$	-2	$1/2$	Positive
$-1 < x < 0$	-0.5	-1	Negative
$0 < x < \infty$	1	2	Positive

The domain is $\{x \mid x < -1 \text{ or } x > 0\}$

46.   The domain of $h(x) = \log_3\left(\dfrac{x}{x-1}\right)$ requires that $\dfrac{x}{x-1} > 0$.

The expression is zero or undefined when $x = 0$ or $x = 1$.

$$f(x) = \dfrac{x}{x-1}$$

Interval	Test Number	$f(x) = \dfrac{x}{x-1}$	Positive/Negative
$-\infty < x < 0$	-1	$1/2$	Positive
$0 < x < 1$	0.5	-1	Negative
$1 < x < \infty$	2	2	Positive

The domain is $\{x \mid x < 0 \text{ or } x > 1\}$.

47. $\ln\dfrac{5}{3} \approx 0.511$

48. $\dfrac{\ln 5}{3} \approx 0.536$

49. $\dfrac{\ln(10/3)}{0.04} \approx 30.099$

50. $\dfrac{\ln(2/3)}{-0.1} \approx 4.055$

51.   For $f(x) = \log_a x$, find a so that $f(2) = \log_a 2 = 2$ or $a^2 = 2$ or $a = \sqrt{2}$.
       (The base a must be positive by definition.)

52.   For $f(x) = \log_a x$, find a so that $f\left(\dfrac{1}{2}\right) = \log_a\left(\dfrac{1}{2}\right) = -4$.

$$a^{-4} = \dfrac{1}{2} \;\rightarrow\; \dfrac{1}{a^4} = \dfrac{1}{2} \;\rightarrow\; a^4 = 2 \;\rightarrow\; a = \sqrt[4]{2}$$

(The base a must be positive by definition.)

53.   B   54.   F   55.   D   56.   H

57.   A   58.   C   59.   E   60.   G

61. $f(x) = \ln(x + 4)$
       Using the graph of $y = \ln x$, shift the
       graph 4 units to the left.
       Domain: $(-4, \infty)$
       Range: $(-\infty, \infty)$
       Vertical Asymptote: $x = -4$

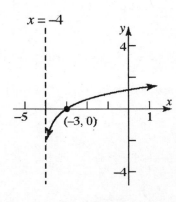

62. $f(x) = \ln(x - 3)$
Using the graph of $y = \ln x$, shift the
graph 3 units to the right.
Domain: $(3, \infty)$
Range: $(-\infty, \infty)$
Vertical Asymptote: $x = 3$

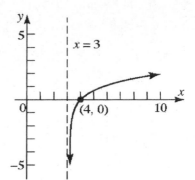

63. $f(x) = \ln(-x)$
Using the graph of $y = \ln x$, reflect the
graph about the y-axis.
Domain: $(-\infty, 0)$
Range: $(-\infty, \infty)$
Vertical Asymptote: $x = 0$

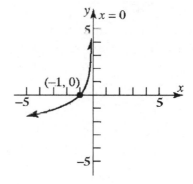

64. $f(x) = -\ln(-x)$
Using the graph of $y = \ln x$, reflect the
graph about the y-axis, and reflect about
the x-axis.
Domain: $(-\infty, 0)$
Range: $(-\infty, \infty)$
Vertical Asymptote: $x = 0$

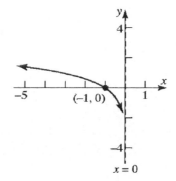

65. $g(x) = \ln(2x)$
Using the graph of $y = \ln x$, compress the
graph horizontally by a factor of $\dfrac{1}{2}$.
Domain: $(0, \infty)$
Range: $(-\infty, \infty)$
Vertical Asymptote: $x = 0$

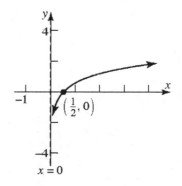

66. $h(x) = \ln\left(\dfrac{1}{2}x\right)$

Using the graph of $y = \ln x$, stretch the
graph horizontally by a factor of 2.
Domain: $(0, \infty)$
Range: $(-\infty, \infty)$
Vertical Asymptote: $x = 0$

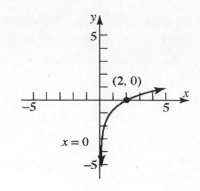

67. $f(x) = 3\ln x$

Using the graph of $y = \ln x$, stretch the
graph vertically by a factor of 3.
Domain: $(0, \infty)$
Range: $(-\infty, \infty)$
Vertical Asymptote: $x = 0$

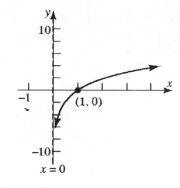

68. $f(x) = -2\ln x$

Using the graph of $y = \ln x$, stretch the
graph vertically by a factor of 2, and
reflect about the x-axis.
Domain: $(0, \infty)$
Range: $(-\infty, \infty)$
Vertical Asymptote: $x = 0$

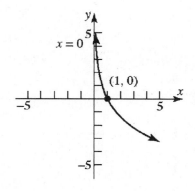

69. $g(x) = \ln(3 - x) = \ln(-(x - 3))$

Using the graph of $y = \ln x$, reflect the
graph about the y-axis, and shift 3 units to
the right.
Domain: $(-\infty, 3)$
Range: $(-\infty, \infty)$
Vertical Asymptote: $x = 3$

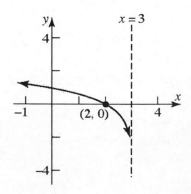

70. $h(x) = \ln(4 - x) = \ln(-(x - 4))$
Using the graph of $y = \ln x$, reflect the
graph about the y-axis, and shift 4 units to
the right.
Domain: $(-\infty, 4)$
Range: $(-\infty, \infty)$
Vertical Asymptote: $x = 4$

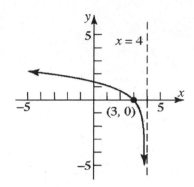

71. $f(x) = -\ln(x - 1)$
Using the graph of $y = \ln x$, shift the
graph 1 unit to the right, and reflect about
the x-axis.
Domain: $(1, \infty)$
Range: $(-\infty, \infty)$
Vertical Asymptote: $x = 1$

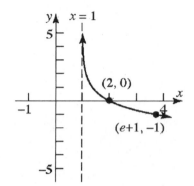

72. $f(x) = 2 - \ln x$
Using the graph of $y = \ln x$, reflect the
graph about the x-axis, and shift 2 units
up.
Domain: $(0, \infty)$
Range: $(-\infty, \infty)$
Vertical Asymptote: $x = 0$

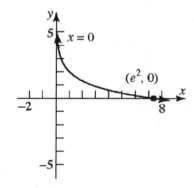

73. $\log_3 x = 2$
$\qquad x = 3^2 \rightarrow x = 9$

74. $\log_5 x = 3$
$\qquad x = 5^3 \rightarrow x = 125$

75. $\log_2(2x + 1) = 3$
$\qquad 2x + 1 = 2^3 \rightarrow 2x + 1 = 8$
$\qquad 2x = 7 \rightarrow x = \dfrac{7}{2}$

76. $\log_3(3x - 2) = 2$
$\qquad 3x - 2 = 3^2 \rightarrow 3x - 2 = 9$
$\qquad 3x = 11 \rightarrow x = \dfrac{11}{3}$

77. $\log_x 4 = 2$
$\qquad x^2 = 4$
$\qquad x = 2 \quad (x \neq -2, \text{ base is positive})$

78. $\log_x\left(\dfrac{1}{8}\right) = 3$
$\qquad x^3 = \dfrac{1}{8} \rightarrow x = \dfrac{1}{2}$

79. $\ln e^x = 5$
$\qquad e^x = e^5 \rightarrow x = 5$

80. $\ln e^{-2x} = 8$
$\qquad e^{-2x} = e^8 \rightarrow -2x = 8 \rightarrow x = -4$

81. $\log_4 64 = x$

$$4^x = 64 \rightarrow 4^x = 4^3 \rightarrow x = 3$$

82. $\log_5 625 = x$

$$5^x = 625 \rightarrow 5^x = 5^4 \rightarrow x = 4$$

83. $\log_3 243 = 2x + 1$

$$3^{2x+1} = 243$$

$$3^{2x+1} = 3^5$$

$$2x + 1 = 5 \rightarrow 2x = 4 \rightarrow x = 2$$

84. $\log_6 36 = 5x + 3$

$$6^{5x+3} = 36$$

$$6^{5x+3} = 6^2$$

$$5x + 3 = 2 \rightarrow 5x = -1 \rightarrow x = -\frac{1}{5}$$

85. $e^{3x} = 10$

$$3x = \ln 10 \rightarrow x = \frac{\ln 10}{3}$$

86. $e^{-2x} = \frac{1}{3}$

$$-2x = \ln\left(\frac{1}{3}\right) \rightarrow x = \frac{\ln\left(\frac{1}{3}\right)}{-2}$$

87. $e^{2x+5} = 8$

$2x + 5 = \ln 8$

$$2x = -5 + \ln 8 \rightarrow x = \frac{-5 + \ln 8}{2}$$

88. $e^{-2x+1} = 13$

$-2x + 1 = \ln 13$

$$-2x = -1 + \ln 13 \rightarrow x = \frac{-1 + \ln 13}{-2}$$

89. $\log_3\left(x^2 + 1\right) = 2$

$$x^2 + 1 = 3^2$$

$$x^2 + 1 = 9 \rightarrow x^2 = 8$$

$$x = \pm\sqrt{8} = \pm 2\sqrt{2}$$

90. $\log_5\left(x^2 + x + 4\right) = 2$

$$x^2 + x + 4 = 5^2$$

$$x^2 + x + 4 = 25$$

$$x^2 + x - 21 = 0$$

$$x = \frac{-1 \pm \sqrt{1^2 - 4(1)(-21)}}{2(1)} = \frac{-1 \pm \sqrt{85}}{2}$$

$$x = \frac{-1 - \sqrt{85}}{2} \text{ or } \frac{-1 + \sqrt{85}}{2}$$

91. $\log_2 8^x = -3$

$$8^x = 2^{-3}$$

$$8^x = \frac{1}{8} \rightarrow 8^x = 8^{-1} \rightarrow x = -1$$

92. $\log_3 3^x = -1$

$$3^x = 3^{-1} \rightarrow x = -1$$

93. $f(x) = \begin{cases} \ln(-x) & \text{if } x < 0 \\ \ln x & \text{if } x > 0 \end{cases}$

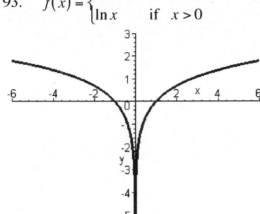

Domain: $(-\infty, 0) \cup (0, \infty)$
Range: $(-\infty, \infty)$
x-intercept: $(-1, 0), (1, 0)$
vertical asymptote: $x = 0$

94. $f(x) = \begin{cases} \ln(-x) & \text{if } x \le -1 \\ -\ln(-x) & \text{if } -1 < x < 0 \end{cases}$

Domain: $(-\infty, 0)$
Range: $[0, \infty)$
x-intercept $(-1, 0)$
vertical asymptote: $x = 0$

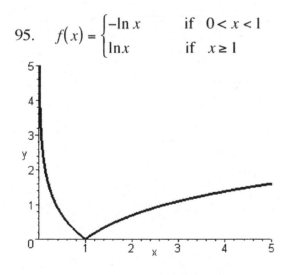

95. $f(x) = \begin{cases} -\ln x & \text{if } 0 < x < 1 \\ \ln x & \text{if } x \ge 1 \end{cases}$

Domain: $(0, \infty)$
Range: $[0, \infty)$
x-intercept: $(1, 0)$
vertical asymptote: $x = 0$

96. $f(x) = \begin{cases} \ln x & \text{if } 0 < x < 1 \\ -\ln x & \text{if } x \geq 1 \end{cases}$

Domain: $(0, \infty)$
Range: $(-\infty, 0]$
x-intercept: $(1, 0)$
vertical asymptote: $x = 0$

97. $P = 100e^{-0.1\,n}$

(a)
$$50 = 100e^{-0.1\,n}$$
$$0.5 = e^{-0.1n}$$
$$\ln(0.5) = -0.1n$$
$$n = \frac{\ln(0.5)}{-0.1}$$
$$n \approx 6.93$$
7 panes of glass are needed.

(b)
$$25 = 100e^{-0.1n}$$
$$0.25 = e^{-0.1n}$$
$$\ln(0.25) = -0.1n$$
$$n = \frac{\ln(0.25)}{-0.1}$$
$$n \approx 13.86$$
14 panes of glass are needed.

98. $pH = -\log_{10}\left[H^+\right]$

(a) $pH = -\log_{10}[0.0000001] = -(-7) = 7$

(b) $4.2 = -\log_{10}\left[H^+\right] \rightarrow -4.2 = \log_{10}\left[H^+\right] \rightarrow \left[H^+\right] = 10^{-4.2}$
$$= 6.31 \times 10^{-5} = 0.0000631$$

99. $w = 50e^{-0.004\,d}$

(a)
$$30 = 50e^{-0.004d}$$
$$0.6 = e^{-0.004d}$$
$$\ln(0.6) = -0.004\,d$$
$$d = \frac{\ln(0.6)}{-0.004} \approx 127.7$$
Approximately 128 days.

(b)
$$5 = 50e^{-0.004\,d}$$
$$0.1 = e^{-0.004d}$$
$$\ln(0.1) = -0.004\,d$$
$$d = \frac{\ln(0.1)}{-0.004} \approx 575.6$$
Approximately 576 days.

100. $A = A_0 e^{-0.35\,n}$

(a)
$$50 = 100e^{-0.35\,n}$$
$$0.5 = e^{-0.35n}$$
$$\ln(0.5) = -0.35\,n$$
$$n = \frac{\ln(0.5)}{-0.35} \approx 1.98 \text{ days}$$
Approximately 2 days.

(b)
$$10 = 100e^{-0.35\,n}$$
$$0.1 = e^{-0.35n}$$
$$\ln(0.1) = -0.35\,n$$
$$n = \frac{\ln(0.1)}{-0.35} \approx 6.58 \text{ days}$$
Approximately 6.6 days.

101. $F(t) = 1 - e^{-0.1t}$

(a) $0.5 = 1 - e^{-0.1t}$

$-0.5 = -e^{-0.1t} \rightarrow 0.5 = e^{-0.1t} \rightarrow \ln(0.5) = -0.1t$

$t = \dfrac{\ln(0.5)}{-0.1} \approx 6.93$

Approximately 7 minutes.

(b) $0.8 = 1 - e^{-0.1t}$

$-0.2 = -e^{-0.1t} \rightarrow 0.2 = e^{-0.1t} \rightarrow \ln(0.2) = -0.1t$

$t = \dfrac{\ln(0.2)}{-0.1} \approx 16.09$

Approximately 16 minutes.

(c)   It is impossible for the probability to reach 100% because $e^{-0.1t}$ will never equal zero.

102. $F(t) = 1 - e^{-0.15t}$

(a) $0.50 = 1 - e^{-0.15t}$

$-0.5 = -e^{-0.15t}$

$0.5 = e^{-0.15t} \rightarrow \ln(0.5) = -0.15t$

$t = \dfrac{\ln(0.5)}{-0.15} \approx 4.62$ minutes

Approximately 5 minutes.

(b) $0.80 = 1 - e^{-0.15t}$

$-0.2 = -e^{-0.15t}$

$0.2 = e^{-0.15t} \rightarrow \ln(0.2) = -0.15t$

$t = \dfrac{\ln(0.2)}{-0.15} \approx 10.73$ minutes

Approximately 11 minutes.

103. $D = 5e^{-0.4h}$

$2 = 5e^{-0.4h}$

$0.4 = e^{-0.4h}$

$\ln(0.4) = -0.4h$

$h = \dfrac{\ln(0.4)}{-0.4} \approx 2.29$ hours

104. $N = P\left(1 - e^{-0.15d}\right)$

$450 = 1000\left(1 - e^{-0.15d}\right)$

$0.45 = 1 - e^{-0.15d} \rightarrow -0.55 = -e^{-0.15d}$

$0.55 = e^{-0.15d} \rightarrow \ln(0.55) = -0.15d$

$d = \dfrac{\ln(0.55)}{-0.15} \approx 3.99$ days

105. $I = \dfrac{E}{R}\left[1 - e^{-\left(\frac{R}{L}\right)t}\right]$

0.5 ampere:

$0.5 = \dfrac{12}{10}\left[1 - e^{-\left(\frac{10}{5}\right)t}\right] \rightarrow 0.4167 = 1 - e^{-2t}$

$e^{-2t} = 0.5833 \rightarrow -2t = \ln(0.5833)$

$t = \dfrac{\ln(0.5833)}{-2} \approx 0.2695$ seconds

1.0 ampere:

$1.0 = \dfrac{12}{10}\left[1 - e^{-\left(\frac{10}{5}\right)t}\right] \rightarrow 0.8333 = 1 - e^{-2t}$

$e^{-2t} = 0.1667 \rightarrow -2t = \ln(0.1667)$

$t = \dfrac{\ln(0.1667)}{-2} \approx 0.8958$ seconds

106. $L(t) = A\left(1 - e^{-kt}\right)$

    (a) $20 = 200\left(1 - e^{-k(5)}\right)$

         $0.1 = 1 - e^{-5k}$

         $e^{-5k} = 0.9$

         $-5k = \ln(0.9)$

         $k = \dfrac{\ln(0.9)}{-5} \approx 0.021$

    (b) $L(10) = 200\left(1 - e^{-0.021\,(10)}\right) = 200\left(1 - e^{-0.21}\right) = 200(1 - 0.811) \approx 38$ words

    (c) $L(15) = 200\left(1 - e^{-0.021(15)}\right) = 200\left(1 - e^{-0.315}\right) = 200(1 - 0.730) \approx 54$ words

    (d) $180 = 200\left(1 - e^{-0.021\,t}\right)$

         $0.9 = 1 - e^{-0.021t}$

$$e^{-0.021t} = 0.1 \rightarrow -0.021t = \ln(0.1) \rightarrow t = \dfrac{\ln(0.1)}{-0.021} \approx 109.65 \approx 110 \text{ days}$$

107. $R = 3e^{kx}$

    (a)

         $10 = 3e^{k(0.06)}$

         $\dfrac{10}{3} = e^{k(0.06)}$

         $\ln\left(\dfrac{10}{3}\right) = k(0.06)$

         $k = \dfrac{\ln\left(\dfrac{10}{3}\right)}{0.06} \approx 20.07$

    (b)

         $R = 3e^{(20.07)(0.17)}$

         $R = 3e^{3.4119} \approx 90.97\%$

    (c)

         $100 = 3e^{(20.07)x}$

         $\dfrac{100}{3} = e^{(20.07)x}$

         $\ln\left(\dfrac{100}{3}\right) = (20.07)x$

         $x = \dfrac{\ln\left(\dfrac{100}{3}\right)}{(20.07)} \approx 0.1747$

    (d)

         $15 = 3e^{(20.07)(x)}$

         $5 = e^{(20.07)(x)}$

         $\ln(5) = (20.07)(x)$

         $x = \dfrac{\ln(5)}{20.07} \approx 0.080$

    (e)   Answers will vary.

108.   Answers will vary.

109.   New $= \text{Old}\left(e^{R\,t}\right)$

Age	Depreciation rate	Age	Depreciation rate
1	$38000 = 36600e^{R\,(1)}$ $\dfrac{38000}{36600} = e^{R}$ $\ln\left(\dfrac{38000}{36600}\right) = R$ $\rightarrow R \approx 0.03754 = 3.8\%$	2	$38000 = 32400e^{R\,(2)}$ $\dfrac{38000}{32400} = e^{2R}$ $\ln\left(\dfrac{38000}{32400}\right) = 2R$ $\dfrac{\ln\left(\dfrac{38000}{32400}\right)}{2} = R$ $\rightarrow R \approx 0.07971 = 8\%$

Age	Depreciation rate	Age	Depreciation rate
3	$38000 = 28750e^{R\,(3)}$ $\dfrac{38000}{28750} = e^{3R}$ $\ln\left(\dfrac{38000}{28750}\right) = 3R$ $\dfrac{\ln\left(\dfrac{38000}{28750}\right)}{3} = R$ $\rightarrow R \approx 0.0930 = 9.3\%$	4	$38000 = 25400e^{R\,(4)}$ $\dfrac{38000}{25400} = e^{4R}$ $\ln\left(\dfrac{38000}{25400}\right) = 4R$ $\dfrac{\ln\left(\dfrac{38000}{24500}\right)}{4} = R$ $\rightarrow R \approx 0.1007 = 10.1\%$

Age	Depreciation rate
5	$38000 = 21200e^{R\,(5)}$ $\dfrac{38000}{21200} = e^{5R}$ $\ln\left(\dfrac{38000}{21200}\right) = 5R$ $\dfrac{\ln\left(\dfrac{38000}{21200}\right)}{5} = R \rightarrow R \approx 0.1167 = 11.7\%$

Exponential and Logarithmic Functions

6.4 Properties of Logarithms; Exponential and Logarithmic Models

1. $\log_3 3^{71} = 71$

2. $\log_2 2^{-13} = -13$

3. $\ln e^{-4} = -4$

4. $\ln e^{\sqrt{2}} = \sqrt{2}$

5. $2^{\log_2 7} = 7$

6. $e^{\ln 8} = 8$

7. $\log_8 2 + \log_8 4 = \log_8(4 \cdot 2) = \log_8(8) = 1$

8. $\log_6 9 + \log_6 4 = \log_6(9 \cdot 4) = \log_6(36) = \log_6(6^2) = 2$

9. $\log_6 18 - \log_6 3 = \log_6\left(\dfrac{18}{3}\right) = \log_6(6) = 1$

10. $\log_8 16 - \log_8 2 = \log_8\left(\dfrac{16}{2}\right) = \log_8(8) = 1$

11. $\log_2 6 \cdot \log_6 4$

$= \log_6\left(4^{\log_2 6}\right) = \log_6\left(\left(2^2\right)^{\log_2 6}\right)$

$= \log_6\left((2)^{2\log_2 6}\right) = \log_6\left((2)^{\log_2 6^2}\right) = \log_6\left(6^2\right) = 2$

12. $\log_3 8 \cdot \log_8 9$

$= \log_8\left(9^{\log_3 8}\right) = \log_8\left(\left(3^2\right)^{\log_3 8}\right)$

$= \log_8\left((3)^{2\log_3 8}\right) = \log_8\left((3)^{\log_3 8^2}\right) = \log_8\left(8^2\right) = 2$

13. $3^{\log_3 5 - \log_3 4} = 3^{\log_3\left(\frac{5}{4}\right)} = \dfrac{5}{4}$

14. $5^{\log_5 6 + \log_5 7} = 5^{\log_5(6 \cdot 7)} = 6 \cdot 7 = 42$

15. $e^{\log_{e^2} 16}$

Simplify the exponent:

$$\text{Let} \quad a = \log_{e^2} 16$$
$$\left(e^2\right)^a = 16$$
$$e^{2a} = 16 = 4^2$$
$$e^a = 4 \rightarrow a = \ln 4$$

Thus, $e^{\log_{e^2} 16} = e^{\ln 4} = 4$

16. $e^{\log_{e^2} 9}$

Simplify the exponent:

$$\text{Let} \quad a = \log_{e^2} 9$$
$$\left(e^2\right)^a = 9$$
$$e^{2a} = 9 = 3^2$$
$$e^a = 3 \rightarrow a = \ln 3$$

Thus, $e^{\log_{e^2} 9} = e^{\ln 3} = 3$

17. $\ln 6 = \ln(3 \cdot 2) = \ln 3 + \ln 2 = b + a$

18. $\ln\left(\dfrac{2}{3}\right) = \ln 2 - \ln 3 = a - b$

19. $\ln(1.5) = \ln\left(\dfrac{3}{2}\right) = \ln 3 - \ln 2 = b - a$

20. $\ln 0.5 = \ln \dfrac{1}{2} = \ln 1 - \ln 2 = 0 - a = -a$

21. $\ln 8 = \ln 2^3 = 3 \cdot \ln 2 = 3a$

22. $\ln 27 = \ln 3^3 = 3 \cdot \ln 3 = 3b$

23. $\ln \sqrt[5]{6} = \ln 6^{1/5} = \dfrac{1}{5} \cdot \ln 6 = \dfrac{1}{5} \cdot \ln(2 \cdot 3) = \dfrac{1}{5} \cdot (\ln 2 + \ln 3) = \dfrac{1}{5} \cdot (a + b)$

24. $\ln\left(\sqrt[4]{\dfrac{2}{3}}\right) = \ln\left(\dfrac{2}{3}\right)^{1/4} = \dfrac{1}{4} \cdot \ln\left(\dfrac{2}{3}\right) = \dfrac{1}{4} \cdot (\ln 2 - \ln 3) = \dfrac{1}{4} \cdot (a - b)$

25. $\log_a\left(u^2 v^3\right) = \log_a u^2 + \log_a v^3 = 2\log_a u + 3\log_a v$

26. $\log_2\left(\dfrac{a}{b^2}\right) = \log_2 a - \log_2 b^2 = \log_2 a - 2\log_2 b$

27. $\log\left(\dfrac{1}{M^3}\right) = \log M^{-3} = -3\log M$

28. $\log\left(10u^2\right) = \log 10 + \log u^2 = 1 + 2\log u$

29. $\log_5 \sqrt{\dfrac{a^3}{b}} = \log_5\left(\dfrac{a^3}{b}\right)^{1/2} = \log_5\left(\dfrac{a^{3/2}}{b^{1/2}}\right) = \log_5 a^{3/2} - \log_5 b^{1/2} = \dfrac{3}{2}\log_5 a - \dfrac{1}{2}\log_5 b$

30. $\log_6\left(\dfrac{ab^4}{\sqrt[3]{c^2}}\right) = \log_6\left(ab^4\right) - \log_6\left(c^2\right)^{1/3} = \log_6 a + \log_6 b^4 - \log_6 c^{2/3}$

$$= \log_6 a + 4\log_6 b - \dfrac{2}{3}\log_6 c$$

31. $\ln\left(x^2\sqrt{1-x}\right) = \ln x^2 + \ln\sqrt{1-x} = \ln x^2 + \ln(1-x)^{1/2} = 2\ln x + \dfrac{1}{2}\ln(1-x)$

32. $\ln\left(x\sqrt{1+x^2}\right) = \ln x + \ln\sqrt{1+x^2} = \ln x + \ln(1+x^2)^{1/2} = \ln x + \dfrac{1}{2}\ln(1+x^2)$

33. $\log_2\left(\dfrac{x^3}{x-3}\right) = \log_2 x^3 - \log_2(x-3) = 3\log_2 x - \log_2(x-3)$

34. $\log_5\left(\dfrac{\sqrt[3]{x^2+1}}{x^2-1}\right) = \log_5\left(x^2+1\right)^{1/3} - \log_5(x^2-1) = \dfrac{1}{3}\log_5\left(x^2+1\right) - \log_5\left(x^2-1\right)$

35. $\log\left[\dfrac{x(x+2)}{(x+3)^2}\right] = \log x(x+2) - \log(x+3)^2 = \log x + \log(x+2) - 2\log(x+3)$

36. $\log\left[\dfrac{x^3\sqrt{x+1}}{(x-2)^2}\right] = \log x^3\sqrt{x+1} - \log(x-2)^2 = \log x^3 + \log(x+1)^{1/2} - 2\log(x-2)$

$$= 3\log x + \dfrac{1}{2}\log(x+1) - 2\log(x-2)$$

37. $\ln\left[\dfrac{x^2-x-2}{(x+4)^2}\right]^{1/3} = \dfrac{1}{3}\ln\left[\dfrac{(x-2)(x+1)}{(x+4)^2}\right] = \dfrac{1}{3}\left[\ln(x-2)(x+1) - \ln(x+4)^2\right]$

$$= \dfrac{1}{3}\left[\ln(x-2) + \ln(x+1) - 2\ln(x+4)\right] = \dfrac{1}{3}\ln(x-2) + \dfrac{1}{3}\ln(x+1) - \dfrac{2}{3}\ln(x+4)$$

38. $\ln\left[\dfrac{(x-4)^2}{x^2-1}\right]^{2/3} = \dfrac{2}{3}\ln\left[\dfrac{(x-4)^2}{x^2-1}\right] = \dfrac{2}{3}\left[\ln(x-4)^2 - \ln\left(x^2-1\right)\right]$

$$= \dfrac{2}{3}\left[2\ln(x-4) - \ln(x-1)(x+1)\right] = \dfrac{2}{3}\left[2\ln(x-4) - \ln(x-1) - \ln(x+1)\right]$$

$$= \dfrac{4}{3}\ln(x-4) - \dfrac{2}{3}\ln(x-1) - \dfrac{2}{3}\ln(x+1)$$

39. $\ln\left(\dfrac{5x\sqrt{1-3x}}{(x-4)^3}\right) = \ln 5x\sqrt{1-3x} - \ln(x-4)^3 = \ln 5 + \ln x + \ln\sqrt{1-3x} - 3\ln(x-4)$

$$= \ln 5 + \ln x + \ln(1-3x)^{1/2} - 3\ln(x-4) = \ln 5 + \ln x + \dfrac{1}{2}\ln(1-3x) - 3\ln(x-4)$$

40. $\ln\left[\dfrac{5x^2\sqrt[3]{1-x}}{4(x+1)^2}\right] = \ln\left(5x^2\sqrt[3]{1-x}\right) - \ln\left(4(x+1)^2\right)$

$$= \ln 5 + \ln x^2 + \ln(1-x)^{1/3} - \left[\ln 4 + \ln(x+1)^2\right]$$

$$= \ln 5 + 2\ln x + \dfrac{1}{3}\ln(1-x) - \ln 4 - 2\ln(x+1)$$

41. $3\log_5 u + 4\log_5 v = \log_5 u^3 + \log_5 v^4 = \log_5(u^3 v^4)$

42. $\log_3 u^2 - \log_3 v = \log_3\left(\dfrac{u^2}{v}\right)$

43. $\log_{\frac{1}{2}}\sqrt{x} - \log_{\frac{1}{2}} x^3 = \log_{\frac{1}{2}}\left(\dfrac{\sqrt{x}}{x^3}\right) = \log_{\frac{1}{2}}\left(\dfrac{x^{1/2}}{x^3}\right) = \log_{\frac{1}{2}} x^{-5/2} = -\dfrac{5}{2}\log_{\frac{1}{2}} x$

44. $\log_2\left(\dfrac{1}{x}\right) + \log_2\left(\dfrac{1}{x^2}\right) = \log_2\left(\dfrac{1}{x}\cdot\dfrac{1}{x^2}\right) = \log_2\left(\dfrac{1}{x^3}\right) = \log_2 x^{-3} = -3\log_2 x$

45. $\ln\left(\dfrac{x}{x-1}\right) + \ln\left(\dfrac{x+1}{x}\right) - \ln(x^2-1) = \ln\left[\dfrac{x}{x-1}\cdot\dfrac{x+1}{x}\right] - \ln(x^2-1) = \ln\left[\dfrac{x+1}{x-1}\div(x^2-1)\right]$

$= \ln\left[\dfrac{x+1}{(x-1)(x-1)(x+1)}\right] = \ln\dfrac{1}{(x-1)^2} = \ln(x-1)^{-2} = -2\ln(x-1)$

46. $\log\left(\dfrac{x^2+2x-3}{x^2-4}\right) - \log\left(\dfrac{x^2+7x+6}{x+2}\right) = \log\left[\dfrac{\left(\dfrac{x^2+2x-3}{x^2-4}\right)}{\left(\dfrac{x^2+7x+6}{x+2}\right)}\right]$

$= \log\left(\dfrac{(x+3)(x-1)}{(x-2)(x+2)}\cdot\dfrac{x+2}{(x+6)(x+1)}\right) = \log\left(\dfrac{(x+3)(x-1)}{(x-2)(x+6)(x+1)}\right)$

47. $8\log_2\sqrt{3x-2} - \log_2\left(\dfrac{4}{x}\right) + \log_2 4 = \log_2\left(\sqrt{3x-2}\right)^8 - (\log_2 4 - \log_2 x) + \log_2 4$

$= \log_2(3x-2)^4 - \log_2 4 + \log_2 x + \log_2 4 = \log_2\left[x(3x-2)^4\right]$

48. $21\log_3\sqrt[3]{x} + \log_3\left(9x^2\right) - \log_3 25 = \log_3\left(x^{1/3}\right)^{21} + \log_3\left(9x^2\right) - \log_3 25$

$= \log_3\left(x^7\cdot 9x^2\right) - \log_3 25 = \log_3\left(\dfrac{9x^9}{25}\right)$

49. $2\log_a 5x^3 - \dfrac{1}{2}\log_a(2x+3) = \log_a\left(5x^3\right)^2 - \log_a(2x-3)^{1/2} = \log_a\left[\dfrac{25x^6}{(2x-3)^{1/2}}\right]$

50. $\dfrac{1}{3}\log\left(x^3+1\right) + \dfrac{1}{2}\log\left(x^2+1\right) = \log\left(x^3+1\right)^{1/3} + \log\left(x^2+1\right)^{1/2} = \log\left[\sqrt[3]{x^3+1}\cdot\sqrt{x^2+1}\right]$

51. $\log_3 21 = \dfrac{\log 21}{\log 3} \approx \dfrac{1.32222}{0.47712} \approx 2.771$

52. $\log_5 18 = \dfrac{\log 18}{\log 5} \approx \dfrac{1.25527}{0.69897} \approx 1.796$

53. $\log_{\frac{1}{3}} 71 = \dfrac{\log 71}{\log\left(\dfrac{1}{3}\right)} = \dfrac{\log 71}{-\log 3} \approx \dfrac{1.85126}{-0.47712} \approx -3.880$

54. $\log_{\frac{1}{2}} 15 = \dfrac{\log 15}{\log\left(\dfrac{1}{2}\right)} = \dfrac{\log 15}{-\log 2} \approx \dfrac{1.17609}{-0.30103} \approx -3.907$

55. $\log_{\sqrt{2}} 7 = \dfrac{\log 7}{\log \sqrt{2}} = \dfrac{\log 7}{\log 2^{1/2}} = \dfrac{\log 7}{\left(\dfrac{1}{2}\log 2\right)} \approx \dfrac{0.84510}{0.5(0.30103)} \approx 5.615$

56. $\log_{\sqrt{5}} 8 = \dfrac{\log 8}{\log \sqrt{5}} = \dfrac{\log 8}{\log 5^{1/2}} = \dfrac{\log 8}{\left(\dfrac{1}{2}\log 5\right)} \approx \dfrac{0.90309}{0.5(0.69897)} \approx 2.584$

57. $\log_\pi e = \dfrac{\ln e}{\ln \pi} \approx \dfrac{1}{1.14473} \approx 0.874$

58. $\log_\pi \sqrt{2} = \dfrac{\ln \sqrt{2}}{\ln \pi} = \dfrac{\ln 2^{1/2}}{\ln \pi} = \dfrac{\left(\dfrac{1}{2}\ln 2\right)}{\ln \pi}$
$\approx \dfrac{0.5(0.69315)}{1.14473} \approx 0.303$

59. $\log_2 3 \cdot \log_3 4 \cdot \log_4 5 \cdot \log_5 6 \cdot \log_6 7 \cdot \log_7 8$
$= \dfrac{\log 3}{\log 2} \cdot \dfrac{\log 4}{\log 3} \cdot \dfrac{\log 5}{\log 4} \cdot \dfrac{\log 6}{\log 5} \cdot \dfrac{\log 7}{\log 6} \cdot \dfrac{\log 8}{\log 7} = \dfrac{\log 8}{\log 2} = \dfrac{\log 2^3}{\log 2} = \dfrac{3\log 2}{\log 2} = 3$

60. $\log_2 4 \cdot \log_4 6 \cdot \log_6 8 = \dfrac{\log 4}{\log 2} \cdot \dfrac{\log 6}{\log 4} \cdot \dfrac{\log 8}{\log 6} = \dfrac{\log 8}{\log 2} = \dfrac{\log 2^3}{\log 2} = \dfrac{3\log 2}{\log 2} = 3$

61. $\log_2 3 \cdot \log_3 4 \cdot \ldots \cdot \log_n (n+1) \cdot \log_{n+1} 2$
$= \dfrac{\log 3}{\log 2} \cdot \dfrac{\log 4}{\log 3} \cdot \ldots \cdot \dfrac{\log(n+1)}{\log n} \cdot \dfrac{\log 2}{\log(n+1)} = \dfrac{\log 2}{\log 2} = 1$

62. $\log_2 2 \cdot \log_2 4 \cdot \ldots \cdot \log_2 2^n = \log_2 2 \cdot \log_2 2^2 \cdot \ldots \cdot \log_2 2^n = 1 \cdot 2 \cdot 3 \cdot \ldots \cdot n = n!$

63. $y = \log_4 x = \dfrac{\ln x}{\ln 4}$ or $y = \dfrac{\log x}{\log 4}$

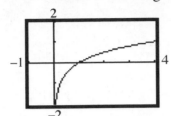

64. $y = \log_5 x = \dfrac{\ln x}{\ln 5}$ or $y = \dfrac{\log x}{\log 5}$

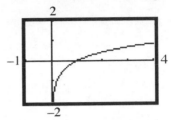

65. $y = \log_2(x + 2) = \dfrac{\ln(x + 2)}{\ln 2}$
or $y = \dfrac{\log(x + 2)}{\log 2}$

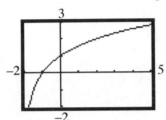

66. $y = \log_4(x - 3) = \dfrac{\ln(x - 3)}{\ln 4}$
or $y = \dfrac{\log(x - 3)}{\log 4}$

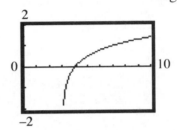

67. $y = \log_{x-1}(x + 1) = \dfrac{\ln(x + 1)}{\ln(x - 1)}$
or $y = \dfrac{\log(x + 1)}{\log(x - 1)}$

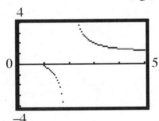

68. $y = \log_{x+2}(x - 2) = \dfrac{\ln(x - 2)}{\ln(x + 2)}$
or $y = \dfrac{\log(x - 2)}{\log(x + 2)}$

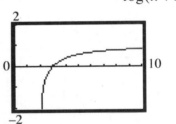

69. $\ln y = \ln x + \ln C$
$\ln y = \ln(xC)$
$y = Cx$

70. $\ln y = \ln(x + C)$
$y = x + C$

71. $\ln y = \ln x + \ln(x + 1) + \ln C$
$\ln y = \ln(x(x + 1)C)$
$y = Cx(x + 1)$

72. $\ln y = 2\ln x - \ln(x + 1) + \ln C$
$\ln y = \ln\left(\dfrac{x^2 C}{x + 1}\right) \rightarrow y = \dfrac{Cx^2}{x + 1}$

73. $\ln y = 3x + \ln C$
$\ln y = \ln e^{3x} + \ln C$
$\ln y = \ln(Ce^{3x})$
$y = Ce^{3x}$

74. $\ln y = -2x + \ln C$
$\ln y = \ln e^{-2x} + \ln C$
$\ln y = \ln(Ce^{-2x})$
$y = Ce^{-2x}$

75. $\ln(y-3) = -4x + \ln C$

   $\ln(y-3) = \ln e^{-4x} + \ln C$

   $\ln(y-3) = \ln\left(Ce^{-4x}\right)$

   $y-3 = Ce^{-4x} \rightarrow y = Ce^{-4x} + 3$

76. $\ln(y+4) = 5x + \ln C$

   $\ln(y+4) = \ln e^{5x} + \ln C$

   $\ln(y+4) = \ln\left(Ce^{5x}\right)$

   $y+4 = Ce^{5x} \rightarrow y = Ce^{5x} - 4$

77. $3\ln y = \dfrac{1}{2}\ln(2x+1) - \dfrac{1}{3}\ln(x+4) + \ln C$

   $\ln y^3 = \ln(2x+1)^{1/2} - \ln(x+4)^{1/3} + \ln C$

   $\ln y^3 = \ln\left[\dfrac{C(2x+1)^{1/2}}{(x+4)^{1/3}}\right]$

   $y^3 = \dfrac{C(2x+1)^{1/2}}{(x+4)^{1/3}}$

   $y = \left[\dfrac{C(2x+1)^{1/2}}{(x+4)^{\frac{1}{3}}}\right]^{1/3}$

   $y = \dfrac{\sqrt[3]{C}(2x+1)^{1/6}}{(x+4)^{1/9}}$

78. $2\ln y = -\dfrac{1}{2}\ln x + \dfrac{1}{3}\ln\left(x^2+1\right) + \ln C$

   $\ln y^2 = -\ln x^{1/2} + \ln\left(x^2+1\right)^{1/3} + \ln C$

   $\ln y^2 = \ln\left[\dfrac{C\left(x^2+1\right)^{1/3}}{x^{1/2}}\right]$

   $y^2 = \dfrac{C\left(x^2+1\right)^{1/3}}{x^{1/2}}$

   $y = \left[\dfrac{C\left(x^2+1\right)^{1/3}}{x^{1/2}}\right]^{1/2}$

   $y = \dfrac{\sqrt{C}\left(x^2+1\right)^{1/6}}{x^{1/4}}$

79. Verifying:

   $\log_a\left(x+\sqrt{x^2-1}\right) + \log_a\left(x-\sqrt{x^2-1}\right) = \log_a\left[\left(x+\sqrt{x^2-1}\right)\left(x-\sqrt{x^2-1}\right)\right]$

   $= \log_a\left[x^2 - \left(x^2-1\right)\right] = \log_a\left[x^2 - x^2 + 1\right] = \log_a 1 = 0$

80. Verifying:

   $\log_a\left(\sqrt{x}+\sqrt{x-1}\right) + \log_a\left(\sqrt{x}-\sqrt{x-1}\right) = \log_a\left[\left(\sqrt{x}+\sqrt{x-1}\right)\left(\sqrt{x}-\sqrt{x-1}\right)\right]$

   $= \log_a\left[x - (x-1)\right] = \log_a\left[x - x + 1\right] = \log_a 1 = 0$

81. Verifying:

   $2x + \ln\left(1+e^{-2x}\right) = \ln e^{2x} + \ln\left(1+e^{-2x}\right) = \ln\left(e^{2x}\left(1+e^{-2x}\right)\right) = \ln\left(e^{2x}+e^{0}\right) = \ln\left(e^{2x}+1\right)$

82. Verifying:

   $\dfrac{f(x+h)-f(x)}{h} = \dfrac{\log_a(x+h) - \log_a x}{h} = \dfrac{\log\left(\dfrac{x+h}{x}\right)}{h} = \dfrac{1}{h}\cdot\log\left(1+\dfrac{h}{x}\right) = \log\left(1+\dfrac{h}{x}\right)^{\frac{1}{h}}$

83. $f(x) = \log_a x$

   $x = a^{f(x)} \rightarrow x^{-1} = a^{-f(x)} = \left(a^{-1}\right)^{f(x)} = \left(\dfrac{1}{a}\right)^{f(x)}$

   $\log_{\frac{1}{a}} x^{-1} = f(x) \rightarrow -\log_{\frac{1}{a}} x = f(x) \rightarrow -f(x) = \log_{\frac{1}{a}} x$

84. $f(AB) = \log_a(AB) = \log_a A + \log_a B = f(A) + f(B)$

85. $f(x) = \log_a x$

$$a^{f(x)} = x \quad \rightarrow \quad \frac{1}{a^{f(x)}} = \frac{1}{x} \quad \rightarrow \quad a^{-f(x)} = \frac{1}{x} \quad \rightarrow \quad -f(x) = \log_a \frac{1}{x} = f\left(\frac{1}{x}\right)$$

86. $f\left(x^\alpha\right) = \log_a x^\alpha = \alpha \log_a x = \alpha \cdot f(x)$

87.   If $A = \log_a M$ and $B = \log_a N$, then $a^A = M$ and $a^B = N$.

$$\log_a\left(\frac{M}{N}\right) = \log_a\left(\frac{a^A}{a^B}\right) = \log_a a^{A-B} = A - B = \log_a M - \log_a N$$

88. $\log_a\left(\dfrac{1}{N}\right) = \log_a N^{-1} = -1 \cdot \log_a N = -\log_a N, \quad a \neq 1$

89.   (a)   Graphing:

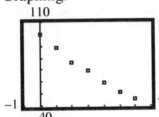

$$A = 100e^{-0.1278(50)}$$

(d) ≈ 0.1678 grams

(e) and (f) Graphing:

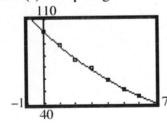

(b) $y = 100(0.88)^x$

$0.88 = e^{\ln(0.88)}$

$\rightarrow y = 100\left(e^{\ln(0.88)}\right)^x = 100e^{\ln(0.88)x}$

$A = A_0 e^{-0.1278t},\ A_0 = 100$

(c)

$100e^{-0.1278t} = 50$

$e^{-0.1278t} = \dfrac{50}{100}$

$e^{-0.1278t} = 0.5$

$\ln\left(e^{-0.1278t}\right) = \ln(0.5)$

$-0.1278t = \ln(0.5)$

$t = \dfrac{\ln(0.5)}{-0.1278} \approx 5.42$ weeks

90.   (a)   Graphing:

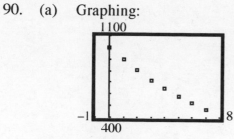

$$A = 999e^{-0.1076(20)}$$

(d) ≈ 116.14 grams

(e) and (f)   Graphing:

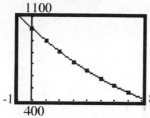

(b) $y = 999(0.898)^t$

$0.898 = e^{\ln(0.898)}$

$\rightarrow y = 999\left(e^{\ln(0.898)}\right)^x = 999e^{\ln(0.898)x}$

$A = A_0 e^{-0.1076t}, A_0 = 999$

(c)

$999e^{-0.1076t} = 500$

$e^{-0.1076t} = \dfrac{500}{999}$

$\ln(e^{-0.1076t}) = \ln\left(\dfrac{500}{999}\right)$

$-0.1076t = \ln\left(\dfrac{500}{999}\right)$

$t = \dfrac{\ln\left(\dfrac{500}{999}\right)}{-0.1076} \approx 6.43$ days

91.   (a)   Graphing:

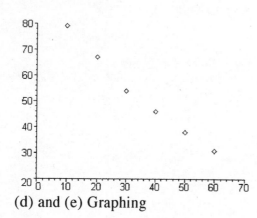

(d) and (e) Graphing

(b) $y = 96(0.98)^x$

$0.98 = e^{\ln(0.98)}$

$\rightarrow y = 96\left(e^{\ln(0.98)}\right)^x = 96e^{\ln(0.98)x}$

$A = A_0 e^{-0.0202t}, A_0 = 96$

(c)

$96e^{-0.0202t} = 60$

$e^{-0.0202t} = \dfrac{60}{96}$

$\ln(e^{-0.0202t}) = \ln\left(\dfrac{60}{96}\right)$

$-0.0202t = \ln\left(\dfrac{60}{96}\right)$

$t = \dfrac{\ln\left(\dfrac{60}{96}\right)}{-0.0202} \approx 23$ shoes

92. **(a)** Graphing:

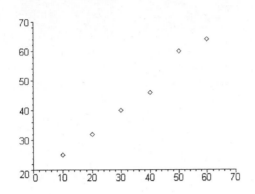

(d) and (e) Graphing:

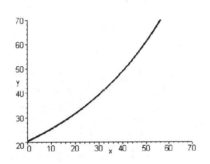

(b) $y = 20.524(1.022)^x$

$1.022 = e^{\ln(1.022)}$

$\rightarrow y = 20.524\left(e^{\ln(1.022)}\right)^x = 20.524 e^{\ln(1.022)x}$

$A = A_0 e^{0.0218t}, \ A_0 = 20.524$

(c)

$20.524 e^{0.0218t} = 45$

$e^{0.0218t} = \dfrac{45}{20.524}$

$\ln\left(e^{0.0218t}\right) = \ln\left(\dfrac{45}{20.524}\right)$

$0.0218t = \ln\left(\dfrac{45}{20.524}\right)$

$t = \dfrac{\ln\left(\dfrac{45}{20.524}\right)}{0.0218} \approx 36 \ \ \text{dresses}$

93. **(a)** Graphing:

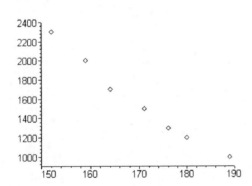

(c) and (d) Graphing:

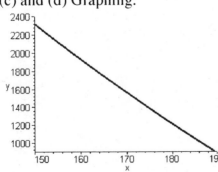

(b)

$y = 32741 - 6071 \cdot \ln x$

$1650 = 32741 - 6071 \cdot \ln x$

$-31091 = -6071 \cdot \ln x$

$\dfrac{-31091}{-6071} = \ln x$

$\dfrac{31091}{6071} = \ln x$

$e^{\left(\frac{31091}{6071}\right)} = e^{\ln x} = x$

$x \approx 168 \ \ \text{computers}$

94.

domain of $f(x) = \log_a x^2$ is all real numbers $\neq 0$

domain of $g(x) = 2\log_a x$ is all real numbers > 0

These two domains are different because the logarithm property $\log_a x^n = n \cdot \log_a x$ holds only when $\log_a x$ exists

Exponential and Logarithmic Functions

6.5 Logarithmic and Exponential Equations

1. $\log_4(x+2) = \log_4 8$
    $x+2 = 8 \to x = 6$

2. $\log_5(2x+3) = \log_5 3$
    $2x+3 = 3 \to 2x = 0$
    $x = 0$

3. $\dfrac{1}{2}\log_3 x = 2\log_3 2$
    $\log_3 x^{1/2} = \log_3 2^2$
    $x^{1/2} = 4 \to x = 16$

4. $-2\log_4 x = \log_4 9$
    $\log_4 x^{-2} = \log_4 9$
    $x^{-2} = 9$
    $\dfrac{1}{x^2} = 9 \to x^2 = \dfrac{1}{9} \to x = \pm\dfrac{1}{3}$
    Since $\log_4\left(-\dfrac{1}{3}\right)$ is undefined, the
    only solution is $x = \dfrac{1}{3}$.

5. $2\log_5 x = 3\log_5 4$
    $\log_5 x^2 = \log_5 4^3$
    $x^2 = 64$
    $x = \pm 8$
    Since $\log_5(-8)$ is undefined, the
    only solution is $x = 8$.

6. $3\log_2 x = -\log_2 27$
    $\log_2 x^3 = \log_2 27^{-1}$
    $x^3 = 27^{-1}$
    $x^3 = \dfrac{1}{27} \to x = \dfrac{1}{3}$

7. $3\log_2(x-1) + \log_2 4 = 5$
    $\log_2(x-1)^3 + \log_2 4 = 5$
    $\log_2 4(x-1)^3 = 5$
    $4(x-1)^3 = 2^5$
    $(x-1)^3 = \dfrac{32}{4}$
    $(x-1)^3 = 8$
    $x-1 = 2$
    $x = 3$

8. $2\log_3(x+4) - \log_3 9 = 2$
    $\log_3(x+4)^2 - \log_3 3^2 = 2$
    $\log_3(x+4)^2 - 2 = 2$
    $\log_3(x+4)^2 = 4$
    $(x+4)^2 = 3^4$
    $(x+4)^2 = 81$
    $x+4 = \pm 9$
    $x = -4 \pm 9$
    $x = 5 \text{ or } x = -13$
    Since $\log_3(-13+4)$ is undefined,
    the only solution is $x = 5$.

9.　$\log x + \log(x + 15) = 2$

　　$\log x(x + 15) = 2$

　　　$x(x + 15) = 10^2$

　$x^2 + 15x - 100 = 0 \rightarrow (x + 20)(x - 5) = 0$

　　　　　$x = -20$ or $x = 5$

Since $\log(-20)$ is undefined, the
only solution is $x = 5$.

10.　$\log_4 x + \log_4(x - 3) = 1$

　　$\log_4 x(x - 3) = 1$

　　　$x(x - 3) = 4^1$

　$x^2 - 3x - 4 = 0 \rightarrow (x + 1)(x - 4) = 0$

　　　　　$x = -1$ or $x = 4$

Since $\log_4(-1)$ is undefined, the
only solution is $x = 4$.

11.　$\ln x + \ln(x + 2) = 4$

　　$\ln x(x + 2) = 4$

　　　　$x(x + 2) = e^4 \rightarrow x^2 + 2x - e^4 = 0$

$$x = \frac{-2 \pm \sqrt{2^2 - 4(1)(-e^4)}}{2(1)} = \frac{-2 \pm \sqrt{4 + 4e^4}}{2}$$

$$= \frac{-2 \pm 2\sqrt{1 + e^4}}{2} = -1 \pm \sqrt{1 + e^4}$$

Since $\ln\left(-1 - \sqrt{1 + e^4}\right)$ is undefined, the only solution is $x = -1 + \sqrt{1 + e^4} \approx 6.456$.

12.　$\ln(x + 1) - \ln x = 2$

$$\ln\left(\frac{x + 1}{x}\right) = 2 \rightarrow \frac{x + 1}{x} = e^2$$

$$x + 1 = e^2 x \rightarrow e^2 x - x = 1 \rightarrow x(e^2 - 1) = 1 \rightarrow x = \frac{1}{e^2 - 1}$$

13.　$2^{2x} + 2^x - 12 = 0$

　　$(2^x)^2 + 2^x - 12 = 0$

　　$(2^x - 3)(2^x + 4) = 0$

　　　　$2^x - 3 = 0$　　　or $2^x + 4 = 0$

　　　　　$2^x = 3$　　　or　　$2^x = -4$

　　　　$x = \log_2 3$　　　No solution

　　　　$x \approx 1.585$

14.　$3^{2x} + 3^x - 2 = 0$

　　$(3^x)^2 + 3^x - 2 = 0$

　　$(3^x - 1)(3^x + 2) = 0$

　　　　$3^x - 1 = 0$　　　or $3^x + 2 = 0$

　　　　　$3^x = 1$　　　or　　$3^x = -2$

　　　　　$x = 0$　　　No solution

15. $$3^{2x} + 3^{x+1} - 4 = 0$$
$$\left(3^x\right)^2 + 3 \cdot 3^x - 4 = 0$$
$$\left(3^x - 1\right)\left(3^x + 4\right) = 0$$
$$3^x - 1 = 0 \quad \text{or} \quad 3^x + 4 = 0$$
$$3^x = 1 \quad \text{or} \quad 3^x = -4$$
$$x = 0 \qquad \text{No solution}$$

16. $$2^{2x} + 2^{x+2} - 12 = 0$$
$$\left(2^x\right)^2 + 2^2 \cdot 2^x - 12 = 0$$
$$\left(2^x - 2\right)\left(2^x + 6\right) = 0$$
$$2^x - 2 = 0 \quad \text{or} \quad 2^x + 6 = 0$$
$$2^x = 2 \quad \text{or} \quad 2^x = -6$$
$$x = 1 \qquad \text{No solution}$$

17. $$2^x = 10$$
$$\log\left(2^x\right) = \log 10$$
$$x \log 2 = 1$$
$$x = \frac{1}{\log 2} \approx 3.322$$

18. $$3^x = 14$$
$$\log\left(3^x\right) = \log 14$$
$$x \log 3 = \log 14$$
$$x = \frac{\log 14}{\log 3} \approx 2.402$$

19. $$8^{-x} = 1.2$$
$$\log\left(8^{-x}\right) = \log 1.2$$
$$-x \log 8 = \log 1.2$$
$$x = \frac{\log 1.2}{-\log 8} \approx -0.088$$

20. $$2^{-x} = 1.5$$
$$\log\left(2^{-x}\right) = \log 1.5$$
$$-x \log 2 = \log 1.5$$
$$x = \frac{\log 1.5}{-\log 2} \approx -0.585$$

21. $$3^{1-2x} = 4^x$$
$$\log\left(3^{1-2x}\right) = \log\left(4^x\right)$$
$$(1 - 2x)\log 3 = x \log 4$$
$$\log 3 - 2x \log 3 = x \log 4 \rightarrow \log 3 = x \log 4 + 2x \log 3 \rightarrow \log 3 = x(\log 4 + 2\log 3)$$
$$x = \frac{\log 3}{\log 4 + 2\log 3} \approx 0.307$$

22. $$2^{x+1} = 5^{1-2x}$$
$$\log\left(2^{x+1}\right) = \log\left(5^{1-2x}\right)$$
$$(x + 1)\log 2 = (1 - 2x)\log 5$$
$$x \log 2 + \log 2 = \log 5 - 2x \log 5 \rightarrow x \log 2 + 2x \log 5 = \log 5 - \log 2$$
$$x(\log 2 + 2\log 5) = \log 5 - \log 2 \rightarrow x = \frac{\log 5 - \log 2}{\log 2 + 2\log 5} \approx 0.234$$

23.

$$\left(\frac{3}{5}\right)^{x} = 7^{1-x}$$

$$\log\left(\left(\frac{3}{5}\right)^{x}\right) = \log\left(7^{1-x}\right)$$

$$x\log\left(\frac{3}{5}\right) = (1-x)\log 7 \rightarrow x(\log 3 - \log 5) = \log 7 - x\log 7$$

$$x\log 3 - x\log 5 + x\log 7 = \log 7 \rightarrow x(\log 3 - \log 5 + \log 7) = \log 7$$

$$x = \frac{\log 7}{\log 3 - \log 5 + \log 7} \approx 1.356$$

24.

$$\left(\frac{4}{3}\right)^{1-x} = 5^{x}$$

$$\log\left(\left(\frac{4}{3}\right)^{1-x}\right) = \log\left(5^{x}\right)$$

$$(1-x)\log\left(\frac{4}{3}\right) = x\log 5$$

$$\log\left(\frac{4}{3}\right) - x\log\left(\frac{4}{3}\right) = x\log 5$$

$$x\log 5 + x\log\left(\frac{4}{3}\right) = \log\left(\frac{4}{3}\right)$$

$$x\left(\log 5 + \log\left(\frac{4}{3}\right)\right) = \log\left(\frac{4}{3}\right)$$

$$x = \frac{\log\left(\frac{4}{3}\right)}{\log 5 + \log\left(\frac{4}{3}\right)} \approx 0.152$$

25.

$$1.2^{x} = (0.5)^{-x}$$

$$\log 1.2^{x} = \log(0.5)^{-x}$$

$$x\log 1.2 = -x\log 0.5$$

$$x\log 1.2 + x\log 0.5 = 0$$

$$x(\log 1.2 + \log 0.5) = 0$$

$$x = 0$$

26.

$$0.3^{1+x} = 1.7^{2x-1}$$

$$\log\left(0.3^{1+x}\right) = \log\left(1.7^{2x-1}\right)$$

$$(1+x)\log 0.3 = (2x-1)\log 1.7$$

$$\log 0.3 + x\log 0.3 = 2x\log 1.7 - \log 1.7$$

$$x\log 0.3 - 2x\log 1.7 = -\log 1.7 - \log 0.3 \rightarrow x(\log 0.3 - 2\log 1.7) = -\log 1.7 - \log 0.3$$

$$x = \frac{-\log 1.7 - \log 0.3}{\log 0.3 - 2\log 1.7} \approx -0.297$$

27.
$$\pi^{1-x} = e^x$$
$$\ln \pi^{1-x} = \ln e^x$$
$$(1-x)\ln \pi = x$$
$$\ln \pi - x \ln \pi = x$$
$$\ln \pi = x + x \ln \pi$$
$$\ln \pi = x(1 + \ln \pi)$$
$$x = \frac{\ln \pi}{1 + \ln \pi} \approx 0.534$$

28.
$$e^{x+3} = \pi^x$$
$$\ln e^{x+3} = \ln \pi^x$$
$$x + 3 = x \ln \pi$$
$$x - x \ln \pi = -3$$
$$x(1 - \ln \pi) = -3$$
$$x = \frac{-3}{1 - \ln \pi} \approx 20.728$$

29.
$$5\left(2^{3x}\right) = 8$$
$$2^{3x} = \frac{8}{5}$$
$$\log 2^{3x} = \log\left(\frac{8}{5}\right)$$
$$3x \log 2 = \log 8 - \log 5$$
$$x = \frac{\log 8 - \log 5}{3 \log 2} \approx 0.226$$

30.
$$0.3\left(4^{0.2x}\right) = 0.2$$
$$4^{0.2x} = \frac{2}{3}$$
$$\log 4^{0.2x} = \log\left(\frac{2}{3}\right)$$
$$0.2x \log 4 = \log 2 - \log 3$$
$$x = \frac{\log 2 - \log 3}{0.2 \log 4} \approx -1.462$$

31. $\log_a(x-1) - \log_a(x+6) = \log_a(x-2) - \log_a(x+3)$

$$\log_a\left(\frac{x-1}{x+6}\right) = \log_a\left(\frac{x-2}{x+3}\right) \rightarrow a^{\left(\log_a\left(\frac{x-1}{x+6}\right)\right)} = a^{\left(\log_a\left(\frac{x-2}{x+3}\right)\right)}$$

so

$$\frac{x-1}{x+6} = \frac{x-2}{x+3} \rightarrow (x-1)(x+3) = (x-2)(x+6)$$

$$x^2 + 2x - 3 = x^2 + 4x - 12 \rightarrow 2x - 3 = 4x - 12 \rightarrow 9 = 2x \rightarrow x = \frac{9}{2}$$

Since each of the original logarithms is defined for $x = \frac{9}{2}$, the solution is $x = \frac{9}{2}$.

32.
$$\log_a x + \log_a(x-2) = \log_a(x+4)$$
$$\log_a\left(x(x-2)\right) = \log_a(x+4)$$
$$x(x-2) = x+4$$
$$x^2 - 2x = x+4$$
$$x^2 - 3x - 4 = 0$$
$$(x-4)(x+1) = 0$$
$$x = 4 \text{ or } x = -1$$

Since $\log_a(-1)$ is undefined, the only solution is $x = 4$.

33. $\log_{\frac{1}{3}}(x^2 + x) - \log_{\frac{1}{3}}(x^2 - x) = -1$

$\log_{\frac{1}{3}}\left(\dfrac{x^2 + x}{x^2 - x}\right) = -1$

$\dfrac{x^2 + x}{x^2 - x} = \left(\dfrac{1}{3}\right)^{-1}$

$\dfrac{x(x+1)}{x(x-1)} = 3 \to x + 1 = 3(x - 1)$

$x + 1 = 3x - 3 \to -2x = -4 \to x = 2$

34. $\log_4(x^2 - 9) - \log_4(x + 3) = 3$

$\log_4\left(\dfrac{x^2 - 9}{x + 3}\right) = 3$

$\dfrac{(x-3)(x+3)}{x+3} = 4^3 \to x - 3 = 64 \to x = 67$

35. $\log_2(x + 1) - \log_4 x = 1$

$\log_2(x+1) - \dfrac{\log_2 x}{\log_2 4} = 1$

$\log_2(x+1) - \dfrac{\log_2 x}{2} = 1$

$2\log_2(x+1) - \log_2 x = 2$

$\log_2(x+1)^2 - \log_2 x = 2$

$\log_2 \dfrac{(x+1)^2}{x} = 2$

$\dfrac{(x+1)^2}{x} = 2^2$

$x^2 + 2x + 1 = 4x$

$x^2 - 2x + 1 = 0$

$(x - 1)^2 = 0$

$x - 1 = 0$

$x = 1$

36. $\log_2(3x + 2) - \log_4 x = 3$

$\log_2(3x+2) - \dfrac{\log_2 x}{\log_2 4} = 3$

$\log_2(3x+2) - \dfrac{\log_2 x}{2} = 3$

$2\log_2(3x+2) - \log_2 x = 6$

$\log_2(3x+2)^2 - \log_2 x = 6$

$\log_2 \dfrac{(3x+2)^2}{x} = 6$

$\dfrac{(3x+2)^2}{x} = 2^6$

$9x^2 + 12x + 4 = 64x$

$9x^2 - 52x + 4 = 0$

$x = \dfrac{52 \pm \sqrt{(-52)^2 - 4(9)(4)}}{2(9)}$

$= \dfrac{52 \pm \sqrt{2560}}{18} \approx 5.70 \text{ or } 0.08$

37. $\log_{16} x + \log_4 x + \log_2 x = 7$

$\dfrac{\log_2 x}{\log_2 16} + \dfrac{\log_2 x}{\log_2 4} + \log_2 x = 7$

$\dfrac{\log_2 x}{4} + \dfrac{\log_2 x}{2} + \log_2 x = 7$

$\log_2 x + 2\log_2 x + 4\log_2 x = 28$

$7\log_2 x = 28$

$\log_2 x = 4$

$x = 2^4 = 16$

38. $\log_9 x + 3\log_3 x = 14$

$\dfrac{\log_3 x}{\log_3 9} + 3\log_3 x = 14$

$\dfrac{\log_3 x}{2} + 3\log_3 x = 14$

$\dfrac{7}{2}\log_3 x = 14$

$\log_3 x = 4$

$x = 3^4 = 81$

39. $\left(\sqrt[3]{2}\right)^{2-x} = 2^{x^2}$

$\left(2^{1/3}\right)^{2-x} = 2^{x^2}$

$2^{\frac{1}{3}(2-x)} = 2^{x^2}$

$\frac{1}{3}(2-x) = x^2 \rightarrow 2-x = 3x^2$

$3x^2 + x - 2 = 0 \rightarrow (3x-2)(x+1) = 0$

$x = \frac{2}{3}$ or $x = -1$

40. $\log_2 x^{\log_2 x} = 4$

$\log_2 x \cdot \log_2 x = 4$

$\left(\log_2 x\right)^2 = 4$

$\log_2 x = -2$ or $\log_2 x = 2$

$x = 2^{-2}$ or $x = 2^2$

$x = \frac{1}{4}$ or $x = 4$

41. $\dfrac{e^x + e^{-x}}{2} = 1$

$e^x + e^{-x} = 2$

$e^x\left(e^x + e^{-x}\right) = 2e^x$

$e^{2x} + 1 = 2e^x$

$(e^x)^2 - 2e^x + 1 = 0$

$\left(e^x - 1\right)^2 = 0$

$e^x - 1 = 0$

$e^x = 1$

$x = 0$

42. $\dfrac{e^x + e^{-x}}{2} = 3$

$e^x + e^{-x} = 6$

$e^x\left(e^x + e^{-x}\right) = 6e^x$

$e^{2x} + 1 = 6e^x$

$(e^x)^2 - 6e^x + 1 = 0$

$e^x = \dfrac{6 \pm \sqrt{(-6)^2 - 4(1)(1)}}{2(1)} = \dfrac{6 \pm \sqrt{32}}{2}$

$= \dfrac{6 \pm 4\sqrt{2}}{2} = 3 \pm 2\sqrt{2}$

$x = \ln\left(3 + 2\sqrt{2}\right)$ or $x = \ln\left(3 - 2\sqrt{2}\right)$

43. $\dfrac{e^x - e^{-x}}{2} = 2$

$e^x - e^{-x} = 4 \rightarrow e^x\left(e^x - e^{-x}\right) = 4e^x \rightarrow e^{2x} - 1 = 4e^x \rightarrow (e^x)^2 - 4e^x - 1 = 0$

$e^x = \dfrac{-(-4) \pm \sqrt{(-4)^2 - 4(1)(-1)}}{2(1)} = \dfrac{4 \pm \sqrt{20}}{2} = \dfrac{4 \pm 2\sqrt{5}}{2} = 2 \pm \sqrt{5}$

$x = \ln\left(2 + \sqrt{5}\right)$

Since $\ln\left(2 - \sqrt{5}\right)$ is undefined; it is not a solution.

44. $\dfrac{e^x - e^{-x}}{2} = -2$

$e^x - e^{-x} = -4 \rightarrow e^x\left(e^x - e^{-x}\right) = -4e^x \rightarrow e^{2x} - 1 = -4e^x \rightarrow (e^x)^2 + 4e^x - 1 = 0$

$e^x = \dfrac{-4 \pm \sqrt{4^2 - 4(1)(-1)}}{2(1)} = \dfrac{-4 \pm \sqrt{20}}{2} = \dfrac{-4 \pm 2\sqrt{5}}{2} = -2 \pm \sqrt{5}$

$x = \ln\left(-2 + \sqrt{5}\right)$

Since $\ln\left(-2 - \sqrt{5}\right)$ is undefined; it is not a solution.

45.   Using INTERSECT to solve:
      $y_1 = \ln(x)\,/\,\ln(5) + \ln(x)\,/\,\ln(3)$
      $y_2 = 1$

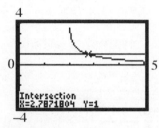

      Intersection
      X=1.9211482 Y=1

      The solution is 1.92.

46.   Using INTERSECT to solve:
      $y_1 = \ln(x)\,/\,\ln(2) + \ln(x)\,/\,\ln(6)$
      $y_2 = 3$

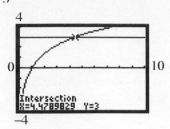

      Intersection
      X=4.4789829 Y=3

      The solution is 4.48.

47.   Using INTERSECT to solve:
      $y_1 = \ln(x+1)\,/\,\ln(5) - \ln(x-2)\,/\,\ln(4)$
      $y_2 = 1$

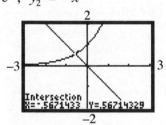

      Intersection
      X=2.7871804 Y=1

      The solution is 2.79.

48.   Using INTERSECT to solve:
      $y_1 = \ln(x-1)\,/\,\ln(2) - \ln(x+2)\,/\,\ln(6)$
      $y_2 = 2$

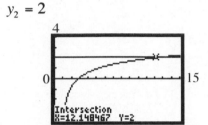

      Intersection
      X=12.148467 Y=2

      The solution is 12.15.

49.   Using INTERSECT to solve:
      $y_1 = e^x$; $y_2 = -x$

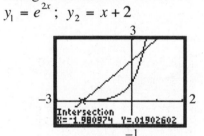

      Intersection
      X=-.5671433 Y=.56714329

      The solution is −0.57.

50.   Using INTERSECT to solve:
      $y_1 = e^{2x}$; $y_2 = x + 2$

      Intersection
      X=-1.980974 Y=.01902602

      Intersection
      X=.44754216 Y=2.4475422

      The solutions are −1.98 and 0.45.

51. Using INTERSECT to solve:
$y_1 = e^x$; $y_2 = x^2$

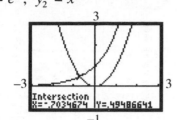

The solution is –0.70.

52. Using INTERSECT to solve:
$y_1 = e^x$; $y_2 = x^3$

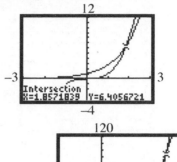

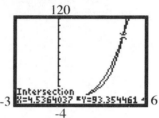

The solutions are 1.86 and 4.54.

53. Using INTERSECT to solve:
$y_1 = \ln x$; $y_2 = -x$

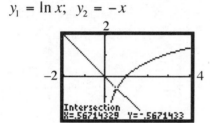

The solution is 0.57.

54. Using INTERSECT to solve:
$y_1 = \ln(2x)$; $y_2 = -x + 2$

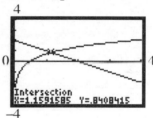

The solution is 1.16.

55. Using INTERSECT to solve:
$y_1 = \ln x$; $y_2 = x^3 - 1$

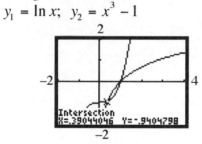

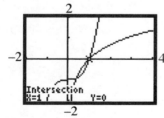

The solutions are 0.39, 1.00.

56. Using INTERSECT to solve:
$y_1 = \ln x$; $y_2 = -x^2$

The solution is 0.65.

57. Using INTERSECT to solve:

$y_1 = e^x + \ln x$; $y_2 = 4$

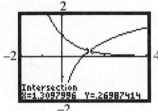

The solution is 1.32.

58. Using INTERSECT to solve:

$y_1 = e^x - \ln x$; $y_2 = 4$

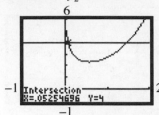

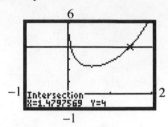

The solutions are 0.05 and 1.48.

59. Using INTERSECT to solve:

$y_1 = e^{-x}$; $y_2 = \ln x$

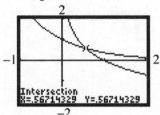

The solution is 1.31.

60. Using INTERSECT to solve:

$y_1 = e^{-x}$; $y_2 = -\ln x$

The solution is 0.57.

Exponential and Logarithmic Functions

6.6   Compound Interest

1. $P = \$100$, $r = 0.04$, $n = 4$, $t = 2$

$$A = P\left[1 + \frac{r}{n}\right]^{nt} = 100\left[1 + \frac{0.04}{4}\right]^{(4)(2)} = \$108.29$$

2. $P = \$50$, $r = 0.06$, $n = 12$, $t = 3$

$$A = P\left[1 + \frac{r}{n}\right]^{nt} = 50\left[1 + \frac{0.06}{12}\right]^{(12)(3)} = \$59.83$$

3. $P = \$500$, $r = 0.08$, $n = 4$, $t = 2.5$

$$A = P\left[1 + \frac{r}{n}\right]^{nt} = 500\left[1 + \frac{0.08}{4}\right]^{(4)(2.5)} = \$609.50$$

4. $P = \$300$, $r = 0.12$, $n = 12$, $t = 1.5$

$$A = P\left[1 + \frac{r}{n}\right]^{nt} = 300\left[1 + \frac{0.12}{12}\right]^{(12)(1.5)} = \$358.84$$

5. $P = \$600$, $r = 0.05$, $n = 365$, $t = 3$

$$A = P\left[1 + \frac{r}{n}\right]^{nt} = 600\left[1 + \frac{0.05}{365}\right]^{(365)(3)} = \$697.09$$

6. $P = \$700$, $r = 0.06$, $n = 365$, $t = 2$

$$A = P\left[1 + \frac{r}{n}\right]^{nt} = 700\left[1 + \frac{0.06}{365}\right]^{(365)(2)} = \$789.24$$

7. $P = \$10$, $r = 0.11$, $t = 2$
$$A = Pe^{rt} = 10e^{(0.11)(2)} = \$12.46$$

8. $P = \$40$, $r = 0.07$, $t = 3$
$$A = Pe^{rt} = 40e^{(0.07)(3)} = \$49.35$$

9. $P = \$100$, $r = 0.10$, $t = 2.25$
$$A = Pe^{rt} = 100e^{(0.10)(2.25)} = \$125.23$$

10. $P = \$100$, $r = 0.12$, $t = 3.75$
$$A = Pe^{rt} = 100e^{(0.12)(3.75)} = \$156.83$$

11. $A = \$100$, $r = 0.06$, $n = 12$, $t = 2$

$$P = A\left[1 + \frac{r}{n}\right]^{-nt} = 100\left[1 + \frac{0.06}{12}\right]^{(-12)(2)} = \$88.72$$

12. $A = \$75$, $r = 0.08$, $n = 4$, $t = 3$

$$P = A\left[1 + \frac{r}{n}\right]^{-nt} = 75\left[1 + \frac{0.08}{4}\right]^{(-4)(3)} = \$59.14$$

13. $A = \$1000$, $r = 0.06$, $n = 365$, $t = 2.5$

$$P = A\left[1 + \frac{r}{n}\right]^{-nt} = 1000\left[1 + \frac{0.06}{365}\right]^{(-365)(2.5)} = \$860.72$$

14. $A = \$800$, $r = 0.07$, $n = 12$, $t = 3.5$

$$P = A\left[1 + \frac{r}{n}\right]^{-nt} = 800\left[1 + \frac{0.07}{12}\right]^{(-12)(3.5)} = \$626.61$$

15. $A = \$600$, $r = 0.04$, $n = 4$, $t = 2$

$$P = A\left[1 + \frac{r}{n}\right]^{-nt} = 600\left[1 + \frac{0.04}{4}\right]^{(-4)(2)} = \$554.09$$

16. $A = \$300$, $r = 0.03$, $n = 365$, $t = 4$

$$P = A\left[1 + \frac{r}{n}\right]^{-nt} = 300\left[1 + \frac{0.03}{365}\right]^{(-365)(4)} = \$266.08$$

17. $A = \$80$, $r = 0.09$, $t = 3.25$

$$P = Ae^{-rt} = 80e^{(-0.09)(3.25)} = \$59.71$$

18. $A = \$800$, $r = 0.08$, $t = 2.5$

$$P = Ae^{-rt} = 800e^{(-0.08)(2.5)} = \$654.98$$

19. $A = \$400$, $r = 0.10$, $t = 1$

$$P = Ae^{-rt} = 400e^{(-0.10)(1)} = \$361.93$$

20. $A = \$1000$, $r = 0.12$, $t = 1$

$$P = Ae^{-rt} = 1000e^{(-0.12)(1)} = \$886.92$$

21. $r_e = \left[1 + \frac{r}{n}\right]^{n} - 1 = \left[1 + \frac{0.0525}{4}\right]^{4} - 1 = 1.0535 - 1 = 0.0535 = 5.35\%$

22. $0.07 = \left[1 + \frac{r}{4}\right]^{4} - 1$

$1.07 = \left(1 + \frac{r}{4}\right)^{4}$ $\rightarrow$ $1 + \frac{r}{4} = 1.0170585$ $\rightarrow$ $\frac{r}{4} = 0.0170585$ $\rightarrow$ $r \approx 6.82\%$

23. $2P = P(1 + r)^3$

   $2 = (1 + r)^3$

   $\sqrt[3]{2} = 1 + r$

   $r = \sqrt[3]{2} - 1 \approx 1.26 - 1 = 0.26 = 26\%$

24. $2P = P(1 + r)^{10}$

   $2 = (1 + r)^{10} \quad \rightarrow \quad \sqrt[10]{2} = 1 + r \quad \rightarrow \quad r = \sqrt[10]{2} - 1 \approx 1.0718 - 1 = 0.0718 = 7.18\%$

25. 6% compounded quarterly:

   $$A = 10,000\left[1 + \frac{0.06}{4}\right]^{(4)(1)} = \$10,613.64$$

   $6\frac{1}{4}\%$ compounded annually:

   $$A = 10,000[1 + 0.0625]^1 = \$10,625$$

   $6\frac{1}{4}\%$ compounded annually yields the larger amount.

26. 9% compounded quarterly:

   $$A = 10,000\left[1 + \frac{0.09}{4}\right]^{(4)(1)} = \$10,930.83$$

   $9\frac{1}{4}\%$ compounded annually:

   $$A = 10,000[1 + 0.0925]^1 = \$10,925$$

   9% compounded quarterly yields the larger amount.

27. 9% compounded monthly:

   $$A = 10,000\left[1 + \frac{0.09}{12}\right]^{(12)(1)} = \$10,938.07$$

   8.8% compounded daily:

   $$A = 10,000\left[1 + \frac{0.088}{365}\right]^{365} = \$10,919.77$$

   9% compounded monthly yields the larger amount.

28. 8% compounded semiannually:

   $$A = 10,000\left[1 + \frac{0.08}{2}\right]^{(2)(1)} = \$10,816$$

   7.9% compounded daily:

   $$A = 10,000\left[1 + \frac{0.079}{365}\right]^{365} = \$10,821.95$$

   7.9% compounded daily yields the larger amount.

29. Compounded monthly:

   $$2P = P\left[1 + \frac{0.08}{12}\right]^{12t}$$

   $$2 = (1.00667)^{12t}$$

   $$\ln 2 = 12t \ln(1.00667)$$

   $$t = \frac{\ln 2}{12 \ln(1.00667)} \approx 8.69 \text{ years}$$

   Compounded continuously:

   $$2P = Pe^{0.08t}$$

   $$2 = e^{0.08t}$$

   $$\ln 2 = 0.08t$$

   $$t = \frac{\ln 2}{0.08} \approx 8.66 \text{ years}$$

30. Compounded monthly:

$$2P = P\left[1 + \frac{0.10}{12}\right]^{12t}$$
$$2 = (1.00833)^{12t}$$
$$\ln 2 = 12t \ln(1.00833)$$
$$t = \frac{\ln 2}{12 \ln(1.00833)} \approx 6.96 \text{ years}$$

Compounded continuously:

$$2P = Pe^{0.10t}$$
$$2 = e^{0.10t}$$
$$\ln 2 = 0.10t$$
$$t = \frac{\ln 2}{0.10} \approx 6.93 \text{ years}$$

31. Compounded monthly:

$$150 = 100\left[1 + \frac{0.08}{12}\right]^{12t}$$
$$1.5 = (1.00667)^{12t}$$
$$\ln 1.5 = 12t \ln(1.00667)$$
$$t = \frac{\ln 1.5}{12 \ln(1.00667)} \approx 5.083 \text{ years}$$

Compounded continuously:

$$150 = 100e^{0.08t}$$
$$1.5 = e^{0.08t}$$
$$\ln 1.5 = 0.08t$$
$$t = \frac{\ln 1.5}{0.08} \approx 5.068 \text{ years}$$

32. Compounded monthly:

$$175 = 100\left[1 + \frac{0.10}{12}\right]^{12t}$$
$$1.75 = (1.00833)^{12t}$$
$$\ln 1.75 = 12t \ln(1.00833)$$
$$t = \frac{\ln 1.75}{12 \ln(1.00833)} \approx 5.62 \text{ years}$$

Compounded continuously:

$$175 = 100e^{0.10t}$$
$$1.75 = e^{0.10t}$$
$$\ln 1.75 = 0.10t$$
$$t = \frac{\ln 1.75}{0.10} \approx 5.60 \text{ years}$$

33. $25,000 = 10,000e^{0.06t}$
$$2.5 = e^{0.06t}$$
$$\ln 2.5 = 0.06t$$
$$t = \frac{\ln 2.5}{0.06} \approx 15.27 \text{ years}$$

34. $80,000 = 25,000e^{0.07t}$
$$3.2 = e^{0.07t}$$
$$\ln 3.2 = 0.07t$$
$$t = \frac{\ln 3.2}{0.07} \approx 16.62 \text{ years}$$

35. $A = 90,000(1 + 0.03)^5 = \$104,335$

36. $A = 200(1 + 0.0125)^5 = \$212.82$ (You get a 1 month grace period.)

37. $P = 15,000e^{(-0.05)(3)} = \$12,910.62$

38. $P = 3,000\left(1 + \frac{0.03}{12}\right)^{(-12)(0.5)} = \$2,955.39$

39. $A = 1500(1 + 0.15)^5 = 1500(1.15)^5 = \$3017$

40. $20 = 15(1 + r)^2 \ \rightarrow \ 1.333 = (1 + r)^2 \ \rightarrow \ 1.155 = 1 + r \ \rightarrow \ r = 0.155 \approx 15.5\%$

41. $850,000 = 650,000(1 + r)^3$

$1.3077 = (1 + r)^3$

$\sqrt[3]{1.3077} = 1 + r \rightarrow r = \sqrt[3]{1.3077} - 1 \approx 0.0935 = 9.35\%$

42. $A = 5000(1 + 0.08)^{-10} = \$2,315.97$

43.   5.6% compounded continuously:

$A = 1000e^{(0.056)(1)} = \$1057.60$

Jim does not have enough money to buy the computer.

5.9% compounded monthly:

$A = 1000\left[1 + \dfrac{0.059}{12}\right]^{12} = \$1060.62$

The second bank offers the better deal.

44.   6.8% compounded continuously for 3 months:

$A = 1000e^{(0.068)(0.25)} = \$1017.15$ -- Amount on April 1.

5.25% compounded monthly for 1 month:

$A = 1017.15\left[1 + \dfrac{0.0525}{12}\right]^{(12)(1/12)} = \$1021.60$ -- Amount on May 1.

45.   Will - 9% compounded semiannually:

$A = 2000\left[1 + \dfrac{0.09}{2}\right]^{(2)(20)} = \$11,632.73$

Henry - 8.5% compounded continuously:

$A = 2000e^{(0.085)(20)} = \$10,947.89$

Will has more money after 20 years.

46.   Value of $1000 compounded continuously at 10% for 3 years:

$A = 1000e^{(0.10)(3)} = \$1349.86$

April will have more money if she takes the $1000 now and invests it.

47. $P = 50,000; \ t = 5$

(a)   Simple interest at 12% per annum:

$A = 50,000 + 50,000(0.12)(5) = \$80,000$

(b)   11.5% compounded monthly:

$A = 50,000\left[1 + \dfrac{0.115}{12}\right]^{(12)(5)} = \$88,613.59$

(c)   11.25% compounded continuously:

$A = 50,000e^{(0.1125)(5)} = \$87,752.73$

Subtract $50,000 from each to get the amount of interest:

(a) $30,000

(b) $38,613.59

(c) $37.752.73

Option (a) results in the least interest.

48. (a) 360 day year:

$$r_e = \left(1 + \frac{0.0425}{360}\right)^{360} - 1 = 1.043413439 - 1 = 0.043413439 = 4.3413439\%$$

(b) 365 day year:

$$r_e = \left(1 + \frac{0.0425}{365}\right)^{365} - 1 = 1.043413475 - 1 = 0.043413475 = 4.3413475\%$$

49. (a) $A = \$10,000$, $r = 0.10$, $n = 12$, $t = 20$ (compounded monthly)

$$P = 10,000\left[1 + \frac{0.10}{12}\right]^{(-12)(20)} = \$1364.62$$

(b) $A = \$10,000$, $r = 0.10$, $t = 20$ (compounded continuously)
$$P = 10,000e^{(-0.10)(20)} = \$1353.35$$

50. $A = \$40,000$, $r = 0.08$, $n = 1$, $t = 17$ (compounded annually)
$$P = 40,000[1 + 0.08]^{-17} = \$10,810.76$$

51. $A = \$10,000$, $r = 0.08$, $n = 1$, $t = 10$ (compounded annually)

$$P = 10,000\left[1 + \frac{0.08}{1}\right]^{(-1)(10)} = \$4631.93$$

52. $A = \$25,000$, $P = 12,485.52$, $n = 1$, $t = 8$ (compounded annually)

$$25,000 = 12,485.52(1 + r)^8$$

$$2.002319487 = (1 + r)^8 \rightarrow 1.090665741 = 1 + r \rightarrow r = 0.090665741 \approx 9.07\%$$

53. (a) $y = \dfrac{\ln 2}{1 \cdot \ln\left(1 + \dfrac{0.12}{1}\right)} = \dfrac{\ln 2}{\ln 1.12} \approx 6.12$ years

(b) $y = \dfrac{\ln 3}{4 \cdot \ln\left(1 + \dfrac{0.06}{4}\right)} = \dfrac{\ln 3}{4 \ln(1.015)} \approx 18.45$ years

(c) $mP = P\left[1 + \dfrac{r}{n}\right]^{nt}$

$m = \left[1 + \dfrac{r}{n}\right]^{nt} \rightarrow \ln m = nt \cdot \ln\left[1 + \dfrac{r}{n}\right] \rightarrow t = \dfrac{\ln m}{n \cdot \ln\left[1 + \dfrac{r}{n}\right]}$

54. (a) $y = \dfrac{\ln 8000 - \ln 1000}{0.10} = 20.79$ years

(b) $35 = \dfrac{\ln 30000 - \ln 2000}{r}$ $\rightarrow$ $r = \dfrac{\ln 30000 - \ln 2000}{35} \approx 0.0774 \approx 7.74\%$

(c) $A = Pe^{rt}$

$$\frac{A}{P} = e^{rt}$$

$$\ln\left(\frac{A}{P}\right) = rt \rightarrow \ln A - \ln P = rt \rightarrow t = \frac{\ln A - \ln P}{r}$$

55. Answers will vary.   56. Answers will vary.   57. Answers will vary.

Chapter 6

Exponential and Logarithmic Functions

6.7   Growth and Decay; Newton's Law; Logistic Models

1. $P(t) = 500e^{0.02t}$

    Find t when $P = 1000$:

    $1000 = 500e^{0.02t}$

    $2 = e^{0.02t}$

    $\ln 2 = 0.02t$

    $t = \dfrac{\ln 2}{0.02} \approx 34.7$ days

    Find t when $P = 2000$:

    $2000 = 500e^{0.02t}$

    $4 = e^{0.02t}$

    $\ln 4 = 0.02t$

    $t = \dfrac{\ln 4}{0.02} \approx 69.3$ days

2. $N(t) = 1000e^{0.01t}$

    Find t when $N = 1500$:

    $1500 = 1000e^{0.01t}$

    $1.5 = e^{0.01t}$

    $\ln 1.5 = 0.01t$

    $t = \dfrac{\ln 1.5}{0.01} \approx 40.55$ hours

    Find t when $N = 2000$:

    $2000 = 1000e^{0.01t}$

    $2 = e^{0.01t}$

    $\ln 2 = 0.01t$

    $t = \dfrac{\ln 2}{0.01} \approx 69.31$ hours

3. Find t when $A(t) = \dfrac{1}{2}A_0$:

    $\dfrac{1}{2}A_0 = A_0 e^{-0.0244t}$

    $\dfrac{1}{2} = e^{-0.0244t}$

    $\ln\left(\dfrac{1}{2}\right) = -0.0244t$

    $t = \dfrac{\ln\left(\dfrac{1}{2}\right)}{-0.0244} \approx 28.4$ years

4. Find t when $A(t) = \dfrac{1}{2}A_0$:

    $\dfrac{1}{2}A_0 = A_0 e^{-0.087t}$

    $\dfrac{1}{2} = e^{-0.087t}$

    $\ln\left(\dfrac{1}{2}\right) = -0.087t$

    $t = \dfrac{\ln\left(\dfrac{1}{2}\right)}{-0.087} \approx 7.97$ days

636

5.   Use $N(t) = N_0 e^{kt}$ and solve for k:
$$1800 = 1000e^{k(1)}$$
$$1.8 = e^k$$
$$k = \ln 1.8 \approx 0.5878$$
When $t = 3$:
$$N(3) = 1000e^{0.5878(3)} = 5832 \text{ mosquitos}$$
Find t when $N(t) = 10,000$:
$$10,000 = 1000e^{0.5878\,t}$$
$$10 = e^{0.5878\,t}$$
$$\ln 10 = 0.5878t$$
$$t = \frac{\ln 10}{0.5878} \approx 3.9 \text{ days}$$

6.   Use $N(t) = N_0 e^{kt}$ and solve for k:
$$800 = 500e^{k(1)}$$
$$1.6 = e^k$$
$$k = \ln 1.6 \approx 0.4700$$
When $t = 5$:
$$N(5) = 500e^{0.4700(5)} = 5243 \text{ bacteria}$$
Find t when $N(t) = 20,000$:
$$20,000 = 500e^{0.4700\,t}$$
$$40 = e^{0.4700\,t}$$
$$\ln 40 = 0.4700t$$
$$t = \frac{\ln 40}{0.4700} \approx 7.85 \text{ hours}$$

7.   Use $P(t) = P_0 e^{kt}$ and solve for k:
$$2P_0 = P_0 e^{k(1.5)}$$
$$2 = e^{1.5k}$$
$$\ln 2 = 1.5k \rightarrow k = \frac{\ln 2}{1.5} \approx 0.4621$$
When $t = 2$:
$$P(2) = 10,000e^{0.4621(2)} = 25,199 \text{ is the population 2 years from now.}$$

8.   Use $P(t) = P_0 e^{kt}$ and solve for k:
$$800,000 = 900,000e^{k(2)}$$
$$\frac{8}{9} = e^{2k}$$
$$\ln\left(\frac{8}{9}\right) = 2k \rightarrow k = \frac{\ln\left(\frac{8}{9}\right)}{2} \approx -0.05889$$
When $t = 4$:
$$P(4) = 900,000e^{-0.05889(4)} = 711,115 \text{ is the population in 1997.}$$

9.   Use $A = A_0 e^{kt}$ and solve for k:

$$\frac{1}{2} A_0 = A_0 e^{k(1690)} \rightarrow \frac{1}{2} = e^{1690k}$$

$$\ln\left(\frac{1}{2}\right) = 1690k \rightarrow k = \frac{\ln 0.5}{1690} \approx -0.00041$$

When $A_0 = 10$ and $t = 50$:

$$A = 10e^{-0.00041(50)} \approx 9.797 \text{ grams}$$

10. Use $A = A_0 e^{kt}$ and solve for k:

$$\frac{1}{2} A_0 = A_0 e^{k(1.3 \times 10^9)} \rightarrow \frac{1}{2} = e^{1.3 \times 10^9 k}$$

$$\ln\left(\frac{1}{2}\right) = 1.3 \times 10^9 k \rightarrow k = \frac{\ln 0.5}{1.3 \times 10^9} \approx -5.3319 \times 10^{-10}$$

When $A_0 = 10$ and $t = 100$: $A = 10e^{-5.3319 \times 10^{-10}(100)} = 9.999999467 \text{ grams}$

When $A_0 = 10$ and $t = 1000$: $A = 10e^{-5.3319 \times 10^{-10}(1000)} = 9.999994668 \text{ grams}$

11. Use $A = A_0 e^{kt}$ and solve for k:

$$\frac{1}{2} A_0 = A_0 e^{k(5600)}$$

$$\frac{1}{2} = e^{5600k}$$

$$\ln\left(\frac{1}{2}\right) = 5600k \rightarrow k = \frac{\ln 0.5}{5600} \approx -0.000124$$

Solve for t when $A = 0.3 A_0$:

$$0.3 A_0 = A_0 e^{-0.000124\, t}$$

$$0.3 = e^{-0.000124\, t}$$

$$\ln 0.3 = -0.000124 t$$

$$t = \frac{\ln 0.3}{-0.000124}$$

$$\approx 9709 \text{ years ago}$$

12. Use $A = A_0 e^{kt}$ and solve for k:

$$\frac{1}{2} A_0 = A_0 e^{k(5600)}$$

$$\frac{1}{2} = e^{5600\, k} \rightarrow \ln\left(\frac{1}{2}\right) = 5600k$$

$$k = \frac{\ln 0.5}{5600} \approx -0.000124$$

Solve for t when $A = 0.7 A_0$:

$$0.7 A_0 = A_0 e^{-0.000124\, t}$$

$$0.7 = e^{-0.000124\, t}$$

$$\ln 0.7 = -0.000124 t$$

$$t = \frac{\ln 0.7}{-0.000124}$$

$$\approx 2876 \text{ years}$$

The fossil is 2876 years old.

13. (a)   Using $u = T + (u_0 - T)e^{kt}$ where $t = 5$,
     $T = 70$, $u_0 = 450$, $u = 300$:

$$300 = 70 + (450 - 70)e^{k(5)}$$

$$230 = 380e^{5k}$$

$$0.6053 = e^{5k}$$

$$5k = \ln 0.6053$$

$$k = \frac{\ln 0.6053}{5} \approx -0.1004$$

$T = 70$, $u_0 = 450$, $u = 135$:

$$135 = 70 + (450 - 70)e^{-0.1004\, t}$$

$$65 = 380e^{-0.1004\, t}$$

$$0.17105 = e^{-0.1004\, t}$$

$$-0.1004\, t = \ln 0.17105$$

$$t = \frac{\ln 0.17105}{-0.1004} \approx 17.6 \text{ minutes}$$

The pizza will be cool enough to eat at 5:18 p.m.

(b) $T = 70,\ u_0 = 450,\ u = 160$:

$$160 = 70 + (450 - 70)e^{-0.1004\ t}$$
$$90 = 380e^{-0.1004\ t} \qquad \ln\left(\frac{90}{380}\right) = \ln e^{-0.1004\ t} = -0.1004\ t$$
$$\frac{90}{380} = e^{-0.1004\ t}$$
$$t = \frac{\ln\left(\dfrac{90}{380}\right)}{-0.1004} \approx 14.35 \text{ minutes}$$

The pizza will be 160°F after about 14.3 minutes.

(c)   As time passes the temperature gets closer to 70°F.

14.   (a)   Using $u = T + (u_0 - T)e^{kt}$ where $t = 2$,
        $T = 38,\ u_0 = 72,\ u = 60$:

$$60 = 38 + (72 - 38)e^{k(2)}$$
$$22 = 34e^{2k}$$
$$0.6471 = e^{2k}$$
$$2k = \ln 0.6471 \qquad\qquad T = 38,\ u_0 = 72,\ t = 7:$$
$$k = \frac{\ln 0.6471}{2} \approx -0.2176 \qquad u = 38 + (72 - 38)e^{-0.2176\ (7)}$$
$$u = 38 + 34e^{-1.5232} \approx 45.4°F$$

After 7 minutes the thermometer reads 45.4°F.

(b)   Find t when $u = 39°\text{F}$
$$39 = 38 + (72 - 38)e^{-0.2176\ t}$$
$$1 = 34e^{-0.2176\ t}$$

$$0.02941 = e^{-0.2176\ t} \ \rightarrow\ -0.2176t = \ln 0.02941 \rightarrow t = \frac{\ln 0.02941}{-0.2176} \approx 16.2 \text{ minutes}$$

(c)   Find t when $u = 45°\text{F}$

$$45 = 38 + (72 - 38)e^{-0.2176\ t}$$

$$7 = (34)e^{-0.2176\ t} \rightarrow \frac{7}{34} = e^{-0.2176\ t}$$

$$\ln\left(\frac{7}{34}\right) = \ln e^{-0.2176\ t} = -0.2176\ t \rightarrow t = \frac{\ln\left(\dfrac{7}{34}\right)}{-0.2176} \approx 7.26 \text{ minutes}$$

The thermometer will read 45°F after about 7.3 minutes.

(d)   As time passes the temperature gets closer to 38°F.

15.   Using $u = T + (u_0 - T)e^{kt}$ where $t = 3$,
$T = 35$, $u_0 = 8$, $u = 15$:

$$15 = 35 + (8 - 35)e^{k(3)} \rightarrow -20 = -27e^{3k} \rightarrow 0.74074 = e^{3k}$$

$$3k = \ln 0.74074 \rightarrow k = \frac{\ln 0.74074}{3} \approx -0.100035$$

At $t = 5$:
$$u = 35 + (8 - 35)e^{-0.100035\,(5)} = 18.63°\text{C}$$
At $t = 10$:
$$u = 35 + (8 - 35)e^{-0.100035\,(10)} = 25.1°\text{C}$$

16.   Using $u = T + (u_0 - T)e^{kt}$ where $t = 10$,
$T = 70$, $u_0 = 28$, $u = 35$:

$$35 = 70 + (28 - 70)e^{k(10)} \rightarrow -35 = -42e^{10k}$$

$$0.83333 = e^{10k} \rightarrow 10k = \ln 0.83333 \rightarrow k = \frac{\ln 0.83333}{10} \approx -0.01823$$

At $t = 30$:
$$u = 70 + (28 - 70)e^{-0.01823\,(30)} = 45.69°\text{F}$$
Find time for temperature of 45°F:
$$45 = 70 + (28 - 70)e^{-0.01823\,t}$$

$$-25 = -42e^{-0.01823\,t} \rightarrow 0.59524 = e^{-0.01823\,t}$$

$$\ln 0.59524 = -0.01823t \rightarrow t = \frac{\ln 0.59524}{-0.01823} \approx 28.5 \text{ minutes}$$

17.   Use $A = A_0 e^{kt}$ and solve for k:
$$15 = 25e^{k(10)}$$

$$0.6 = e^{10k} \rightarrow \ln 0.6 = 10k \rightarrow k = \frac{\ln 0.6}{10} \approx -0.0511$$

When $A_0 = 25$ and $t = 24$:
$$A = 25e^{-0.0511\,(24)} = 7.33 \text{ kilograms}$$

Find t when $A = \frac{1}{2} A_0$:
$$0.5 = 25\,e^{-0.0511\,t}$$

$$0.02 = e^{-0.0511\,t} \rightarrow \ln 0.02 = -0.0511t \rightarrow t = \frac{\ln 0.02}{-0.0511} \approx 76.6 \text{ hours}$$

18.   Use $A = A_0 e^{kt}$ and solve for k:
$$10 = 40e^{k(2)}$$

$$0.25 = e^{2k} \rightarrow \ln 0.25 = 2k \rightarrow k = \frac{\ln 0.25}{2} \approx -0.6931$$

When $A_0 = 40$ and $t = 5$:
$$A = 40e^{-0.6931(\,5)} = 1.25 \text{ volts}$$

19. Use $A = A_0 e^{kt}$ and solve for k:

$$\frac{1}{2}A_0 = A_0 e^{k(8)}$$

$$0.5 = e^{8k} \rightarrow \ln 0.5 = 8k$$

$$k = \frac{\ln 0.5}{8} \approx -0.0866$$

The farmers need to wait about 27 days before using the hay.

Find t when $A = 0.1A_0$:

$$0.1A_0 = A_0 e^{-0.0866\,t}$$

$$0.1 = e^{-0.0866\,t} \rightarrow \ln 0.1 = -0.0866\,t$$

$$t = \frac{\ln 0.1}{-0.0866} \approx 26.6 \text{ days}$$

20. Using $u = T + (u_0 - T)e^{kt}$ where $t = 2$,
$T = 325$, $u_0 = 75$, $u = 100$:

$$100 = 325 + (75 - 325)e^{k(2)} \rightarrow -225 = -250e^{2k}$$

$$0.9 = e^{2k} \rightarrow 2k = \ln 0.9 \rightarrow k = \frac{\ln 0.9}{2} \approx -0.05268$$

Find time for temperature of 175°F:

$$175 = 325 + (75 - 325)e^{-0.05268\,t}$$

$$-150 = -250e^{-0.05268\,t} \rightarrow 0.6 = e^{-0.05268\,t} \rightarrow \ln 0.6 = -0.05268\,t$$

$$t = \frac{\ln 0.6}{-0.05268} \approx 9.7 \text{ hours}$$

The hotel may serve their guests about 9.7 hours after noon or at 9:42 p.m.

21. (a) $P(0) = \dfrac{0.9}{1 + 6e^{-0.32\,(0)}} = \dfrac{0.9}{1 + 6 \cdot 1} = \dfrac{0.9}{7} = 0.1286$

(b)   The maximum proportion is the carrying capacity, 0.9.

(c) $$0.8 = \frac{0.9}{1 + 6e^{-0.32\,t}}$$

$$0.8\left(1 + 6e^{-0.32t}\right) = 0.9 \rightarrow 1 + 6e^{-0.32t} = 1.125 \rightarrow 6e^{-0.32t} = 0.125$$

$$e^{-0.32t} = 0.020833 \rightarrow -0.32t = \ln(0.020833)$$

$$t = \frac{\ln(0.020833)}{-0.32} \approx 12.1$$

80% of households will own VCR's in 1996 (t = 12).

22.   (a) $P(0) = \dfrac{0.9}{1 + 3.5e^{-0.339\,(0)}} = \dfrac{0.9}{1 + 3.5 \cdot 1} = \dfrac{0.9}{4.5} = 0.2$

(b)   The maximum proportion is the carrying capacity, 0.9.

(c) $$0.75 = \dfrac{0.9}{1 + 3.5e^{-0.339t}}$$

$$0.75\left(1 + 3.5e^{-0.339t}\right) = 0.9 \rightarrow 1 + 3.5e^{-0.339t} = 1.2 \rightarrow 3.5e^{-0.339t} = 0.2$$

$$e^{-0339t} = 0.05714 \rightarrow -0.339t = \ln(0.05714)$$

$$t = \dfrac{\ln(0.05714)}{-0.339} \approx 8.4 \text{ months}$$

23.   (a)   As $t \to \infty$, $e^{-0.439\,t} \to 0$. Thus, $P(t) \to 1000$. The carrying capacity is 1000.

(b) $P(0) = \dfrac{1000}{1 + 32.33e^{-0.439\,(0)}} = \dfrac{1000}{33.33} = 30$

(c) $$800 = \dfrac{1000}{1 + 32.33e^{-0.439\,t}}$$

$$800\left(1 + 32.33e^{-0.439t}\right) = 1000 \rightarrow 1 + 32.33e^{-0.439t} = 1.25$$

$$32.33e^{-0.439t} = 0.25 \rightarrow e^{-0439t} = 0.007733$$

$$-0.439t = \ln(0.007733) \rightarrow t = \dfrac{\ln(0.007733)}{-0.439} \approx 11.076 \text{ hours}$$

24.   (a)   As $t \to \infty$, $e^{-0.162\,t} \to 0$. Thus, $P(t) \to 500$. The carrying capacity is 500.

(b) $P(20) = \dfrac{500}{1 + 83.33e^{-0.162\,(20)}} = \dfrac{500}{4.2635} \approx 117.27 \text{ or } 117$

(c) $$300 = \dfrac{500}{1 + 83.33e^{-0.162t}}$$

$$300\left(1 + 83.33e^{-0.162t}\right) = 500 \rightarrow 1 + 83.33e^{-0.162\,t} = 1.6667$$

$$83.33e^{-0.162t} = 0.6667 \rightarrow e^{-0.162t} = 0.0080$$

$$-0.162t = \ln(0.0080) \rightarrow t = \dfrac{\ln(0.0080)}{-0.162} \approx 29.8 \text{ years}$$

Exponential and Logarithmic Functions

6.8   Logarithmic Scales

1. $L(10^{-5}) = 10 \log\left(\dfrac{10^{-5}}{10^{-12}}\right) = 10 \log 10^{7} = 10 \cdot 7 = 70$ decibels

2. $L(10^{-3}) = 10 \log\left(\dfrac{10^{-3}}{10^{-12}}\right) = 10 \log 10^{9} = 10 \cdot 9 = 90$ decibels

3. $L(0.15) = 10 \log\left(\dfrac{1.5 \times 10^{-1}}{10^{-12}}\right) = 10 \log\left(1.5 \times 10^{11}\right)$

$= 10\left(\log\left(1.5\right) + \log\left(10^{11}\right)\right) = 10\left(\log\left(1.5\right) + 11\right) \approx 111.76$ decibels

4. $L(10^{-9.8}) = 10 \log\left(\dfrac{10^{-9.8}}{10^{-12}}\right) = 10 \log 10^{2.2} = 10 \cdot 2.2 = 22$ decibels

5. $L(x) = 10 \log\left(\dfrac{x}{10^{-12}}\right) = 130$ decibels

$10 \log\left(\dfrac{x}{10^{-12}}\right) = 130 \rightarrow \log\left(\dfrac{x}{10^{-12}}\right) = 13$

$\log\left(x \cdot 10^{12}\right) = 13 \rightarrow \log(x) + \log\left(10^{12}\right) = 13$

$\log(x) + 12 = 13 \rightarrow \log(x) = 1 \rightarrow 10^{\log(x)} = 10^{1}$

$x = 10^{1} = 10$ watts per square meter

6.   We compute $L(50x) - L(x)$

$$L(50x) - L(x) = 10\log\left(\frac{50x}{10^{-12}}\right) - 10\log\left(\frac{x}{10^{-12}}\right) = 10\left(\log\left(\frac{50x}{10^{-12}}\right) - \log\left(\frac{x}{10^{-12}}\right)\right)$$

$$= 10\log\left(\frac{\left(\frac{50x}{10^{-12}}\right)}{\left(\frac{x}{10^{-12}}\right)}\right) = 10\log\left(\left(\frac{50x}{10^{-12}}\right)\cdot\left(\frac{10^{-12}}{x}\right)\right) = 10\log(50) \approx 16.99 \;\; \text{decibels}$$

7. $M(10) = \log\dfrac{10}{10^{-3}} = \log 10^4 = 4$

8. $M(1210) = \log\dfrac{1210}{10^{-3}} = \log(1210000) \approx 6.08$

9.   Mexico City:

$$\log(x \cdot 10^3) = 8.1$$

$$\log(x) + \log(10^3) = 8.1$$

$$\log(x) + 3 = 8.1$$

$$\log(x) = 5.1$$

$$10^{\log x)} = 10^{5.1}$$

$$x = 10^{5.1} \approx 125892.54$$

San Francisco: $M(x) = \log\left(\dfrac{x}{10^{-3}}\right) = 6.9$

$$\log(x \cdot 10^3) = 6.9$$

$$\log(x) + \log(10^3) = 6.9$$

$$\log(x) + 3 = 6.9$$

$$\log(x) = 3.9$$

$$10^{\log x)} = 10^{3.9}$$

$$x = 10^{39} \approx 7943.28$$

10.   We compute $M(x_1) - M(x_2) = 1$

$$\log\left(\frac{x_1}{10^{-3}}\right) - \log\left(\frac{x_2}{10^{-3}}\right) = 1 \rightarrow \log\left(\frac{\left(\frac{x_1}{10^{-3}}\right)}{\left(\frac{x_2}{10^{-3}}\right)}\right) = 1$$

$$\log\left(\left(\frac{x_1}{10^{-3}}\right)\cdot\left(\frac{10^{-3}}{x_2}\right)\right) = 1 \rightarrow \log\left(\frac{x_1}{x_2}\right) = 1$$

$$10^{\log\left(\frac{x_1}{x_2}\right)} = 10 \rightarrow \frac{x_1}{x_2} = 10 \rightarrow x_1 = 10x_2 \rightarrow x_1 - x_2 = 9x_2$$

11.   Delta Center

$$L(x_1) = 10\log\left(\frac{x_1}{10^{-12}}\right) = 110 \ \text{decibels}$$

$$10\log\left(\frac{x_1}{10^{-12}}\right) = 110$$

$$\log\left(x_1 \cdot 10^{12}\right) = 11$$

$$\log(x_1) + \log\left(10^{12}\right) = 11$$

$$\log(x_1) + 12 = 11$$

$$\log(x_1) = -1$$

$$10^{\log(x_1)} = 10^{-1}$$

$$x_1 = 10^{-1} = 0.1$$

NBA guidelines

$$L(x_2) = 10\log\left(\frac{x_2}{10^{-12}}\right) = 95 \ \text{decibels}$$

$$10\log\left(\frac{x_2}{10^{-12}}\right) = 95$$

$$\log\left(x_2 \cdot 10^{12}\right) = 9.5$$

$$\log(x_2) + \log\left(10^{12}\right) = 9.5$$

$$\log(x_2) + 12 = 9.5$$

$$\log(x_2) = -2.5$$

$$10^{\log(x_2)} = 10^{-2.5}$$

$$x_2 = 10^{-2.5} \approx 0.0032$$

Therefore $\dfrac{x_1}{x_2} = \dfrac{0.1}{0.0032} = 31.25$, which means that the crowd noise was approximately 31 times louder than NBA guidelines allow.

Exponential and Logarithmic Functions

6.R   Chapter Review

1. $f(x) = \dfrac{2x+3}{5x-2}$

$y = \dfrac{2x+3}{5x-2}$

$x = \dfrac{2y+3}{5y-2}$ Inverse

$x(5y-2) = 2y+3$

$5xy - 2x = 2y+3$

$5xy - 2y = 2x+3$

$y(5x-2) = 2x+3$

$y = \dfrac{2x+3}{5x-2}$

$f^{-1}(x) = \dfrac{2x+3}{5x-2}$

Domain of f =

range of f^{-1} = all real numbers except $\dfrac{2}{5}$

Range of f =

domain of f^{-1} = all real numbers except $\dfrac{2}{5}$

2. $f(x) = \dfrac{2-x}{3+x}$

$y = \dfrac{2-x}{3+x}$

$x = \dfrac{2-y}{3+y}$ Inverse

$x(3+y) = 2-y$

$3x + xy = 2-y$

$xy + y = 2 - 3x$

$y(x+1) = 2 - 3x$

$y = \dfrac{2-3x}{x+1}$

$f^{-1}(x) = \dfrac{2-3x}{x+1}$

Domain of f =
range of f^{-1} = all real numbers except -3

Range of f =
domain of f^{-1} = all real numbers except -1

3. $f(x) = \dfrac{1}{x-1}$

$y = \dfrac{1}{x-1}$

$x = \dfrac{1}{y-1}$ Inverse

$x(y-1) = 1$

$xy - x = 1$

$xy = x + 1$

$y = \dfrac{x+1}{x}$

$f^{-1}(x) = \dfrac{x+1}{x}$

Domain of f =
range of f^{-1} = all real numbers except 1

Range of f =
domain of f^{-1} = all real numbers except 0

4. $f(x) = \sqrt{x-2}$

$y = \sqrt{x-2}$

$x = \sqrt{y-2}$ Inverse

$x^2 = y - 2$ $x \geq 0$

$y = x^2 + 2$ $x \geq 0$

$f^{-1}(x) = x^2 + 2$ $x \geq 0$

Domain of f =
range of f^{-1} = all real numbers greater than or
                        equal to 2

Range of f =
domain of f^{-1} = all real numbers greater than or
                        equal to 0

5. $f(x) = \dfrac{3}{x^{1/3}}$

$y = \dfrac{3}{x^{1/3}}$

$x = \dfrac{3}{y^{1/3}}$ Inverse

$xy^{1/3} = 3$

$y^{1/3} = \dfrac{3}{x}$

$y = \dfrac{27}{x^3}$

$f^{-1}(x) = \dfrac{27}{x^3}$

Domain of f =
range of f^{-1} = all real numbers except 0

Range of f =
domain of f^{-1} = all real numbers except 0

6.　　$f(x) = x^{1/3} + 1$ 　　　　　Domain of $f =$
　　　　$y = x^{1/3} + 1$ 　　　　　range of f^{-1} = all real numbers

　　　　$x = y^{1/3} + 1$ 　　Inverse
　　　　　　　　　　　　　　Range of $f =$
　　　　$y^{1/3} = x - 1$ 　　　　　domain of f^{-1} = all real numbers

　　　　$y = (x - 1)^3$

　　$f^{-1}(x) = (x - 1)^3$

7.　$\log_2\left(\dfrac{1}{8}\right) = \log_2 2^{-3} = -3\log_2 2 = -3$

8.　　$\log_3 81 = \log_3 3^4 = 4\log_3 3 = 4$

9.　$\ln e^{\sqrt{2}} = \sqrt{2}$ 　　　　10.　$e^{\ln 0.1} = 0.1$ 　　　11.　$2^{\log_2 0.4} = 0.4$

12.　$\log_2 2^{\sqrt{3}} = \sqrt{3}\log_2 2 = \sqrt{3}$

13.　$\log_3\left(\dfrac{uv^2}{w}\right) = \log_3 uv^2 - \log_3 w = \log_3 u + \log_3 v^2 - \log_3 w = \log_3 u + 2\log_3 v - \log_3 w$

14.　$\log_2\left(a^2\sqrt{b}\right)^4 = 4\log_2\left(a^2\sqrt{b}\right) = 4\left(\log_2 a^2 + \log_2 b^{1/2}\right) = 4\left(2\log_2 a + \dfrac{1}{2}\log_2 b\right)$

　　　　　$= 8\log_2 a + 2\log_2 b$

15.　$\log\left(x^2\sqrt{x^3 + 1}\right) = \log x^2 + \log\left(x^3 + 1\right)^{\frac{1}{2}} = 2\log x + \tfrac{1}{2}\log\left(x^3 + 1\right)$

16.　$\log_5\left(\dfrac{x^2 + 2x + 1}{x^2}\right) = \log_5(x + 1)^2 - \log_5\left(x^2\right) = 2\log_5(x + 1) - 2\log_5 x$

17.　$\ln\left(\dfrac{x\sqrt[3]{x^2 + 1}}{x - 3}\right) = \ln\left(x\sqrt[3]{x^2 + 1}\right) - \ln(x - 3) = \ln x + \ln\left(x^2 + 1\right)^{1/3} - \ln(x - 3)$

　　　　　　$= \ln x + \dfrac{1}{3}\ln\left(x^2 + 1\right) - \ln(x - 3)$

18.　$\ln\left(\dfrac{2x + 3}{x^2 - 3x + 2}\right)^2 = 2\ln\left(\dfrac{2x + 3}{x^2 - 3x + 2}\right) = 2\left(\ln(2x + 3) - \ln(x - 2)(x - 1)\right)$

　　　$= 2\left(\ln(2x + 3) - \ln(x - 2) - \ln(x - 1)\right) = 2\ln(2x + 3) - 2\ln(x - 2) - 2\ln(x - 1)$

19.　$3\log_4 x^2 + \dfrac{1}{2}\log_4 \sqrt{x} = \log_4\left(x^2\right)^3 + \log_4\left(x^{1/2}\right)^{1/2} = \log_4 x^6 + \log_4 x^{1/4} = \log_4 x^6 \cdot x^{1/4}$

　　　　　　　　$= \log_4 x^{25/4} = \dfrac{25}{4}\log_4 x$

20. $-2\log_3\left(\dfrac{1}{x}\right)+\dfrac{1}{3}\log_3\sqrt{x}=\log_3\left(x^{-1}\right)^{-2}+\log_3\left(x^{1/2}\right)^{1/3}=\log_3 x^2+\log_3 x^{1/6}$

$$=\log_3 x^2\cdot x^{1/6}=\log_3 x^{13/6}$$

21. $\ln\left(\dfrac{x-1}{x}\right)+\ln\left(\dfrac{x}{x+1}\right)-\ln\left(x^2-1\right)=\ln\left(\dfrac{x-1}{x}\cdot\dfrac{x}{x+1}\right)-\ln\left(x^2-1\right)=\ln\left[\dfrac{\left(\dfrac{x-1}{x+1}\right)}{x^2-1}\right]$

$$=\ln\left(\dfrac{x-1}{x+1}\cdot\dfrac{1}{(x-1)(x+1)}\right)=\ln\dfrac{1}{(x+1)^2}=\ln(x+1)^{-2}=-2\ln(x+1)$$

22. $\log\left(x^2-9\right)-\log\left(x^2+7x+12\right)=\log\left(\dfrac{(x-3)(x+3)}{(x+3)(x+4)}\right)=\log\left(\dfrac{x-3}{x+4}\right)$

23. $2\log 2+3\log x-\dfrac{1}{2}\left[\log(x+3)+\log(x-2)\right]=\log 2^2+\log x^3-\dfrac{1}{2}\log\left[(x+3)(x-2)\right]$

$$=\log 4x^3-\log((x+3)(x-2))^{1/2}=\log\left[\dfrac{4x^3}{\left((x+3)(x-2)\right)^{1/2}}\right]$$

24. $\dfrac{1}{2}\ln\left(x^2+1\right)-4\ln\dfrac{1}{2}-\dfrac{1}{2}\left[\ln(x-4)+\ln x\right]=\ln\left(x^2+1\right)^{1/2}-\ln\left(\dfrac{1}{2}\right)^4-\dfrac{1}{2}\ln(x(x-4))$

$$=\ln\left(x^2+1\right)^{1/2}-\ln\left(\dfrac{1}{2}\right)^4-\ln(x(x-4))^{1/2}=\ln\left[\dfrac{\left(x^2+1\right)^{1/2}}{\dfrac{1}{16}(x(x-4))^{1/2}}\right]$$

25. $\log_4 19=\dfrac{\log 19}{\log 4}\approx 2.124$ 26. $\log_2 21=\dfrac{\log 21}{\log 2}\approx 4.392$

27. $\ln y=2x^2+\ln C$
    $\ln y=\ln e^{2x^2}+\ln C$
    $\ln y=\ln\left(Ce^{2x^2}\right)\rightarrow y=Ce^{2x^2}$

28. $\ln(y-3)=\ln\left(2x^2\right)+\ln C$
    $\ln(y-3)=\ln\left(2x^2\cdot C\right)$
    $y-3=2Cx^2\rightarrow y=2Cx^2+3$

29. $\ln(y-3)+\ln(y+3)=x+C$
    $\ln(y-3)(y+3)=x+C$
    $(y-3)(y+3)=e^{x+C}$
    $y^2-9=e^{x+C}$
    $y^2=9+e^{x+C}$
    $y=\sqrt{9+e^{x+C}}$

30. $\ln(y-1)+\ln(y+1)=-x+C$
    $\ln(y-1)(y+1)=-x+C$
    $(y-1)(y+1)=e^{-x+C}$
    $y^2-1=e^{-x+C}$
    $y^2=1+e^{-x+C}$
    $y=\sqrt{1+e^{-x+C}}$

31. $e^{y+C} = x^2 + 4$
     $\ln e^{y+C} = \ln(x^2 + 4)$
     $y + C = \ln(x^2 + 4)$
     $y = \ln(x^2 + 4) - C$

32. $e^{3y-C} = (x+4)^2$
     $\ln e^{3y-C} = \ln(x+4)^2$
     $3y - C = \ln(x+4)^2$
     $3y = 2\ln(x+4) + C$
     $y = \dfrac{2\ln(x+4) + C}{3}$

33. $f(x) = 2^{x-3}$
     Using the graph of $y = 2^x$, shift the graph
     3 units to the right.
     Domain: $(-\infty, \infty)$
     Range: $(0, \infty)$
     Horizontal Asymptote: $y = 0$

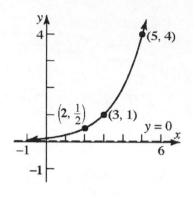

34. $f(x) = -2^x + 3$
     Using the graph of $y = 2^x$, reflect the
     graph about the x-axis, and shift
     vertically 3 units up.
     Domain: $(-\infty, \infty)$
     Range: $(-\infty, 3)$
     Horizontal Asymptote: $y = 3$

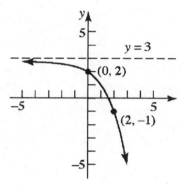

35. $f(x) = \dfrac{1}{2} \cdot 3^{-x}$
     Using the graph of $y = 3^x$, reflect the
     graph about the y-axis, and shrink
     vertically by a factor of $\dfrac{1}{2}$.
     Domain: $(-\infty, \infty)$
     Range: $(0, \infty)$
     Horizontal Asymptote: $y = 0$

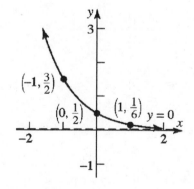

36. $f(x) = 1 + 3^{2x}$
Using the graph of $y = 3^x$, shrink the

graph horizontally by a factor of $\dfrac{1}{2}$, and

shift vertically 1 unit up.
Domain: $(-\infty, \infty)$
Range: $(1, \infty)$
Horizontal Asymptote: $y = 1$

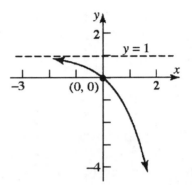

37. $f(x) = 1 - e^x$
Using the graph of $y = e^x$, reflect about
the x-axis, and shift up 1 unit.
Domain: $(-\infty, \infty)$
Range: $(-\infty, 1)$
Horizontal Asymptote: $y = 1$

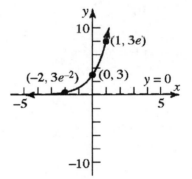

38. $f(x) = 3e^x$
Using the graph of $y = e^x$, stretch
vertically by a factor of 3.
Domain: $(-\infty, \infty)$
Range: $(0, \infty)$
Horizontal Asymptote: $y = 0$

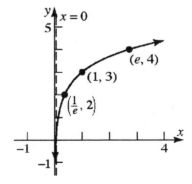

39. $f(x) = 3 + \ln x$
Using the graph of $y = \ln x$, shift the
graph up 3 units.
Domain: $(0, \infty)$
Range: $(-\infty, \infty)$
Vertical Asymptote: $x = 0$

40. $f(x) = \dfrac{1}{2}\ln x$

Using the graph of $y = \ln x$, shrink

vertically by a factor of $\dfrac{1}{2}$.

Domain: $(0, \infty)$

Range: $(-\infty, \infty)$

Vertical Asymptote: $x = 0$

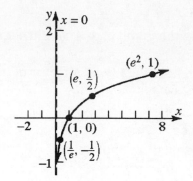

41. $f(x) = 3 - e^{-x}$

Using the graph of $y = e^x$, reflect the
graph about the y-axis, reflect about the
x-axis, and shift up 3 units.

Domain: $(-\infty, \infty)$

Range: $(-\infty, 3)$

Horizontal Asymptote: $y = 3$

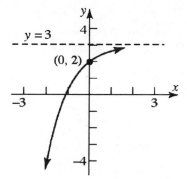

42. $f(x) = 4 - \ln(-x)$

Using the graph of $y = \ln x$, reflect the
graph about the y-axis, reflect about the x-
axis, and shift up 4 units.

Domain: $(-\infty, 0)$

Range: $(-\infty, \infty)$

Vertical Asymptote: $x = 0$

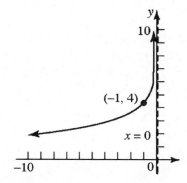

43. $4^{1-2x} = 2$

$\left(2^2\right)^{1-2x} = 2$

$2^{2-4x} = 2^1$

$2 - 4x = 1 \rightarrow -4x = -1 \rightarrow x = \dfrac{1}{4}$

44. $8^{6+3x} = 4$

$\left(2^3\right)^{6+3x} = 2^2$

$2^{18+9x} = 2^2$

$18 + 9x = 2 \rightarrow 9x = -16 \rightarrow x = -\dfrac{16}{9}$

45. $3^{x^2+x} = \sqrt{3}$

$3^{x^2+x} = 3^{1/2}$

$x^2 + x = \dfrac{1}{2} \rightarrow 2x^2 + 2x - 1 = 0 \rightarrow x = \dfrac{-2 \pm \sqrt{4 - 4(2)(-1)}}{2(2)} = \dfrac{-2 \pm \sqrt{12}}{4} = \dfrac{-2 \pm 2\sqrt{3}}{4} = \dfrac{-1 \pm \sqrt{3}}{2}$

$x = \dfrac{-1 - \sqrt{3}}{2}$ or $x = \dfrac{-1 + \sqrt{3}}{2}$

46.

$$4^{x-x^2} = \frac{1}{2}$$

$$\left(2^2\right)^{x-x^2} = 2^{-1} \rightarrow 2^{2x-2x^2} = 2^{-1}$$

$$2x - 2x^2 = -1 \rightarrow 2x^2 - 2x - 1 = 0 \rightarrow x = \frac{-(-2) \pm \sqrt{4 - 4(2)(-1)}}{2(2)} = \frac{2 \pm \sqrt{12}}{4} = \frac{2 \pm 2\sqrt{3}}{4} = \frac{1 \pm \sqrt{3}}{2}$$

$$x = \frac{1 - \sqrt{3}}{2} \quad \text{or} \quad x = \frac{1 + \sqrt{3}}{2}$$

47. $\log_x 64 = -3$

$$x^{-3} = 64$$

$$\left(x^{-3}\right)^{-1/3} = 64^{-1/3} \rightarrow x = \frac{1}{\sqrt[3]{64}} = \frac{1}{4}$$

48. $\log_{\sqrt{2}} x = -6$

$$x = \left(\sqrt{2}\right)^{-6} = \left(2^{1/2}\right)^{-6} = 2^{-3} = \frac{1}{8}$$

49.

$$5^x = 3^{x+2}$$
$$\log\left(5^x\right) = \log\left(3^{x+2}\right)$$
$$x\log 5 = (x+2)\log 3$$
$$x\log 5 = x\log 3 + 2\log 3$$
$$x\log 5 - x\log 3 = 2\log 3$$
$$x(\log 5 - \log 3) = 2\log 3$$
$$x = \frac{2\log 3}{\log 5 - \log 3}$$
$$x \approx 4.301$$

50.

$$5^{x+2} = 7^{x-2}$$
$$\log\left(5^{x+2}\right) = \log\left(7^{x-2}\right)$$
$$(x+2)\log 5 = (x-2)\log 7$$
$$x\log 5 + 2\log 5 = x\log 7 - 2\log 7$$
$$x\log 5 - x\log 7 = -2\log 7 - 2\log 5$$
$$x(\log 5 - \log 7) = -2\log 7 - 2\log 5$$
$$x = \frac{-2\log 7 - 2\log 5}{\log 5 - \log 7}$$
$$x \approx 21.133$$

51.

$$9^{2x} = 27^{3x-4}$$
$$\left(3^2\right)^{2x} = \left(3^3\right)^{3x-4}$$
$$3^{4x} = 3^{9x-12}$$
$$4x = 9x - 12 \rightarrow -5x = -12$$
$$x = \frac{12}{5}$$

52.

$$25^{2x} = 5^{x^2-12}$$
$$\left(5^2\right)^{2x} = 5^{x^2-12}$$
$$5^{4x} = 5^{x^2-12}$$
$$4x = x^2 - 12$$
$$x^2 - 4x - 12 = 0 \rightarrow (x-6)(x+2) = 0$$
$$x = 6 \quad \text{or} \quad x = -2$$

53. $\log_3 \sqrt{x-2} = 2$

$$\sqrt{x-2} = 3^2$$

$$x - 2 = 9^2 \rightarrow x - 2 = 81 \rightarrow x = 83$$

54.

$$2^{x+1} \cdot 8^{-x} = 4$$
$$2^{x+1} \cdot \left(2^3\right)^{-x} = 2^2$$
$$2^{x+1} \cdot 2^{-3x} = 2^2$$
$$2^{-2x+1} = 2^2$$
$$-2x + 1 = 2 \rightarrow -2x = 1 \rightarrow x = -\frac{1}{2}$$

Chapter 6   Exponential and Logarithmic Functions

55.
$$8 = 4^{x^2} \cdot 2^{5x}$$
$$2^3 = \left(2^2\right)^{x^2} \cdot 2^{5x}$$
$$2^3 = 2^{2x^2+5x}$$
$$3 = 2x^2 + 5x \rightarrow 0 = 2x^2 + 5x - 3$$
$$0 = (2x-1)(x+3) \rightarrow x = \frac{1}{2} \text{ or } x = -3$$

56.
$$2^x \cdot 5 = 10^x$$
$$\ln\left(2^x \cdot 5\right) = \ln 10^x$$
$$\ln 2^x + \ln 5 = \ln 10^x$$
$$x \ln 2 + \ln 5 = x \ln 10$$
$$x(\ln 2 - \ln 10) = -\ln 5$$
$$x = \frac{-\ln 5}{\ln 2 - \ln 10} = 1$$

57.
$$\log_6(x+3) + \log_6(x+4) = 1$$
$$\log_6(x+3)(x+4) = 1$$
$$(x+3)(x+4) = 6^1$$
$$x^2 + 7x + 12 = 6$$
$$x^2 + 7x + 6 = 0$$
$$(x+6)(x+1) = 0$$
$$x = -6 \text{ or } x = -1$$
The logarithms are undefined when $x = -6$, so $x = -1$ is the only solution.

58.
$$\log_{10}(7x-12) = 2\log_{10} x$$
$$\log_{10}(7x-12) = \log_{10} x^2$$
$$7x - 12 = x^2$$
$$x^2 - 7x + 12 = 0$$
$$(x-4)(x-3) = 0$$
$$x = 4 \text{ or } x = 3$$

59.
$$e^{1-x} = 5$$
$$1 - x = \ln 5$$
$$-x = -1 + \ln 5$$
$$x = 1 - \ln 5 \approx -0.609$$

60.
$$e^{1-2x} = 4$$
$$1 - 2x = \ln 4$$
$$-2x = -1 + \ln 4$$
$$x = \frac{1 - \ln 4}{2} \approx -0.193$$

61.
$$2^{3x} = 3^{2x+1}$$
$$\ln 2^{3x} = \ln 3^{2x+1}$$
$$3x \ln 2 = (2x+1)\ln 3$$
$$3x \ln 2 = 2x \ln 3 + \ln 3$$
$$3x \ln 2 - 2x \ln 3 = \ln 3$$
$$x(3\ln 2 - 2\ln 3) = \ln 3$$
$$x = \frac{\ln 3}{3\ln 2 - 2\ln 3}$$
$$x \approx -9.327$$

62.
$$2^{x^3} = 3^{x^2}$$
$$\ln 2^{x^3} = \ln 3^{x^2}$$
$$x^3 \ln 2 = x^2 \ln 3$$
$$x^3 \ln 2 - x^2 \ln 3 = 0$$
$$x^2(x \ln 2 - \ln 3) = 0$$
$$x^2 = 0 \text{ or } x = \frac{\ln 3}{\ln 2}$$
$$x = 0 \text{ or } x \approx 1.585$$

63. $h(300) = (30(0) + 8000)\log\left(\frac{760}{300}\right) = 8000\log 2.53333 = 3229.5$ meters

64. $h(500) = (30(5) + 8000)\log\left(\frac{760}{500}\right) = 8150\log 1.52 = 1482$ meters

65. $h(x) = 10000$

$$10000 = (30(-100) + 8000)\log\left(\frac{760}{x}\right)$$

$$10000 = (5000)\log\left(\frac{760}{x}\right)$$

$$2 = \log\left(\frac{760}{x}\right)$$

$$10^2 = 10^{\log\left(\frac{760}{x}\right)}$$

$$100 = \frac{760}{x} \rightarrow x = \frac{760}{100} = 7.6 \text{ mm}$$

66. $h(x) = 10000$

$$8900 = (30(5) + 8000)\log\left(\frac{760}{x}\right)$$

$$8900 = (8150)\log\left(\frac{760}{x}\right)$$

$$\frac{8900}{8150} = \log\left(\frac{760}{x}\right) \rightarrow 10^{\left(\frac{8900}{8150}\right)} = 10^{\log\left(\frac{760}{x}\right)}$$

$$10^{\left(\frac{8900}{8150}\right)} = \frac{760}{x} \rightarrow 10^{1.092} \approx \frac{760}{x}$$

$$\rightarrow x \approx \frac{760}{10^{1.092}} = 61.488 \text{ mm}$$

67. $P = 25e^{0.1d}$

(a) $P = 25e^{0.1(4)}$
    $= 25e^{0.4}$
    $= 37.3$ watts

(b) $50 = 25e^{0.1d}$
    $2 = e^{0.1d}$
    $\ln 2 = 0.1d$
    $d = \dfrac{\ln 2}{0.1} = 6.9$ decibels

68. $L = 9 + 5.1\log d$

(a) $L = 9 + 5.1\log 3.5 \approx 11.8$

(b) $14 = 9 + 5.1\log d$
    $5 = 5.1\log d$

$$\log d = \frac{5}{5.1} \approx 0.9804$$

$$d \approx 10^{0.9804} \approx 9.56 \text{ inches}$$

69. (a) $P = 90 - 80\left(\dfrac{3}{4}\right)^5 \approx 71.02\%$

(b) $P = 90 - 80\left(\dfrac{3}{4}\right)^{10} \approx 85.5\%$

(c) as $t \rightarrow \infty$, $P = 90 - 80\left(\dfrac{3}{4}\right)^t \rightarrow 90 - 0 = 90\%$

(d) $40 = 90 - 80\left(\dfrac{3}{4}\right)^t \rightarrow -50 = -80\left(\dfrac{3}{4}\right)^t \rightarrow \dfrac{5}{8} = \left(\dfrac{3}{4}\right)^t \rightarrow \ln\left(\dfrac{5}{8}\right) = \ln\left(\dfrac{3}{4}\right)^t$

$$\rightarrow \ln\left(\frac{5}{8}\right) = t \cdot \ln\left(\frac{3}{4}\right) \rightarrow t = \frac{\ln\left(\frac{5}{8}\right)}{\ln\left(\frac{3}{4}\right)} \approx 1.63 \text{ months}$$

(e) $70 = 90 - 80\left(\dfrac{3}{4}\right)^t$

$$-20 = -80\left(\frac{3}{4}\right)^t \rightarrow 0.25 = \left(\frac{3}{4}\right)^t \rightarrow \ln(0.25) = \ln\left(\frac{3}{4}\right)^t$$

$$\rightarrow \ln(0.25) = t \cdot \ln\left(\frac{3}{4}\right) \rightarrow t = \frac{\ln(0.25)}{\ln\left(\frac{3}{4}\right)} \approx 4.82 \text{ months}$$

70. $m = 55.3 - 6\ln(10000 - 5000) = 55.3 - 6\ln(5000) \approx 4.2$ months

71.   (a) $n = \dfrac{\log 10000 - \log 90000}{\log(1 - 0.20)} = 9.85$ years

      (b) $n = \dfrac{\log 0.5i - \log i}{\log(1 - 0.15)} = \dfrac{\log\left(\dfrac{0.5i}{i}\right)}{\log 0.85} = \dfrac{\log 0.5}{\log 0.85} = 4.27$ years

72. $A = 10000\left(1 + \dfrac{0.04}{2}\right)^{(2)(18)} = 10000(1.02)^{36} = \$20{,}398.87$

73. $P = A\left(1 + \dfrac{r}{n}\right)^{-nt} = 85000\left(1 + \dfrac{0.04}{2}\right)^{-2(18)} = \$41{,}668.97$

74.   (a) $5000 = 620.17e^{r(20)}$

              $8.0623 = e^{20r}$

              $\ln(8.0623) = 20r \rightarrow r = \dfrac{\ln(8.0623)}{20} \approx 0.10436 \approx 10.436\%$

      (b) $A = 4000e^{0.10436(20)} = \$32{,}249.24$

              The bank's claim is correct.

75. $L(10^{-4}) = 10\log\left(\dfrac{10^{-4}}{10^{-12}}\right) = 10\log(10^{8}) = 10 \cdot 8 = 80$ decibels

76.   Chicago: $M(x) = \log\left(\dfrac{x}{10^{-3}}\right) = 3.0$ San Francisco: $M(x) = \log\left(\dfrac{x}{10^{-3}}\right) = 6.9$

      $\log(x \cdot 10^{3}) = 3.0$ $\log(x \cdot 10^{3}) = 6.9$

      $\log(x) + \log(10^{3}) = 3$ $\log(x) + \log(10^{3}) = 6.9$

      $\log(x) + 3 = 3$ $\log(x) + 3 = 6.9$

      $\log(x) = 0 \rightarrow 10^{\log(x)} = 10^{0} \rightarrow x = 10^{0} = 1$ $\log(x) = 3.9 \rightarrow 10^{\log(x)} = 10^{3.9} \rightarrow x = 10^{3.9} \approx 7943.28$

77. $A = A_0 e^{kt}$

      $\dfrac{1}{2}A_0 = A_0 e^{k(5600)}$

      $0.5 = e^{5600\,k} \rightarrow \ln 0.5 = 5600k \rightarrow k = \dfrac{\ln 0.5}{5600} \approx -0.000124$

      $0.05A_0 = A_0 e^{-0.000124\,t}$

      $0.05 = e^{-0.000124\,t} \rightarrow \ln 0.05 = -0.000124t \rightarrow t = \dfrac{\ln 0.05}{-0.000124} \approx 24{,}159$ years ago

78. Using $u = T + (u_0 - T)e^{kt}$ where $t = 5$,
$T = 70$, $u_0 = 450$, $u = 400$:

$$400 = 70 + (450 - 70)e^{k(5)} \rightarrow 330 = 380e^{5k}$$

$$0.86842 = e^{5k} \rightarrow 5k = \ln 0.86842 \rightarrow k = \frac{\ln 0.86842}{5} \approx -0.028216$$

Find time for temperature of 150°F:
$$150 = 70 + (450 - 70)e^{-0.028216\,t} \rightarrow 80 = 380e^{-0.028216\,t}$$

$$0.210526 = e^{-0.028216\,t} \rightarrow \ln(0.210526) = -0.028216t \rightarrow t = \frac{\ln(0.210526)}{-0.028216} \approx 55.2 \text{ minutes}$$

79. (a) Graphing:

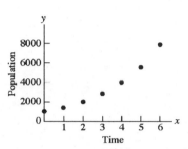

(c) $N = 1000e^{0.3466(7)} \approx 11314$ bacteria

(b) $y = 1000\left(\sqrt{2}\right)^x$

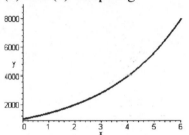

$\sqrt{2} = e^{\ln\sqrt{2}} \rightarrow y = 1000\left(e^{\ln\sqrt{2}}\right)^x = 1000e^{(\ln\sqrt{2})x}$

$N = N_0 e^{0.3466t}, N_0 = 1000, k = 0.3466$

(d) and (e) Graphing:

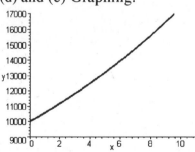

80. (a) Graphing:

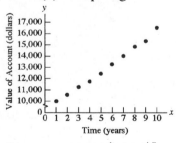

(b) $y = 10014(1.057)^x$

$1.057 = e^{\ln 1.057}$

$\rightarrow y = 10014\left(e^{\ln 1.057}\right)^x = 1000e^{(0.0554)x}$

(c) $A = 10014e^{0.0554(35)} \approx \$69699.90$

(d) and (e) Graphing:

$\rightarrow A = A_0 e^{0.0554t}, A_0 = 10014, k = 0.0554$

81. $P = P_0 e^{kt} = 5,840,445,216e^{0.0133(3)} = 6,078,190,457$

82. $A = A_0 e^{kt}$

$$\frac{1}{2}A_0 = A_0 e^{k(5.27)} \rightarrow \frac{1}{2} = e^{5.27k} \rightarrow \ln 0.5 = 5.27k \rightarrow k = \frac{\ln 0.5}{5.27} \approx -0.13153$$

In 20 years: $A = 100e^{-0.13153(20)} = 7.2$ grams; In 40 years: $A = 100e^{-0.13153(40)} = 0.52$ grams

83.   (a) $P(0) = \dfrac{0.8}{1 + 1.67e^{-0.16(0)}} = \dfrac{0.8}{1 + 1.67} = 0.2996$

   (b)   0.8

   (c)   Graphing:

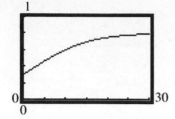

   (d)   Using INTERSECT we have:

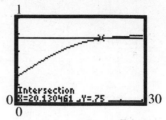

75% use Windows 98 in 2018.